DOGIEL: General Protozoology

GENERAL
PROTOZOOLOGY

.

GENERAL
PROTOZOOLOGY

BY

V. A. DOGIEL

REVISED BY

J. I. POLJANSKIJ

AND

E. M. CHEJSIN

SECOND EDITION

OXFORD
AT THE CLARENDON PRESS
1965

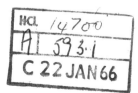

Oxford University Press, Ely House, London W. 1

GLASGOW   NEW YORK   TORONTO   MELBOURNE   WELLINGTON
CAPE TOWN   SALISBURY   IBADAN   NAIROBI   LUSAKA   ADDIS ABABA
BOMBAY   CALCUTTA   MADRAS   KARACHI   LAHORE   DACCA
KUALA LUMPUR   HONG KONG

PREFACE

Biologists have always given great attention to Protozoa because of the striking peculiarity that they combine features of both the single cell and the complete organism in their organization. A number of large and valuable monographs and books of the advanced type have been written concerning different aspects of their morphology and biology, and many reviews dealing with the taxonomy of various groups of Protozoa have appeared. In some works Protozoa have been examined from medical and veterinary points of view. For example, in 1930 two books by Russian authors appeared—*Veterinary Protozoology* by V. V. L. Yakimov and *The Pathogenetic Protozoa, Spirochetes and Fungi* by G. V. Epstein.

Comparatively little has been written on the more general aspects of Protozoology. Among other books, *The Biology of the Protozoa* by G. Calkins (1933), *Protozoa in Biological Research* edited by G. Calkins and F. Summers (1945), and *General Protistology* by V. A. Dogiel (1951) deserve to be mentioned. These, as well as some other large textbooks (*Lehrbuch der Protozoenkundë*, 1–6 Auflage, by F. Doflein and E. Reichenow (1909–53); *Protozoology* by C. Wenyon (1925); and others) in which a great deal of attention was paid to the general aspects of Protozoology, played an important role in the development of this aspect of the subject.

Nowadays, however, these books have become rather out of date. Within the last 10–15 years, studies of unicellular organisms have advanced very quickly owing to the development and employment of new methods of investigation of the cell. Tremendous progress in electron microscopy, biochemistry, and cytophysiology has enriched our knowledge of Protozoa and allowed expansion into new aspects of research on unicellular animals.

Some new reviews and monographs have appeared which treated Protozoa from different points of view. Among the most significant contributions the following books must be mentioned: *Biochemistry and Physiology of Protozoa* edited by A. Lwoff (vol. i, 1951) and by A. Lwoff and S. Hutner (vol. ii, 1955), *The Genetics of Paramecium aurelia* by G. Beale (1954), *The Biochemistry of Intracellular Parasitism* by J. Moulder (1962), and *Electron-microscopical Structure of Protozoa* by D. Pitelka (1963). However, in some new textbooks on Protozoology, such as *Protozoologie* by O. Jirovec *et al.* (1953), *Protozoologie* by R. Hall (1953), *Protozoology* by R. Kudo (first edition 1931, fourth edition 1954), *Introduction to the Study of Protozoa* by D. Mackinnon and R. Hawes (1961), as well as in *Traité de Zoologie* edited by P. Grassé (1952–3), general problems of Protozoology have not received much attention. Only in the *Protozoologie* by K. Grell (1956) and in the recently published *Introduction to Protozoology* by R. Manwell (1961) are the general aspects of Protozoology touched upon more thoroughly.

The vast amount of material obtained from recent research in the field of Protozoology has created an urgent need for summarizing the new facts available. It has made us think that such a work ought to be done as soon as possible, taking into consideration that the basis of the book had already been created in *General Protistology* written by our teacher, the late Professor V. A. Dogiel, and published in the USSR in 1951. In this textbook a good deal of data concerning the morphology, ecology, and evolution of Protozoa were generalized at the level of the fifties.

Thus this new book represents a remade, extended, and advanced version of Dogiel's *General Protistology*. Some old data have been withdrawn from it, while a lot of new findings have been included. Several chapters and sections have been rewritten, including those on the nucleus and reproduction, life-cycles, and the species problem. The chapters devoted to the organization of the cytoplasm, fibrillar structures, and the physiology of metabolism have been enlarged. In 1962 the Russian edition, entitled *General Protozoology*, was published by the Publishing House of the Academy of Sciences of the USSR. The English translation of the book was made from the manuscript, some additions being made to the Russian edition. As concerns literature sources used, most of them terminate in 1961 and only a few papers of 1962 were included in the reference list and referred to in the text.

Nowadays, Protozoology has undergone such a tremendous development that it seems next to impossible, in one book, to elucidate and to cover all aspects equally; greatest attention is given to the morphology, reproduction, and evolution of Protozoa; questions of physiology and biochemistry of Protozoa are covered much less completely. Aspects of medical and veterinary Protozoology are not touched upon at all, though some general questions concerning host–parasite relationship are dealt with in the chapter devoted to the ecology of Protozoa.

Protozoological problems are being studied throughout the world. A great deal of work is being done in the Soviet Union, but many of the Russian papers remain relatively unknown in Western Europe and on the American continent. In the present book the authors have endeavoured to evaluate, to an equal degree, the contributions made by both Russian and Western protozoologists.

In some chapters debatable points of view are expressed on, for example, the question of 'neuromotor apparatus', the species problem in Protozoa, and regularities in the evolution within the phylum. In the authors' opinion scientific discussions are always fruitful because they allow the truth to be born.

We are very much obliged to Dr. C. A. Hoare, F.R.S., who so kindly edited the English text of the book and without whose help the book could not have been published in England.

We owe a debt of gratitude to the staff of the laboratory of cytology of unicellular organisms of the Institute of Cytology in Leningrad—Drs. K. M. Sukhanova, I. B. Raikov, M. N. Golikova, T. V. Beyer, T. M. Poznanskaya, A. A. Dobrovolski, G. I. Sergejeva, N. N. Bobyljeva, and Dr. L. N. Seravin, a scientific worker of the Department of Invertebrates of the University of Leningrad—for their efforts in preparing the Russian text for publication.

We would also like to thank N. G. Korobova for her labour in making most of the figures exhibited in this book.

J. I. POLJANSKIJ
E. M. CHEJSIN

Institute of Cytology, Leningrad

CONTENTS

I

THE CYTOPLASM OF THE PROTOZOA, ITS ORGANOIDS AND INCLUSIONS

STRUCTURE AND COMPOSITION OF THE CYTOPLASM

THE body of the Protozoa, like that of the multicellular organisms, is built mainly of cytoplasm and the nucleus. We prefer not to use the wide term 'protoplasm', since there is no general agreement about its meaning. The term was first suggested by Purkinje in 1839 for the substance from which an animal embryo developed. Since Mohl's work in the second half of the nineteenth century it became widely used to cover the whole of the living matter of the cell, including its nucleus. On the other hand, many investigators use this term in a much more limited sense, to denote all living parts of the cell except the nucleus. In this case protoplasm becomes synonymous with cytoplasm. Elementary manifestations of life, and above all metabolism, are closely linked with these main components. Apart from the cytoplasm and the nucleus the body contains various kinds of organoids, metaplasmic and alloplasmic substances (inclusions, skeletal elements, and others), which play an important part in the structure and functions of the Protozoa. A precise distinction between these two types of component is not always easy to draw, and to a certain extent it is a matter of convention. Inclusions such as fat drops should certainly be considered as metaplasmic, but supporting fibrillar structures are not so easily classified. These solid intracellular skeletal filaments do not apparently take a direct part in the processes of metabolism; they are comparatively stable formations and should be classified as alloplasmic structures. During the process of multiplication, as well as encystment some of these skeletal structures are transformed into the basic matter of the cytoplasm, to be differentiated again later. Such transformations can be explained by the submicroscopic structure of the cytoplasm and the capacity of its protein molecules and their aggregates to change their structure, to unite into complexes, and to undergo a series of partly reversible transformations.

The problem of the elementary structure and the composition of cytoplasm as the main substratum of life has long attracted the attention of investigators. Attempts were made and still continue to be made to explain the elementary manifestations of life by the structure and properties of the cytoplasm. Since in these attempts the study of the Protozoa has played an important part, we shall give a short account of this subject, although it lies outside the field of protozoology.

The investigation of the chemical composition of the cytoplasm has been approached almost exclusively through the study of multicellular organisms to which an extensive literature is devoted. The minute size of the body of the Protozoa is naturally a drawback to its biochemical investigation. The chemical composition of the myxomycete plasmodium, formed mainly of cytoplasm and nuclei, has been most comprehensively examined. In the opinion of many protozoologists the Myxomycetes are an order of the class Sarcodina. Kiesel's (1925, 1927) data on the chemical composition of the organic matter (dry residue) of two species of Myxomycetes, *Reticularia lycoperdon* and *Lycogala epidendron*, are given in the following table.

Substances	Reticularia lycoperdon	Lycogala epidendron
Protein (except plastin) and nucleoproteid	20·65	18·37
Plastin (albumen-like) . . .	8·42	11·96
Nucleic acid (free and bound) .	3·68	
Nitrous extractive substances . .	12·0	5·20
Oil and pigment	17·85	37·51
Lecithins	4·67	
Cholesterine	0·58	1·16
Oil of Lipoproteins (?). . . .	1·20	0·66
Polycyclic alcohol		0·26
Resinous substances, partly products of secondary changes		4·29
Unknown lipoids		1·20
Volatile acids		0·26
Reducing carbohydrates . . .	2·74	0·53
Non-reducing carbohydrates (without glycogen, trehalose)	5·32	1·06
Glycogen	15·24	13·10
Myxoglucosan	1·78	1·79
Unknown substances . . .	5·87	2·65

Apart from organic substances the cytoplasm always contains large amounts of water. The percentage content of water in the body of the Protozoa has not been determined accurately, while the water content of multicellular organisms is rarely below 60 per cent. (by weight), and at times reaches 98 per cent. (medusae, comb-jellies).

Inorganic salts, primarily the cations K, Ca, Mg, also Na and Fe, and the anions Cl, PO_4, NO_3 are always present in the cytoplasm. Inorganic salts are present in the cytoplasm partly as ions in solution and partly more or less closely bound with organic compounds. Inorganic salts play an important role in the cytoplasm, particularly by their influence on its aggregate state and its permeability.

Various enzymes with powerful effects on metabolism have been found in the cytoplasm of Protozoa. Proteases and carbohydrases have been detected, and the occurrence of lipases, which seemed doubtful to Staniewicz (1910), has been confirmed by Barbarin (1937a, b). Complex systems of respiratory enzymes, such as oxidases and peroxidases (Roskin and

Levinson, 1926), cytochrome oxidase, and the yellow respiratory enzyme, flavin, have also been traced in the cytoplasm of numerous Protozoa. Acid and alkaline phosphatases, which are enzyme systems controlling different aspects of metabolism, have been comprehensively studied in the ciliates (see Hutner and Lwoff, 1955).

Although the cytoplasm and nucleus are composed of many diverse organic and inorganic substances, their main constituents are represented by proteins which are of special importance in living processes.

As shown by the data cited above concerning the chemical composition of the Myxomycetes the nucleic acids are important components. These compounds are usually closely linked with proteins, forming nucleoproteins, and play an important part in the living processes of the cells of multicellular organisms and the Protozoa. Desoxyribonucleic acid (DNA) is a component of the cell nucleus (in the chromosomes) and acts as the main agent in the transmission of hereditary characteristics. Ribonucleic acid (RNA) plays an important role in the synthesis of proteins and is found both in the nucleus and in the cytoplasm.

The fat-like substances or lipids are important chemical components of the cytoplasm and are essential for metabolism. Their chemical nature varies. Some lipids (phosphatides) contain phosphorus. According to some biochemists, such as Lepeschkin, a considerable part of the cytoplasmic lipids is closely bound with the proteins, forming lipoprotein complexes.

Chemical analysis of the cytoplasm always reveals the presence of neutral fats and carbohydrates in noticeable quantities. These components should be regarded in general as food reserves which take part in metabolism and are the source of energy in the cell. Carbohydrates and fats in the cytoplasm of the Protozoa occur usually in the form of inclusions.

A knowledge of the structure and the aggregate state of the cytoplasm is most important for the understanding of the living processes taking place within the body of a protozoon. Several so-called morphological theories of the structure of cytoplasm were advanced at the end of the nineteenth and the beginning of the twentieth centuries. The general feature of these theories, which were based mainly on the study of fixed and stained preparations, was a tendency to discover a structure of the cytoplasm common to plants, animals, and Protozoa, by means of which the main processes of life could be explained. In the eighties Flemming developed the theory of fibrillar structure of the cytoplasm. According to this investigator the ground substance of cytoplasm is composed of fibril, the gaps between them being filled with a fluid. Somewhat later Altmann expounded the granular theory which was further developed by Heidenhain, Reinke, and others. According to this theory, the basic structure of cytoplasm is formed by very fine granules or bioblasts. These granules are endowed with the fundamental living properties, in particular that of multiplication by binary fission. Altmann and his followers regarded every cell as a sum of more elementary vital units.

Among the morphological theory of the structure of cytoplasm, the spumoid-alveolar theory is the most fully developed. It was first suggested by Otto Bütschli and further developed by the works of Rhumbler. During the nineties of the last century and the first two decades of the present century it became widely accepted. This acceptance was due to the fact that it provided a fairly satisfactory explanation for certain peculiarities of cell structure, of the physical state of the cytoplasm, and of the simplest forms of amoeboid locomotion and ingestion of food.

At present Bütschli–Rhumbler's theory, like other morphological theories, is only of historical interest, in spite of all its importance in the development of the study of the structure and fundamental properties of cytoplasm. Further stages in the study of the cytoplasm and nucleus are closely linked with the progress of colloidal chemistry and the chemistry of proteins, as well as with the development and improvement of methods of examining cells *in vivo*. Among these the following have acquired special importance: examination in a dark field and polarized light, the application of micromanipulators, ultracentrifugation, microphotography in ultraviolet light, and vital staining. Recently the electron microscopic examination of Protozoa has considerably advanced the study of the ultramicroscopic structure of cytoplasm, nucleus, and organoids, while further refinements were introduced by the technique of fluorescence microscopy. Microchemical analysis of cells, which has developed so rapidly lately, has also contributed much to our knowledge of the cytoplasm and the nucleus.

Numerous observations made by different methods have shown that the basic substance of the cytoplasm in the Protozoa is either of fluid or semi-fluid consistency. This is evident from the fact that, when a protozoon is crushed in water, drops of its cytoplasm acquire a more or less regular spherical shape. When Protozoa such as *Paramecium*, *Stylonychia*, or *Stentor* come into contact with a bubble of air, the outer layer of their body, the pellicle, is liquefied, and the cytoplasm stretches out in a fine layer along the line of the air–water interface, thus indicating the fluid state of the cytoplasm (Lepeschkin, 1925).

Diverse figures have been obtained as the result of measurements of the internal viscosity of various Protozoa made by the methods of centrifugation and by observation of particles in Brownian movement. According to Heilbrunn (1929) the viscosity coefficient[1] of the cytoplasm of *Amoeba dubia* (Fig. 1) is 1·9 at 18° C., while in a different species of *Amoeba* it was found to be 5·2. According to Fetter (1926) the viscosity coefficient of

---

[1] The unit of viscosity coefficient, known as poise, expresses the rate of fall of a body in a given liquid. For comparison, here are the viscosity coefficients of certain liquids: acetaldehyde 0·2215, chloroform 0·5640, water 1·000, ethyl alcohol 1·192, 3 per cent, egg albumen 1·200, castor oil 1020·0 glycerine 1069·0.

Paramecium endoplasm is extremely high, viz. between 8027 and 8726; this may be due to the occurrence of fibrillar structures in the cytoplasm, rather than to the properties of the ground substance of the endoplasm. Moreover, it has been shown that the viscosity of the cytoplasm depends to a considerable extent on the conditions in the external environment of the protozoon, particularly the temperature. Heilbrunn found that the viscosity of

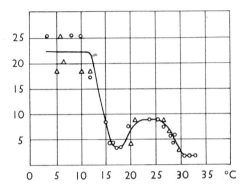

FIG. 1. Viscosity of the cytoplasm of amoeba. Temperature (° C.) is plotted on the abscissa, and viscosity (time in seconds required for a crystal in the cytoplasm to move through half the length of the cell under the influence of gravity) on the ordinate. (From Heilbrunn, 1929.)

the cytoplasm of *Amoeba dubia* increased from 1·8 to 25 with a decrease in temperature from 18° to 2·5° C. (Fig. 1).

The specific gravity of protozoal cells, the main mass of which is represented by cytoplasm, has been determined by many investigators. Several different methods have been used: determination of the rate of free fall in water and salt solutions, pycnometry, and centrifugation in water and other liquids. The first results, obtained at the end of the nineteenth century, gave very high figures for the specific gravity of Protozoa; thus the specific gravity of *Paramecium aurelia* was given as 1·25. These data, which were shown to be completely erroneous, have been quoted for a long time in tables and in textbooks. The specific gravity of Protozoa, as shown by later determinations, proved to be considerably lower. The results of some determinations of specific gravities are given in the following table.

As seen from the table the figures obtained by different determinations are fairly similar, varying between 1·02 and 1·08.

The hydrogen ion concentration (pH) in the cytoplasm has been studied by many investigators, some of whom used various Protozoa for this purpose. The method of indicators has been used in most work on intracellular pH. The indicators were introduced into the cytoplasm either by microinjection or in a solid state. In some cases the Protozoa were placed in an indicator solution and stained supravitally. The numerous results were mostly concordant. The pH of the cytoplasm of *Amoeba dubia* is 6·6–7·2, according to Pollack (1928) and 6·9 according to Chambers (1928), while in *A. proteus* it is 6·4–7·3 (Date, 1931). All these data indicate a practically neutral (Ph = 7·0) reaction of the cytoplasm.

SPECIFIC GRAVITY OF VARIOUS PROTOZOA

Name of organism	Specific gravity
Naegleria	1·045
Entamoeba coli (cysts) . . .	1·068–1·070
Hartmanella hyalina (cysts) . . .	1·084
Dunaliella viridis	1·069
Chlamydomonas Dangeardi . . .	1·077–1·091
Chlamydomonas pulvisculus . . .	1·046–1·072
Paramecium sp.	1·048–1·049
Paramecium caudatum . . .	1·038–1·039
Stentor coerulueas	1·016
Bursaria sp.	1·0142

The stability of the intracellular pH is conditioned by the buffering capacity of the cytoplasm in the living cell. However, the concentration of hydrogen ions in the cytoplasm does not remain stable but, according to some data, it changes with the physiological state of the protozoon. Pantin found that the pH of amoeba ectoplasm decreases from 7·3 to 6·8 during the formation of pseudopodia; Date (1931) has made similar observations, showing that under resting conditions the pH of an amoeba was 6·7–7·3, while during active movement it decreased to 6·5–7·0. Acidification of the cytoplasm has also been observed during reversible injury (Nasonov and Aleksandrov, 1937).

Many of the basic properties of the cytoplasm of the Protozoa are the result of its being a complex system of hydrophile colloids. Large and complex protein molecules are the main components of the dispersion phase in the cytoplasmic colloidal system. Most investigators agree that the dispersion medium is composed of water and the substances dissolved in it.[1] In an ultramicroscopic examination of the cytoplasm of living Protozoa in a dark field the main mass of the cytoplasm appears to be optically empty, only some organoids and some inclusions (chondriosomes, drops of fat, minute granules of protein-microsomes) being luminescent. The absence of opalescence and luminescence in the main substance of the cytoplasm is an indication of the hydrophilic character of its colloids. This is due to the fact that in hydrophile colloids the molecules of water surround and become closely linked with the individual micelles (particles) of the protein dispersion phase. A so-called solvate aqueous membrane is formed, in which the water

[1] A different point of view as to the nature of the dispersion medium has been given by Lepeschkin (1936a, b), who believes that the dispersion medium is a complex compound of proteins and lipids, which he calls vitaproteid or vitaid.

molecules are orientated perpendicularly to the micelles. The layers of water molecules further removed from the micelles are less and less regularly orientated, passing gradually to the irregular distribution of molecules characteristic of liquids (Fig. 2). Owing to the presence of the solvate membrane, there is no sharp delimitation between the dispersion medium and the micelles, therefore the incident rays are not reflected by the micelles and the hydrophile colloid is optically empty. The extreme variability of cytoplasmic structure and its aggregate state is related to the colloidal state of its proteins. The structure of the cytoplasm changes with the physiological state of the protozoon and with the conditions in the surrounding medium. In contrast with the former concept of a stable uniform structure of cytoplasm, postulated by the morphological theories, a wide variability of its

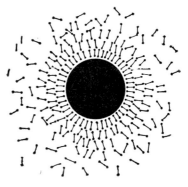

Fig. 2. Structure of solvate membrane around particle of hydrophile colloid. (From Dogiel, 1951.)

structure has now been established. Processes of reversible gelation, with a conversion of the protein colloids from the state of a liquid aggregate (sol) to a jelly (gel) take place continuously. As a result of these processes taking place on the periphery of the cytoplasm, denser outer layers are formed: the pellicle and the ectoplasm. The reversible processes of gelation are closely linked with the simplest forms of amoeboid movement.

As shown by numerous investigations on members of different classes of Protozoa, the structure and aggregate state of cytoplasm are greatly influenced by conditions in the environment, such as: changes in salt content (Fig. 3), osmotic pressure, hydrogen-ion concentration, temperature, and the action of electric currents. As an example, here are some data on the changes in the state of the cytoplasm of *Amoeba radiata* under the influence of diverse external factors, taken from Giersberg (1922). Giersberg used weak solutions of various substances, in which the amoeba lived for days and even weeks without interrupting its movement and multiplication. It was shown that hydrochloric acid and sodium hydroxide usually produced a swelling of the hydrophile colloids. When *A. radiata* was placed in weak solutions of hydrochloric acid or sodium hydroxide (0·00015 M), the protein granules were gradually dissolved and all the cytoplasm became transparent and homogeneous. Exposure for a few days to these solutions caused further swelling and hydration with the appearance of tiny drops of liquid in the cytoplasmic colloid. As these drops accumulated the cytoplasm acquired a kind of alveolar structure. In weak solutions of sugar or sodium acetate the cytoplasm gradually became dehydrated, its movements were slowed down, and a large number of protein granules accumulated in it

Under the influence of weak solutions of salts (Li Cl, K Cl, Na Cl, Ca Cl$_2$) the cytoplasm grew darker when observed by transmitted light and the number of granules increased. These reversible intra-vital changes of microscopically visible structures are accompanied by alterations in the form of the pseudopodia. Numerous other investigators, some quoted above, have referred to similar changes in cytoplasmic structure under the influence of various factors.

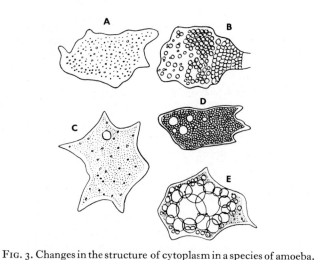

Fig. 3. Changes in the structure of cytoplasm in a species of amoeba.

(*A*) original form; (*B*) increase of the grains due to the action of dehydrating substances; (*C-E*) changes under influence of substances promoting swelling. (Giersberg, 1922.)

These investigations show that the structures of cytoplasm described previously by the supporters of the morphological theories, although occurring under certain conditions, cannot be considered as fundamental structures determining the living properties of the cytoplasm.

General non-specific changes, linked with colloido-chemical processes, are brought about in the cytoplasm of the Protozoa, as in plant and animal cells, by various external injurious factors. The term 'paranecrosis' was suggested in 1934 by Nasonov and Aleksandrov for these complex changes. According to them, paranecrosis is characterized by: (1) a decrease in the dispersion capacity of the cytoplasmic nuclear colloids, (2) an increase of cytoplasmic viscosity, preceded at times by a decrease, (3) an increased affinity of the cytoplasm and nucleus for certain staining agents (Nasonov and Aleksandrov, 1940). The whole of this complex of changes characterizing paranecrosis has been observed in various representatives of the Protozoa. Ultramicroscopic observations of the paranecrotic changes of the cytoplasm and nucleus have been made by Makarov (1936) on *Vorticella*, *Pyxidium*, and *Colpidium*. The cytoplasm of an intact ciliate seen in a dark field is optically empty; its nucleus (macronucleus) is also either completely colourless or has a feeble blue luminescence. However, when subjected to reversible injuries (e.g. the action of weak acetic acid) the ultramicroscopic picture resolved is quite different: the macronucleus acquires a strong fluorescence and becomes milky-white in colour, while the cytoplasm shows signs of a diffuse fluorescence of varying degree. These paranecrotic changes are reversible, but under a larger dose of the injuring agent the cytoplasm and nucleus coagulate irreversibly.

Nasonov and Aleksandrov put forward the denaturation theory of injury to explain the nature of the changes occurring in the cytoplasm during paranecrosis. According to this theory the complex of changes in the colloidal properties of the cytoplasm produced by injury is conditioned by reversible denaturation of the original proteins.

In their normal environment Protozoa are exposed to the action of various external factors, so that paranecrotic changes must also occur under natural conditions, and represent a form of reversible changes in the structure and aggregate state of the cytoplasm and nucleus. Nasonov (1932) and Makarov (1940) have observed, in their research on certain parasitic ciliates living under anaerobic conditions in the stomach of ruminants, that the cytoplasm and nucleus of these forms, when in the natural medium of their habitat, were in a practically continuous state of paranecrosis.

The problem of the submicroscopic molecular structure of cytoplasm has been very much in the limelight during the last 10–15 years. This problem is of the greatest importance for the understanding of the most intimate processes taking place within the cell, but it lies far outside the field of protozoology. Therefore we shall restrict ourselves to a few remarks on the subject. Judging by the basic properties of cytoplasm mentioned above, the colloidal particles composing it are not spherical. One of the basic properties of cytoplasm is the formation of highly viscous gels, although the concentration of its dispersed phase represents only a fraction of that of its dispersion medium, which is mainly water. In some cases cytoplasm exhibits birefringence. Among the Protozoa this has been observed in the pseudopodia of the radiolarian *Thalassicola* and the testacean rhizopod *Miliola*. These data confirm the old observations of Engelmann (1875) on the birefringence of the axopods of the heliozoan *Actinosphaerium*, and indicate the presence in cytoplasm of submicroscopic particles with birefringence which probably depends on their shape and structure.

In a non-differentiated cytoplasm lacking birefringence, individual submicroscopic particles (submicrons) are irregularly distributed, so that the cytoplasm is isotropic. Likewise, the capacity of the cytoplasm to stretch into long thin filaments (for example the rhizopodia of rhizopods) does not conform with the conception of spherical submicrons.

The majority of investigators now agree that the colloidal particles in the cytoplasm are rod-shaped or filamentar, though spherical or nearly spherical particles may possibly exist side by side with them. Some advocates of the fibrillar submicroscopic structure of cytoplasm (Frey-Wyssling, 1948) attribute to it most of the fundamental properties of cells, such as the preservation of the shape of the cell, the physical properties of the cytoplasm, the dissociation of enzymes, and others. It has been accepted by most investigators that the fibrillar submicrons of cytoplasm are built of polypeptide chains of amino acids linked by their side chains with various other chemical components—lipids, enzymes, and others. The differentiation of various microscopically visible fibrillar structures (supporting fibrils, myofibrils) takes place as a result of an orderly orientation of the submicrons of the cytoplasm and their partial dehydration.

In spite of the large amount of research on this question, the problem of the submicroscopic structure of cytoplasm is far from being solved. Various, often contradictory, points of view are expressed on it. Nevertheless the presence in cytoplasm of rod-shaped or filamentar colloidal particles, often called structural proteins, is most probable, as indicated by many facts, some of which are given above. Our knowledge of the submicroscopic structure of cytoplasm has been greatly enlarged during the last 10–15 years by electron-microscopic research. Numerous investigations have been carried out by this method on various tissues and cells of multicellular organisms and Protozoa. Many investigators have described special small granules or microsomes in the cytoplasm with a diameter of 100–200 Å (Brachet, 1957). These granules are rich in RNA and in lipids. Most cytologists think that they take an active part in the synthesis of cytoplasmic proteins. Apart from these microsomes, some special lamellated, composed of a series of membranes arranged in parallel pairs, have been recorded in the cytoplasm, especially in the glandular cells. Each membrane is no more than 40 Å thick, and minute grains, similar to the microsomes, known as Palade's small granules or ultramicrosomes, usually lie along the membrane (Palade, 1955). These structures are called the 'ergastoplasm', thereby restoring the old term suggested in 1897 by Garier for basophilic cytoplasmic inclusions, though many workers used the term 'endoplasmic reticulum' instead of ergastoplasm. It has been suggested that the microsomes are formed as a result of the breaking up of ergastoplasm (Porter, 1954, 1955). However, the occurrence of microsomes and ergastoplasm in the cytoplasm of the Protozoa has not yet been properly studied. 'Granule-bearing membranes' forming an endoplasmic network have been observed in the cytoplasm of certain Protozoa, for example in the amoeba, *Hartmannella astronyxis* (Deutsch and Swann, 1959); in flagellates, *Trichomonas* (Anderson and Beams, 1959) and *Trichonympha* (Grimstone, 1959); in Astomatous ciliates (de Puytoras, 1958), *Colpidium colpoda* (Chejsin and Mosevič, 1962), and *Paramecium caudatum* (Schneider, 1960); in gregarines (Grassé and Théodorides, 1958). We have also observed in *P. caudatum* (Fig. 4.) granular membranes of the endoplasmic network forming canals with distensions in the shape of small vacuoles or bubbles. However, no granular membranes were observed in *Euplotes* (Roth, 1956), *Pyrsonympha* (Grasse, 1956), and in the gregarine *Melanoplus* (Beams *et al.*, 1959). The functional significance of the endoplasmic network in various Protozoa has

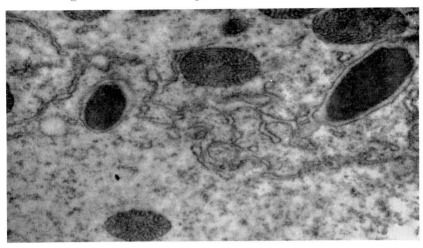

FIG. 4. Endoplasmic reticulum in cytoplasm of *Paramecium caudatum*. (Electron-micrograph, ×40,000: Original.)

not yet been fully elucidated. It is probable that on the surface of the granular membranes, as well as in connexion with the minute granules of RNA scattered between the membranes and the cytoplasm, synthesis of proteins is taking place. The synthesized substances are probably distributed throughout the whole cell through the canals of the endoplasmic network.

The problem of the permeability of cytoplasm is most important for the understanding of many aspects of the physiology of the Protozoa. The concentration of salts and other soluble substance in the cell (including that of the Protozoa) is not the same as in the surrounding medium. A cell is certainly not a simple osmometer, into which various substances penetrate by osmosis from the surrounding medium until the concentrations are equalized. For example, in the freshwater Protozoa the salt concentration in the cytoplasm is considerably higher than in the surrounding medium. Cytoplasm has a selective permeability. Two different theories have been advanced to explain the peculiarities of cell permeability. In one of them the characteristics of cell permeability are explained by the occurrence of a special submicroscopic membrane, with selective permeability, at the interface between the cytoplasm and the surrounding liquid medium. Overton, in the nineties, published the first comprehensive theory of membrane permeability, according to which the cells are enclosed in a delicate lipid membrane. Overton thinks that substances most soluble in lipids penetrate most easily into the cell. The membrane theory was later modified considerably because many phenomena could not be explained by it. Traube (1904) expounded his view that penetrability depends mainly on the adsorption conditions at the cell surface, rather than on differential solubility in lipids. Substances more readily absorbed would penetrate into the cell more easily. Some workers have pointed out the significance of the usual negative charge on the cell membrane which prevents the penetration of similarly charged ions.

According to the 'ultra-filter' theory, the cell membrane is regarded as a fine sieve, and penetration through it depends on the size and configuration of the molecules and ions, and on their electric charges. Some investigators (Wilbrandt, 1938; Höber, 1945) combine the ultra-filter theory with that of the lipid covering, assuming that some substances penetrate into the cell by dissolving in the lipid sections of the membrane, while others pass through the ultra-pores. This theory, with various modifications, is widely accepted.

Though much research has been done on this problem, many aspects of cell permeability cannot be explained by the membrane theories. In particular the well-known fact of the change of permeability with the physiological state of the cell is difficult to explain in terms of the membrane concept.

Soviet cytophysiologists Aleksandrov, Nasonov, and Trošin and their collaborators have severely criticized the membrane theory. They think that the penetration of a substance into a cell (including that of a protozoon) and the distribution of the substance between the cell and the surrounding medium depend on the properties of the ground substance of the cytoplasm, viz. its proteins, rather than on the selective properties of some hypothetical submicroscopic cell membrane.

A change in the adsorption properties of the proteins of the cytoplasm and nucleus, in particular as a result of injury and paranecrosis, is, according to Nasonov and Aleksandrov (1940), the main cause of change in cytoplasmic permeability. 'We think that it is time to renounce the cell membrane concept as a general principle and to seek for the solution of a whole series of so far mysterious physiological problems in the properties of the whole mass of living matter rather than in some or other properties of a hypothetical cell membrane.'

In our opinion, the advantage of the Nasonov–Aleksandrov theory lies in the fact that it associates the fundamental properties of the cytoplasm with its protein substratum, instead of attributing them to hypothetical surface membranes arbitrarily endowed with various properties.

In accepting the adsorption theory of the distribution of substances between the cell and the medium there is no need to deny the occurrence on the surface of the cell of very thin membranes formed at the boundary between the cytoplasm and the medium. On the contrary, the occurrence of such membranes, with a thickness of about 100 Å, has been confirmed by the latest data of electron microscopy. The difference between the membrane and the adsorption theories does not lie in the acceptance or denial of the presence of membranes, but in the estimation of their relative significance in the distribution of substances between the cell and the medium. The peculiar properties of the membrane are held to be responsible by the former theory, while according to the adsorption theory the distribution of substances is conditioned by the properties of the main mass of the cytoplasm.

In the Protozoa the ground substance of the cytoplasm is not uniform; it is usually differentiated into zones or layers. In some cases these cytoplasmic layers are very variable, being readily converted one into another during the life processes of the protozoon (for instance in amoebae); in other cases these differentiations are more permanent. Let us consider as an example the differentiation of the cytoplasm of a large amoeba, *Amoeba proteus* (Fig. 5), as described in a series of papers by Mast (1926a–1927).

The body of the amoeba is enclosed in a thin (0·25μ) elastic and apparently strong membrane, referred to by Mast as the plasmolemma. G. Pappas (1959) has shown, by electron microscopic analysis of *A. proteus*, that the plasmolemma consists of extremely thin fibrils, with a diameter of 80 Å, lying parallel to each other. Beneath the plasmolemma is a layer of fluid cytoplasm which becomes thickest in the region where pseudopodia are formed. Still deeper within the body of the amoeba is a fairly thick layer of jelly-like cytoplasm—Mast's plasmagel (this layer is comparable to the ectoplasm of more highly organized Protozoa)—in which the contractile vacuole lies. Finally, beneath the plasmagel is the central fluid part of the cytoplasm, the plasmasol, which is occupied by the nucleus.

All these differentiations of amoebic cytoplasm are reversible: plasmagel and plasmasol are continuously being converted into each other during the process of pseudopodium formation. When the plasmalemma is damaged, it is readily reformed from the layers underneath it.

In other classes of Protozoa the differentiation of the cytoplasm is more stable. In the majority of flagellates, ciliates, and sporozoa (for instance gregarines) a pellicle is differentiated at the surface of the body by a thickening of the cytoplasm. The pellicle is often very thin and elastic, so that changes in body shape are not prevented. Many flagellates (such as *Astasia*, *Distigma*, and others) can easily change the shape of their body.

In others a denser pellicle enables the body to retain a permanent shape characteristic for the given species. An examination of the structure of the pellicle of some ciliates (*Paramecium, Colpidium, Condylostoma*, and others) by electron microscopy has shown that it is composed of two layers disposed at some distance from each other (Fig. 6). Each layer in its turn is composed of two compact membranes separated by a less dense substance (Sedar and Porter, 1955; Ehret and Powers, 1959; and others). The outer surface of the

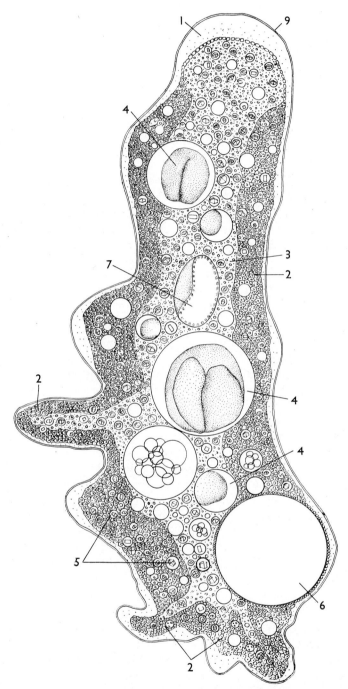

FIG. 5. Optical section of *Amoeba proteus*.

1, contractile vacuole; 2, food vacuole; 3, nucleus; 4, food vacuole; 5, layer of dense cytoplasm (endoplasm); 6, layer of fluid cytoplasm (ectoplasm); 7, plasmolemma. (From Mast, 1926.)

pellicle of some species of flagellates (certain euglenoids) is sculptured with minute denticles, papillae, &c. Under the pellicle there is usually a layer of ectoplasm. Strictly speaking the pellicle should be regarded as a thickened outer layer of ectoplasm. The ectoplasm differs from the inner endoplasm in having a greater density and a smaller number of inclusions, and by the absence of food vacuoles. In living organisms the ectoplasm appears to be lighter in colour than the endoplasm, and it frequently presents a regular alveolar structure.

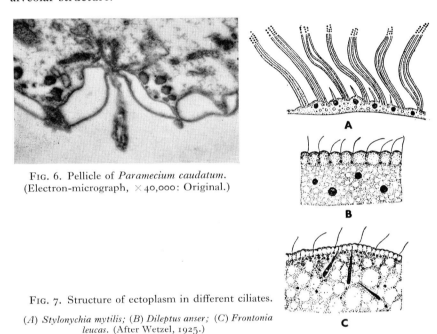

FIG. 6. Pellicle of *Paramecium caudatum*.
(Electron-micrograph, ×40,000: Original.)

FIG. 7. Structure of ectoplasm in different ciliates.

(*A*) *Stylonychia mytilis;* (*B*) *Dileptus anser;* (*C*) *Frontonia leucas.* (After Wetzel, 1925.)

Wetzel (1925) distinguished the following main types of ectoplasmic structure in the ciliates (Fig. 7): (*a*) simple pellicle with endoplasm directly beneath it (e.g. *Stylonychia*); (*b*) pellicle+alveolar layer: the pellicle is succeeded by a layer of ectoplasm of alveolar structure, in which the alveolae lie parallel in one row, while the endoplasm lies directly below the alveolar layer (e.g. *Dileptus, Bursaria*); (*c*) pellicle +alveolar layer+cortical plasma: in this type of ectoplasmic structure the alveolar layer overlies another layer of thickened homogeneous plasma called the cortical plasma, the deeper layers of which grade into the endoplasm (e.g. *Frontonia, Paramecium*).

The differentiation of the cytoplasm into layers is particularly complex in ciliates of the order Entodiniomorpha (parasitic in the alimentary tract of hoofed animals). Strelkov (1939), in his comprehensive study of the morphology of this group, distinguishes the following layers (Fig. 8): (*a*) the cuticle, formed of three distinct layers, (*b*) the ectoplast—the external layer of much thickened protoplasm, including fibrillar structures, (*c*) the boundary membrane—a thin membranous structure separating the ectoplast from the deeper layers of the cytoplasm, (*d*) the endoplasmic sac—the largest central part of the cytoplasm, where the processes of digestion take place.

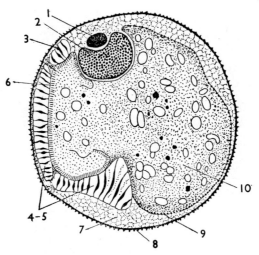

FIG. 8. Cross-section through body of *Epidinium ecaudatum* (Ophryoscolecidae Entodiniomorpha).

1, micronucleus; 2, macronucleus; 3–5, skeletal plates; 6, pharyngeal fibril; 7, ectoplasm; 8, cuticle; 9, longitudinal fibrils; 10, endoplasmic sac. (From Strelkov, 1939.)

In spite of the considerable complexity and relative stability of cytoplasmic differentiation found in the higher Protozoa, the different parts can be converted one into another in the course of their life activities and development. These transformations are based on colloido-chemical changes of the cytoplasmic proteins. During the formation of cysts, which is of frequent occurrence in many ciliates, the differentiation of the cytoplasm into layers disappears, and a dense protective cyst-wall is formed. Differentiation of the cytoplasm takes place again when the ciliate hatches from the cyst (excystment). Analogous processes take place during a sexual reproduction by fission or agamogony, and in some cases after conjugation.

The cytoplasm of the Protozoa contains numerous organoids and inclusions of varying physiological significance, the nature of which will be considered in a separate section.

MITOCHONDRIA OR CHONDRIOSOMES

The cytoplasm of Protozoa is rich in various kinds of granular inclusions of different size, shape, chemical composition, and physiological significance. Among the multiformity of inclusions, one type of granular bodies, known as mitochondria or chondriosomes, has in the last 40–50 years especially attracted the attention of investigators. First discovered in the cells of Metazoa and then in those of the most diverse organs and tissues, mitochondria were later found, with the same uniformity, in the cytoplasm of the Protozoa.

Mitochondria can be detected by special technique based on their following characteristics. Typical mitochondria stain black or brown-grey when treated with osmic acid (not so deeply, however, as the Golgi apparatus), reduce pyrogallol, are preserved by liquids which fix lipids, and are basophilic. On the other hand, when treated with acetic acid, they are stained either very slightly or not at all. Finally, intravital staining with Janus-green is characteristic of them. The identification of mitochondria, however, is frequently difficult, since the same staining reactions are characteristic not only of them but, to a certain extent, of the lipids, and, moreover, characteristic reactions are not always obtained with the mitochondria as themselves, for example, the selective reaction with Janus-green. Chondriosomes can also be detected in living bodies, especially by the method of phase-contrast microscopy.

The first work of any importance in the field of protozoology belongs to Fauré-Fremiet (1910), who has investigated the mitochondria in ciliates and has demonstrated their wide distribution in this group of Protozoa. This was followed by a series of works on mitochondria in Protozoa. Among them may be noted the investigations of Joyet-Lavergne (1926) and others on Sporozoa, and the works of Russian scientists—such as Poljanskij (1934), Rumjancev and Vermel (1925), Cinger (1929), and others.

Mitochondria (Fig. 9) are minute bodies, which are either spherical or rod-shaped (mitochondria proper) or rosary-shaped (chondriomites) or filamentar (chondrioconts) forms scattered in the cytoplasm; the whole complex of these structures in the cell has the general name of the chondriosome.

Spherical mitochondria of different Protozoa vary in size from $0 \cdot 5\,\mu$ to $1 \cdot 5\,\mu$, but are more or less constant for each species. Rod-shaped mitochondria and chondrioconts may even reach a larger size, viz. up to $3 \cdot 5\,\mu$. Their number is large and cannot be determined.

In recent years our knowledge of the structure of mitochondria has been considerably enlarged as a result of intensive research carried out by electron microscopy on various multicellular cells and Protozoa. It was found that in spite of the variety of their external appearance and size, the inner ultramicroscopic structure of different organisms is very much the same (Sedar and Porter, 1955; Sedar and Rudzinska, 1956; Randall and Jackson, 1958; Pappas, 1959; and others). Each chondriosome has a double membrane (Fig. 10). Numerous digitiform processes in the shape of tubules (microvilli) are given off from its inner membrane into its cavity. The intervals between the tubes are probably filled with a fluid. In the cells of multicellular organisms, the mitochondria have a similar structure.

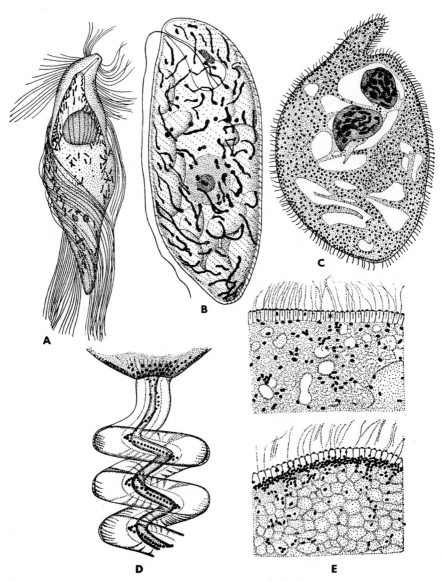

Fig. 9. Mitochondria of various Protozoa.

(A) *Trichonympha agilis* (Duboscq and Grassé, 1933); (B) *Euglena* (Hollande, 1942); (C) *Trachelius ovum* (Fauré-Fremiet, 1910); (D) *Vorticella convellaria*: stalk (Fauré-Fremiet, 1910); (E) *Bursaria truncatella*: from underneath, neutral individual; from above, conjugation. (Poljanskij, 1934.)

They differ, however, from the protozoal mitochondria, in that the inner processes from the walls are not tubules but represent incomplete partitions (cristae mitochondriales). However, in some Protozoa (*Euglena*) such partitions are also present in mitochondria. The presence of microvilli and cristae increases the internal surface in the mitochondria considerably. This is probably of importance for their enzymic activity.

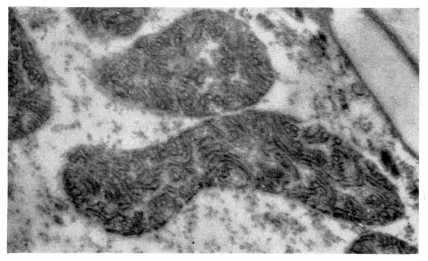

FIG. 10. Mitochondria of *Paramecium caudatum*. (Electron-micrograph: Original.)

Proteins are the main chemical constituents of mitochondria, which contain in addition fats (glyceroses), various lipids (among them phospholipids), and small quantities of ribonucleic acid. Moreover, mitochondria are the carriers of complex enzyme systems.

At a first glance no regularity can be observed in the distribution of chondriosomes: they seem to be scattered more or less uniformly throughout the whole cytoplasm. However, a careful perusal of the abundant literature on the subject shows that, as a general rule, the less differentiated the various organoids in the body of Protozoa are, the smaller their variety, and the more uniform the structure of the cytoplasm, the more regular is the distribution of chondriosomes. On the contrary, with the increase of the internal differentiation of the cytoplasm a more regular and definite distribution—though it varies in different cases—of chondriosomes in the body is more frequently observed. Thus there is a uniformly scattered distribution of mitochondria in *Trichamoeba*, Vermel (1925) notes the irregular distribution of mitochondria in the cytoplasm of *Amoeba hydroxena*, Sassuchin (1929) writes the same about *Endamoeba blattae*, while Rumjancev and Vermel (1925) state that in *Actinosphaerium* 'there is no regularity in the distribution of the chondriosome'. However, the distribution of mitochondria in Mastigophora and Ciliata is frequently more definite. In *Peranema* mitochondria lie directly under its pellicula along its spiral bands. In *Haematococcus pluvialis* mitochondria are distributed mostly around its pyrenoids and under its pellicula.

The arrangement of mitochondria in a row in the stalk of *Vorticella* (Fig. 9) (Fauré-Fremiet), their clustering around the contractile vacuole (noted by many investigators), and their sub-pellicular arrangement in many ciliates, all provide evidence of definite pattern in the distribution of mito-chondria in ciliates. In some cases, moreover, it has been possible to demonstrate a regular modification of the distribution of mitochondria in the course of the life-cycle of ciliates. Thus, Poljanskij (1934) has shown that in the neutral individuals of *Bursaria* the mitochondria are distributed more or less uniformly in the cytoplasm, but during conjugation they move in large numbers to the periphery, forming a thick layer under the ecto-plasm and around the products of division of the micronuclei (Fig. 9).

In an attempt to draw a general conclusion from these data, Horning (1927) says that mitochondria tend to accumulate in the neighbourhood of various boundary membranes, crowding at times around the macronucleus of ciliates (*Nyctotherus*) and especially around its food vacuoles. It seems to us that the majority of the data observed conform to Horning's concept.

A uniform distribution of mitochondria is commonly found in those forms of Sporozoa which have a spherical body, devoid of organelles, such as the intra-cellular stages of Coccidia, while in gregarines, fixed by the protomerite to the intestinal wall of its host, the anterior part of the body is usually more or less free of mitochondria (Joyet-Lavergne, 1926). Thus, apparently, in Sporozoa a greater morphological differentiation is linked with the differentiation in the distribution of mitochondria.

The fate of mitochondria during the multiplication of Protozoa is an important problem. How is the number of mitochondria, reduced during multiplication, restored? Are the new mitochondria formed only by division of the old ones, or can they appear anew in the cytoplasm similarly to the grains of glycogen, starch, &c.? The early investigators of the mitochondria in Protozoa (for example, Fauré-Fremiet, 1910) already established the capacity of mitochondria to multiply by binary fission, and this was con-firmed by all later data. Fauré-Fremiet (Fig. 11) gives an excellent picture of the gradual stretching out of mitochondria, of the swelling of both their ends in the form of a dumb-bell, and their final constriction into two parts. This kind of fission is most easily observed during division of the protozoon itself, for example in ciliates. It is much more difficult to prove the forma-tion of mitochondria *de novo* in the cytoplasm.

However, indirect evidence of this is provided by observations (on *Trypanosoma, Amoeba, Flabellula,* and *Monocystis*) that mitochondria, normally absent in certain Protozoa, might temporarily appear in their plasma under the effect of some external factors. Horning mentions the absence of mitochondria in gregarines at some definite stages of their development (in sporozoites)—thereby indicating that they are newly formed at other stages. However, such observations do not appear convincing to us, the less so since the method of diagnosis of the presence of mitochondria is not quite reliable, because their characteristic reactions, either to staining or other techniques, are sometimes difficult to obtain.

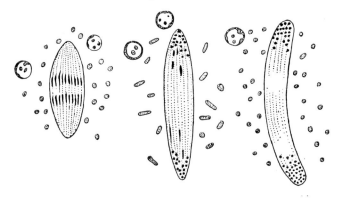

FIG. 11. Division of mitochondria and of the micronucleus in *Carchesium polypinum* observed *in vivo*. (Fauré-Fremiet, 1910.)

It has also been suggested that mitochondria can be evolved from microsomes (for a survey of the literature, see Runnström, 1952). There is, however, no definite proof of this, especially in the case of Protozoa.

The problem of the functional significance of the chondriosomes and the part played by them in the cell in general and in the body of Protozoa in particular is very complicated; and has not been fully investigated although there is abundant and extremely contradictory literature on the subject. The different and at times contradictory opinions expressed in regard to the role of chondriosomes is due partly to the fact that until quite recently only morphological methods were applied to the study of their function; it was approached by the study of their distribution, their topographic relation to other cell organoids and inclusions. Much progress has been made only in the last ten years, owing to a wide application of cytophysiological and biochemical methods of research. The isolation of the pure chondriosome fraction from the cell by fractional centrifugation was of special importance. The enzyme systems linked with the chondriosomes were defined and analysed by biochemical examination of the homogenates of chondriosomes obtained by centrifugation. Most of the investigations were made on Metazoan cells.

Many investigators described the part played by chondriosomes in the formation of certain organoids of the cell (for example myofibrils) and in the accumulation of food reserves (for instance glycogen). However, these data, mostly obtained from various Metazoan cells by morphological methods, cannot be considered as sufficiently reliable.

As has been established by the above-mentioned new methods, chondriosomes are bearers of a number of enzyme systems and their role in the life of the cells is therefore important. Already in 1926 Joyet-Lavergne stated, on the basis of not very accurate cytochemical reactions, that mitochondria act as centres of oxydation-reduction processes. These data were fully confirmed by subsequent investigations. It is now established that chondriosomes are carriers of a complex enzyme system, stimulating the reactions of the Krebs cycle, based on the conversion of pyruvic acid and accompanied by dehydration and decarboxylation. Moreover, chondriosomes are linked with a system of cytochromes, upon which the final stages of dehydration up to the formation of water depend.

All the chemical conversions linked with the enzyme systems of the chondriosome are accompanied by liberation of energy. Chondriosomes contain a set of enzymes, by the action of which the energy of the substratum is converted into a form in which it is utilized by the cell for its work and for the processes of synthesis; such is, generally speaking, the function of chondriosomes in the physiology of the cell and in that of Protozoa. At present there is abundant experimental evidence in cytology indicating that in the cells of multicellular organisms mitochondria are specialized for various functions of the tissues. Thus, for example, some mitochondria in the muscles are closely connected with the production of ATP, the source of energy in the muscle contraction; in a number of cases mitochondria are found to be associated with the secretory activity, &c. The function of mitochondria in Protozoa may also be specific: thus there are numerous data indicating their role in intracellular digestion.

An accumulation of chondriosomes has been observed round the food vacuoles in amoebae (Mast and Doyle, 1935) and ciliates. Chondriosomes are, possibly, the source of the enzymes of hydrolytic digestion. Accumulation of chondriosomes in the ectoplasm of many ciliates is probably linked with their role as liberators of energy required for the activity of cilia. In a number of cases mitochondria in Protozoa are closely linked with the formation and deposition of reserve substances (glycogen, lipid granules, and others) in the cytoplasm. Many investigators have recorded the deposition of glycogen and lipid granules within mitochondria. All this is in agreement with their enzyme activity, as described above.

FOOD RESERVES OF THE CYTOPLASM

In the process of nutrition, part of the food taken in is generally utilized directly, while a certain part, as a result of complex metabolism, is deposited in the cytoplasm of the Protozoa in the form of reserve food, to be consumed later in the processes of growth and multiplication. Reserve substances are of varied chemical nature: they are composed of carbohydrates, fats, and proteins. In most cases a protozoon has the capability of forming in its cytoplasm food reserves of different chemical composition. However, some groups are distinguished from others by the composition of their reserve food. Various carbohydrates are the most common reserve food among Protozoa.

Carbohydrates. Starch and allied substances (paramylum) are formed mainly in autotrophic coloured Protozoa, i.e. in some Mastigophora.

The occurrence of starch proper has been proved for two orders of flagellates: Phytomonadida and Cryptomonodida.

In Euglenida starch is replaced by an allied carbohydrate, paramylum, which does not give the colour reactions characteristic of starch; for instance, it is not stained blue by iodine. At times paramylum forms large inclusions in the cytoplasm, their shapes being characteristic of definite different species: transparent calyxes in *Euglena gracilis* and spiral whorls in *E. sanguinea*, &c.

Starch and paramylum synthesis is frequently genetically linked with pyrenoids, although the exact function of the latter is not fully explained. Pyrenoids are mostly spherical structures situated within the chromatophores or closely adjacent to them. They are capable of division and this is often simultaneous with that of the organism itself. There are some indications, however, of the capacity of pyrenoids to be formed anew. Their connexion with the formation of polysaccharides seems most probable since the pyrenoids are often tightly enclosed in a laminated paramylum membrane. Pyrenoids have a homogeneous structure; they show some affinity for nuclear stains; and, according to some authors (Czurda, 1933*a, b*), they are of protein nature.

However, starch may be formed also in flagellates devoid of pyrenoids, either in the form of small granules, or, as has been mentioned above, in the form of large inclusions.

It is interesting to note that a number of flagellates—*Polytoma* (Phytomonadida), *Chilomonas*, *Astasia* (Euglenida), and others—retain their ability to synthesize starch, although they have lost their chromatophores and their capacity for autotrophic feeding.

Glycogen and its allied carbohydrates (paraglycogen) are the most common food reserves in Protozoa (Fig. 12). However, the difference between glycogen and paraglycogen (a term introduced by Bütschli), viz. their solubility in water, is not sufficiently definite or precise. Thus glycogen is soluble in cold water, while paraglycogen is practically insoluble in it, but is soluble in hot water. There are also intermediate stages between these extremes. Apparently in some Protozoa glycogen combines chemically with proteins, giving rise to glycoproteids which are less soluble in water than glycogen. Paraglycogen appears usually in the form of small granules, which are stained by iodine to a brown-grey or purple-grey colour, and turn wine-red on addition of strong sulphuric acid. After prolonged boiling with dilute sulphuric acid glycogen is converted into a reducing sugar. An intensive staining with Best's carmine and a number of other characteristic microchemical reactions (PA5 reaction) are obtained both with glycogen and paraglycogen.

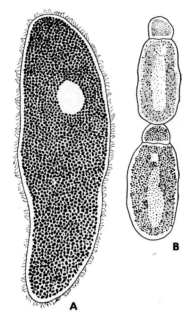

The endoplasm of gregarines is filled with rounded granules of paraglycogen with a star-shaped centre. *Difflugia* possesses two types of granules: small homogeneous spheres and larger oval-shaped bodies with a central granule. In the latter case the small body contains apparently two types of substances. The oval-shaped small bodies of *Difflugia* are not completely soluble in ptyalin, and, judging by their colour reactions, they contain glycoprotein as well as glycogen.

In Entodiniomorpha paraglycogen occurs in the endoplasm in the form of granules with a denser spherical central part; moreover, some of the glycogen is distributed also in the skeletal plates, occupying the inside of the mesh of which the plates are formed. The so-called glycogen 'vacuoles' found in the cysts of many parasitic amoebae, in the amoeboid sporoplasm of many Myxosporidia, &c., is the other type of paraglycogen accumulations.

FIG. 12. Glycogen inclusions in various Protozoa.

(*A*) *Balantidium elongatum* (original figure by K. M. Suchanova). (*B*) *Gregarina limnophili* (original figure by J. A. Stein).

Attempts have been made in the last fifteen years to explain the process of the formation of paraglycogen aggregates. It was found that in some cases their deposition is in some way connected with mitochondria. For instance, in *Ichthyophthirius* paraglycogen appears in the shape of minute droplets inside the spherical mitochondria; the latter then bursts, and its remnants, in the shape of rods, stick to the surface of the glycogen granules in the process of formation, and are then gradually dissolved. Joyet-Lavergne (1926) mentions only a close morphological contact between the mitochondria and paraglycogen granules in gregarines, but did not recognize a genetic link between them. In any case paraglycogen granules may be formed in the cytoplasm without the participation of mitochondria.

It is interesting that the formation of glycogen is dependent on temperature. Zinkin (1929) notes that in *Stentor* glycogen is accumulated at low temperatures and consumed at high temperatures. In the flagellate *Cryptobia helicis* glycogen granules are formed in close contact with the cords of the parabasal body in winter; these glycogen aggregates are absent in the summer.

The dependence of glycogen accumulation on the state of nutrition of the animal is even more evident. Stores of glycogen disappear during starvation periods, and grow larger during abundant feeding. The causal correlation between the absence of glycogen and starvation is clearly seen in the ciliate family *Ophryoscolecidae*: during abundant feeding with starch their cytoplasm is filled with glycogen granules after $2\frac{1}{2}$ hours. However, 16 hours after feeding remnants of glycogen are left only in some parts of the cytoplasm. Observations on certain regional accumulation and consumption of glycogen in *Trichonympha* are most curious. Its cytoplasm is divided by a special paranuclear corbula into two—the anterior and posterior sections. Both sections contain glycogen (Fig. 13), but during

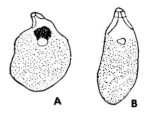

FIG. 13. Glycogen in *Trichonympha agilis*. (*A*) normal individual; (*B*) individual that had lost glycogen reserve after fall of temperature and increase of O₂ pressure. (After Yamasaki, 1937.)

starvation it disappears first from the large posterior section, and only later from the corbula, after which the animal dies. However, when termites with *Trichonympha* are placed in an atmosphere of oxygen at a low temperature, the glycogen first disappears from the corbula, and the animal perishes, even when some glycogen is left in the posterior half of its body. Therefore Yamasaki (1937), in our opinion, was not quite right in concluding that the synthesis and accumulation of glycogen takes place only in the posterior part of the body, while its consumption is restricted to the corbula. Trypanosomes were found to be constantly poor not only in glycogen but in all other carbohydrates. In these flagellates the accumulation of food reserves presents great difficulties, owing to their intensive metabolism: trypanosomes consume in a day an amount of sugar equal to three times the weight of their body.

Thus in Protozoa glycogen is frequently found only at some stages of their life-cycle, depending on the above-mentioned and other factors. There is a tendency to accumulate glycogen and other reserve substances during the stages of macrogametes and zygotes, especially when they pass over to the resting state. Chejsin (1947, 1958) records only minute amounts of glycogen in the schizonts and macrogametocytes of *Eimeria*, while in macrogametes there is a mass accumulation of glycogen granules; moreover fat droplets appear near the centre of the gametes, and protein granules on the periphery. When isogametes are formed during the sexual process, reserve substances may be deposited in both partners: for example, according to Dogiel (1935), in *Polytoma* both kinds of gametes differ greatly from neutral individuals in that the former are packed with paramylum granules.

Leucosin is a carbohydrate most characterstic of the flagellate order Chrysomonadida, in which it is found either in the form of highly refractive globules, or as spheres lying in the posterior part of the body.

Fats and lipids

Under this title are included all fats and lipids, deposited as granules or drops (Fig. 14), during the active stage of the life of Protozoa and consumed

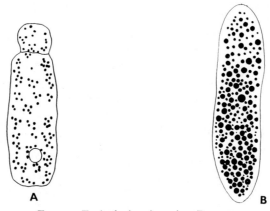

FIG. 14. Fat inclusions in various Protozoa.

(*A*) *Gregarina limnophili* (original drawing by J. A. Stein).
(*B*) *Balantidium elongatum* (original drawing by K. M. Suchanova).

by them either during starvation or encystation. Fat reserves have been found in many Protozoa, which is not in conformity with the low capacity of the protozoon to digest fats. Direct data on fat digestion exist mainly for amoebae, which digest drops of cod-liver oil, olive oil, cotton-seed oil, &c., swallowed by them. The ability of ciliates to digest the fats from fatty emulsions (*Paramecium*, *Balantidium*) has also been proved. It is noteworthy that large fat inclusions are observed mostly among the planktonic and especially in marine Protozoa. Thus, large oil-drops are deposited in the radiolarians *Spumellaria*, especially in its central capsule. Fats, apparently, also occur in the body of *Phaeodoria*, which sometimes even suffer from fatty degeneration of their plasma and nucleus. Oil-drops, sometimes coloured yellow or orange, are frequently found in the cytoplasm of Peridinea. In *Noctiluca* the plasmatic strands are studded with minute droplets of oil throughout the whole body. Fat inclusions are frequent also in the fresh-water plankton Mastigophora, which possess chromatophores.

In the cases cited fat inclusions are obviously playing a double role, viz. of food reserves and of hydrostatic apparatus. Moreover, the luminescence capacity of many Dinoflagellata, the radiolarians and especially *Noctiluca*, is linked with the presence of fat inclusions: thus in *Noctiluca* the minute fat-drops scattered in its cytoplasm are luminescent. Luminescence is usually stimulated by external irritations, such as shaking, electric currents, the action of alkalis or acids; moreover the presence of oxygen is essential for luminescence.

Nirenstein (1905) was the first to observe an accumulation of fat reserves in the form of small droplets in feeding *Paramecium*, in which large amounts were stored when the diet was suitable. Since then this phenomenon has been observed in the case of many Protozoa. The fat content in a cell may sometimes be very considerable, thus the amount of fats in coccidia of *Eimeria gadi* reaches 3·55 per cent. and in *Noctiluca* even 12 per cent. of their dry weight. However, the visible fats in the cytoplasm form only a part of the whole reserve in the cell, since some of the lipids combine with the proteins and cannot be traced by the microtechnical methods used for the detection of fats. Some idea of such combined lipids can be obtained only by special methods. Thus Heilbrunn (1936) demonstrated an increase of lipid granules in *Amoeba proteus* by placing them in a dilute solution of ammonia salts; in his opinion it was due to an increase of alkalinity in the cytoplasm, resulting in the splitting of lipoproteins into protein and lipid components. Lipoproteins are, apparently, decomposed also by ultra-violet light. According to Sassuchin's experiments (1929) a rise of temperature has the same effect on the cytoplasm of *Opalina*. In some cases special physiological and ecological conditions leading to an accumulation of fat in the plasma have been established. Thus, according to the data of Zweibaum (1922) in *Paramecium*, and those of Zinkin (1930) in *Stentor*, there is an accumulation in the case of oxygen deficiency in the surrounding medium, whereas it disappears with an increase of oxygen content in water. On the basis of these data Zinkin has succeeded in correlating the change in the amount of fat in *Stentor* plasma with certain seasonal phenomena in fresh-water reservoirs. Thus these organisms are enriched with fat in the winter when the access of oxygen to the water is made difficult by the ice cover, and the hydrogen sulphide of the ooze, retained in the water, binds up the oxygen present. An accumulation of considerable amounts of fat inclusions in the plasma has also been observed during conjugation in some ciliates (*Bursaria*: Poljanskij, 1934).

The paradoxical appearance of the so-called 'hunger fat' in ciliates has been noted by Barbarin (1937a, b, 1938), Izjumov, and others (1947). On an abundant diet ciliates contain large amounts of glycogen, as well as fat. These reserves disappear gradually on prolonged starvation but later fat reappears in the cytoplasm, apparently being formed as a result of the decomposition of the lipoprotein complex of the animal's cytoplasm. This is the so-called 'hunger fat'. The appearance of this fat might probably be connected with the phenomenon of fatty degeneration, observed in certain Protozoa during their transition to the state of depression.

Thus, for example, droplets of fat appear in the degenerating oocysts of coccidia; in *Aulacantha* fatty degeneration may take place at the expense of the plasma of the central capsule and as the result of nuclear changes.

Some specimens of *Actinophrys* revealing a state of depression by their decreased rate of division, and by other symptoms, contain an abnormally large number of fat inclusions, and after a time show a typical fatty degeneration. Complete absence of fat or minute traces of it characterize only a few blood Protozoa, especially the trypanosomes at a certain phase of their life-cycle.

Sometimes, apparently, the presence or absence of fat in the plasma can serve to a certain extent as a specific criterion; according to Chejsin (1930), the ciliate *Mesnilella multispiculata* is completely free of fat reserves, whereas the other five species of this genus investigated by him produce them.

Protein reserve substances

This term covers both the protein inclusions proper, and also substances which, together with carbohydrates and lipids, contain proteins, amino acids, nucleic acids, and some others. Only a few of this type of inclusions have been investigated in sufficient detail by microchemical methods, and therefore there is much confusion in their nomenclature and identification; e.g. chromidia, volutin, metachromatic granules, basophile granules, chromatoid bodies, protein crystals, &c.

Chromidia. Chromidia are no longer considered as chromatin inclusions, emerging from the nucleus into the cytoplasm and capable of reproducing new nuclei in the plasma. All the examples of this kind of nucleus formation have been shown to be based on inaccurate and erroneous observations by investigators during the first two decades of the twentieth century. Therefore, the theory of chromidia has been abandoned and, to avoid misunderstanding, the term 'chromidia' should not be used.

Volutin of metachromatic granules. These inclusions are found in the cytoplasm of the small Protozoa such as amoebae flagellates, gregarines, and coccidia, but are absent in ciliates. Volutin was first found in algae and bacteria by Mayer. With methylene blue it stains a metachromatic colour, i.e. violet or pink. Volutin is usually represented by spherical granules of different size.

Reichenow (1909) observed in the flagellate *Haematococcus pluvialis* the effect of phosphorus in the surrounding medium on the accumulation of volutin in the cytoplasm. *Haematococcus* grown in a medium rich in phosphorus has a greatly increased volutin content; whereas in a medium poor in phosphorus it is rapidly consumed and is not restored (Fig. 15). Reichenow's suggestion (1929) that the chemical composition of volutin is similar to that of nucleic substances has been confirmed by further investigations. According to van den Berghe (1946) volutin consists mainly of ribonucleic acid (RNA); this is confirmed by its characteristic cytochemical reactions, and by the fact that volutin is dissolved by ribonuclease, the enzyme specific for RNA.

Chromatoid bodies are inclusions in the cytoplasm of many parasitic amoebae, which are deeply stained by iron haematoxilin. They are mostly found in the form of long or short rods, and the fact that they occur in encysted individuals is an indication of their being food reserves. According to Ray and Sen Gupta (1954) these bodies contain in Entamoeba histo-lytica some amount of DNA and RNA. On the contrary, in *E. invadens*, after Barker and Deutsch (1958), the chromatoid bodies contain only RNA and non-specific proteins. An electron microscopic study has shown these

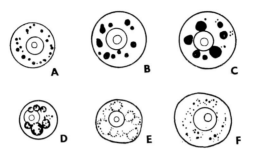

Fig. 15. 'Volutin' in *Haematococcus pluvialis*.

(*A*)–(*C*) accumulation of volutin in nutrient medium rich in phosphorus; (*D*)–(*F*) gradual disappearance of 'volutin' in medium poor in phosphorus. Nucleus visible in centre of cell. (After Reichenow, 1909.)

bodies to consist of linearly arranged dense rounded granules, approximately 70 Å in diameter. The latter become flattened after ribonuclease treatment. In an encysted amoebae the chromatoid bodies gradually disappear.

Protein crystalloids. Among the crystalline inclusions with an excretion function, which are widely distributed among the Protozoa, some may represent reserve substances. Such, apparently, as the protein crystalloids in radiolarian isospores, while *Amoeba proteus* possesses two types of crystals in the form of plates and bipyramids; the plate crystals are apparently composed of leucine.

II

THE NUCLEUS OF PROTOZOA AND ITS DIVISION

RESTING NUCLEUS

THE problems concerning the resting nucleus and the different methods of nuclear division in Protozoa, are of special interest owing to the diversity of nuclear apparatus in different groups of Protozoa. In contrast to the nuclear structure of Metazoa, which are represented by two or three main types, in Protozoa the nuclei and their methods of multiplication are so varied that it is very difficult to relate their form and construction to any common pattern. This seems to indicate that the nuclear structure in Protozoa is passing through an unstable phase of evolution, when it has not yet acquired the uniformity and stability reached by the nuclear apparatus of the Metazoa.

The number of nuclei

In most cases the cells of Protozoa contain a single nucleus. However, in all classes of Protozoa there are forms—sometimes they are numerous—which possess several or even a large number of nuclei. But even such multinucleate Protozoa always start their life-cycle with a single nucleus.

The position of the nuclei

The nucleus or nuclei are always situated in the endoplasm. This is the only feature of their position that is invariable. Otherwise the position of the nucleus in uninucleate forms depends on a number of factors, and chiefly on the shape of the body of the organism and on the character of its locomotion. It may be said that, other conditions being equal, the nucleus has a tendency to occupy the central position in the body. This is understandable if we take into consideration the part played by the nucleus in controlling the activity of the body of the protozoon. When the body is spherical, and its activity is reduced to a minimum, the nucleus occupies the central or subcentral position. This is the case in uninucleate radiolarians, heliozoans, motionless coelomic gregarines, schizonts of the coccidia, and others.

In a differently shaped body (most frequently elongated), with organs of locomotion (flagella) having a polar arrangement, the nucleus has a tendency to move to the end of the body which carries the locomotor organoids. This tendency, observed mostly in flagellates, is partly due to the fact that their nucleus is frequently in direct contact with their locomotor apparatus—either, as is commonly the case, by means of rhizoplasts running from the base of the flagella, or by some other method. The various Zoomastigina are most frequently characterized by the anterior position of their nucleus. The representatives of the orders Polymastigina and Hypermastigina can, with very few exceptions, be referred to as the type with an anterior nucleus. The same can be said of the majority of Protomonadina, while the numerous exceptions among them ('I'rypanosomidae) to a certain extent confirm the rule. Thus, the base of the single flagellum in *Trypanosoma* is shifted towards the posterior end of the body, while their nucleus lies approximately in the centre of their elongated body; but it may be assumed that the nucleus which was formerly situated at the anterior end has undergone a secondary displacement to the centre corresponding to the translocation of its locomotor apparatus. In most Rhizomastigida the nucleus is shifted to the extreme anterior end of the body, from which the flagellum is given off but moves to the centre of the body only when that becomes spherical (*Dimorpha*), or when the rhizoplast of the flagellum terminates near the posterior end of the body (Rhizomastix). In Phytomonadina and in all Dinoflagellata the anterior position of the nucleus is not sharply pronounced; in part this corresponds to the change in the position of the locomotor apparatus: as is known, in most Dinoflagellata the bases of both flagella start approximately from the equator of the body.

The cilia of the ciliates are not connected with the macronucleus; their body is usually elongated, while in their locomotion there is a definite tendency for one end to be directed forwards. In this combination of characters it is usual for the nucleus to be oval in shape and situated approximately in the centre of the body while the development of the cilia, mainly at one end of the body, does not affect the position of the nucleus. These facts lead to the following conclusions: first, that the movement of Protozoa does not depend on the position of the nucleus; secondly, that the position of the nucleus and to some extent its form are such as to serve uniformly the surrounding territory of its plasma. When the shape of the body approaches a sphere this is secured by the central position of the nucleus: for an elongated shape of the body by the position of the nucleus in the centre of its long axis, and in the case of a greater extension of the body by a correspondingly greater extension of the nucleus itself, as in *Streblomastix strix*, among the Polymastigina, and in a number of ciliates (Astomata, Heterotricha).

In the vast majority of cases the position of the nucleus is strictly fixed, but in some forms where the shape of the body is subject to wide variations (amoeba) or where the endoplasm is considerably displaced with the contraction of the ectoplasmic covering (some gregarines), the nucleus too may move within the body.

The shape of the nuclei

The basic shape of the nucleus is a sphere, i.e. in its basic shape the nucleus is, apparently, governed by the law relating to the shape of a drop

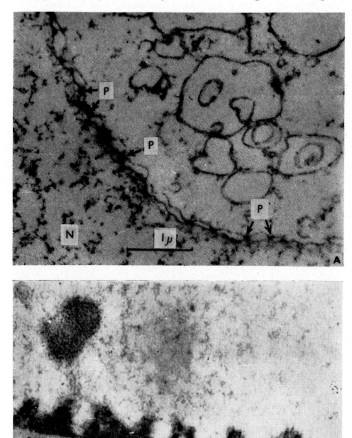

FIG. 16. Nuclear membrane (electron-micrograph, ×60,000).

(*A*) nuclear membrane of *Pelomyxa carolinensis*; *P*, pore in membrane; *N*, nucleus. (After Pappas, 1959.) (*B*) nuclear membrane of gregarine *Stylocephalus*. (After Grassé and Théorodidès, 1957.)

of liquid suspended in another liquid with which it does not mix. However, the mixing of the nuclear substance with the protoplasm is prevented by the presence of a special nuclear membrane, but not by any physical or chemical factors. When the nuclear membrane is ruptured, it can be observed that the contents of the vesicular nuclei flow into the plasma.

The presence of a membrane, as a morphologically distinct part of the nucleus both in unicellular and multicellular organisms, has been confirmed by electron-microscopy. However, the question regarding the fine structure of the nuclear membrane is not yet solved; and the data given in the literature are very contradictory. Most workers have described the membrane as consisting of two layers (the outer and inner membranes) separated by a transparent space (Pappas, 1959, for amoebae, Randall and Jackson, 1958, for *Stentor polymorphus* and others). Many investigators have described pores in the nuclear membrane (Fig. 16). According to Pappas, the diameter of the pores in *Amoeba proteus* is 640 Å, and a nucleus contains many thousands of pores. The pores probably play an important part in the metabolic processes between the cytoplasm and the nucleus; and certain substances (for example, RNA) leave the nucleus through the pores.

Grassé and Théodoridès (1957), who studied the ultramicroscopic picture of the nucleus in gregarines of the family Stylocepholidae consider that their nuclear membrane consists of a row of closely adjacent minute alveoles (Fig. 16) giving an impression of a double contoured membrane.

A dense fibrillar network with numerous apertures is observed directly under the nuclear membrane in some Protozoa (*Amoeba proteus*, Pappas, 1959, gregarines of the family Stylocepholidae, Grassé and Théodoridès, 1957). This network apparently does not occur in all the Protozoa studied: according to Pappas, it is absent in *Hartmannella rysodes*.

As regards the shape of the nucleus a distinction should be drawn between the nuclei of the so-called vesicular type and the macronuclei of ciliates. The rounded form described above is especially characteristic of the former kind, while the shape of macronuclei is much more varied.

The true or vesicular nuclei very rarely deviate from their typical round or oval shape. Only in male gametes of many Sporozoa (for instance in Coccidia, Haemosporidia), when the microgamete is very poor in cytoplasm, is the nucleus of the gamete drawn out in a narrow band invested only by a thin edging of plasma.

The only known exception as regards the shape of the nucleus in vegetative individuals is found in the gregarine *Callintrochlamys* (Fig. 17), described by Dogiel (1910) from the digestive tract of the plankton amphipode *Phronima*. It has a regular rounded nucleus, but very numerous, twisted processes, which are somewhat longer than the radius of the nucleus, are given off from the periphery of the nucleus; each process represents a hollow evagination of the nuclear membrane into the anterior of which the cavity of the nucleus with its nuclear fluid is prolonged. These processes form a radial halo around the nucleus. The significance of the processes evidently consists in an increased metabolism between the plasma and the nucleus.

The basic types of nuclei and their structure

The nuclei of Protozoa have several components, combining differently to form diverse types of nuclei.

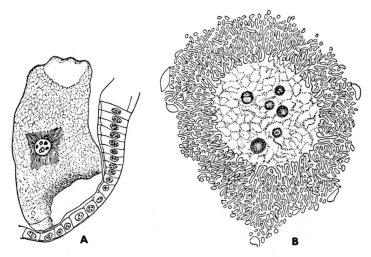

FIG. 17. Nucleus of gregarine *Callintrochlamys phronimae.*

(*A*) section through whole individual attached to gut wall of crustacean *Phronima*; (*B*) section of nucleus of gregarine at high magnification: convoluted tubes around the nucleus are protruded from the nuclear membrane. (After Dogiel, 1910.)

Morphologically the interkinetic nuclei of the Protozoa are extremely varied (Fig. 18). Let us now consider briefly the basic components of the nucleus. The structure of the nuclear membrane has been discussed above. All nuclei contain nuclear sap (karyolymph), the quantity of which varies considerably. Some vesicular nuclei (in growing gamonts of gregarines, macrogametes of coccidia) are very rich in nuclear sap; other nuclei (macronucleus of ciliates, and nuclei of numerous dinoflagellates) are, on the contrary, poor in karyolymph. All the most important transitional stages can be traced between these two extreme cases. The problem of the nature and composition of the nuclear sap has not been properly studied. Conclusions have mainly to be drawn from analogy with the nuclei of multicellular organisms. The nuclear sap is not liquid, it contains proteins, including those rich in the SH-groups, and small amounts of RNA are apparently dissolved in it.

The nucleoli (the 'Nucleolarsubstanz' of Bělăr, 1926) are indispensable components of the interkinetic nucleus of the Protozoa. As to their chemical nature, it is now known that the nucleoli consist mainly of RNA bound in most cases with a protein base. In some case there is a large nucleolus forming the so-called karyosome (Fig. 18, *J*) which occupies the central position. In other cases several nucleoli are distributed along the periphery, either directly under the nuclear membrane or at some distance from it (Fig. 18, *N*). In some Protozoa (the gregarine *Diplocystis*) the nucleoli take the shape of a considerably twisted flask, in others they imitate the chromosomes in appearance (*Euglypha*, Fig. 18, *G*). In the majority of macronuclei in ciliates the nucleoli are scattered throughout the whole nucleus as

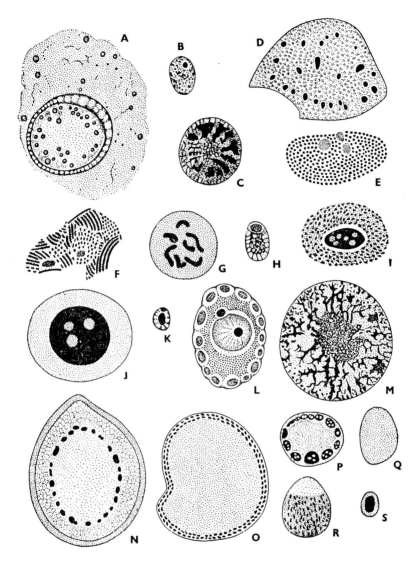

FIG. 18. Resting nucleus (interphase) of different Protozoa.

(*A*) *Aggregata*, macrogamete; (*B*) *Trichomonas muris*; (*C*) *Actinosphaerium*, nucleole forms rosette; (*D*) *Epidinium ecaudatum*, macronucleus; (*E*) *Ceratium fuscus*; (*F*) *Dinophysis* (Dino-flagellata); (*G*) *Euglypha*; (*H*) *Caryolysus*, sporokinete; (*I*) *Euglena*; (*J*) *Amoeba sphaero-nucleus*; (*K*) *Trypanosoma brucei*; (*L*) *Chilodon cucullus*, macronucleus; (*M*) *Aulacantha scolymantha*; (*N*) *Entamoeba blattae*; (*O*) *Amoeba cristalligera*; (*P*) *Amoeba terricola*; (*Q*) *Iso-tricha ruminaceum*, micronucleus; (*R*) *Paramecium caudatum*, micronucleus with chromatin cap; (*S*) *Paramecium aurelia*, micronucleus. (After Bělǎr, 1926, from various authors.)

granules of different sizes. In some cases a vacuole is seen inside the nucleolus, and there is a membrane around it (for instance, in the coccidium *Aggregata*, Fig. 18, *A*). The nucleoli containing RNA correspond in most cases to the structures which were formerly called the nuclear substance or plastin (Bělăr, 1926). RNA is now considered to play a most important role in the protein synthesis within the cell. As has been mentioned above RNA is encountered not only in the nucleoli but also in the cytoplasm. It is possible that the RNA in the cytoplasm is of nuclear origin (Brachet, 1957). In this connexion the observations of I. Raikov (1959*b*) on the ciliate *Geleia nigriceps*, in which nucleoli rich in RNA are periodically expelled from the macronucleus into the cytoplasm, are of special interest. Nucleoli have not been found in the micronuclei of the ciliates.

The influence of external conditions on the structure of the nucleoli and on their accumulation in the nucleus has been shown in some Protozoa, and this is in accord with the idea of their active role in synthetic processes. For instance, Gromova (1941) has shown that under all kinds of unfavourable conditions (e.g. starvation, low temperature) the number of nucleoli in *Paramecium caudatum* decreases while they become larger in size. On the other hand, under favourable conditions, a large number of minute nucleoli appear in the macronucleus.

It has been shown that in the case of a few Protozoa (for instance, *Holomastigotoids tusitala*, according to Cleveland) the development of nucleoli is closely linked with special regions of chromosomes (nucleolus-forming) in an analogous way to what takes place in the cells of multicellular plants and animals.

Chromatin, representing a nucleoprotein of desoxyribonucleic acid (DNA), is an important and indispensable component of the nucleus. Its protein components usually belong to the group of histones. DNA (chromatin) of the nucleus is revealed by the Feulgen nucleal reaction, while by ultra-violet microscopy it has a characteristic absorption spectrum. Various other cytochemical methods have been recently developed for the detection of DNA in the nucleus, but we shall not discuss them here.

The chromatin component of the interkinetic nucleus is usually directly linked morphologically with the chromosomes, which appear during karyokinesis. The quantity and distribution of chromatin in a resting nucleus, as well as of the nucleoli, may vary considerably (Fig. 18), and so it is difficult to classify the resting nuclei of Protozoa.

In most textbooks the resting nuclei of the Protozoa are divided into two main types: the vesicular nuclei and the massive nuclei. The nuclei of the first type are more common, and the arrangement of their components is more varied. However, the nuclei cannot be classified into types solely on the basis of data relating to the resting nucleus, since resting nuclei of similar structure often vary greatly in the pattern of their division.

At the present state of knowledge we believe that the following five types of protozoan nuclei should be recognized: (1) vesicular, or ovular, nuclei, (2) spermatic type of nuclei, (3) chromosome nuclei, (4) macro-nuclei of ciliates, and (5) polyploid nuclei of radiolarians. It has to be kept in mind, however, that this classification is to a considerable degree provisional. It is based mainly on the morphology of the resting nucleus and partly on the pattern of its division and its chromosome structure. It should be stressed that neither the structure of a nucleus nor the pattern of its division have any phylogenetic significance, as some protozoologists have tried to ascribe to them in the first decade of this century (Calkins, 1911). As has been shown by the study of the nuclear apparatus of the Protozoa, the structure of the nucleus in closely related forms may differ widely and, on the other hand, it may be similar in species far removed from each other. Only in some cases is a definite type of nucleus characteristic of a certain group of Protozoa (macronuclei of ciliates, dinokaryons in Dinoflagellata).

1. *Vesicular, or ovular, nuclei.* This type of nuclear structure is the most widely distributed among various groups of Protozoa. The nuclei are usually either spherical or oval in shape, and they possess a clearly defined membrane and a considerable amount of karyolymph. The central part of the nucleus is often occupied by a more or less large nucleolus (karyosome, with a high content of RNA). The chromatin components (originating directly from the chromosome) are distributed along the periphery, around the karyosome, sometimes directly under the nuclear membrane. This type of nuclear structure is found in many Mastigophora (for instance in Trypanosomidae (Fig. 18, *K*), Euglenidae), in some Rhizopoda (*Amoeba sphaeronucleus* (Fig. 18, *J*), genera *Entamoeba*, Arcella, and others). The nucleoli are frequently represented by granules of various shapes, either clustered in the centre (*Euglypha*, Fig. 18, *G*) or distributed along the periphery (*Amoeba terricola*, Fig. 18, *P*).

The nucleoli may be distributed in the nucleus without any particular order. In gregarines during the growth of the gamont, and in the growing macrogametes of coccidia, the vesicular nucleus reminds one very much of the germinal vesicle of the oocyte: there is a large nucleolus rich in RNA, but the DNA in the karyolymph is in a state which does not give a positive Feulgen reaction. Here the chromosomes reach a high degree of unspoiling which renders them invisible by the usual methods of optical investigation.

In a number of cases the nucleoli and the chromatin elements of the nucleus are very closely intermixed as it were (*Actinosphaerium*, Fig. 18, *C*). Nuclei of this type are very similar in structure to the macronuclei of ciliates. Finally, in a few cases, as in the foraminifer, *Myxotheca arenilega* (Fig. 19) (Grell, 1956*a*), the chromosomes of vesicular nuclei are only partly despiralized and are clearly seen in the interphase. The vesicular nuclei, on the whole, are an artificial group with, for the most part, one common feature, viz. the presence of a considerable amount of karyolymph in the nucleus.

2. *Nuclei of the spermatic type.* We include in this group the micronuclei of ciliates. In the majority of cases a resting micronucleus has a roundish-oval shape, a clearly defined nuclear membrane, and a homogeneous, inner mass of chromatin, which is deeply coloured with nuclear stains (Fig. 18, *S*). Sometimes one end of the micronucleus remains unstained, forming a small cap (Fig. 18, *R*). This cap represents the centrosome component of

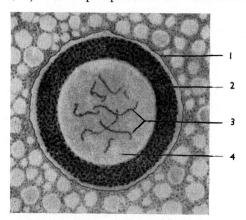

FIG. 19. Resting nucleus of gamont of *Myxo-theca arenilega* (Foraminifera).

1, nuclear membrane; 2, nucleolar substance, RNA; 3, chromosomes; 4, basic substance of nucleus (nuclear sap). (After Grell, 1956.)

the nucleus. As stated previously by us (Dogiel, 1937) the structure of the micronuclei is similar to that of the heads of spermatozoa; moreover, this similarity seems to be determined by the necessity to localize all the chromatin of the nucleus within the small volume of the micronucleus or spermatozoon. Micronuclei never have any nucleoli, and apparently there is never any RNA in them, although Moses (1950) has recorded a small amount of RNA diffused through the nucleus in the micronuclei of *Paramecium caudatum*.

3. *Chromosome nuclei.* This peculiar type of nuclear structure is characterized by the retention in the interphase of all the chromosomes, which either undergo no uncoiling or undergo it to a very limited extent. This type of nuclei are, therefore, as it were permanently in the state of prophase. In the most typical form such nuclei are found in Dinoflagellata (Fig. 18, *F*). Apart from the chromosomes and the karyolymph they usually contain one or several nucleoli (RNA). Chatton calls this type of nuclei in Dinoflagellates 'dinokaryons'. Grassé and Dragesco (1957) have recently confirmed by electron microscopy that in the interphase the chromosomes of various Dinoflagellata are considerably coiled. The nuclei of some other flagellates (Hypermastigina), inhabiting the digestive tract of termites,

should apparently also be included in this group of chromosome nuclei. As has been shown by the numerous investigations of Cleveland, Grassé and his collaborators, in these flagellates considerably coiled chromosomes, easily detected even at small microscopic magnification, are retained in the interphase (Fig. 20).

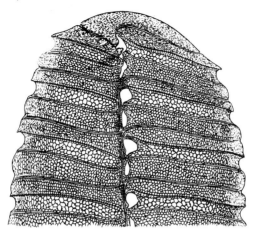

FIG. 20. *Trichonympha* (Polymastigina).

4. *Macronuclei of ciliates.* The macronuclei of the majority of ciliates represent massive nuclei, poor in karyolymph, rich in chromatin (DNA), and usually in RNA as well. The external shape of the macronuclei of different ciliates varies considerably: they are sometimes round (species of the genus *Prorodon*), bean-shaped or kidney-shaped (several Peritricha), band-like (many Astomata), rosary-shaped (*Spirostomum ambiguum, Stentor*). In some ciliates the macronucleus acquires the shape of a branched net (*Chromulina*), or breaks up into a large number of granules (*Dileptus anser*). In some cases the branched macronucleus looks like an amoeba that has put out its pseudopodia (*Rhizocargum* among Astomata), in other cases the macronucleus has dendriform branches in the interior of the body itself, or it gives off branches into the outgrowths of the body (in some Suctoria). The strongly branched macronucleus—whose shape is probably due to intense metabolic processes between it and the cytoplasm —invariably acquires a more simple shape (oval or ribbon-like) during division.

Typical macronuclei have a pronounced membrane enclosing a large number of DNA nucleoproteids, in the form of granules, filaments, &c., which are distributed usually more or less uniformly in the small amount of karyolymph. Owing to the abundance of DNA, the true macronuclei give a very sharp nucleal Feulgen reaction and are coloured intensively with the so-called 'nuclear stains'. The granular mass of the chromatin (DNA) of the macronuclei usually contains intranuclear nucleoli, varying in number and distribution, and giving a precise reaction for RNA (Fig. 18, *D*). As has been noted above, the number and distribution of nucleoli depends to a great extent on external conditions (nutrition, temperature, &c.). The abundance in macronuclei of substances containing DNA apparently depends on its high degree of polyploidy and is characterized by a special pattern of multiplication, described in detail below.

Side by side with this typical structure of macronuclei, some ciliates possess another type of structure, probably more primitive phylogenetically. Joseph had shown as early as 1907 that the macronuclei of the ciliate *Loxodes* resemble in their structure the vesicular nuclei. Later investigations (Rossolimo, 1916; Bogdanovic, 1930; Fauré-Fremiet, 1954; Rajkov, 1959) have shown that the macronuclei of *Loxodes* have a large central nucleolus (karyosome) rich in RNA, and granules of chromatin (DNA) distributed on the periphery (under the membrane). In contrast to typical macronuclei the nuclei of *Loxodes* are very poor in chromatin. The most interesting characteristic of *Loxodes* macronuclei is their incapacity to divide: during division of the ciliate they are formed anew at the expense of the micronuclei. It has been shown by more recent investigations (Fauré-Fremiet, 1954; Rajkov, 1958) that in a large number of ciliates the macronuclei are similar to those of *Loxodes* (general Trachelocerca, Geleia, Remanella, and some others—Rajkov, 1958, 1959). These macronuclei, comparatively poor in DNA, are unable to divide. Cytophotometrical investigations of Rajkov, Chejsin, and Buze (1963) showed that the macronuclei of *Loxodes* are really diploid, but not polyploid, as in the overwhelming majority of ciliates. The significance of these interesting data in the understanding of the origin of nuclear dimorphism in ciliates will be discussed later (p. 65).

5. *Polyploid nuclei of radiolarians.* This type of structure of the nuclear apparatus is found in some radiolarians of the order Phaeodaria (for instance in *Aulacantha*). These are very large nuclei which contain large amounts of chromatin material (DNA), often distributed radially in the nucleus (Fig. 18, *M*). Within the chromatin are scattered nucleoli. These nuclei are called the primary nuclei, since during the process of radiolarian multiplication they may break up into a large number of small swarmer nuclei.

The large amount of DNA in the primary nuclei of Radiolaria is a result of the high state of polyploidy—due to endomitoses. The most peculiar pattern of their multiplication is discussed on p. 65.

As the nuclear apparatus of Radiolaria has so far not been sufficiently investigated, it is impossible to tell how widely this type of nuclear structure is distributed among the Radiolaria.

The cell centre and the centrioles

The centriolar apparatus, especially clearly pronounced during the division of the nuclei, is connected with the nucleus of the Protozoa either temporarily or permanently. This apparatus is considered to be the kinetic centre of the cell, among other things in relation to nuclear division. The position and structure of this central apparatus vary greatly in different Protozoa; they will be considered in more detail in the description of the various types of division. Here it may be noted that the main forms of the kinetic centre are represented by the following structures. The centrosome, a spherical body, lies within the cytoplasm, and stains deeply with ferric haematoxylin. A minute granule, the centriole, is sometimes observed in the centre of the centrosome; it is often double, since the division of the centrosome is preceded by the division of the centriole. In many cases there is only one centriole, while the centrosome is absent. On the other hand, in some cases the centrosome is replaced by a more extensive plasmatic mass, with indefinite border-lines, known as the centrosphere, which stains more weakly with iron haematoxylin.

Electron miscroscopic studies of centrioles in metazoan cells showed that they have an aspect of a hollow cylinder. Its wall consists of nine longitudinal fibrils, just as in the basal body. Among the Protozoa only the centrioles of polymastigote flagellates have so far been studied in the electron microscope. Their structure proved to be identical to the centrioles of metazoan cells. In Trichomonas, the undulating membrane, the axostyle, the parabasal filament, and the costa are all connected with the centriole (Anderson and Beams, 1959), while in Trichonympha a complex centriolar apparatus, connected with the rostral tube, is formed in the anterior end of the body (Pitelka and Schooley, 1958). In ciliates, true intranuclear centrioles are found on the poles of dividing micronuclei. Finally, according to Cleveland's description, in many Hypermastigina the centrioles may be temporarily greatly elongated, assuming a rod-shaped form. The position of the centriolar apparatus also varies. In Mastigophora it is in most cases closely connected with the base of the flagellum or flagella. In some Heliozoa (*Actinophrys, Rhaphidiophrys*) the centrosome lies in the very middle of the body, and the axial filaments of the pseudopodia converge in it. Finally, in ciliates, as has been mentiond above, the centriole is included in the micronucleus, lying under its membrane. There are frequent cases when the centriole appears only during the division of the nucleus, but cannot be distinguished during the resting state. It is possible that during this period it lies inside the resting nucleus, which would recall its position inside the micronucleus in ciliates.

The division of the nucleus

The division of the cell of uninucleate Protozoa is invariably accompanied by the division of the nucleus; only in multicellular Protozoa can division of a particular individual be accompanied only by a redistribution of its nuclei without their fission.

The pattern of division of the nuclei in Protozoa displays an even greater variety than does the structure of the nucleus.

In some Protozoa the centrosome reveals a peculiar pattern during division, while the chromatin part of the nucleus shows a typical picture of division in other groups, on the contrary, the centrosome goes through a typical series of changes, whereas the chromosomal part undergoes certain modifications. The behaviour of each part of the nucleus—viz. nucleolus, achromatic spindle, the chromosomes, and the centrosomes—is to a certain degree subject to different changes. Therefore we cannot accept the complicated nomenclature for the various modes of nuclear division suggested first by Alekseev (more than ten terms) and later by Chatton (promitosis, mesomitosis, metamitosis, &c.), and we propose to divide the main patterns of division into groups without attaching any phylogenetic meaning to this grouping.

Karyokinesis or mitosis

This type in its main features consist of the same consecutive phrases as those in mitosis of cells of Metazoa; however, it has a number of deviations which frequently complicate the patterns of the division.

Typical mitosis proceeds in the following manner (Fig. 21). A nucleus about to divide contains a certain number of long, intertwined filamentar chromosomes. At the very beginning of the division, in the prophase stage, the chromosomes form a more or less compact bundle which becomes less compact as the thin, long chromosomes become somewhat shorter. At this period it can be seen that each chromosome consists of two spirally twisted chromonemes. Moreover, two types of spiral can be distinguished: a larger one forming 10–13 coils and another, smaller spiral forming a large number of coils and usually clearly visible during meiosis (see Chapter VII). At a certain moment the prophase chromosomes become split longitudinally into two chromatids, each of which consists of one chromoneme, enclosed in a sheath or matrix. These two chromatin elements are either disposed parallel to each other, or frequently they may be twisted into a spiral. By the end of the prophase a gradual shortening and thickening of the chromosomes takes place as a consequence of the process of coiling of the chromonemes, which consists in a decrease of the number of coils of the spiral and in an increase of their diameter (Fig. 22). Further, during the so-called prometaphase each chromoneme becomes doubled (Fig. 22), and the chromosome thus consists of two adjacent chromatids, each of which in its turn is divided into two chromonemes (semi-chromatids). It should be noted that the duplication of chromonemes, observed in prometaphase, probably occurs earlier, before the separation of the chromatids in anaphase.

The nuclear membrane is in most cases dissolved at the stage of prometaphase.

Parallel with these processes, at the beginning of prophase, the centriole, lying inside the centrosome situated alongside the nucleus, divides into two centrioles, which move to the two opposite poles of the nucleus as

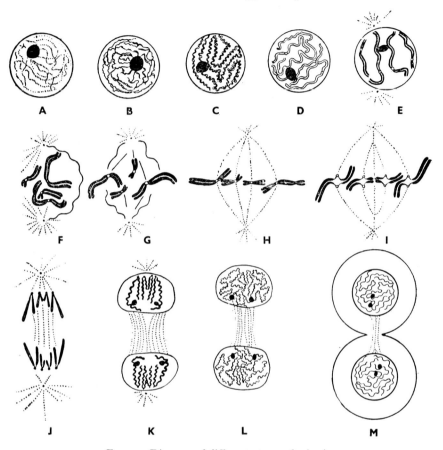

FIG. 21. Diagram of different stages of mitosis.

(A) interphase; (B), (C), (D), (E) prophase in which there is observed a progressive contraction and condensation of the chromosomes (each composed of two chromatids); (F), (G) prometaphase, the spindle is beginning to form, and nuclear membrane is disappearing; (H), (I) metaphase; (J) anaphase; (K), (L), (M) telophase. The centromere is indicated by a clear circle in each chromosome. (After de Robertis, Novinski, and Saez, 1954.)

the prometaphase approaches. From these poles run rays, forming the achromatic spindle.

The structure of chromosomes is usually most clearly seen at the stage of prophase. It is frequently possible to observe that the chromonemes consist of thickenings—chromomeres, of a specific shape and size, linked together by interchromomere threads. The basic part of the chromosomes is formed by euchromatin, with a comparatively low content of nucleic acids; in addition there are some portions of heterochromatin, characterized by a considerable concentration of DNA. In the interphase nucleus these heterochromatin portions remain in the form of small bodies, which are deeply stained by basic dyes; these bodies represent the chromocentres.

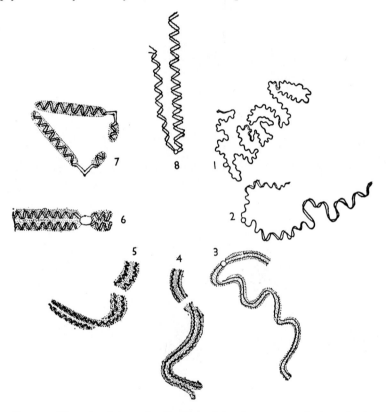

FIG. 22. Diagram of the cycle of coiling of the chromoneme during mitosis.

1, interphase with the relic of spiral and superspiral; 2, 3, 4, prophase showing the relic spiral and formation of matrix around each chromoneme; 5, prometaphase with the chromoneme of each chromotid duplicated; 6, metaphase showing each chromatid with two chromonemes, which form a major and minor spiral; 7, anaphase; 8, telophase. The centromeres are indicated by clear circles. (After de Robertis, Novinski, and Saez, 1954.)

Some specialized areas can be distinguished in the chromosomes: the primary constriction with a centromere or kinetochore localized in it. This is the area where the threads of the spindle are fixed, and it plays an important role in the mechanism of mitosis. Secondary constrictions usually separate some small end-sections of the chromosomes, the so-called satellites. Finally it is possible to distinguish a special region of the chromosome, forming the nucleolus. Some investigators (D'Angelo, 1946) assume the existence of a membrane in the chromosomes.

Chromosomes, shortened as a result of coiling, move during the prometaphase to the centre of the achromatin spindle which is in the process of formation and at the stage of metaphase are distributed along its equator, forming the equatorial plate. If at the beginning of prophase the chromosomes seem to consist of chromonemes extended to their greatest length, by the time of metaphase the chromosomes reach their shortest length, forming a very dense spiral, composed, as in prometaphase, of four chromonemes.

During the metaphase some of the threads of the spindle, running from the poles, are fixed to the centromere area of the chromosome: moreover the centromere is situated either terminally, or more frequently medially, somewhere along the extension of the chromosome. The anaphase separation of chromatids (chromosomes), which appear to be pulled apart by the threads of the spindle, begins from it. At the beginning of anaphase stage the two chromatids of each chromosome gradually separate from each other, moving towards the opposite poles of the spindle, each chromatid becoming a daughter chromosome which is already duplicated, i.e. consists of two chromonemes.

The last stage, or telophase, begins from the moment when the two chromosomes which have already approached the poles come close to each other. Finally, the reconstruction of the two daughter nuclei takes place. The matrix of the chromosomes loses its stainability and the chromonemes become visible, uncoiling of the chromatin threads takes place, and concurrently the chromosomes become longer and thinner. As a result of it the complex nuclear network is restored and the nuclear membrane is formed, while the nucleolus, which disappeared at the beginning of prophase, also reappears. It is formed near a particular area of the nucleus-forming chromosome, which is usually located terminally.

Thus two daughter nuclei are produced as a result of mitosis. The division of the cytoplasm of the cell follows more or less closely on the division of the nucleus.

All the details of mitosis and of the chromosome structure described above have recently been investigated mainly in the cells of plants and animals, whereas the different Protozoa have not been studied so thoroughly. Cleveland (1956a) has given a most comprehensive description of mitosis occurring in some Polymastigina and Hypermastigina from the guts of cockroaches and termites. Judging from these data, and from the few experimental results available, there is no difference in principle in the fine structure of the chromosomes and their behaviour during mitosis between Protozoa and multicellular animals and plants.

We can now consider some peculiarities of the mitosis in different representatives of the Protozoa. Two main types of nuclear division can be distinguished—eumitosis and paramitosis—according to the classification of mitoses given by Bělǎr in his large and comprehensive monograph on the nuclear structure and nuclear division of Protozoa. According to Grassé (1952) the orthomitoses and pleuromitoses correspond more or less to these two types. The eumitotic pattern of nuclear division which corresponds more closely to that in multicellular animals has been observed in the

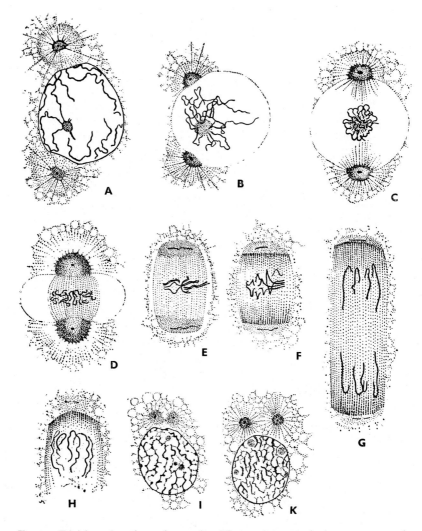

FIG. 23. Division of nucleus of gregarine *Monocystis magna* during gametogenesis.

(*A*), (*B*) prophase; (*C*) transition to metaphase; (*D*), (*E*) early and late metaphases; (*F*), (*G*), (*H*) anaphase; (*I*), (*K*) telophase. (After Bělǎr, 1926.)

majority of Protozoa. It is characterized by the development of dense and comparatively short prophase chromosomes and their arrangement during metaphase along the equator of the achromatic spindle.

The greatest similarity to the mitosis of Metazoa is observed in that of certain gregarines (*Monocystis, Stylocephalus* (Fig. 23)) or in the representatives of Heliozoa (*Dimorpha, Oxnerella,* and others) both in the presence of the centrosome during the whole process of nuclear division and between fissions, and in the behaviour of the chromosomes.

However, the division of the eumitotic nucleus may proceed with some deviations from the typical pattern of mitosis. This concerns first of all the nuclear membrane, which is frequently retained during mitosis, while the achromatic spindle lies inside the nucleus. This phenomenon is observed in many amoebae (*Entamoeba*), Heliozoa (*Actinophrys*, Fig. 24), some representatives of Polymastigina (*Pyrsonympha, Oxymonas, Notila, Saccinobaculus*, and others), and it occurs during division of the micronuclei in ciliates (Fig. 25). In some cases the centrosome lies outside the nucleus at its poles (*Vahlkampfia, Entamoeba, Trichomonas*); in others it is inside under the nuclear membrane, for instance, in *Oxymonas*, or in the micronuclei of many ciliates (*Stentor, Carchesium*, and others).

In some forms division of euchromatic nuclei proceeds without the formation of centrioles, although centrospheres are clearly visible on the poles of the nucleus (amoebae, *Hartmannella*, Heliozoa, the rhizopods *Euglypha* (Fig. 26), *Patellina*, and others).

The resting stage of these forms has the appearance of a typical or atypical karyosome nucleus (with diffuse karyosome in *Actinophrys*). Even before the division or at its very beginning an achromatic plasmatic sphere appears in close proximity to the nucleus; it is sometimes (*Hartmannella, Euglypha*) radial, sometimes (Heliozoa) without plasmatic rays; it divides and moves to the two poles of the nucleus, in which an intranuclear spindle is formed. All these nuclei are characterized by a very slight stretching of the nucleus during the first phases of multiplication. As a consequence during the metaphase and even at the beginning of the anaphase the nucleus is only slightly elongated, and is shaped like a blunt oval, so the rays of the nuclear spindle lie practically parallel, and do not converge towards the poles. The slight extension of the nucleus at this time leads to another structural peculiarity, namely a great width of the equatorial plate, which consists of a large number of short, fine granular chromosomes.

A more comprehensive study might very likely reveal the presence of minute centrioles in all these cases. Finally, there may also be mitoses without centrospheres, as has been observed in testaceous rhizopods *Pamphagus*, in *Pelomyxa*, and in flagellates (*Rhizochrysis, Chlamydomonas, Cryptomonas, Achromonas, Zelleriella*), and also in the micronuclei of some ciliates (*Trachelocerca* and others). In Pamphagus, for instance, a centrosphere has not been discovered, but the pattern of its mitosis resembles in every other respect that of the Heliozoa. Likewise, in the division of micronuclei without centrosomes in, for instance, *Trachelocerca margaritata* (Rajkov, 1957), it is characterized by the formation of very thin filaments of the achromatin spindle, which converges towards the poles of the nucleus. Rod-shaped chromosomes, forming at anaphase two typical

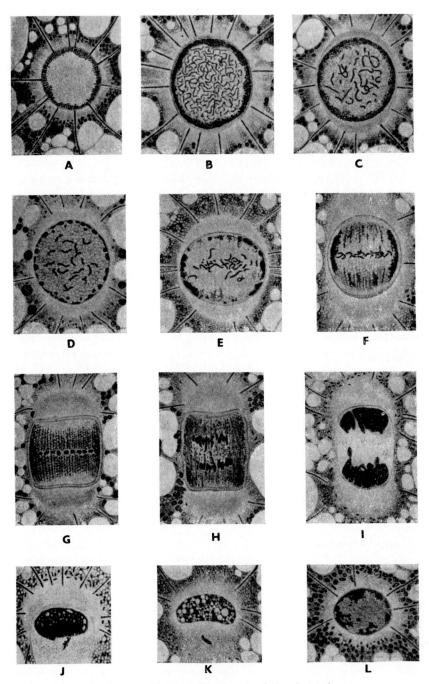

FIG. 24. Division of nucleus in *Actinophrys sol*.

(*A*) resting nucleus; (*B*), (*C*), (*D*) early and late prophases; (*E*) prometaphase; (*F*), (*G*) early and late metaphases; (*H*) anaphase; (*I*), (*J*) telophases; (*K*), (*L*) reconstruction of new nucleus. (After Bělǎr, 1926.)

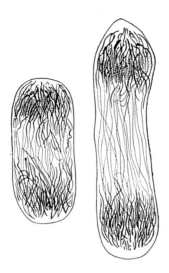

FIG. 25. Mitosis of micronucleus in *Paramecium cauda-tum*, anaphase. (After Chen, 1940.)

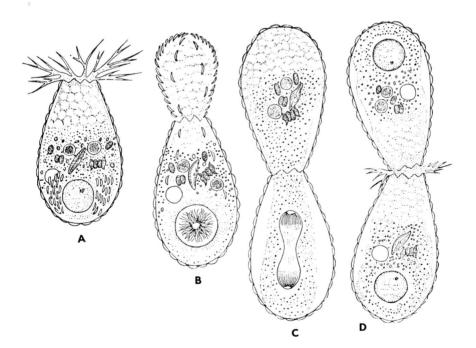

FIG. 26. Division of *Euglypha alveolata* (Testacea).

(*A*) before division, skeletal plates lie near nucleus; (*B*) formation of plasmatic bud on whose surface skeletal plates are arranged; (*C*) division of nucleus, new membrane formed from skeletal plates; (*D*) formation of a new individual, into which nucleus moves. (After Sevjakov, 1887.)

daughter-plates, are concentrated on the equator of the spindle during metaphase (Fig. 27).

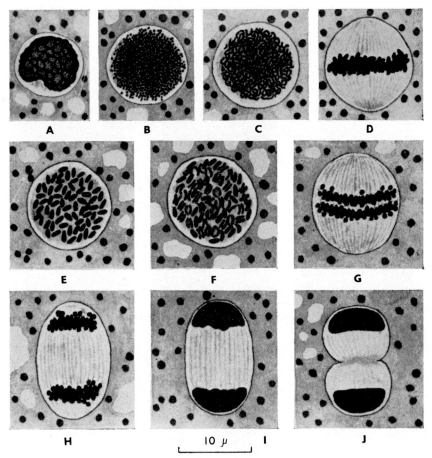

FIG. 27. Division of micronucleus of *Trachelocerca dogieli.*

(*A*) chromatin network; (*B*) grains of chromatin; (*C*) spiremaphase; (*D*) metaphase; (*E*) metaphase, appearance from pole; (*F*) longitudinal splitting of chromosomes; (*G*), (*H*) anaphase; (*I*) early telophase; (*J*) late telophase. (After Rajkov, 1958.)

The paramitotic type of nuclear division, observed in some Coccidia (*Aggregata* and others), in many Hypermastigina and Polymastigina, and in many parasitic Dinoflagellata (Bělǎr, 1926; Grassé, 1952) deviates most from the typical pattern of mitosis.

Paramitosis (pleuromitosis, according to Grassé, 1952) is characterized by the absence during division of the typical metaphase stage, when the chromosomes are distributed on the equator of the spindle and the achromatin spindle proceeds extranuclearly. However, the behaviour of the chromosomes during paramitosis does not differ essentially from that in usual mitosis.

The closest approach to a typical mitosis is the karyokinetic division occurring during sporogony in the coccidium *Aggregata* (Fig. 28) parasitizing in crabs and cephalopod molluscs (with an alternation of these hosts).

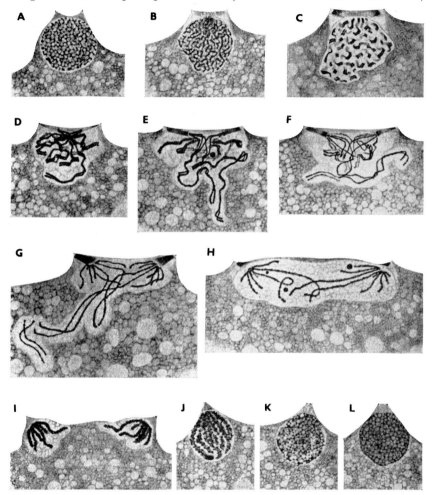

FIG. 28. Division of nucleus during sporogony in *Aggregata eberthi*.

(*A*), (*B*) prophase; (*C*) prometaphase; (*D*)–(*G*) anaphase; (*H*)–(*I*) telophase. (After Bělǎr, 1926.)

Here the extranuclear centrosomes are retained for some time on the poles of the spindle; in prophase the chromosomes are split longitudinally and only during the metaphase stage is the behaviour of the chromosomes somewhat atypical. They are not distributed on the achromatic spindle, since they do not pass through its centre, but tangentially along the edge of the nucleus. Each elongated chromosome is attached to the spindle only by one of its ends. This is due to the terminal position of the centromeres (kinetochores) of the chromosomes. All the remaining parts of the chromosomes lie away from the spindle, and does not form an equatorial plate. As a result at anaphase the divergent chromatids (daughter chromosomes) form two bundles of parallel threads.

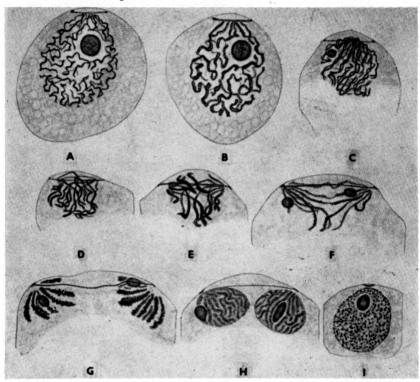

FIG. 29. Division of nucleus in *Merodinium* sp. (Parasitic Peridineans from the radiolarian *Collozoum inerme*.)

(*A*)–(*C*) prophase with formation of long, curved, filamentary chromosomes; (*D*)–(*F*) three stages of movement of chromosomes towards poles, early telophase; (*G*)–(*H*) late telophase; (*I*) interphase nucleus. (After Bělǎr, 1926.)

In other Coccidia (*Klossia, Karyolysus*) a similar behaviour of the chromosomes is linked with a complete absence of centrosomes and a feeble development of the achromatic spindle.

In parasitic Dinoflagellata (*Syndinium, Merodinium*, and others), with their few chromosomes, mitosis proceeds in a way similar to that of *Aggregata*. In *Merodinium* (Fig. 29), a parasite on the radiolarian *Collozoum*, a centrodesmose is formed between the centrosomes during division, and the chromosomes, having the terminal position of centromeres, stretch out towards the poles by their ends, without being connected with the spindle.

A centrodesmose is likewise formed in the free-living peridian *Oxyrrhis marina*, and during the whole course of division the karyosome is retained, while the chromosomes extend along the axis of the nucleus, divide, and move end-first towards the poles. During this process (Fig. 30) centro-

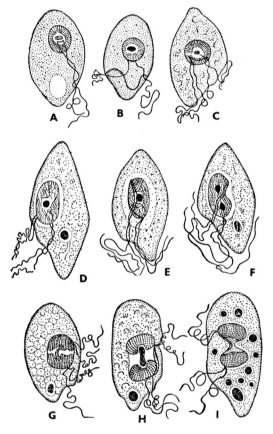

FIG. 30. Division of *Oxyrrhis marina* (Dinoflagel-lata).

(*A*) early prophase and division of basal body; (*B*) new formation of flagella during metaphase; (*C*) anaphase and division of intranuclear body; (*D*)–(*E*) telophase; (*F*) centrodesmose visible; (*G*)–(*I*) reconstruction of resting nucleus. (After Hall, 1925.)

meres have not been observed on chromosomes. The division of the nucleus of *Syndinium* is characterized by the absence of centrosomes and centrodesmose, the behaviour of their chromosomes being similar to that in the preceding case.

The division of the nucleus of *Noctiluca* proceeds according to an original pattern: they retain a large centrosphere throughout their life cycle. During division the centrosphere elongate in a direction perpendicular to the extension of the nucleus. The nucleus then encloses the extended centro-sphere, around which it bends in the form of a crescent, while the numerous chromosomes are disposed inside the nucleus in such a way that their ends are turned to the nuclear spindle, in a manner very reminiscent of *Aggregata*. The opposite ends of the chromosomes are directed away from the achro-matic spindle.

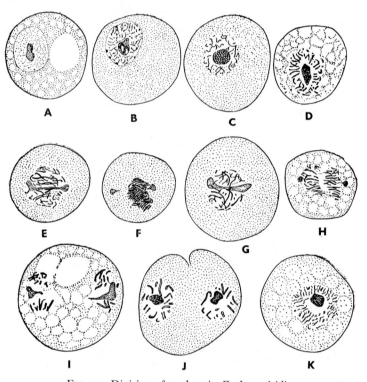

FIG. 31. Division of nucleus in *Euglena viridis*.

(*A*) resting nucleus; (*B*)–(*D*) prophase; (*E*), (*F*) metaphase; (*G*)–(*I*) anaphase; (*J*), (*K*) telophase. (After Bělǎr, 1926.)

Bělǎr (1926) includes the division of certain Euglenidae in the paramitotic type. Thus in *Euglena* (Fig. 31) the resting nucleus contains a central karyo-some, with chromatin granules scattered round it. During prophase the karyosome stretches out in the direction of the axis of the nucleus and the chromosomes become thread-like in shape, and stain deeply. During meta-phase the chromosomes lengthen, become double, and occupy the whole nucleus, lying along its axis, while an equatorial plate is not formed. The karyosome retained throughout division is constricted, acquiring the shape of a dumb-bell. The two halves of the karyosome become rounded and pass into the daughter nuclei. Thus in the division of the nucleus of *Euglena* a centrosome and an achromatic spindle are formed and the thin nuclear membrane and a karyosome are retained, but the equatorial plate is not formed.

The division of the paramitotic nucleus was studied most comprehensively in some representatives of Hypermastigina (Cleveland, 1938a, b; Grassé and Hollande, 1951) from the gut of cockroaches (*Cryptocercus, Blatta*) and termites. They are characterized by the centriole being a permanent structure, visible not only during the division of the nucleus, and by an extranuclear achromatic spindle in the shape of a more or less dense bundle of threads. The paired centrioles in some species (*Joenia, Lophomonas*, and others) have the shape of short stalks or small granules. In many Hypermastigina (*Barbulanympha, Holomastigotes, Pseudotrichonympha*, and others) the centrioles have the form of long rods, the anterior end of which is rounded and has a terminal granule, while the posterior end is pointed and surrounded by a bright spherical zone, which Cleveland regards as the centrosome. During division the latter adjoins the exterior surface of the nuclear membrane lying on the poles of the nucleus. In *Barbulanympha* rays run from the pointed end of the centrioles, some of them forming the spindle, while the others are fixed to the centromeres of the chromatids. The centromeres occupy a terminal position in the chromosomes. Their centromere ends are directed towards the nuclear membrane, which is retained during division, and are attached to it (Fig. 32). On account of this the daughter chromosomes running to the poles are always stretched out like straight bands, and have not got the angular shape with two limbs, as occurs when the centromere occurs somewhere along each chromosome. The duplication of the centrioles begins during the early prophase, and takes place at the terminal granule of the anterior end. Then the rod-like centriole grows and the centrosome is formed. By the end of mitosis and of the fission of the flagellate both daughter individuals again possess two fully developed centrioles. The same process occurs either similarly or with slight deviations in the other Hypermastigina (Cleveland, 1957). It is of importance that all the nuclear elements and the centrosome apparatus are clearly visible in living individuals during mitosis and interkinesis when examined by phase contrast microscopy (Fig. 33).

In the pyriform nucleus of *Holomastigotoides tusitala*, lying in the anterior third of the body, there are two comparatively long, bent chromosomes, which are, as it were, suspended backwards from the anterior end of the nucleus. The anterior ends of both chromosomes carrying the centromeres become linked with the flagellar bands running in a spiral from the anterior end and coil round the body several times. The centrioles start at the anterior end of the 4th and 5th flagellar bands and follow the latter closely from $1\frac{1}{2}$ of the bands. There they separate from the bands and approach the anterior margin of the nucleus, where they produce a permanent achromatic spindle, which is connected with the centromeres of both chromosomes. Thus the chromosomes are permanently connected with the flagellar bands from one division to another. The chromosome centromeres adhere closely to the nuclear membrane, at the point where the centriolar filament

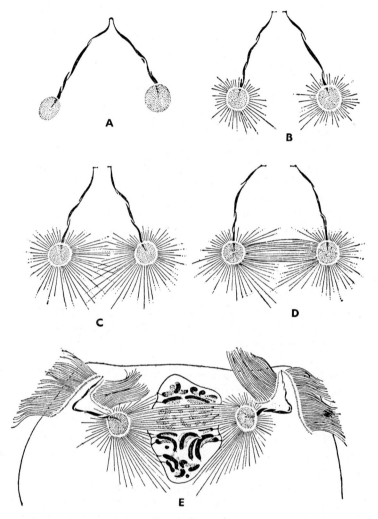

Fig. 32. Division of nucleus and centrioles in *Barbulanympha* (Polymastigida).

(*A*)–(*D*) division of centrioles; (*A*) interphase, (*B*)–(*D*) prophase; (*E*) anterior end of body of flagellate with nucleus in anaphase stage. (After Cleveland, 1938.)

approaches it. The chromosomes are easily distinguishable from each other, for one is longer than the other. In the former there are two nucleoli, one situated terminally, the other at the side, while the shorter chromosome has only one terminal nucleolus in contact with it. These nucleoli always arise at the same place on the chromosome and are connected with it by means

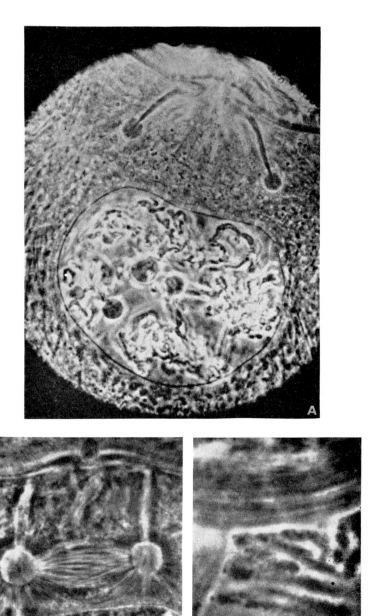

FIG. 33. Stages of division of *Barbulanympha* (Polymastigina), observations
on living specimens by phase contrast.

(*A*) beginning of formation of spindle between centrosomes; (*B*) spindle during late
prophase; (*C*) spiral chromosomes, united with nuclear membrane by kinetochores.
(After Cleveland, 1953.)

of a fine fibril. The nucleoli disappear during anaphase and appear again during telophase, i.e. they are absent for only a short period. At the beginning of division at prophase the chromosomes appear as long and thin large filaments, with small coils of spiral chromonemes, which are retained

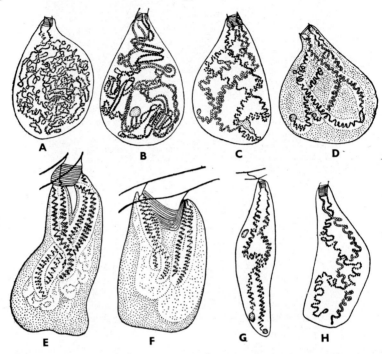

FIG. 34. Nuclear division of *Holomastigotoides tusilata.*

(*A*)–(*H*) successive stages of coiling and uncoiling of chromosomes during mitosis. (After Cleveland, 1949.)

throughout the whole process of nuclear division. A similar structure is also observed in *H. rosei* (Grassé and Hollande, 1951). The duplication of the chromosomes takes place next, as well as their shortening and the formation of major coils of the spiral of the chromonemes. Later the chromonemes are enclosed in the matrix, becoming still shorter and thicker owing to their coiling. At this stage longitudinal division of the nucleus takes place, and the chromosomes, which had become shortened and thickened to their maximum, are separated into two daughter nuclei, after which the chromosomes begin to grow longer, the major spiral is uncoiled, and the matrix disappears (Fig. 34).

From the foregoing account of karyokinetic division in Protozoa it is seen that in general this process does not manifest as much diversity as was thought earlier when Bělǎr wrote his monograph (1926). The pattern of mitosis in Protozoa reveals more and more similarity with analogous processes in Metazoa. Undoubtedly the group of organisms undergoing eutomitotic division, i.e. the one nearest to typical mitosis, will gradually widen, while that of the various aberrant cases of deviation will diminish. Moreover the study of mitosis in various protozoa proves that at present it is quite impossible to arrange them in a phylogenetic series which would illustrate the history of the gradual development of the process of karyokinesis.

Investigations carried out during the last two decades have made it possible to discover in the chromosome apparatus of Protozoa those details of their minute structure which had been described for the nuclei of multicellular organisms. The processes of the coiling up of chromosomes during their transition from prophase to metaphase, and their uncoiling in telophase have been discovered in representatives of Hypermastigina: *Holomastigotoides rosei*, *H. tusitala*, *Pseudotrichonympha introflexibilis*, and others (Grassé, 1939, 1952, 1953; Cleveland, 1949*a*, *b*; Grassé and Hollande, 1951); as well as in foraminifera (for instance, *Patellina corrugata* (Le Calvez, 1938)).

In the case of the large chromosomes of certain Hypermastigina (e.g. *Holomastigotoides*, Cleveland, 1949*a*, *b*) it is possible to establish in the later prophase the appearance of a matrix around the chromoneme, and its disappearance during transition to the telophase.

In a number of cases (*Aggregata*, *Zelleriella*) moniliform thickenings, which may probably be identified with chromomeres, are observed lying along the chromosomes.

Chromosome areas with centromeres, frequently terminally located, are clearly distinguished (Fig. 34). They have been found in this position, for instance, in different Hypermastigina (*Barbulanympha*, *Holomastigotoides*), in Dinoflagellata (Grassé, 1952; Cleveland, 1938*a*, *b*, 1949*a*), and in Coccidia (*Aggregata*, *Klossia*, and others). The presence of a terminal centromere may be inferred mainly from the behaviour of the chromosomes during anaphase (Grassé, 1952).

Data on nucleolus-forming areas in the chromosomes of Protozoa are comparatively scarce. Their terminal position has been noted for *Holomastigotoides tusitala* (Fig. 34), while in *H. rosei* they are distributed along the chromosome itself. The terminal position of nucleolus-forming elements is also characteristic of certain chromosomes in *Aggregata*. In *Zelleriella* (Opalinina) the formation of the nucleolus is associated with a large area extending along a specific chromosome (Fig. 35). Thus in *Z. elliptica*, of its twenty-four chromosomes two pairs are nucleolus-forming, whereas in *Z. louisianensis* there are three such pairs out of the total number (Chen, 1943).

The rule concerning the fixed number of chromosomes in a given species is fully applicable to Protozoa. As regards the chromosomal complexes there are types of organisms among the Protozoa. Some are haploid with a

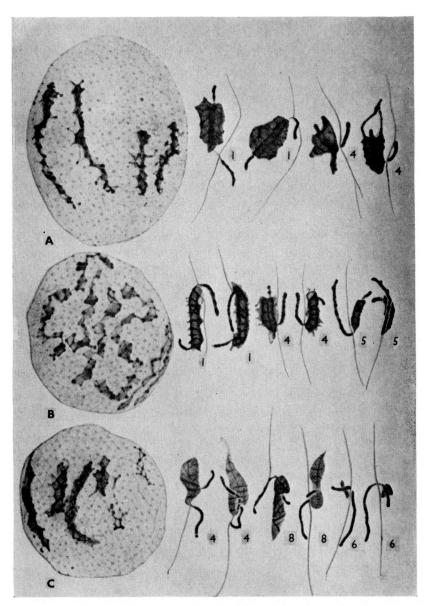

FIG. 35. Resting nuclei and nucleoli linked with chromosomes in different species of *Zelleriella*.

(*A*) *Z. elliptica*; (*B*) *Z. louisianensis*; (*C*) *Z. intermedia*; individual chromosomes with adjacent nucleoli are indicated by numerals. (After Chen, 1948.)

zygotic reduction, others are diploid with a gametic reduction of chromosomes. The majority of the flagellates and sporozoa belong to the first type; the ciliates, opalinas, and apparently the sarcodina to the second.

As shown by the appended table the number of chromosomes among the protozoans varies greatly.

NUMBER OF CHROMOSOMES IN DIFFERENT PROTOZOA

Species	Class order	Haploid number	Author, year
Entamoeba histolytica .	Rhizopoda, Amoebina	6	Kofoid and Swezy, 1925
Discorbis vilardeboanus .	Rhizopoda, Foraminifera	6	Le Calvez, 1951
Allogromia laticolaris	Rhizopoda, Foraminifera	10	Arnold, 1955
Rotaliella heterocaryotica	Rhizopoda, Foraminifera	18	Grell, 1957
Rotaliella roscoffensis	Rhizopoda, Foraminifera	9	Grell, 1957
Patellina corrugata .	Rhizopoda, Foraminifera	24	Le Calvez, 1951
Rubratella intermedia .	Rhizopoda, Foraminifera	8	Grell, 1958
Glabratella sulcata .	Rhizopoda, Foraminifera	9	Grell, 1958
Actinophrys sol . .	Rhizopoda, Heliozoa	22	Bělǎr, 1922
Chlamydomonas sp. .	Flagellata, Phytomonadida	10	Pascher, 1916
Trypanosoma lewisi .	Flagellata, Protomonadida	3	Walcott, 1952
Trypanosoma cruzi .	Flagellata, Protomonadida	3	Noble, McRary, and Beaver, 1953
Notila proteus . .	Flagellata, Polymastigida	14	Cleveland, 1950
Spirotrichonympha polygura . . .	Flagellata, Hypermastigida	2	Cleveland, 1938
Spirotrichosoma normum . . .	Flagellata, Hypermastigida	12	Cleveland and Day, 1958
Spirotrichosoma submagnum . .	Flagellata, Hypermastigida	24	Cleveland and Day, 1958
Spirotrichosoma promagnum . .	Flagellata, Hypermastigida	24	Cleveland and Day, 1958
Spirotrichosoma paramagnum . .	Flagellata, Hypermastigida	48	Cleveland and Day, 1958

As a rule, it is not possible to detect any correlation between the number of chromosomes and the systematic position of the protozoa, but certain groups are characterized by one or another number of chromosomes. Thus in Myxosporidia this number is frequently $2n=6$; in ciliates it is usually higher than 20, while in Monocystidae it varies from 4 to 8 chromosomes. The highest number of chromosomes is found mainly in Hypermastigina and in many ciliates. In certain protozoa the large number of chromosomes may be connected with polyploidy (Chen, 1940; Grell, 1956). The micronuclei of some races of *Paramecium bursaria* have up to 70 chromosomes with a comparatively small micronucleus (Fig. 36), while in others this figure rises to several hundred (Fig. 36, *h*, *v*), with a larger micronucleus (Chen, 1940). The large number of chromosomes (up to 500) in *Amoeba*

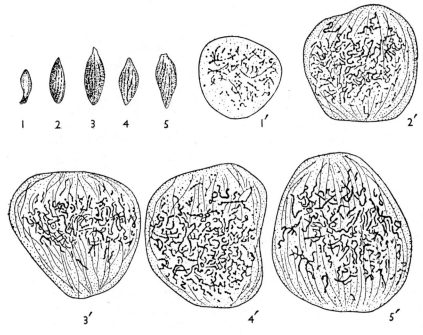

FIG. 36. *Paramecium bursaria.*

Top left: micronuclei of five races in interphase. In other figures: micronuclei of same races during prophase of first progamous division. (After Chen, 1940.)

proteus may possibly also be explained by the phenomenon of polyploidy. Tetraploid (in their micronucleus) forms of ciliates are known in Chilodon (MacDougal, 1955). Cleveland and Day (1958) have described several species of *Spirotrichosoma* (Hypermastigina) where the number of chromosomes are a multiple of 12. They probably originated as polyploids from the 12 chromosome species *S. normum*. This kind of polyploidy occurs usually as a result of the interruption of the process of mitosis, or as a consequence of some abnormalities during the fusion of their pronuclei (Chen, 1940*a*, *b*).

The formation of chromosome aggregates or collective chromosomes in the micronucleus of *Colpidium campilum* during asexual multiplication should be specially noted. Devidé and Geitler (1947) consider that these large aggregates of chromosomes, consisting of separate 'true' chromosomes, divide transversely and in vegetative division their number is not constant.

However, during mitosis the same number of 'true' chromosomes are always formed. Hence there is a constant number of chromosomes peculiar to each species of Protozoa, and the previous contrary data should be regarded as erroneous, being based on mistakes in observation, due to the minute dimensions of the nuclei and chromosomes in the majority of Protozoa.

The metaphase chromosomes are frequently comparatively uniform in appearance, either as small rods or spheres, and there is therefore no question about their individual differences. However, there are some cases, though so far they are few, of obvious morphological differences between the chromosomes of one set. This is clearly seen in *Aggregata*, where the 6 haploid chromosomes are threadlike and easily distinguishable from each other by their shape and size (Dobell, 1925). The individuality and succession of the chromosomes through the whole life cycle of *Aggregata* is fairly well pronounced.

According to Wolcott (1954, 1957), the two chromosomes in the nucleus of the schizont of the malarial plasmodia of man and monkey are of unequal length, one being shorter than one micron, the other longer. The individuality of the chromosomes is to a certain extent manifest in certain Hypermastigina, *Barbulanympha*, *Trichonympha*, and others. Cleveland (1949, 1954*a*, *b*, *c*) and Chen (1948) noted permanent differences in the size of certain chromosomes in *Zelleriella*.

Special forms of nuclear division

Nuclear division of some protozoa differs significantly from eumitosis and paramitosis in the behaviour of the chromosomes, although externally the division itself, in a number of cases, resembles typical mitosis. Such division is characteristic of the polyenergid nuclei (Hartmann, 1909, 1952), which are complex formations resulting from the union of several or even many simple (diploid or haploid) monoenergid nuclei. This process occurs in the radiolarians and ciliates. Thus the polyenergid nuclei are in effect polyploid.

The radiolarian *Aulacantha scolymantha* (Grell, 1953*c*, 1956*a*, *b*) possesses a very large nucleus rich in DNA, called the 'primary', which Grell considers to be a highly polyploid nucleus. As was shown by Bogert (1900, 1909), during agamic multiplication by binary division, more than 1,000 chromosomes are formed within the 'primary' nucleus. Grell (1953*a–c*) has explained that during the division of this 'primary' nucleus, numerous chromosomes assemble in the equatorial region of the nucleus, and then each of them splits longitudinally. Subsequently, however, in contrast with mitosis, both chromatids move to one side to form part of one of the daughter nuclei (Fig. 37). According to Grell's data, the chromosomes, formed at the division of the 'primary' nuclei, are complex structures consisting of a series of linearly arranged simple chromosomes joined by their

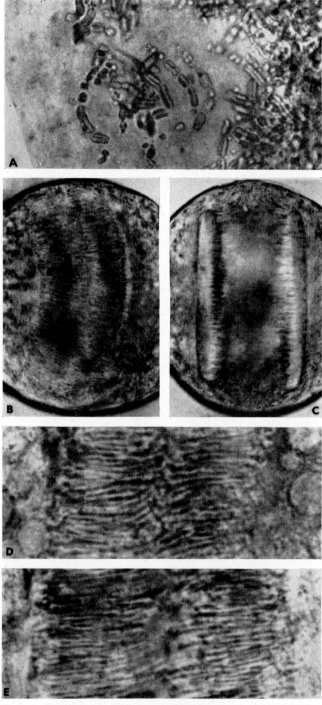

Fig. 37. Division of highly polyploid (primary) nucleus in *Aula-cantha scolymantha*.

(*A*) section of part of central capsule, chromosomes in endomitosis; (*B*) early, and (*C*) late stage of divergence of daughter plates; (*D*), (*E*) same at high magnification. (After Grell, 1958.)

ends. They represent, as it were, 'collective chromosomes' (Sammelchromosomen), corresponding to a whole, probably haploid, chromosome complex, i.e. one genom. Thus during the division into two of radiolarians with a large nucleus a distribution (or segregation) between the daughter nuclei of numerous similar genoms takes place, and not mitosis. Grell called this special form of division 'genom segregation'. Since all the genoms are equivalent, in such a process there is evidently no divergence of the chromatids belonging to one collective chromosome.

The duplication of the collective chromosomes is not a mitotic cleavage, but, in the opinion of Grell, it represents an endomitosis, which serves to retain at one level the degree of polyploidy of the nucleus that is being reduced as a result of division (Fig. 37).

During the formation of swarmers in *Aulacantha* the 'primary' polyploid nucleus breaks up into numerous small 'secondary' nuclei, containing a normal diploid set of chromosomes (10–12 chromosomes or one genom); the collective chromosomes break up into simple chromosomes. When large radiolarian is developed from swarmers polyploidization by means of successive endomitoses takes place in the nucleus parallel with its growth. An approximately 100-ploid nucleus is formed as a result. At the same time the integration of chromosomes into larger complexes—collective chromosomes—takes place.

Grell's above-mentioned conception about the structure and division of the nucleus of *Aulacantha* has been subjected to criticism by Cachon-Enjumet (1961), who published a big article on morphology of *Aulacantha* and other Phaeodaria.

According to Cachon-Enjumet, the long chromosomes of Phaeodaria are not complex chromosomes ('Sammelchromosomen' of Grell), their chain-like appearance being caused by secondary constrictions. She considers the division of the nucleus of *Aulacantha* to be mitosis, and describes migration of divided chromosome halves (chromatids) to opposite poles, thus denying the existence of endomitosis and of subsequent segregation of genoms. Cachon-Enjumet believes the descriptions of subdivision of the polyenergid nucleus in secondary nuclei of zoospores to be erroneous. She insists that the latter nuclei are not stages of nuclear transformation of *Aulacantha*, but belong to parasitic Dinoflagellates and have nothing to do with the life cycle of the radiolaria. The polyploid nature of the nucleus of *Aulacantha* is subjected to doubts.

Thus the question of the nature of the nucleus of Phaeodaria, which seemed to be solved following Grell's investigations, has again become complicated and needs further studies. In any case, if we discard the hypothesis of the polyenergid and polyploid nature of the radiolarian primary nucleus, the presence of a huge number of chromosomes therein immediately becomes hardly explicable.

As in the case of the radiolarian nucleus, the division of the macronucleus of ciliates is characterized by several peculiarities. Externally its division proceeds like amitosis: round or oval macronuclei are transversely constricted, and after rupture the two halves move in opposite directions into the anterior and posterior daughter-individuals. In the case of the elongated

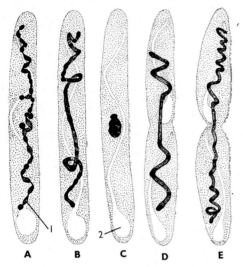

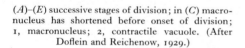

FIG. 38. Ciliate *Spirostomum ambiguum*.

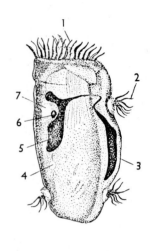

FIG. 39. Ciliate *Tripalmaria dogieli* f. minor.

(*A*)–(*E*) successive stages of division; in (*C*) macronucleus has shortened before onset of division; 1, macronucleus; 2, contractile vacuole. (After Doflein and Reichenow, 1929.)

1, adoral zone of cirri; 2, anterior cluster of cirri; 3, dorsal region of macronucleus; 4, posterior vacuole; 5, abdominal region of macronucleus; 6, micronucleus; 7, anterior vacuole. (After Strelkov, 1931.)

or branched macronuclei, the nucleus may shorten or in some cases it may even acquire a round or oval form, before the beginning of the division. This is observed, for instance, in *Stentor*, *Spirostomum* (Fig. 38), *Tripalmaria dogieli* (Cycloposthiidae Entodiniomorpha) (Fig. 39).

The macronucleus of this last-named species, described by Gassovskij (1918), has a very queer shape. In all the Cycloposthiidae and Ophryoscolecidae the macronucleus usually lies on the right side of the body along the dorsal edge: it normally has an elongated form, sometimes slightly bent in the form of a hook at the anterior end. In *Tripalmaria* the anterior end of the nucleus is not only bent ventrally but it reaches the ventral edge of the body, bends backwards, and reaches the posterior third of the body. Thus the nucleus is composed of a large dorsal piece, of a thin anterior connecting bridge, and of a large abdominal piece. It is interesting that in *Tripalmaria* the micronucleus lies within a groove in the abdominal lobe of the macronucleus. At the beginning of division the abdominal lobe of the nucleus together with the micronucleus as well as the connecting part move back to the dorsal side, and the nucleus acquires the simple, elongated form usual for Cycloposthiidae, after which it proceeds to divide. In other words, during division both nuclei temporarily revert to the characteristic ancestral position of the Cycloposthiidae.

In the behaviour of nuclei of complex configuration there are two interesting features. First, the change of shape of their macronucleus is an indication that its division is not a simple constriction of a homogeneous nuclear substance, proceeding in any direction, but a process which is probably preceded by a certain regrouping of the particles in the macronucleus. Secondly the macronucleus reverts to a simpler external form before its division. On the basis of what takes place in *Tripalmaria*, it may be supposed that this process represents a recapitulation of ancestral characters.

During the budding of Astomata (*Radiophrya*) the long ribbon-like macronucleus is unequally constricted. In the parasitic suctorian *Tachiblaston ephelotensis* the macronucleus produces consecutively a large number of buds. However, behind the apparent simplicity of the division of the macronucleus, complex processes are concealed testifying to the absence here of true amitosis.

In ciliata the macronucleus, rich as a rule in chromatin (DNA), plays an exceptionally important role in their vegetative life. Individuals deprived of a macronucleus perish rapidly: the presence of at least part of the macronucleus is necessary for the regeneration of most ciliata. In amicronucleate strains, obtained experimentally, the macronucleus ensures the normal functioning of the cell. The macronucleus is a genetically active nucleus in the sense that the genes localized in it determine the phenotype of the ciliate (Kimball, 1942; Sonneborn, 1954a, b; Beale, 1954), and others.

At the same time the micronuclei are genetically inactive nuclei (Sonneborn, 1947). On the contrary, during conjugation the activity of the micronuclei comes to the fore, while the old macronucleus is destroyed, and a new one is formed from part of the products of synkaryon division.

The genetic activity of macronucleus does not fit in well with the occurrence of amitosis, since the continuity of the genetically active chromosome material is secured by the mechanism of longitudinal cleavage of chromosomes during division, which does not occur in amitosis.

Attempts were made to explain the genetic activity of the macronucleus by its polyploid character (Piekarski, 1941; Geitler, 1941; Grell, 1950, 1953a-c; Fauré-Fremiet, 1953a, b; Sonneborn, 1947; Raikov, 1957; Poljanskij and Raikov, 1960). According to this hypothesis, the chromatin of the macronucleus is linked with the chromosomes, which multiply repeatedly by means of endomitosis during the development of the macronucleus, after conjugation, or autogamy, from the diploid nucleus of the synkaryon. Therefore the macronucleus contains a large number of chromosome sets (genoms). A number of data can be cited in favour of the polyploid character of macronuclei.

In a number of cases during the development of the macronucleus primordium (*Anlage*), a phenomenon similar to the longitudinal cleavage of chromosomes was observed. This process has been described by Poljanskij (1934) for *Bursaria truncatella*, by Peškovskaja (1936, 1948) for *Climacostomum* and *Stylonychia*, and by Grell (1949, 1953*a*) for the suctorian *Ephelota gemmipara*. In this process each chromosome divides longitudinally and a bundle of 2–4 or even 8 chromatids (Fig. 40) is produced as a result, but no spindle is formed. Grell calls this process endo-

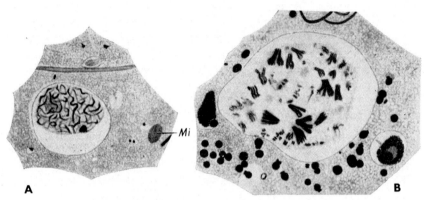

A   **B**

Fig. 40. Development of primordium of macronucleus in *Ephelota gemmipara* (Suctoria).

(*A*) early stage; (*B*) late stage, showing endomitotic cleavage of chromosomes. (After Grell, 1949.)

mitosis. However, Egelhaaf (1955), while examining the development of the macronucleus-Anlage- in *Paramecium bursaria* did not find in it any evidence of endomitosis. Chromosomes which have developed at an early stage of development of the macronucleus-Anlage- seem later to disappear and the enrichment of the macronucleus in DNA proceeds without any visible cleavage of the chromosomes.

No chromosomal elements are usually seen in the definitive macronucleus, which have most frequently a granular structure. However, new data has now begun to accumulate as a result of improvement of the microscopical technique. They show that in some cases it is possible to recognize chromosome-like structures in the definitive macronucleus. Grell (1950, 1952) describes thread-like chromatin formations in the macronucleus of Tachyblaston and Tokophrya (Suctoria). Analogous patterns were observed by Schwartz (1958) in *Paramecium bursaria*, by Mügge (1957) in *Vorticella campanula*, by Ruthmann and Heckmann (1961) in *Bursaria truncatella*. But the presence of thread-like Feulgen-positive (i.e. DNA-containing) structures does not yet provide a final proof that these structures are chromosomes. In this respect, more convincing are Ruthmann's (1963) observations on the macronucleus of *Loxophyllum meleagris*. Chromosomes were observed in the latter, which resembled, according to their form and structure, the micronuclear chromosomes. In a number of cases this author could state their chain-like end-to-end arrangement. This allows to suggest that the chromosomes of each genom unite here to form more complex aggregates—'Sammelchromosomen', just as it was described by Grell (1953c) in *Aulacantha*.

Among the proofs of the chromosomal composition of the macronucleus, Rajkov's (1962) data on the structure and division of the macronucleus of *Nassula ornata* are of special significance. In this ciliate no morphologically definite chromosomes are visible in the interphase macronucleus, which is nevertheless DNA-rich. The chromatin is represented there by many interlaced strands. At the beginning of division of the ciliate, several hundreds of thread-like chromosomes appear in the macronucleus and undergo longitudinal splitting (Fig. 44). Thus, typical endomitosis occurs in this case. After its completion the chromosomes become despiralized and morphologically poorly distinguishable, forming the network, which is characteristic for the interphase macronucleus. Only after this the macronucleus begins to stretch and to constrict into two halves. Consequently, a chromosome duplication carried out by endomitosis precedes the division of the macronucleus.

Direct continuity between the chromosomes of the initial stage of the development of the macronucleus-Anlage- and the chromatin of the final macronucleus has not yet been established, and this fact is, of course, a strong argument against the hypothesis of polyploidy of the macronucleus. Grell (1953a–c), however, considers that the 'disappearance' of the endomitotic chromosomes in the macronucleus is connected with their uncoiling and the transition of the developing macronucleus-Anlage- to interphase.

The chromosomes may quite possibly be present in the definitive macronucleus in the form of aggregates, with hardly distinguishable structure. This suggestion has been supported by the data of Piekarski (1939, 1941) for *Colpoda steinii*. In the macronucleus of this species, before division in the reproduction cysts, eight chromatin Feulgen-positive structures— aggregates—are formed, and four of these aggregates get into the daughter macronucleus; but during the following division only two do this. The author believes that each of these structures is a haploid complex of chromosomes (a genom), while the division itself is a segregation of genoms. If that is so the macronucleus of *Colpoda* is only octoploid.

Moses (1950) considers that the macronucleus of *Paramecium caudatum* is 80-ploid, since the total amount of DNA and RNA and proteins is approximately 40 times greater in the macronucleus that in the diploid micronucleus. Rajkov, Chejsin, and Buze (1963) found that the macronucleus of *P. caudatum* is 160-ploid. In a closely related species, *P. aurelia*, the macronucleus contains 430 times more DNA than the micronucleus and thus should be considered as 860-ploid (Woodard, Gelber, and Swift, 1961).

In *P. calkinsi* the macronucleus is approximately 600-ploid, but in *P. utrinum* only 20-ploid. In *Nassula ornata* the macronucleus proved to be 230-ploid. In *Epistylis articulata* the amount of DNA in its macronucleus is 720 times greater than in its micronucleus (Seshachar and Dass, 1954). The maximum degree of polyploidy (5,000 μ) recorded so far was for the macronucleus of *Bursaria truncatella* (Ruthmann and Heckmann, 1961).

The capacity of regeneration of even a small part of the macronucleus is substantive proof of its polyploid nature (*Stentor*, Schwartz, 1935; *Paramecium*, Sonneborn, 1947). This can be explained only by the fact that each part of the macronucleus contains several genoms, therefore the regeneration of even a small fragment of the old macronucleus proceeds by endomitosis, i.e. by an increase in the number of genoms. Since the smallest defects in the structure of the chromosomes cannot be repaired by the mechanism of autoproduction of the chromosomes themselves, this is the most probable theory.

If we accept the hypothesis of the polyploidy of the macronucleus—and it seems to be the most plausible one—the 'amitotic' division of the macronucleus can be considered as a 'segregation of genoms'. However, contrary to the radiolarians, the nucleus of ciliates has lost the capacity to break up into monoenergid nuclei and a micronucleus is never formed from a macronucleus.[1] It may be assumed that the increase of the degree of polyploidy of the macronucleus, as in the 'primary' nucleus of the radiolarians, takes place during its division by endomitosis.

The question of the way by which the integrity of single genoms (chromosome sets) is maintained at macronuclear division still remains open. It is possible that chromosomes belonging to one genom become united into complexes ('Sammelchromosomen'). Some evidence for such a suggestion is provided by the above-mentioned observations of Ruthmann (1963) on the macronucleus of Loxophyllum, where the chromosomes show a chain-like arrangement. However, this important question needs further investigation.

In many ciliates the macronucleus goes through a periodic reorganization or even undergoes from time to time a complete change. These processes are partly linked with sexual reproduction (see Chapter VII), but in a series of cases the reorganization of the macronucleus takes place at each division independently of conjugation, autogamy, and endomixis. These reorganization processes vary in character. The changes in the macronucleus which take place in many Hypotricha before division are particularly interesting. During the shortening of the macronucleus of *Euplotes patella*, in readiness for division, two clear transverse zones appear at its ends, known as the reorganization zones.

Each zone is restricted at the place where it joins the remaining part of the

---

[1] The date of Schwartz, 1956, on the regeneration of a micronucleus in *P. Bursaria* from fragments of the macronucleus is in need of verification.

nucleus by a transverse band of a material which stains much more deeply with the basic dyes. Both zones move towards each other to the centre of the nucleus, while both the ends of the nucleus which are left behind grow richer in chromatin. Finally, both zones meet at the centre of the nucleus, which then acquires an oval shape and is constricted into two.

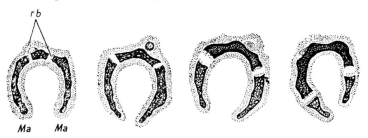

FIG. 41. Reorganization of macronucleus in *Aspidisca lynceus.* Two reorganization bands move from middle of horseshoe-shaped macronucleus towards both its ends. (After Summers, 1935.)

In *Euplotes woodruffi* the reorganization zones of the nucleus appear at the ends of the right branch and at the base of the T-shaped nucleus. As the right zone moves to the centre, it reorganizes both branches and a part of the base, while the lower zone reorganizes the rest of the base. The same is observed also in the macronucleus of *E. eurystomus.* In this species, however, additional reorganization bands can be formed, not only at the ends of the nucleus, but also in other places, often in its central part (Kimball and Prescott, 1962). In *Aspidisca lynceus* (Fig. 41) the reorganization bands start at the middle of the C-shaped nucleus (Summers, 1935), and travel towards the two ends, as they do in exceptional cases in *E. eurystomus.* The reorganized macronucleus becomes shortened and goes on to divide.

Gall (1959) has studied the inclusion of the specific precursor of DNA— thymidine labelled with tritium (H^3)—in *Euplotes* macronucleus. It was found that the inclusion occurs only during a short interval of time immediately before division, and corresponds to the passage of the 'reorganization band' through the macronucleus (Fig. 42). Gall suggests that the reorganization band is nothing else than a wave of endomitotic reduplication running along the macronucleus.

Kimball and Prescott (1961), having applied the same method of autoradiography, showed that not only DNA but also proteins were synthesized in the reorganization band. Therefore, these authors propose to call the reorganization band 'replication band' (1962).

Raabe (1947) found extremely complex changes in the macronucleus during the division of *Urostyla grandis* (Fig. 43). The *Urostyla* macronucleus is of a diffuse nature, and consists of a hundred small nuclei (fragments of the nucleus, measuring $7 \cdot 3 \, \mu$). At the approach of division these nuclei

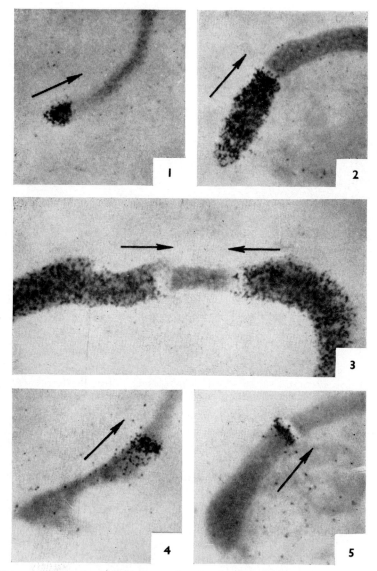

FIG. 42. Reorganization of macronucleus in *Euplotes eurystomus* before division. Inclusions H³, thymidine in macronucleus (autoradiographic method). Direction of movement of reorganization band marked by arrow.

1–3, successive phases of the inclusion of labelled thymidine in ciliates kept in solution containing the isotope from the very beginning of reorganization; 4–5, inclusion of labelled thymidine in ciliates placed in solution containing it after reorganization has started, and left there for three hours. Synthesis of DNA occurs only in region of reorganization band. (After Gall, 1959.)

become rounded and are fused into a huge 'division macronucleus'. As the body of the ciliate undergoes fission 'the division macronucleus' divides successively into 2, 4, and 8 nuclei, and at this stage the daughter individuals are separated from each other. Later the normal multiplicity of macronuclei

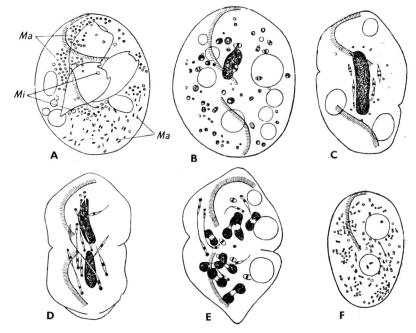

FIG. 43. Division of Ciliate *Urostyla grandis*.

(*A*) pre-division stages, numerous, already partly rounded, macronuclei (Ma) and micro-nuclei (Mi) in prophase; (*B*) beginning of fusion of macronuclei; micronuclei in meta- and anaphases; (*C*) large macronucleus formed by fusion of small macronuclei, extended in length; micronuclei partly resting, partly in meta- and anaphases; (*D*) division of large macronucleus; micronuclei in telophase; (*E, F*) third stage of macronuclear division, with numerous macro- and micronuclei. (After Raabe, 1946.)

is restored by their successive divisions; it should be emphasized that the restoration is a result of division and not of simple fragmentation. In *Urostyla grandis* the reorganization of the nucleus takes place as early as the stage of the diffuse macronucleus; in each of the small nuclei a 'reorganization zone' appears in the form of a transverse band.

The reorganization of the macronucleus may also manifest itself by the elimination of part of the chromatin, taking place either during its division or having no connexion with it. The ejection of part of the material of the macronucleus during division has been recorded for many Ciliata Holotricha; it may proceed in various ways.

In a number of forms a kind of residual body, which is later reabsorbed in the plasma, is formed on the constriction of the dividing macronucleus. This is observed in *Colpidium, Glaucoma, Ancistruma, Conchophthirius,* and others. In Chilodonella and *Ichthyophthirius* elimination takes place immediately after division, while in *Uroleptus* and *Trichodina* it occurs immediately before. Calkins (1930) has found that in *Uroleptus* each of the eight macronuclei ejects its terminal 'reorganization zone' into the plasma before its fusion with all the others into the 'division nucleus'.

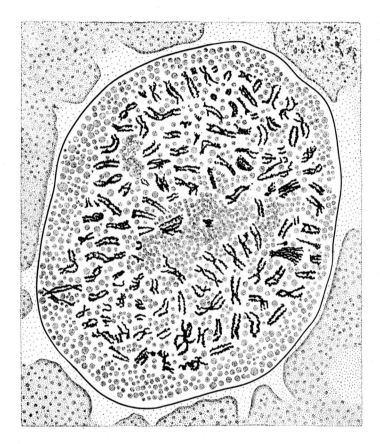

Fig. 44. Endoanaphase stage of endomitosis in macronucleus of *Nassula ornata* prior to division.   Feulgen staining.   (After Rajkov, 1962*b*.)

Chromatin elimination from the macronucleus not associated with division was first described in *Paramecium aurelia*, and called *hemixis* (Diller, 1936). This author distinguishes several morphological types of hemixis. In essence, the process is an extrusion of an appreciable quantity of Feulgen-positive material, in the state of fairly large fragments, from the macronucleus into the cytoplasm before division of the ciliate. Later these fragments become gradually resorbed. A similar phenomenon is observed in *P. caudatum, Epistylis, Tokophrya* (Seshachar, 1946; Rudzinska, 1956) and in resting cysts of many Colpodidae (Beers, 1946).

A very peculiar process of reorganization of the nuclear apparatus, which can be considered as a special form of hemixis, was described in *Nassulopsis lagenula* by Tuffrau (1962). During division of the macronucleus, a long connective strand is formed between the daughter nuclei. In the middle of this strand, a small Feulgen-positive chromatin aggregation is elaborated. Such a picture can be seen, as mentioned above, in many ciliates. But usually this chromatin aggregation later becomes discarded and resorbed in the cytoplasm. In *N. lagenula*, the process is different. One daughter-cell receives only a daughter macronucleus, while the other one, a daughter macronucleus and the chromatin aggregation. It is the daughter macronucleus of the latter cell that degenerates and becomes resorbed, and instead of it a new macronucleus develops from the chromatin aggregation, which was formed on the connective strand between the daughter nuclei. Thus, the daughter cells receive after division macronuclei formed by different ways: one is a product of division, while the other develops from a small chromatin aggregation on the connective strand. The interpretation of this process still remains obscure.

The significance of chromatin elimination from macronuclei is not quite clearly understood: there are several theories about this process.

Some investigators (Calkin, 1930; Woodruff, 1941) regard this phenomenon as a process of 'purification' of the macronucleus from the products of metabolism. Others (Painter, 1945; Dass, 1950; and others) think that the ejection of chromatin is a means of transferring the nucleic acids from the nucleus into the cytoplasm, where they are necessary for the process of growth associated with division. This view is supported by data on the increase of the amount of RNA in the plasma after chromatin elimination. In the case of the predator *Woodruffia*, which obtains nucleic acids with its food, there is no elimination of chromatin as there is in the others (Colpodidae, Evans, 1944). This assumption is possible only if DNA is really transformed into RNA of the cytoplasm; this, however, has not yet been proved (Brachet, 1957). Finally, there is an opinion that chromatin elimination is a means of regulating the degree of polyploidy of the macronucleus, preventing the hyperploid tendency and 'ageing' of the macronucleus (Fauré-Fremiet, 1953).

This point of view is supported by the fact that the species in which chromatin elimination accompanies every division (*Tetrachymena, Colpidium*) are the ones that can be cultivated for a long time without conjugation, autogamy, and endomixis. Chromatin elimination may quite possibly also play a role both in the regulation of the degree of polyploidy and in the transfer of part of the nucleic acids into the cytoplasm. In any case this problem is in need of further investigation.

The phenomenon of the so-called continuity of the chromosomes, i.e. the preservation of the individuality of the chromosomes during the interphase, is of great interest. The continuity of chromosomes finds some support in the repetition of the same pattern of mitosis in each new generation of dividing nuclei, in the constant number of chromosomes and their individuality, as well as in the data from experimental genetics of the Protozoa and Metazoa. Although the chromosomes become difficult to distinguish in the interphase and the matrix is dissolved, in some cases the preservation of individual uncoiled chromosomes can be detected. Moreover in the nuclei of the chromosome type (see above) the chromonemes remain coiled, and in some Hypermastigina Cleveland (1953) has observed these structures even *in vivo*.

However, this phenomenon cannot be considered as definitely proved, and the structure of the interkinetic nucleus cannot be finally established without the use of electron microscopy.

III

SKELETAL AND FIBRILLAR
STRUCTURES IN PROTOZOA

SKELETAL or supporting structures, in a broad sense, are present in the majority of Protozoa, and have the following functions. (1) The skeleton serves to protect the organism against various harmful external influences both mechanical and chemical, and to a certain extent against the biotic ones, i.e. the predators. (2) The role of supporting elements as formative elements is just as important. The definite constant shape of the body peculiar to certain organisms is frequently determined by the presence of solid supporting structures either inside it or on its surface (Radiolaria, some of the Mastigophora and Ciliata). (3) The skeleton serves as the point of attachment of muscles; consequently it is the point of application for forces produced by the muscles.

Among the Protozoa the first two functions of the skeleton are predominant, since the third, which plays such an important role in Metazoa, is rarely encountered among Protozoa.

All the skeletal organoids are formed as a result of the activity of the cytoplasm, and in some cases they apparently represent simply thickened gelatinized protoplasm. In most cases, however, skeletal structures are the product of a secretion of the cytoplasm. In contrast to the living or euplasmatic parts of the cell, all these types of 'dead' structures are known as alloplasmatic.

The different types of skeletal structures of Protozoa can be classified into groups based on two main criteria; on the one hand, according to the chemical composition of the skeleton, on the other, to its morphological structure and functions.

Chemical composition

The supporting elements of Protozoa belong according to their chemical composition to one of two groups—those having organic and inorganic skeletons.

Organic skeleton. The organic skeleton is more primitive than the mineral one. This is evident from the fact that a more or less pronounced organic substratum is present in all mineral skeletons.

In Protozoa the most primitive type of an organic skeleton is, apparently, a temporary secretion of tectin, a mucoid substance secreted by many Protozoa. Chemically tectin (or pseudochitin) is a protein combined with carbohydrate component (glycoproteid). In some cases a gelatinous layer serves as an organic protective substance; its exact composition is unknown, but it is probably related to mucin. In plant Protozoa the membrane some-times consists of cellulose. True chitin is very rarely encountered in Pro-tozoa.

The cuticular shells of rhizopods, flagellates, and some ciliates (for instance, Tintinnoidea) are formed by protozoal pseudochitin. The mem-branes of the individuals of colonial Volvocidae consist of a gelatinous substance. Cellulose is widely distributed among Dinoflagellata. Dogiel (1922) has recorded the presence of cellulose in the skeleton of ciliates of the sub-order Entodiniomorpha. Their skeletal plates give colour reactions characteristic of cellulose without any previous treatment: they turn violet with iodinated zinc chloride, and blue with iodine and sulphuric acid. As this animal cellulose differs from the ordinary one (in greater solubility in alkalies and acids) it is called 'ophryoscolecin'. P. Schulze (1927) denies the cellulose nature of ophryoscolecin, but regards the plates as being an accumulation of glycogen, since under certain conditions the skeleton is stained grey-brown by iodinated zinc chloride.

After a careful examination of the skeleton of Entodiniomorpha Strelkov (1929) came to the conclusion that it contains a substance similar to cellu-lose, of the type known as hemicellulose.

Inorganic skeleton. An inorganic skeleton usually originates in the form of mineral deposits embedded in a more or less developed organic matrix. These deposits are most frequently composed of silica (SiO_2) or calcium carbonate ($CaCo_3$).

The shells of some testaceous Rhizopoda (*Euglypha, Quadrula,* and others), the skeleton of Heliozoa and Radiolaria (except for *Acantharia*), and the elegant skeleton of the miniature Silicoflagellata and some Chryso-monadida (*Mallomonas* and others) are composed of silica.

Averincev (1906) and Rhumbler (1891) were of the opinion that in rhizopods the silica forms a chemical compound with some organic substance.

Calcium carbonate skeletons are widespread among Foraminifera and much less frequently encountered among some Mastigophora (Cocco-lithophoridae). Exceptionally large beds of calcium carbonate are produced by enormous deposits of Foraminiferan shells, which form thick strata or whole mountain ranges.

The shells of Foraminifera are composed of 90 per cent. calcium carbo-nate, and 10 per cent. silica, magnesium sulphate, and other admixtures.

One of the radiolarian orders—Acantharia—is characterized by a celestin ($SrSO_4$) skeleton. Bütschli discovered this fact while examining the skeleton of a sedentary aberrant radiolarian (*Podactinelius*), and later confirmed it in other Acantharia. This is proved not only by the solution reactions and the form of the crystals precipitated from the solution, but also by the characteristic pink-coloured flame obtained on burning the solution of skeletal spicules in hydrochloric acid in a platinum loop.

The mineral skeleton is sometimes composed of iron oxide, as in the cement of the shell of the rhizopod *Haplophragmium*; an admixture of iron was also found in the membrane of the stalks of the colonial flagellatum Anthophysa.

Barium was found in the skeleton membrane of the unusual xenophyophora, which apparently belong to the group Flagellata.

The morphology of the skeleton

According to which of the main functions of skeletal forms is predominant in a given case, the skeletal structures of Protozoa may assume diverse shapes, forming several different groups.

Although their classification into groups is to some extent artificial, it is convenient for practical purposes. First of all the skeletons can be separated into two types: the external and internal. They differ not only in their position in the body, but even more in their function.

External skeleton. (1) *The skeleton forming a complete covering.* This group includes protective structures closely adhering to the body and covering its entire surface. The starting-point of this type of skeleton is the gradual thickening of the outer layers of the ectoplasm. In many Protozoa the exterior layer of the ectoplasm is differentiated into a denser pellicle which is usually so flexible as to allow the animal to change its form or perform metabolic movements. On further hardening of the ectoplasm the body of the animal loses some of its capacity to alter its shape. Such examples are presented by certain species of *Euglena* (*E. acus*), *Phacus*, and some ciliates, the body of which is covered by a dense, sometimes double-contoured cuticle (Entodiniomorpha).

The pellicle may be either smooth, or possess different sculptural patterns (Fig. 45), which are especially varied in ciliates. A dense pellicle is often called 'cuticle'.

The cuticular membrane may be differentiated into separate plates (Fig. 46), adjoining each other and separated by seams. Examples of this are found in the ciliates of the genus *Coleps*, which has several transverse belts of cuticular plates. However, the armour of *Coleps* and of some other ciliates is euplasmatic in character, being composed of very dense ectoplasm.

Most Dinoflagellata have a continuous skeleton. The lower representatives of this order (Gymnodiniaceae) are covered only by a thin pellicle, while in other forms there is a continuous cellulose shell consisting of two halves or valves. In Protocentraceae the armour is composed of two integral halves; in other armoured Dinoflagellata the anterior and posterior halves of the cuirass are differentiated into a certain number of plates laid out in a definite pattern. The two halves of the armour are divided by an annular equatorial groove or girdle (cingulum). The plates of the armour are

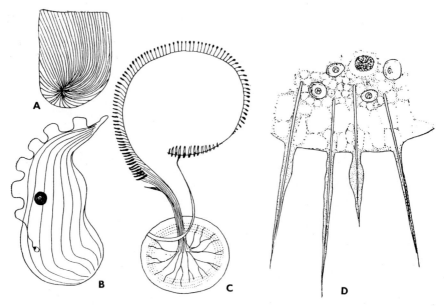

FIG. 45. Supporting structures in Protozoa.

(A) pellicular fibrils in *Euglena ehrenbergi*; (B) same in *Trypanosoma rotatorium*; (C) intraplasmatic fibrillar skeleton in *Licnophora* (Heterotricha); (D) part of a heliozoan, *Actinosphaerium eichhorni*, with nuclei, pseudopodia, and axial filaments. (From different authors.)

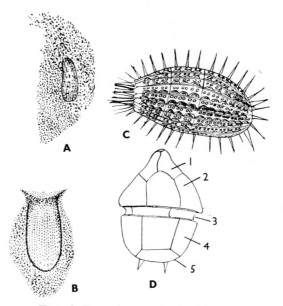

FIG. 46. Protective coverings in Protozoa.

(A), (B) *Colpidium colpoda* ciliates within tectin membranes secreted by them; (C) *Coleps hirtus* (Ciliata, Holotricha) with armour of cuticular plates; (D) *Gonyaulax spirifer* (Dinoflagellata) with armour of cellulose plates, arranged in five rows (1–5). (After various authors.)

disposed in the form of irregular circlets, among which may be distinguished the anterior or apical circlet, the precingular, postcingular, and posterior antapical plates. There is also the singular plate, protecting the equatorial groove, and some additional plates.

The armour of Dinoflagellata extends into horns, leaf-like processes, and other appendages, which increase its surface, and represent adaptations to a plankton mode of life.

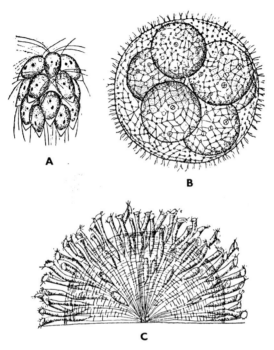

FIG. 47. Colonial protozoa invested in gelatinous membranes.

(A) *Spondylomorum quaternarium* (Mastigophora); (B) *Volvox aureus* (Mastigophora); (C) *Ophrydium versatile* (peritrichous ciliates); (A, after Stein, 1883; B, after Klein, 1888; C, after Kent, 1880–2).

The gelatinous coverings form a special group of continuous skeletons (Fig. 47). They are particularly well developed in some colonial flagellates of the family Volvocidae, in *Syncrypta*, and some others. In Volvocidae (*Pandorina*, *Eudorina*, *Volvox*, and others) the gelatinous, fairly dense coverings of separate individuals are in close contact with each other, and the colony becomes a gelatinous sphere with numerous individuals inserted in it. Each individual has a continuous covering with only a narrow channel through which the flagella emerge, while in *Volvox*, there are also several tangentially arranged tubules, through which the individual zooids communicate with their neighbours by means of inter-cellular bonds. In some sessile, colonial choanoflagellates (*Phalansterium*) and in sessile, colonial

Peritricha of the genus *Ophrydium* the individuals of the colony are enclosed in a common, irregularly shaped, gelatinous mass.

In some free-living ciliates (*Trachelophyllum, Nassula,* and others) outside the pellicle the body is enclosed in a thin, gelatinous layer, through which the bases of the cilia pass. In other ciliates (*Colpidium* and others) similar coverings are formed only under special conditions, e.g. on addition to the culture of various poisonous substances in weak concentrations. In that case the ectoplasm of the animals secretes a large number of minute rod-like bodies or granules, consisting of tectin. Electron microscopic examination has shown that in *Colpidium colpoda* there are numerous secretory ampoules under the pellicle which discharge a gelatinous tectin membrane on to the surface of the body (Chejsin, Mosevič, 1962). Tectin with its high swelling capacity in water forms round the animal a spacious, loose protective case, easily broken through later and abandoned by the ciliate. These tectin cases are thus temporary and short-lived; however, the coverings secreted in a similar manner by many other protozoa become dense and are transformed into permanent shells.

(2) *Skeletons in the form of a shell or test.* These include coverings in loose contact with the body, provided with an opening through which the animal can protrude itself. Shells are widespread among Protozoa; they are encountered both among the creeping and the plankton representatives of Sarcodina, Ciliata, and, less frequently, among Mastigophora.

The testaceous Rhizopoda, namely Thecamoebina, have originated from naked amoeboid organisms. The first step in the formation of a shell consists in the secretion of a thin organic membrane by the ectoplasm of the animal, which at first adheres closely to the body and has an aperture for the pseudopodia. This membrane then becomes detached from the body and denser, being finally transformed into a true shell. In forms like *Pyxidicola*, only the upper part of the body is covered by the shell, whereas all the lower part lies uncovered on the substratum. The next stage of the development is represented by a bag-like skeleton, with the entire body of the animal contracted and drawn into the shell, which has the shape of a spherical pot (certain species of Difflugia) or a watch glass, but with its edges turned inwards. In the majority of Rhizopoda there is a tendency to narrow down the opening or pylome, which serves for the protrusion of pseudopodia, so as to offer a better protection to the contents of the shell, which by now has acquired a pear-shaped form. The development of the shell in Testacea does not go any further. However, in Foraminifera the evolution of the shell proceeds considerably further (Fig. 48). The contraction of the mouth leads naturally to a corresponding decrease in the number of pseudopodia, i.e. organoids for capturing the food. In many Foraminifera this disadvantage is compensated by the formation in the shell, apart from the main opening, of numerous minute ($2-15\,\mu$ in diameter) wall pores, through which thin, threadlike pseudopodia protrude.

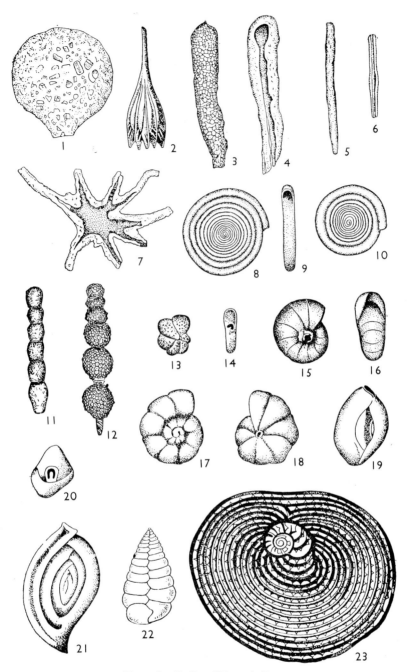

FIG. 48. Shells of Foraminifera.

1, *Saccammina sphaerica*; 2, *Lagena plumigera*; 3, *Hyperammina elongata*, general view of shell;
4, cross-section of same; 5, *Rhabdammina linearis;* 6, section of same; 7, *Astrorhyza limicola* with
exposed wall; 8, 9, *Ammodiscus incertus*; views from side and narrow edge; 10, *Cornuspira
involvens*; 11, *Rheophax nodulosus*; 12, *Nodosaria hispida*; 13, 14, *Haplophragmoides canariensis*,
viewed from the side and from mouth; 15, 16, *Nonion umbilicatus* viewed from the side and from
mouth; 17, 18, *Discorbis vesiculatus* viewed from above and below; 19, 20, *Quinqueloculina
seminulum*, views from side and from mouth; 21, *Spiroloculina depressa*; 22, *Textularia sagittula*;
23, *Archiacina verworni*. (After Cushman, 1948.)

In the more primitive cases the shell or test is composed of pseudochitin. Such shells, for example in *Arcella*, commonly consist of a structureless inner layer and an alveolar outer layer of hexagonal prisms. Rhumbler (1911) thought that the prisms originated in the form of microscopic drops, which solidified on contact with water, and as the result of mutual pressure, acquired the shape of prisms. The pseudochitinous matrix of the shell is frequently incrusted with extraneous solid particles, the organic substance acting as a mere cement for binding these particles. The particles differ greatly in their nature; granules of quartz, limestone, or more rarely ooze, serve for the construction of the shell. Empty shells of other smaller Foraminifera, the siliceous armour of diatoms or spicules of Porifera, are also often used for this purpose. In some cases a strict selection of the building material is observed. Such, for example, as the elongated, rice-grain-shaped shell of the foraminiferan *Technitella*; it is completely covered by a very uniform layer of sponge spicules which imparts to the surface of the shell a soft, silky, milky-white gloss. The foreign particles are first taken in by the pseudopodia and only later deposited on the surface of the shell. These represent the agglutinated type of shells.

In the majority of shells of recent Foraminifera the organic matrix is impregnated with mineral substances, absorbed by the body of the animal: the shell is thus either silicified or calcified. The transition to purely calcareous shells is presumably effected by agglutinated shells, in which the binding cement gradually begins to predominate over the extraneous particles while impregnation with lime takes place concurrently.

Finally, the exogenous particles disappear altogether, leaving a white calcified cement. Lime shells have an alveolar structure, their walls consisting of four or five rows of alveoli, the walls of which are densely covered with grains of calcium carbonate. It is to be noted that the particles of calcium carbonate have a definite optical orientation. When examined in polarized light with crossed Nicol prisms the chamber of every shell gives a pretty rainbow-like display of colours and the so-called negative dark cross. Hence every chamber behaves in the polarized light as a single spherocrystal consisting of radial fibres of calcite.

In the siliceous shells of Testacea, silica is usually separated into small, irregular bodies, formed of spherules stuck together (*Lequereusia*) sometimes closely resembling quartz grains, hence their name 'pseudoquartz'. However, they are easily distinguished from sand grains by their rounded edges, their optical properties, and by the fact that their convexity corresponds to that of the shell walls. In other siliceous Testacea the silica forms thin polygonal (*Nebela*) or square (*Quadrula*) plates or elliptic plates (*Euglypha*).

Palaeontological data bear evidence that the phylogenetic development of foraminiferan shells has also proceeded in the sequence mentioned. Thus Silurian and Devonian strata of the Palaeozoic contain merely stone moulds (the so-called 'nuclei') of the shell's interior (pseudochitin). It is only in the

Carboniferous period that Foraminifera appear suddenly in a large variety of forms, which moreover belong to the agglutinated, sandy type. In addition, dimorphic species, building their shells from particles of sand or from calcareous cement are mixed with the former. True calcareous forms were rare at that time. The same predominance of sandy forms continues during the Permian period, but during the Triassic period the number of calcareous forms begins to increase. Beginning from Jurassic period the light, and at the same time, very strong, purely calcareous shells become predominant: their number is double that of the sandy ones, and by the Tertiary period the number of calcareous Foraminifera is four times greater than that of sandy ones.

The shape of foraminiferan shells is extremely varied. However, Rhumbler demonstrated conclusively that the development of the shape of the shell is governed by a tendency to strengthen it, while the variety of its form is conditioned by the fact that different groups of Foraminifera use different means for strengthening it. The so-called single-chambered species (Monothalamia) are undoubtedly the most primitive of Foraminifera, for their shells are simple and whole. Oval-shaped sacs of the *Saccamina* type with one mouth can be regarded as the basic type in Monothalamia: a drop of liquid plasma which has secreted around itself the sticky base of the shell with extraneous particles adhering to it. Long, tubular shells, open at one end (*Rhabdammina*) may have been produced by an increased growth of such shells at the edge of the mouth. Those species *Rhabdammina* and *Hyperammina*, in which the tube or side branches open at both ends, may be regarded as a ramification of these forms.

However, with excessive elongation these shells can be easily broken; moreover the locomotion of these rod-like shells is difficult. In this connexion there is a tendency among Foraminifera to shorten the tube, while retaining the same volume. Thus, for example, there may be a gradual widening of the shell as it grows, with the production of a funnel-shaped structure (*Jaculella*). Their defect consists in the mouth becoming too wide and open to the hazards of the outer world.

Another way of shortening the tubular shell is by coiling it into a spiral. Its coils are at first very irregular (*Tolypammina*); but in other cases the spiral acquired an extremely regular appearance (*Ammodiscus*). The last stage in the perfection of monothalamous forms is a combination of the two processes—a coiling and a widening at the terminal coils of the spiral (*Cornuspira*).

The many-chambered forms (Polythalamia) have descended from Monothalamia. The polythalamous condition originated as the result of a change in the method of growth; namely, the growth of the shell ceases to be continuous and becomes periodical; periods of increased growth alternate with periods of rest, and one chamber is added during each period of growth. The initial development of polythalamous forms is seen in long, tubular shells, in which slight constrictions are frequently found indicating the periodicity of their growth. This periodicity is apparently advantageous to the animal in that it relieves it of the necessity of continuously building on to its case. The capacity of the newly formed sections of the shell (chambers) is increased most efficiently by their acquiring a spherical shape, since a sphere has the smallest surface for a given volume. Examples of this are found in *Nodosinella, Rheophax*, and others. However, such forms and the simple tubular ones are easily broken, especially at their constrictions. Therefore new chambers in other forms are not added to the very end of the preceding one, but their basal part encloses the end part of the preceding chamber, producing a telescopic arrangement of the chambers. Another way of strengthening the chamber is again by coiling. In this case, owing to the diverse patterns of coiling and of contact between the new chambers, the older forms of the shell could change in various ways. The chamber formed first is called the proloculus, around which growth of the later ones proceeds.

The spiral type of shell is the most common in Polythalamia; it is encountered in all the families, but is predominant among the highest sand and calcareous shells. In the simplest case all the coils of the spiral lie in the same plane—a 'planospiral'. However, the spiral coils are much more often arranged in different planes, as in a snail shell, the spiral becoming conical in shape—a 'turbospiral'. This type does not break so readily.

The cycloid type (Orbitolitidae) is recognized by the ring-shaped form of its later chambers and by their division into numerous, small, secondary chambers. This construction is the result of the replacement of the single, slit-like mouth, extending along the periphery of the last chamber by numerous minute mouths. At first the chambers are arranged in the form of a flat spiral, but later the central, spiral part of the shell is bordered by new chambers along the whole edge, forming concentric rings. The acervuline type is characterized by an irregular formation of new chambers in various places, and frequently several at a time; this becomes possible owing to the increase in size of some of the wall-pores, through which the cytoplasm runs out, forming new chambers. In this case the original part of the shell may be of the spiral type (*Globigerina, Planorbulina*). Finally, there is also the textularid type of growth in the form of a plaited braid (*Textularia, Bolivina*).

The radial, calcareous spicules on the shells of Globigerinidae have a definite and very important purpose, since they serve to increase the surface and decrease the specific gravity of these foraminifera; i.e. they facilitate their floating in the plankton.

The shells of Mastigophora are of little morphological interest. In free-living species, for instance in the family Trachelomonadidae, shells or cases have a simple sac-like shape, with a narrow mouth at one end, from which the flagellum emerges. In other cases, namely in sessile and plankton

Dinobryon, and in collared Monadid flagellates, a similar sac-like shell has a wide mouth, for the extrusion of the individual itself, while in sessile forms a flat sole or a slender stalk is developed on its lower (posterior) end. Such shells usually consist of pseudochitin; while in sessile forms they are

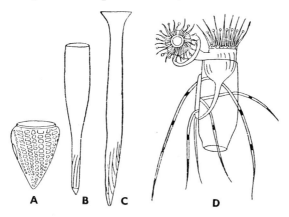

FIG. 49. Various forms of tintinnoid ciliates.

(*A*) *Ptychocylis;* (*B*), (*C*) two species of *Xystonella;* (*D*) *Tintinnus inquilinus* attached to diatoms; ciliates in a state of division. (Different authors from Dogiel, 1951.)

occasionally gelatinous. In Ciliata shell-type skeletons are found almost exclusively in sessile Peritricha and in some Suctoria and especially in the plankton group of Tintinnoinea. The last represent a large group of plankton forms, whose body is hidden in an oblong posteriorly pointed shell, while the anterior end with its spiral zones of adoral membranelles protrudes through the opening of the shell, and serve for the locomotion of the animal. The shells of Tintinnoinea (Fig. 49) are interesting because, in spite of the general simplicity of their structure, they are specially adapted to the plankton form of life, though not for flotation, as the Radiolaria, but for active swimming with their mouth end forwards. These adaptations are first of all reflected in the shape of the shell. The majority of Tintinnoinea have a narrow shell drawn out in length, thereby decreasing the resistance to the liquid met with during progression. Moreover, in a number of genera and species the surface of the shell is not smooth, but sculptured in the direction of its posterior end, with spirally twisted skeletal ridges running in one direction. This torpedo-like construction of the shell gives a greater speed to the rotatory movement of the swimming ciliate around its longitudinal axis. At the same time, however, in certain species of *Tintinnus* the anterior edge of the shell is slightly bent backwards, which is more of a hindrance than of a help in their forward movement. Brandt (1907) suggests that this peculiar shape of the shell, with its rim turned back, is of assistance in the frequent interruptions of the movement of these ciliates. Moreover, in the case of a ciliate passively sinking, with its shell turned downwards, this flap increases its friction with water, retaining the animal within the layer most suitable for it.

The Tintinnoinea also possess adaptations which increase the strength of its shell, while retaining its light weight. Thus a large number of genera possess a sculpture in the form of a raised network made up of narrow rods and trabeculae on the surface of the shell. Such retiform ornamentations greatly increase the strength of the shell without increasing its weight.

Among other ciliates, one species, *Stichotricha* (Hypotricha), sometimes builds a small narrow tube, open at both ends, and hides in it. The method of construction of this tube has not been studied precisely. Among the Heterotricha the marine genus *Folliculina* builds a bottle-shaped, pseudo-chitinous shell, lying on the substratum, but with a 'neck' through which the anterior end of the body with the complex adoral spiral protrudes, rising above the substratum.

Among the sessile Peritricha and Suctoria many more forms are supplied with a shell. Some Peritricha have a recumbent bottle-shaped shell, like that in Folliculina, for instance *Lagenophrys*; others (*Vaginicola*) build a shell in the shape of a small cylindrical tube, yet others (*Cothurnia*) build a similar shell on a stalk-like support. Ivanovski (1918) has observed that the free stage (swarmer) of *Cothurnia* after settling down first secretes a small stalk and only the basal part of the shell.

The secretion of the remaining part is effected when the animal alternately contracts its body, which becomes thicker, at the same time applying the edge of its peristome to that of the finished portion of the shell, and then expanding and becoming thinner when it detaches itself from the shell. While in contact with the edge of the shell the peristome secretes new layers of its covering. In swimming Tintinnoinea the shell is formed during the process of budding (Schweyer, 1909). Before its separation a naked bud first of all secretes behind the peristome a viscous, slimy substance which sets in the form of a ring. During a forward rotary movement of the animal fresh amounts of the secretion flow backwards along the body, gradually covering it with the material of the shell until the bud tears itself off.

More or less similar shell forms, i.e. sessile and stalked, are encountered in some of the fixed Suctoria.

Internal skeleton. The internal skeleton, lying within the cytoplasm, may be divided, in the first place, into two kinds: the continuous ones and those composed of separate supporting elements.

(1) *Continuous internal skeleton.* Found only in radiolarians. The central portion of their body, consisting of endoplasm and containing a nucleus or nuclei, is separated from the ectoplasm by a special thin membrane, forming the so-called central capsule, which represents the internal skeleton. The capsule is secreted by the cytoplasm, and in its structure it resembles to a

certain extent the shells of certain foraminifera; it consists of pseudochitin, and communicates with the extra-capsular plasma by means of minute pores. The central capsule does not protect the whole body but only its most vital part. This was shown already in 1867 by the experiments of Schneider on *Thalassicolla*, in which an animal deprived of all its extra-capsular plasma readily regenerated it in a few days; and, on the contrary, an individual from which the central capsule was removed rapidly perished.

The central capsule is usually spherical, changing only subject to the general contour of the body, or according to the shape of the mineral skeleton of the radiolarian. It can thus become elliptic in shape (*Amphilonche*) or give out radial processes. In *Lithoptera*, for instance, four outgrowths of the central capsule are formed corresponding to the most highly developed spines of the mineral skeleton. In a large radiolarian *Cytocladus*, the capsule produces long dichotomous ramifications, their number corresponding to that of the branches of its single, huge skeletal spine.

The most primitive relationships are encountered, apparently, in the Spumellaria, where the spherical capsule is uniformly perforated by pores scattered over its surface. In Acantharia the arrangement is much the same, but the pores of the central capsule are collected into groups (round the base of the spines) following the geometrically regular arrangement of the skeletal spines. In lower members of Acantharia the central capsule is undeveloped. In other orders of radiolarians the pores are concentrated together, forming larger openings. Thus in Phaeodaria the central capsule acquires a bilateral structure, with one pole of the capsule occupying the main opening (astropyle), while the two others lie on each side of it (parapyle). The opening has a complex structure, and bears a special process, or small proboscis; however, the functional significance of the separate parts of this apparatus is so far little known.

In the last large order of radiolarians, Nassellaria, the capsule is monaxonic carrying at one of its poles a single opening covered by a special sieve-like lid, through which the pseudopodia emerge. Evidently, in general, the central capsule, which at first had only a protective function, later led to considerable complication of the apparatus for capturing food, which had developed among all the Sarcodina only in Radiolaria.

(2) *Internal skeleton consisting of separate skeletal structures.* This large group of structures may be subdivided into two types: (*a*) structures of non-fibrillar character, including mainly internal skeletons of mineral composition; (*b*) fibrillar supporting structures representing elastic elements of filamentar, or rod-shaped, structure of organic nature, which are closely connected with the cytoplasm. These formative elements of the protozoan cells, or morphonemes, are not easily distinguished from the system of fibrils, which have a different functional significance; however, the morphonemes together with the latter constitute in the body of a large number of

Protozoa a complex system of different kinds of fibrillar structures, the study of which is one of the most urgent problems of modern protistologists.

The majority of non-fibrillar structures are represented by the mineral interior skeletons of radiolarians and heliozoans. This skeleton consists of separate mineral siliceous spicules—in practically all radiolarians and the heliozoans, in which it occurs—or of celestite—in the radiolarians of the order Acantharia.

Already Haeckel (1862, 1887), who devoted several monographs to radiolarians, noted the exceptional diversity of their skeletal forms. All the possible architectonic forms, distinguished by Haeckel in the system of promorphology, are encountered in the subclass Radiolaria. There is no doubt that Radiolaria have the highest potential capacity of form-development and of complication of their outer shape, possessed by any single cell in the construction of the skeleton. Moreover, in some radiolarian orders the enormous variety of forms is reached by the development of a single, very simple initial form.

The radiolarian skeleton is always laid out in the form of separate mineral spicules; they frequently fuse into elaborate complexes or even a continuous shell (Fig. 50); this, however, is a secondary phenomenon. Thus the radiolarian skeleton in its origin is very similar to that of Porifera: in both cases the skeleton originates in the shape of fine spicules, which in radiolarians are laid out inside the gelatinous ectoplasm, and in Porifera inside a gelatinous mesogloea, but only in specialized scleroblasts.

Among the Radiolaria only a few representatives of Spumellaria, Nassellaria, and Phaeodaria are completely devoid of a skeleton.

Moreover, in a certain number of species of all the radiolarian orders the skeleton consists of separate spines or spicules freely distributed in the plasma (Fig. 51). In Spumellaria the spicules are numerous, in some forms being usually monaxial (*Thalassoplancta*) in others the majority of the spicules becoming tetraxial, like the monaxon spicules of some siliceous Porifera; they represent the so-called trianes and amphitriaenes, or tetraxon spicules, consisting mainly of one longitudinal axis and three shorter axes given off from it at different angles to the longitudinal axis, and at an angle of 120° to each other. These axes may branch out farther, thus complicating their structure. We believe that the basic form of the Nassellarian skeleton may be derived from a similar triaene form—with these differences, however: first, that their central capsule was originally protected only by one large skeletal spine, and, secondly, that two of the axes of this triaene-like needle are united for a certain distance, after which they become duplicated in the distal direction.

Among Phaeodaria primitive relationships are encountered in the family Aulacanthidae, whose skeleton is formed by two kinds of monaxon spicules: (*a*) thin tangential ones, and (*b*) larger, massive radial ones. Finally,

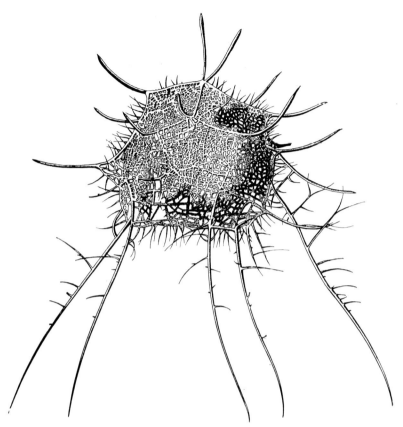

Fig. 50. Radiolarian *Oroscena regalis* (order Spumellaria), one of the largest radiolarians, up to 5 mm. in diameter. (After Haecker, 1908.)

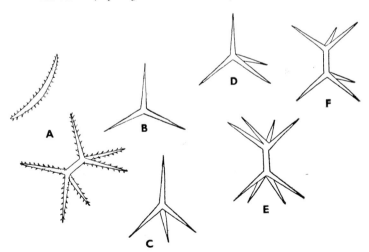

Fig. 51. Structure of the spicules in two orders of Radiolaria.

Spumellaria: (*A*) *Thalassosphaera*; (*B*) *Lamproxanthium pandora*; (*C*) *Thalassoxanthium medusinum*. Nassellaria: (*D*) *Plagoniscus*; (*E*) *Polyplagia octacantha*; (*F*) *Plagonium*. (After Dogiel, 1951.)

in the most primitive Acantharia there are numerous monaxial needles, intersecting each other in the centre.

The very formation of spicules in Acantharia (Fig. 52) proceeds from the centre to the periphery; moreover, concentrically formed new layers may frequently be observed on the surface of the spicules.

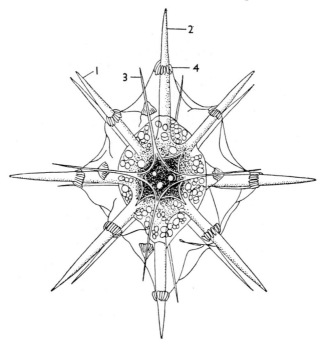

FIG. 52. Radiolarian *Acantostaurus* (Acantharia).

1, tropical spines; 2, equatorial spines; 3, polar spines; 4, myofrisks.
(After Sevjakov, 1926.)

The siliceous skeleton of Phaeodaria (Fig. 53) is formed in a different way. According to Haecker (1908), the primordial type of this skeleton appears in the form of very fine 'primitive' spicules arranged in a definite pattern, round which a long drop of fluid jelly, 'the Gallert vacuole', is formed, which is covered by a thin layer of a special live plasma. The organic (horny) contours of the final skeleton are formed from it. Their complex silicification takes place only when these contours are completed.

The shape of the radiolarian skeleton is most varied, but according to Haeckel two types are most widely distributed: the astroid, with its radial spicules more or less converging to its centre; and the spheroid, consisting of latticed spheres or tangential layers of spicules, distributed on the periphery of the body.

The astroid skeleton predominates in Acantharia, although it is subject to many modifications. The primitive Acantharia (suborder Holacantha) is characterized by 10 spicules bound together in the centre of the body. The skeleton of the great majority of Acantharia is formed by 20 radial needles converging in the centre of the animal. The needles are regularly arranged according to Müller's law. Their protruding ends are disposed in

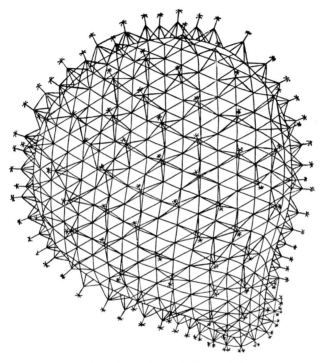

FIG. 53. *Sagenoscena irmingeriana* (Phaeodaria). Pyriform skeleton surrounded by layer of needle-like 'tents' to weaken effect of impact with solid bodies. (After Haecker, 1908.)

5 concentric circles, each containing 4 spicules, which form a corresponding number of belts on the surface of the body. One belt is formed by 4 equatorial needles, on each side of which, at an angle of 30° and alternating with the equatorial needles, there are 2 belts of tropical spicules; finally, at an angle of 45° to the equatorial needles, and strictly under and above them, are 2 belts of polar needles.

No other pattern of distribution is observed in Acantharia (Sevjakov, 1926). The so-called laws of Haeckel, Brandt, and others mentioned in the literature, Sevjakov interprets as modifications of Müller's law. A further variation is introduced into this geometrical regularity, first of all by the different degree of development of the different needles of the skeleton. Quite frequently all the four (*Lithoptera*) or two (*Amphilonche*) of the equatorial spicules become strongly predominant over the others. In this way plate-like or spindle-shaped skeletons are produced. Converging in the centre of the animal's body, the needles of Acantharia become there more or less closely linked with each other, forming a continuous skeleton. In the simplest case the inner ends of the needles are provided with short cones inserted between the proximal cones of other, neighbouring needles. In other species these cones are transformed into polyhedral pyramids, thereby securing a more stable coupling between the bases of the needles. However, in all these types of attachment the needles fall apart under pressure on the skeleton. But in the third group of Acantharia the ends of the spicules in contact with each other are immovably fused together by a mineral cement of the same composition as the needles themselves, with the result that the skeleton acquires the greatest strength.

Among the siliceous Radiolaria, in Spumellaria the spheroid skeleton is predominant, its rudiment in primitive forms being represented by numerous tangential spicules, scattered in the ectoplasm. These spicules may become fused by their ends, forming a lattice sphere which may be tenuous like a cobweb, or massive, depending on the thickness of the trabeculae between the meshes of the sphere. The central capsule lies inside the sphere. In many Spumellaria the skeleton consists not of one but of several concentric lattice spheres, connected with each other by radial needles and formed consecutively as the plasmatic body of the animal grows beyond the limits of the first sphere. It has been observed that in some species the lattice secondary spheres originate in the form of tangential processes diverging in all directions from the radial needles; moreover, the processes of the neighbouring needles converge at their ends (as in Acantharia). The spherical skeleton may either be flattened into a disk or extended in one direction, becoming oval or elliptical. There are some large, deep-water Spumellaria in which the whole skeleton consists of a single large needle, representing as it were two tetraradial needles united by one of their radii.

The skeleton of Nassellaria is, probably, the least varied. Its initial element is represented by a single needle of the type of a tetraradial triaene. One of its rays points upwards, the other three are directed downwards, enclosing the central capsule. Separate rays may produce side branches, which either unite into rings, or, more frequently, enclose the three needles of the tripod in the shape of a perforated helmet, the vertex of which is prolonged into the apical needle while the edges of the lower opening of the helmet are continued into the three basal needles. The helmet may be extended along the long axis, being transformed into a 2-, 3-, or multiple-tiered form, or, on the contrary, become flattened from above downwards, forming a hexagonal openwork cobweb, and so on. Another type of Nassellaria skeleton is produced when the branches of the basic needle are connected with each other by means of two or three smooth or spiny rings, lying in different planes: annular skeletons.

Particularly varied and difficult to bring under a general pattern is the skeleton of Phaeodaria. The most primitive form belongs, apparently, to representatives of Aulacanthidae, whose spherical body is pierced through by an irregular bunch of radial monaxial needles, and is surrounded on the periphery by a layer of very thin tangential spicules: both the former and the latter are hollow. Thus in this case there is a combination of astroid and spheroid skeletons. Further (in Aulosphaeridae and Sagosphaeridae) either

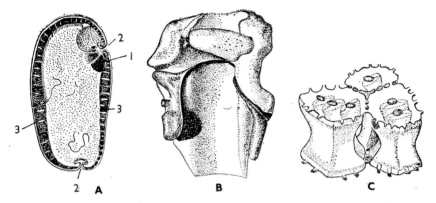

FIG. 54. Skeletal structure in ciliates.

(*A*) transverse section through ciliate *Cycloposthium*; (*B*) reconstruction of skeleton and nucleus of *Tripalmaria dogieli*; (*C*) reconstruction of several skeletal prisms of which the plates of *Cycloposthium* are composed. 1, macronucleus; 2, skeletal groove; 3, two skeletal plates. (After Strelkov, 1929.)

a fusion or articulation of the ends of the tangential needles into a delicate latticed sphere may take place; or else a strengthening of the trabeculae of the sphere, so that it becomes more massive and is perforated only by narrow apertures (Castanellidae). It is much more difficult to explain the origin of the compact yellow-brown, urn-like shells of Challengeridae and Tuscaroridae, as well as the extremely complex bicuspid shells of Coelodendridae. The development of a protection for the capsule proceeds parallel with that of the radial processes, which serve partly for the increase of the surface of the body, and partly for a further strengthening of its spherical skeleton, especially in forms living at great depths.

The variety of adaptations and the enormous number of species of Radiolaria (more than 6,000) with a comparatively similar mode of life leads to a large number of parallelisms and convergences (see section on convergence phenomena, Ch. IX) within the same class in different orders, and especially within the same order.

Apart from the mineral internal skeleton, the extremely original plate-skeleton of the ciliate order Entodiniomorpha (Figs. 54 and 55) also belongs to the group of the non-fibrillar internal supporting apparatus. In the body of the majority of genera of these ciliates, under the cuticle there are one, two, or several thin plates of different shapes. In addition to strengthening the surface of the body (*Cycloposthium*), these plates may support the walls of the enormous gullet of these ciliates, thereby protecting it from injuries caused by coarse particles of food (bits of grass, pieces of cellulose). These plates are most frequently composed of one layer of prisms, extending perpendicularly to the surface of the body, giving the plates an alveolar structure (see Fig. 54, *a*). The walls of the prisms and their contents consist of two different substances. Within the family Ophryoscolecidae, from the rumen of the ruminants, it is possible to trace the gradual evolution of this skeletal apparatus from forms devoid of skeleton to those in which there appears one narrow, lateral plate on the right side, then a second, and ultimately a third, which enclose the cytopharynx from three sides, &c.

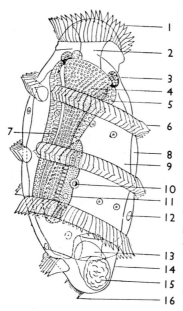

FIG. 55. *Polydinium mysoreum* (Ophryoscolecidae) from intestine of elephant.

1, adoral spiral; 2, oesophagus; 3, dilatation of skeletal plate; 4, right skeletal plate; 5, left plate; 6, spirals of membranelles; 7, dorsal skeletal plate; 8, ectoplasm; 9, endoplasm; 10, micronucleus; 11, macronucleus; 12, contractile vacuole; 13, rectum; 14, caudal lobe; 15, accumulation of excrement; 16, caudal cilia. (After Kofoid, 1935.)

Fibrillar supporting system of Protozoa. The problem of fibrillar structures of Protozoa was elucidated by Koltsov (1911), who was the first to investigate the development of the formative elements of the cells of both Metazoa and Protozoa. He came to the conclusion that if a cell with a more or less fluid aggregate state and a naked surface has a permanent shape, which diverges considerably from the spherical, and moreover does not form any outer cover or shell, there must be some inner morphogenetic elements, either in the form of a solid skeleton of different shapes or in the form of fibrillar structures, imparting to the drops of fluid a specific form. It has been suggested that such purely supporting fibrils are distinguished by their simple monophasic character from other contractile fibres, which are characterized as complex diphasic structures, and are composed of an elastic skeleton and a fluid cytoplasm, as has been proved in the structure of the contractile stalk of the Vorticellidae. However, the view regarding the diphasic character of all the contractile elements in Protozoa has not been confirmed by the latest researches by means of electron microscopy. Apart from the data on the two types of fibrils in Protozoa, some facts have appeared pointing to the existence of a third type of fibril—the conductile fibrils, or neurophanes, so called to distinguish them from the myonemes and morphonemes, i.e. the contractile and supporting fibrils. At the same time the problem of the fibrillar system of Protozoa becomes more complicated because of the difficulty of localizing in specific fibrils, just one, and not any other, of the functions peculiar to fibrils. In any case it has been proved that the function of a series of fibrils of Protozoa is purely formative; we shall now turn to the description of this particular type of fibrils.

Supporting fibrillar structures are most weakly manifested in Sarcodina. In amoebae distinct fibrillar structures are absent altogether. The first indication of a fibrillar structure of supporting and locomotor significance appear in Foraminifera, the long anastomizing pseudopodia of which, according to Doflein's observations (1909), reveal in a dark field a fine denser axial filament. These are apparently euplasmatic structures produced during the temporary transition of sol into gel, which are as readily transformed again into the liquid phase.

The presence of these fibrillar elements inside the pseudopodia indicates their probable double function, namely supporting and locomotor, since, as in the case of Foraminifera, the very stretching out of pseudopodia, which is an act of movement, is difficult to imagine without a simultaneous gelatinization of the axial filament. In the heliozoans *Actinosphaerium* and *Actinophrys*, according to Roskin (1925), in the axopodia, formed by digitiform evaginations of a small section of the body, fine fibrils may be observed in the centre. As the axopodium becomes extended these fibrils draw together and fuse, forming a denser shaft. It is very stable, disappearing only during encystation and fission. Roskin believes that they function to a considerable extent as a skeletal framework supporting the permanent shape of the animal's body. In the axial rod of the axopodia of Heliozoa (*Actinosphaerium, Actinophrys*) longitudinal, densely packed filaments or fibrils with a common membrane were revealed by electron microscopy (Wohlfarth-Bottermann and Krüger, 1954; Anderson and Beams, 1960). In *Actinosphaerium nucleofilum* fibrils of various lengths, measuring 60–125 Å in diameter, and orientated along the axopodium, are seen in the axial rod. They penetrate into the endoplasm, where some of them reach the surface of the nucleus. The axial rod of axopodia exhibits double refraction, pointing to the regular orientation of the fibrillar structures, as was noted long ago by Roskin (1925). Among the Sporozoa definite fibrils of a purely supporting function (Fig. 60) have been discovered in gregarines (Roskin and Levinson, 1929). Apart from myonemes, which will be discussed later, a whole system of small, fine, monophasic supporting fibrils running between the myonemes mostly in a longitudinal direction (in *Nematocystis*) has been traced in gregarines. These morphonemes differ from the contractile fibrils in that the diameter of the morphonemes does not change during contraction of the body, but they acquire an irregularly twisted form.

The supporting fibrils of the gregarines represent an independent system, which does not show any connexion with their nuclear and centrosome apparatus.

On the contrary, the fibrillar apparatus of Mastigophora is usually in one way or another linked with the locomotor organoids for the basic unit of which Chatton (1924) proposed the term 'kinetid' (see page 132). The purely supporting parts in the locomotor supporting system are difficult to distinguish since they are in most cases closely linked with the locomotor apparatus. Thus, in many free-living (*Euglena acus*, *Menoidium*, *Crypto-monas*, and others) and parasitic flagellates (*Rhizomastix*, *Cercomonas*, and others) the base of the flagellum and its basal granule extend into the depth of the cytoplasm in the form of a so-called rhizoplast, which either ends in the plasma or is attached to the nuclear membrane, or lastly is connected with the centrosome in the neighbourhood of the nucleus. The rhizoplast forms part of the kinetid. It is difficult to determine whether this fibril has a supporting or conducting function, but since the rhizoplast sometimes ends in the plasma, and is not connected with the nucleus or centrosome, it evidently also serves as a support, by anchoring the base of the flagellum in the cytoplasm.

A further stimulus to the development of fibrillar structures is the growing complexity of the flagellum apparatus. Thus a more solid basal fibril (costa), evidently having a supporting function, runs along the base of the undulating membrane in some intestinal flagellates (*Trichomonas*). A rudi-mentary basal fibril is also present in certain polymastigine parasites of termites, which have a considerably developed trailing flagellum that has not yet fused with the body into a membrane; in such forms (for example, *Devescovina*) only a very short supporting platelet (cresta), evidently also of a fibrillar nature, lies at the base of the trailing flagellum.

In Mastigophora the next stage in the development of the fibrillar system is the differentiation of a special axial apparatus, or axostyle. The axostyle, extending in the form of an elastic axis from the anterior end of the body to the posterior, plays in the flagellates the same role in the support of the body as the astroid mineral skeleton plays in radiolarians. The axostyle reaches its highest development in various members of Polymastigina and Hyper-mastigina. It is connected with the basal granules and in some cases also with the nucleus (Fig. 56).

In its simplest form the axostyle is found in *Protrichomonas legeri* (Alekeef, 1912), in the intestine of the fish *Box Salpa*. In this genus the rhizoplast is absent and a fine filamentar axostyle, which extends almost to the posterior extremity of the body, is given off directly from the basal granules of the flagella. In *Monocercomonas* a similar axostyle fibril reaches the posterior pole of the body and even protrudes beyond it. In certain species of *Trichomonas* and *Hyperdevescovina* and others the posterior end of the axostyle protrudes beyond the body, and at the point of emer-gence it is encircled by several coils of a spirally twisted fibril. In some

flagellates from termites it can be seen that the axostyle consists in fact of
a bundle of finer filaments, while in *Trichomonas* and *Joenia* it even forms
a hollow transparent tube, apparently composed of small filaments stuck
together. Its posterior end is drawn out to a point, and a group of sidero-

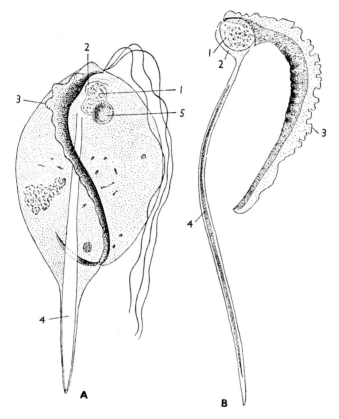

FIG. 56. *Gigantomonas herculea* from intestine of termite *Hodotermes mosambicus*.

(*A*) general view of entire flagellate; (*B*) locomotor-supporting apparatus, separated from
body. 1, nucleus; 2, anterior end of axostyle surrounding nucleus; 3, edge of undulating
membrane; 4, axostyle; 5, parabasal body. (After Dogiel, 1916.)

philous granules of unknown significance may be present in its lumen. The
axostyle is still more complex in certain Hypermastigida. Thus, in *Lophomonas blattarum* the anterior end of the axostyle is swollen in the form of
a bulb which encloses the round nucleus of the animal. Evidently here as
in one very large trichomonad *Gigantomonas* (Fig. 56), discovered by Dogiel
in termites, the axostyle has the character of a fibrillar sheath, serving not
only as a support for the body, but also as a protective envelope for the
nucleus. In *Gigantomonas* the whole complex composed of flagella, undulating membrane, basal granules, axostyle, and nucleus encompassed by it is

squeezed out from the animal's body under pressure as a single indivisible whole. This was the reason why Dogiel called the whole complex (except the nucleus) the 'locomotor-supporting apparatus'. The axostyle of a number of Hypermastigida from termites (*Holomastigotoides, Spirotrichonympha,* and others) also have the appearance of a bundle of filaments enclosing the nucleus in its anterior part. In *Pyrsonympha* and *Dinenympha* the axostyle is shaped like a narrow band given off from the centrosome and extending to the posterior end of the body. The axostyle of *Pyrsonympha* is peculiar in

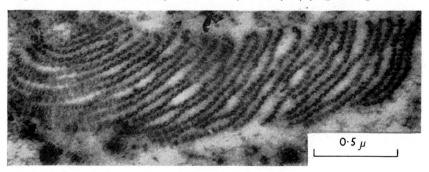

FIG. 57. Axostyle of *Pyrsonympha*, transverse section (electron-micrograph, ×). (After Grassé, 1956.)

its capacity for contraction. In addition to the axostyle a long, fine, non-contractile shaft—the paraxostyle—with a fibrillar structure, runs from the centrosome. It has been shown by electron microscopy that the axostyle of *Pyrsonympha verteus* (Grassé, 1956) consists of longitudinal, slightly bent platelets, their number varying in different individuals from 14 to 74; each of these platelets consists of the finest longitudinal fibrils, which are not homogeneous, but are of tubular structure (Fig. 57). The fibrils of the axostyles are similar to the elastic fibrils of the stalk in Peritricha (see below). Their function is not yet clear. In other flagellates (*Joenia, Foaina*), examined by means of electron microscopy, numerous very fine, longitudinal fibrils, fused with each other, are visible in the non-contractile axostyle.

A system of fine, longitudinal fibrils is encountered inside the long process (attachment rostellum) at the anterior end of the body of certain Polymastigina (*Proboscidiella, Oxymonas,* Fig. 58). The ends of these fibrils penetrate from the rostellum deep into the body of the flagellates. According to Kofoid and Swezy (1926) these fibrils are contractile. This problem, however, is not yet solved.

Certain Polymastigina possess another system of fibrils, apparently unconnected with the basal granules of their flagella; namely *Chilomastix* has a special fibril, skirting the edge of the cytostome. In Lamblia, there are two layers of para-axonemal tubular fibrils, which are unconnected with the basal bodies and have apparently a supporting function (Chejsin, in press). The parabasal filament of certain Trichonymphidae also have a similar function. The filament is cross-striated with a periodicity of 380–540 Å, like collagen fibrils, and thus resembles the costa of Trichomonas and the root fibril of Chilomonas. These structures doubtless have a supporting

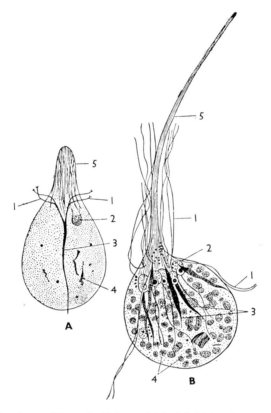

FIG. 58. Flagellates of the order Polymastigida, inhabiting the gut of termites.

(*A*) *Oxymonas dimorpha* (from Connel); (*B*) *Proboscidiella kofoidi*. 1, flagella; 2, nuclei; 3, axostyles; 4, food; 5, rostellum of a fibrous structure. (After Kirby, 1928.)

function. Thus the Mastigophora have fairly varied fibrillar supporting structure.

The fibrillar supporting system of Ciliata is the most difficult to describe, since part of their fibrillar structures, formerly described as supporting elements, are at present regarded as being at least partially conducting elements. Therefore the account of the supporting fibrils in ciliates should be restricted to cases where there is no doubt about their supporting function.

In assessing the supporting function of various fibrils, apart from other considerations, the following criteria should be kept in mind: the absence of a connexion between any given fibrils and the ciliary apparatus; their connexion with definite structures in need of support; the presence of definite elastic properties in the given structures, &c.

On this basis the supporting function of several types of fibrils occurring in the body of the ciliates Entodiniomorpha may be recognized. They contain a complex system of supporting filaments under the cuticle, and systems of supporting fibrils enclosing the endoplasmic sac, pharyngeal fibrils, fibrils within the walls of the anal tube, its suspensory fibrils, &c. The system of branching fibrils, lying within the caudal spines of Ophryoscolecidae and imparting to the spines a certain elasticity, deserves our special attention. All these systems of fibrils are in no way connected with the locomotor apparatus of these ciliates.

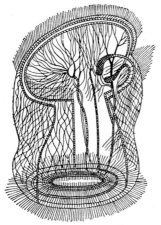

FIG. 59. Fibrillar structure in body of the ciliate *Trichodina*; especially strongly developed within the mouth and attaching disk. (After Peškovskaja, 1923.)

The supporting function of the ecto- and endoplasmatic fibrils or rods of many Astomata, which are arranged longitudinally on the ventral side of their body (*Mrazekiella*, *Metaradiophrya*, and others), cannot be disputed. Their ultrastructure is characterized by a cross-striation with periodicity of about 500 Å (de Puytorac, 1959). These formations are elastic and compact. A similar function is ascribed to the fibrils extending ventrally in the pellicula of several ciliates from the guts of sea urchins and molluscs (*Entodiscus*, *Entorhipidium*, *Lechriopyla*).

There can be no doubt about the supporting function of at least some of the fibrils with which the suckers of certain parasitic ciliates are abundantly equipped. Chejsin (1933) considers that the network of fibrils in the sucker of *Ptychostomum* from the intestine of oligochaetes has a supporting function. Peškovskaja (1923) attributes the same function to the system of fibrils of Trichodina (Fig. 59) and in particular to that of its suckers. An abundant system of annular and radial fibrils was found in the sucker of *Haptophrya*. Bush (1934), it is true, regards part of them as conducting elements, and part as myonemes, but without any doubt a certain part of these fibrils is elastic in nature.

The fibrils of the suspension apparatus (karyophore) of the macronucleus, differentiated in several endoparasitic ciliates (*Nyctotherus*, *Balantidium*, *Clevelandia*), undoubtedly have a supporting function. It is probable that the so-called kinetodesmata, which run along the body beneath the pellicle, have a supporting function. This interpretation is supported by the fact that the cross-striated ultrastructure of kinetodesmata resembles that of collagen fibrils of Metazoa.

In general it is evident that the internal fibrillar skeleton of ciliates is neither less widely distributed nor less varied than that of the Mastigophora.

Contractile fibrils or myonemes. Intraplasmatic contractile elements are encountered among members of all classes of Protozoa, although among the Sarcodina they have been recorded only for some radiolarians. These elements usually bear the character of myonemes, i.e. they are contractile fibrils, with a definite position in the body. Myonemes are distinguishable from other fibrillar structures of the protozoal organism first of all by direct observation of the contraction of the fibrils *in vivo*, their diameter increasing during contraction and decreasing during extension. A considerable contractility and variability of the shape of that part of the protozoan body, where the supposed myonemes are most highly developed, might serve as indirect indication of the contractile character of the fibrils examined. However, the contractile function of the fibrils cannot always be definitely proved even when these characteristic features are present.

The myonemes are distributed mostly in the superficial layers of the body of the protozoon. Thus in certain gregarines fine, annular, contractile fibrils lie under the cuticle. Sevjakov (1892) has recorded them in *Clepsidrina blattarum*. They are linked by oblique anastomosa, forming a common sub-cuticular 'muscular' network. Roskin and Levinson (1929) have described two layers of myonemes in some Monocystidea (Fig. 60): more powerful longitudinal and more delicate annular myonemes, the distribution of which is similar to the muscles of the dermomuscular sac in flatworms. These authors have described in other Monocystidae, viz. in the family Selenidiidae, only longitudinal myonemes, and these only in a small, quite definite number (eight).

In addition to these surface myonemes, in several species of gregarines from New Guinea Oligochaeta, special deep myonemes have been discovered. In *Graterocystis* they diverge radially from the small depression on the anterior end of the body to its outer wall; in *Beccaricystis* the central axis of the body is covered by a latticed sheath of fibrils, which are regarded as myonemes. Finally, Choanocystoides possess within the walls of the sucker a myoneme ring, analogous to sphincter muscles of many Metazoa.

In some gregarines (especially among coelomic Myocystidae) the body may contract considerably as a result of the activity of myonemes. This is accompanied by the contraction of the whole outer case of denser ectoplasm together with the cuticle, while the endoplasm with the nucleus is driven many times from one end of the body to the other. The highest development of the myoneme system is observed in ciliates. Among them *Stentor* and *Spirostomum* have an indisputable contractile system, the arrangement of which is comparatively simple (Fig. 61). In the alveolar layer of the ectoplasm there are numerous ribbon-like myonemes, running from the anterior to the posterior end of the body.

The myonemes extend along the ciliary rows towards the anterior end of the body, branching repeatedly in *Stentor*. Apart from these longitudinal myonemes there are similar fibrils in the peristome, also following the ciliary rows. Contraction of the body of ciliates is accompanied by a considerable shortening and thickening of the myonemes.

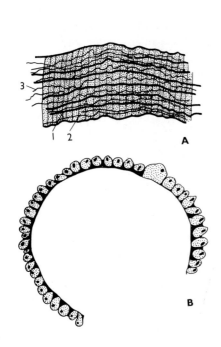

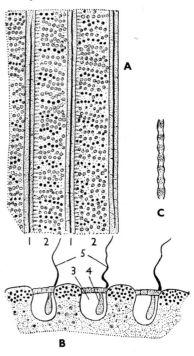

Fig. 60. Myonemes in gregarines *Nematocystis*.

(*A*) tangential and (*B*) transverse section through body of gregarine; 1, longitudinal myonemes; 2, annular myonemes; 3, sinuous supporting fibrils. (After Roskin and Levinson, 1929.)

Fig. 61. Myonemes of *Stentor coeruleus*.

(*A*) seen from surface; (*B*) in cross-section; (*C*) isolated piece of myoneme. 1, longitudinal rib; 2, intermediate band; 3, canal in which myoneme (4) lies; 5, cilium. Schematized from examination by light microscope. (After Schröder, 1907.)

Formerly (Roskin, 1915) it was thought that the myonemes of *Stentor* had a diphasic structure. Moreover, according to Dierks (1926) the myonemes show a transverse striation. New data on the structure of these myonemes, obtained by electron microscopy, do not support this notion, but provide evidence of a different structure (Fauré-Fremiet and Rouiller, 1955; Randall, 1956, 1959). The myonemes of *Spirostomum* seem to consist of approximately ten longitudinal fibrillar bands or plates. These fibrils, of about 250 Å in diameter, have a denser outer layer and a less dense inner core. In *Stentor* the myonemes, running along its body parallel with the rows of cilia and seen through a light microscope as a whole, are, according to the electron microscopic investigations of Randall and Fitton Jackson (1958) represented by two systems of fibrils (Fig. 62).

One system, corresponding to band-like myonemes, visible in living objects, is situated beneath the pellicle in the ectoplasm and is constituted by kinetodesmata running along the infusorian body parallel to the cilia. The kinetodesmata consist of long and thin fibrils, approximately 200 Å in diameter. In *Stentor*, each kinetodesma contains about 500 such fibrils arranged in several longitudinal rows, which form very fine plates or bands.

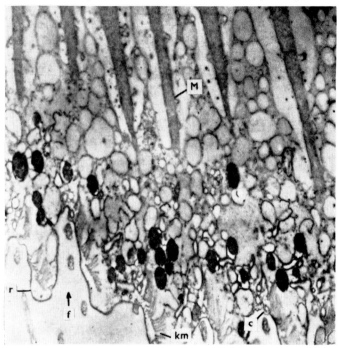

FIG. 62. Electron-micrograph of myonemes of *Stentor*.

Transverse section of lower half of body. (*M*) endoplasmic myonemes (R-band); (*km*) kinetodesmata; (*c*) cilia; (*f*) grooves of ectoplasm; (*r*) ribs. × 40,000. (After Randall and Jackson, 1958.)

The number of the latter, as well as that of the fibrils, changes along the ciliate body. Thickening and shortening of the myonemes corresponding to the kinetodesmata, which is observed *in vivo*, allows us to assume that the birefringent and longitudinally oriented kinetodesmal fibrils have in *Stentor* a function of contractility. Probably, the co-ordination of ciliary movement is also accomplished through these fibrils.

The other system of contractile fibrils is represented by the so-called 'endoplasmic myonemes' (Fauré-Fremiet et Rouiller, 1959) or 'M-bands' (Randall and Jackson, 1958). They are lying in the cytoplasm deeper than the kinetodesmata, and are present only in the posterior body half of *Stentor* (Fig. 62). These band-like myonemes run parallel to the ciliary rows beneath the kinetodesmata. As well as the latter, they become thicker upon body contraction, which testifies to their contractile function. Similar endoplasmic myonemes were found beneath the body surface in some Peritricha (Fauré-Fremiet et Rouiller, 1959), which are able to modify strongly their body shape. Endoplasmic myonemes either have an amorphous structure, or show finest fibrillar elements oriented along the myoneme. They resemble somewhat the fibres of smooth muscle cells of Metazoa. Randall and Jackson note that various authors, who studied the myonemes in fixed ciliates in the light microscope, dealt probably with the endoplasmic myonemes, which are well visible in contracted specimens only, whereas in living specimens the more superficial kinetodesmata were labelled as myonemes. It is most probable that the kinetodesmata cause only an insignificant contraction of the anterior part of the *Stentor* body, whereas the endoplasmic myonemes lead to a considerable contraction of the medium and hind regions of the ciliate body.

The contents of the stalk canal of many solitary or colonial Peritricha, in which it has been studied by numerous investigators, undoubtedly bears a contractile character. According to Koltsov (1911), who studied *Zoothamnium alternans*, the stalk of this ciliate is covered outside by an elastic, cuticular sheath which supports it in an erect position when the myonemes are at rest. The space between the sheath of the stalk and the myoneme is filled with fluid. The myoneme itself is a cylindrical cord, surrounded by a thin membrane and differentiated into two concentric layers of plasma (Fig. 63). The outer layer, or thecoplasm, is granular in structure; the inner layer, or kinoplasm, is homogeneous and highly refractile. The boundary between the thecoplasm and kinoplasm is marked by a layer of fine fibrils running along the whole myoneme. When the stalk is functioning its sheath and its fine longitudinal fibrils are firm, elastic, structures which mechanically straighten out the stalk. The contractile part of the stalk is its central fluid column, viz. the kinoplasm, while the contraction of the stalk is due to the change in the surface tension on the boundary between the kinoplasm and the thecoplasm. The stalk ceased to be contractile, while the kinoplasm breaks into drops (which can be produced artificially in hypotonic solutions). On emerging from the stalk into the body of the ciliate the myoneme of the stalk is extended into a complex system of finer myonemes. Such are the annular myonemes around the peristome, the retractors of the adoral disk, the annular myonemes of the basal part of the body, and some others.

The stalks of certain Peritricha and Chonotricha have in recent years been investigated in considerable detail by electron microscopy (Rouiller, Fauré-Fremiet, and Gauchery, 1956; Randall, 1956, 1959), and our conception of them is now more precise. It has been shown that the contractile stalk of *Zoothamnium*, *Carchesium*, and *Vorticella* (Fig. 63) consists of two clearly distinguishable parts: the central core or canal, into which the endoplasm of the zooid is prolonged, and its sheath or annulus. The core is filled with an amorphous mass enclosed in a fine membrane, and sometimes fibrillar structures can be distinguished in the canal. Thus in *Vorticella* the canal contains bundles of filaments 30–40 Å in diameter (Sotelo and Trujillo-Cenoz, 1959). This fibrillar complex is usually called 'spasmoneme'. Therefore the central canal is similar in structure to the endoplasmic myonemes of other ciliates (for instance, *Stentor*). In the annulus are clearly visible numerous very fine tubes consisting of filamentous elements arising from the scopula (the differentiated zone of the aboral part of the zooid) and extending through the whole length of the stalk. According to Rouiller, Fauré-Fremiet, and Gauchery (1956) in *Opercularia* and *Zoothamnium*, and to Randall (1959) in *Carchesium*, these tubular fibrils have a cross-striation. The annulus of *Carchesium* and *Zoothamnium* contains more than a hundred of such fibrils, that of *Vorticella* only about twenty. The fibrils have a diameter of about 1,400 Å. According to Fauré-Fremiet, Favard, and Curasso (1962), numerous canaliculi are revealed electron microscopically in the non-contractile stalk of *Epistylis articulata*. Their walls consist, like axonemata, of nine extraciliary fibrils having a characteristic double cross-striation, with a larger period of about 400 Å and a half-period of 220 Å. These extraciliary fibrils approach the kinetosomes of the scopular cilia and come into contact with the kinetosomal walls, but they are not prolongations of the kinetosomal fibrils. Apparently the fibrils of the canalicular walls are elastic elements of the stalk, resembling in their structure collagen fibres. The contraction of the stalk is probably associated with the central canal; this

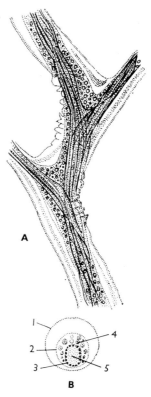

FIG. 63. Structure of main stalk of *Zoothamnium alternans*.

(*A*) lower part of main stalk with two side branches; (*B*) section through stalk. 1, outer sheath; 2, inner sheath; 3, skeletal fibrils; 4, kinoplasm; 5, thecoplasm. (After Koltzov, 1911.)

view is supported by the fact that such a structure is absent in the stalks of *Epistilis*, *Opercularia* (Peritricha), and *Chilodochona* (Chonotricha), which cannot contract. The fibrils of the annulus may be elastic structures. The central canal with its membrane may be compared in its function with the sarcoplasm and sarcolemma of the muscle fibres in Metazoa. It corresponds completely to the inner layer (kinoplasm) of the myoneme of the stalk of *Zoothamnium*, according to Koltzov's description. At the same time Koltzov's observations on the occurrence of a layer of thecoplasm in the myoneme and of fibrils between this layer and the kinoplasm has not been confirmed by data from electron microscopy. The question of the bio-chemical mechanism of stalk contraction in Vorticella and the role of ATP in this process are not yet completely clear. According to Levine (1960), adenosine triphosphate has been found to be localized in the contractile apparatus of Vorticellids. The stalk displayed more activity of ATP-ase in the spasmoneme sheath than in the spasmoneme itself. Further investi-gations are undoubtedly required for the elucidation of the construction and mechanism of contraction in such a complex structure as the stalk of Peritricha.

The myonemes of the parasitic Entodiniomorpha are most diversified and specialized. Both Dogiel (1926) and Strelkov (1939), who have made detailed studies of these elements in many representatives of the group, recognize first of all the existence of a powerful bundle of myonemes, acting as a retractor of the adoral disk, as well as the presence of annular sphincters, surrounding the opening to the vestibule of the cytopharynx, while a similar sphincter and retractor are situated in the walls of the dorsal labium, covering the dorsal zone of the cirri, and in the annular labium of the caudal cirri, in forms like *Tripalmaria*.

Dogiel and Strelkov disagree in their interpretation of other plasmatic fibrils, such as those surrounding the endoplasmic sac and the annular fibrils in the walls of the anal tube or in the excretory duct of the contractile vacuole. Dogiel is inclined to regard them as contractile, whereas Strelkov recognizes their supporting function. It is interesting to note that in their distribution the myonemes of many protozoa find an analogy in certain muscles of Metazoa. The retractors of the anterior end of the body to the myonemes of the rectal tube, the excretory canal, and the contractile vacuole are good examples of it.

There are comparatively few data on the myonemes of the flagellates. Only in certain Trichonymphidae parasitic in termites, Kofoid and Swezy describe two layers of myonemes—annular and longitudinal—lying on the boundary of the ecto- and endoplasm. The annular layer lies outward from the longitudinal, as in the dermomuscular sac of the majority of worms. Moreover, according to Bernstein (1928), the base of the tube of the head organ in *Trichonympha turkestanica* is surrounded by a powerful sphincter.

The so-called tentacle of the *Noctiluca* is an example of the transversely striated contractile structures. At the entrance to the peristome of *Noctiluca* there is a fairly thick, band-shaped tentacle, reaching to approximately half the length of the body, and performing slow beats (2–9 per minute). The transversely striated tentacle consists of regularly alternating lighter and darker sections. The tentacle resembles the transversely striated muscle-fibres both in function, i.e. contraction, and in structure.

To the two examples given should be added the data on the myonemes of Radiolaria and Acantharia (Fig. 64) described by Sevjakov (1926). At the points where the radial spicules of Acantharia emerge from the body they are enclosed in cone-like extensions of the extracapsular substance; moreover, these extensions are fixed to the spicules by varying numbers (from 2 to 30) of short, longitudinal, contractile bands surrounding the axis of each spicule in the shape of a ringlet. Haeckel has called these contractile

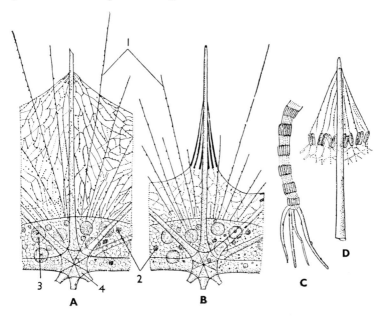

FIG. 64. Contractile apparatus in *Acanthometron pellucidum*.

(*A*) when extended; (*B*) when the gelatinous layer is compressed; (*C*) separate contractile element (myofrisk); (*D*) terminal portion of spicule surrounded by myofrisks. 1, pseudopodia; 2, nuclei; 3, zooxanthellae; 4, central attachment of twenty radial spicules. (After Sevjakov, 1926.)

bands 'the myofrisks', but their functions are exactly the same as those of the myonemes in other protozoa. The number of myonemes varies in different families of Acantharia, and serves as a reliable systematic and phylogenetic character. The number of myonemes is smaller in radiolarians of the primitive families and in young individuals of the more highly specialized ones. Their number increases up to a definite limit by the division of the original small number of myoneme rudiments. The myonemes of Acantharia have several extremely interesting morphological peculiarities. Their shortness and comparatively great thickness are the first to strike the eye—they are attached by one end to the spicule, by the other to the extracapsular plasma: as a result the extension of the plasma is stretched round the spicule in the form of a tent. Another characteristic of the myonemes is their transverse striation. It is clearly seen that they are composed of alternating sections, staining deeply and weakly by nuclear dyes. On irritation, for instance, by electric current, the myonemes contract fairly rapidly, thereby causing the extracapsular substance to extend over the framework of spicules; the volume of the body of the radiolarian is thus increased, while its weight remains constant; this results in an increase of their buoyancy.

The series of analogies noted by us between the contractile fibres of Protozoa and Metazoa is indisputable; however, their existence is not at all surprising. The constructive element of a muscular system consists of very fine muscle fibrils, which are intracellular in both Protozoa and Metazoa. This explains their histological coincidences (smoothness and transverse striation). The similarity in the distribution of the contractile elements is no greater than the analogies between the digestive and skeletal systems in unicellular and multicellular organisms.

Conductile fibrils and the problem of the 'nervous system' in protozoa

The problem of whether Protozoa have a system of special conductile fibrils, similar in function to the nerve fibres of Metazoa, and serving to coordinate the activity of the different organoids, arose in a concrete form at the very beginning of this century. Even before that Schuberg (1890) had given a detailed description of the system of myonemes in the ciliate *Stentor* which reacts rapidly to various stimuli by a pronounced contraction of its body. In 1903 Neresheimer used some new staining methods for the ciliate *Stentor*, and with the help of Mallory's stain he discovered a new, hitherto unknown system of fibrils, which in his opinion had a nervous function; he called them the neurophanes. Like the myonemes the neurophanes spread in the shape of a bouquet from the posterior to the anterior end of the body of *Stentor*, running approximately parallel to the myonemes, but differing from them in their staining properties. Neresheimer also demonstrated that substances with a paralysing effect on the nervous system of higher animals have the same effect on *Stentor*, by stopping its movements. Moreover, in some cases fine side-branches of neurophanes which enter into contact with the myonemes were seen.

From these facts Neresheimer came to the conclusion that among the more highly developed Protozoa there was a differentiated system of nerve fibrils, or neurophanes.

The further elucidation of this problem owes much to the investigation of Sharp (1914) on the organization of *Diplodinium* (*Epidinium*) *ecaudatum* (Fig. 65) belonging to the ciliate order Entodiniomorpha, inhabiting the rumen of the ruminants. These ciliates have a very complex structure (Fig. 65). Their body is equipped with an adoral spiral and a dorsal arch of cirri, covered by a special plasmatic fold—the dorsal lobe; the rest of the body is enclosed in a dense cuticle. The anterior pole of the body bulges somewhat forwards in the form of the so-called parietal protuberance. Using Mallory's stain, Sharp discovered in *Epidinium* an area of specially differentiated plasma at the base of the parietal protuberance above the

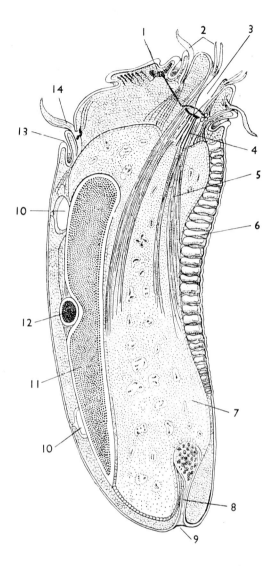

FIG. 65. Longitudinal optical section through the ciliate *Epidinium ecaudatum*. (Ophryoscolecidae).

1, motorium; 2, adoral cirri; 3, mouth (cytostome); 4, conductile fibrils of pharynx; 5, contractile fibrils of pharynx; 6, skeletal plate; 7, endoplasm; 8, rectal tube; 9, anus (cytopyge); 10, contractile vacuoles; 11, macronucleus; 12, micronucleus; 13, dorsal lobe; 14, dorsal zone of cirri. (After Sharp, 1914.)

pharynx; from this area is given off a system of fibrils directed mainly to locomotor organoids (cirri and myonemes). Sharp called this section the motor centre or motorium. In the body of the ciliate only the motorium and micronucleus stain bright red by Mallory's method. Sharp called the motorium and the bundles of fibrils running from it the 'neuromotor apparatus'. According to Sharp's description the fibrils of this apparatus innervate the cirri of the adoral spiral and the dorsal arch, forming a delicate adoral ring from which fibrils run to the pharyngeal myonemes. A cluster of fibrils also runs from the parietal protuberance, which in Sharp's opinion has a sensory function. Sharp's investigations laid the foundation of the American school of study of the conductile system in ciliates. The American research on the subject is characterized by their recognition of the entire neuromotor apparatus as a physiological and morphological complex, controlled from a definitely localized nervous centre, the motorium. In accordance with this view, this nervous centre is invariably searched for by American investigators, even when the pictures observed did not provide sufficient evidence of its existence. As a matter of fact, however, the structures described as motorium have the appearance of either a local thickening of fibrils, or even of artifacts. Moreover, the extreme variety of forms and distribution of the motorium in different ciliates raises a certain doubt. Thus the motorium is in various cases situated at the bottom of the pharynx, or above it, or at the base of the anterior sucker (in *Haptophrya*); sometimes it is a ring, or a ribbon, or a small irregular bundle; in other cases additional centres are recorded side by side with the main motorium (*Entodiscus*, according to Powers, 1933).

The research of the American protistologists on the 'neuromotor apparatus' of ciliates was seriously criticized by many investigators in different countries. Thus, Sharp's data on the presence of a motorium in various Ophryoscolecidae were not confirmed in the detailed investigation of these forms by Bretschneider (1934), who considers the complex system of fibrils discovered by him mainly as a supporting apparatus. Likewise, Strelkov (1939), in his comprehensive work on the morphology and systematics of Ciliata Entodiniomorpha from the Equidae, was unable to discover either a motorium or any other elements of a neuromotor apparatus in them. He records the presence of different fibrils not united into a single system, and having a supporting function. Other investigators of the fibrillar structures in Ciliata, e.g. Ten Kate (1927, 1928) and Lewinson (1941), also do not accept the ideas of the American workers regarding the neuromotor apparatus.

However, the theory of Sharp and others concerning the neuromotor apparatus of ciliates of the family Ophryoscolecidae has been revived in a somewhat different form by researches carried out by Fernandez-Galiano (1949) and Noirot-Timothée (1960). According to the latter (Fig. 66) there are three main groups of fibrils in *Epidinium*: a perioesophageal ring, an anterior dorsal arch, and a posterior dorsal arch, including a large motorium with numerous fibrils running from it to the periphery. Noirot-Timothée expresses her opinion on the function of all this fibrillar apparatus with great caution, without denying, however, its possible transmitting and co-ordinating role.

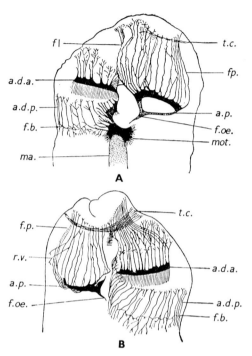

FIG. 66. *Epidinium ecaudatum* (Ophryoscolecidae): system of argentophile fibrils.

(*A*) anterior part of ciliate from right side; (*B*) same from left side; a.d.a., anterior dorsal arch; a.d.p., posterior dorsal arch; a.p., peripharyngeal annulus; f.1., fibril 1; f.b., basal fibril; f.oe., oesophageal fibril; f.p., adoral fibrils; ma., macronucleus; mot., motorium; r.v., ventral ramification; t.c., fibres lying at base of ciliary apparatus. (After Noirot-Timothée, 1960.)

However, it should be pointed out that the system of fibrils described by Noirot-Timothée does not correspond in any way to that described by Sharp for the same organism; therefore Sharp's and Noirot-Timothée's 'motorium' are two different things (compare Figs. 65 and 66). Further research on the problem is evidently needed.

Another approach to the problem of the fibrillar apparatus of ciliates is connected with the examination of the sub-pellicular structures, detectable by silver or gold-impregnation of dry or moist-fixed preparations. Klein and Gelei carried out these investigations independently and almost simultaneously in 1925–6. During the same period Chatton, Lwoff, and their collaborators also studied this problem by means of a modified method of silver impregnation.

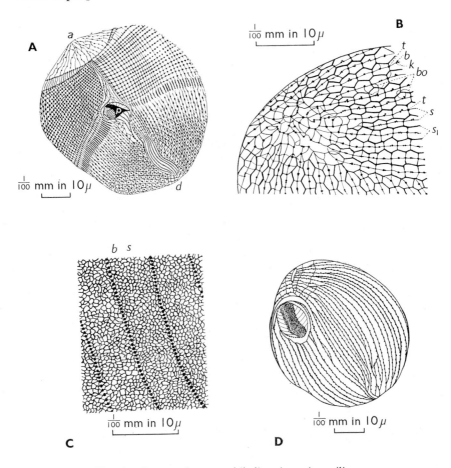

FIG. 67. System of argentophile lines in various ciliates.

(*A*) *Urocentrum turbo*: *a*, apical pole; *d*, distal pole; *p*, basal plate of cytostome; (*B*) apical pole of *Paramecium aurelia*: *a*, argentophile line of direct connexion; *s*, argentophile line of indirect link; *t*, trichocysts; *k*, supplementary grains (Nebenkörner); *bo*, fibrils linking basal bodies, trichocysts, and supplementary grains; *b*, basal body; (*C*) part of body of *Stentor igneus*; *b*, basal bodies; *s*, argentophile lines; (*D*) *Glaucoma scintillans*. (After Klein, 1926, 1927.)

We can now consider briefly the basic research done on this problem. Already at the beginning of this century, Schuberg (1905) had discovered fine fibrils in the ectoplasm, which connected the basal granules of one row of cilia with each other. Klein, who has applied his 'dry' silver method since 1926, has described in a number of papers the presence of an extremely complex system of fibrils, blackened by silver—the silver-line system—in the ectoplasm of various groups of ciliates. This system forms a closed network including all the basal granules of the cilia and the trichocysts. The pattern of the silver-line system may vary considerably (Fig. 67). Sometimes it is a fine meshed network or a row of meridional lines with a few transverse commisures, &c. The silver lines may have a different arrangement in various parts of the body of the ciliate (Fig. 67). Klein distinguishes two types of fibrils among the silver lines. Some of them directly link the basal granules of the cilia and the trichocysts: they represent the 'directly connected system'; the others are linked only indirectly, through the direct system, with the basal granules—this is the 'indirectly connected system'. This distinction is very clear for instance in *Paramecium*, where the fibrils of the directly connected system form longitudinal rows, while the indirect system is situated under the hexagonal projections of the pellicle, which form the characteristic pellicular surface-sculpture of *Paramecium*. Klein distinguishes simple and complex fibrils. In the case of very dense, finely meshed networks, these are composed of extremely fine elementary fibrils. In other cases (for instance in *Paramecium*) the network consists of finer fibrils and then it is composed of several elementary fibrils. According to Klein, the latter also enter the cilia, forming its axial part. Thus the silver-line system is composed of fibrils, basal granules, and cilia.

Klein attributes most varied and essential functions to the system of argentophile fibrils. In his later papers, especially in his big work of 1943, he calls it 'the neuro-formative system' (neuroformium). According to Klein, one of its functions is the conduction of stimuli and the co-ordination of the beats of the cilia. However, apart from this 'nervous function' Klein attributes to it other most important ones. The basal granules originate in the loops of the network, and from these the cilia are formed. Hence, during division of the ciliates, the neuroformative system is the material from which the new ciliary apparatus is formed. The laying down and development of new peristomes during the division of the ciliates also begins, according to Klein, with the transformation of the silver lines. At the site of the future peristome a dense lattice is formed (Fig. 68), which is used as a material for the construction of membranes, membranelles, &c., with their basal apparatus. In Klein's words, the silver-line system is 'an active organ capable of independent changes, representing formative reactions to given influences arising from the animal's body'.

J. Gelei (1932) and his son G. Gelei (1937) give a different explanation of the subpellicular structures in ciliates impregnated with silver. J. Gelei has divided Klein's silver-line system into two completely different categories of structures by using very refined methods of fixation of the material (instead of drying), followed by impregnation with silver and gold salts, as well as by special methods of staining (toluidine blue). J. Gelei detected some subpellicular fibrils linking together the basal granules of cilia. These fibrils are neuronemes and their function consists in conducting the stimulus and co-ordination of the activity of the ciliary apparatus. These fibrils correspond to Klein's 'directly connected system'. As regards the 'indirectly connected system', it is not associated, according to Gelei, with the conducting apparatus and in the majority of cases is not even of fibrillar structure. It is a case of silver impregnation of pellicular structures (in

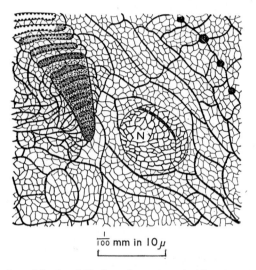

$\overline{100}$ mm in 10 μ

FIG. 68. Section of body of *Euplotes* from ventral side. Formation of new peristomial field (*N*) during division. Silver impregnation. (After Klein, 1926.)

Paramecium of the ridges of the hexagonal depressions). All these structures have a supporting function and they play no role in the conduction of stimuli.

Gelei's concept was complicated by the fact that his son G. Gelei (1937) found in three species of *Paramecium* a third system of fibrils situated at the level of the basal granules and somewhat below them. This fibrillar network consists of longitudinal, transverse, and diagonal strands, which are directly connected with one another at the points where the fibrils intersect. The meshes of this network are smaller and more numerous than those of the outer network; and they are also more irregular. This third network covers the whole periphery of the body, extending to the walls of the peristome and the vestibule of the pharynx. However, Gelei was unable to detect any connexion between the third network and the other two, and its function remains so far unknown.

Further additions to our knowledge of the fibrillar structures in *Paramecium*, used as a standard, were made by Lund (1933), who examined these structures in the pharyngeal apparatus of this ciliate by the same methods of silver impregnation (Fig. 69). Lund discovered an extremely complicated system of fibrillar networks, corresponding to the complex function of the pharynx and its ciliary apparatus: the strands of the network form several areas or separate systems, running in various directions under the pellicle.

Lund's work is chiefly important for his establishment of a main and additional motorium in the walls of the pharynx (Fig. 69, *B*).

While G. Gelei's study (1937) of the fibrillar structure of the peristome

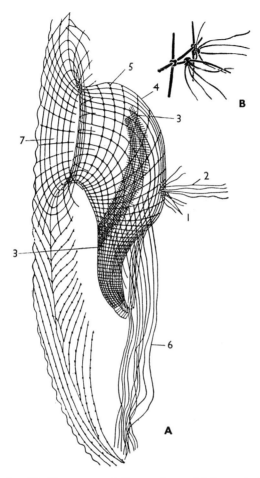

FIG. 69. Fibrillar system of *Paramecium multimicronucleatum*.

(*A*) diagram of pharyngo-oesophageal network of fibrils and fibrils running from it into endoplasm; (*B*) diagram of motorium; 1, motorium; 2, fibrils running from it into endoplasm; 3, anterior and posterior ends of thickened part of network of fibrils; 4 and 5, longitudinal and annular pharyngeal fibrils; 6, fibrils running from pharynx into endoplasm; 7, peristomial fibrils. (After Lund, 1933.)

and pharynx of *Paramecium* has in general confirmed Lund's observations, it differs essentially in the fact that Gelei failed to detect any motoria.

Lund's observations of the surface structures of *Paramecium* are similar to those of G. Gelei. In his opinion only the fibrils connecting the basal granules represent conducting elements. As regards the polygonal network

(Klein's 'indirectly connected system'), Lund regards it simply as a sculpture on the pellicle.

Finally, as early as 1930, but especially in 1935–6, Chatton introduced into this problem a very important modification by pointing out that in ciliates, under the rows of cilia, there are double rows of granules of different significance, not merely rows of basal granules. One row corresponds on the whole to the centrioles of the flagella of Mastigophora and like these is capable of multiplication. In 1937 Chatton referred to these granules simply as centrosomes, whereas earlier he called them kinetosomes. Each centrosome is formed as the result of division of a pre-existing centrosome. Along the row of centrosomes lies a parallel tract of granules, while above each of them arises a corresponding cilium. These granules, apparently, correspond to the additional granules of Gelei and Klein. Chatton and Lwoff (1930) call them the parabasomes. A parabasome originates from the centrosome, but is not capable of independent multiplication and disappears when its own cilium has perished.

Chatton and Lwoff used the term 'infraciliature' for the set of centrosomes and parabasomes. The problem of infraciliature will be discussed in greater detail in the next chapter on locomotor organoids. Here, however, it may be noted that the main point of the French investigator's concept of infraciliature is the idea of its continuity. Kinetosomes (centrosomes) originate from their own kind only by their regeneration and cannot be formed *de novo*. Even in cases when reduction of the ciliary apparatus takes place (for instance during encystation) the infraciliature is retained and the cilia are reconstructed from it later. Therefore, contrary to Klein's opinion, Chatton and Lwoff deny the possibility of a new formation of the basal apparatus and of the cilia themselves from the loops of the silver-line system. The elements of the infraciliature are usually connected with each other by fibrils—the kinetodesmata, which correspond to Gelei's neuronemes and probably have a conducting function. As regards the other elements of Klein's silver-line system, Chatton and Brachon (1935) and other French investigators emphatically deny their role in the formation of interciliary connexions, and regard them as structures completely independent of these. Chatton (1937) uses for the whole network of argentophilic lines the general term of 'argyrome' in contrast to the kinetodesma and infraciliature set which he calls the kinetome.

Chatton and his pupils have discovered a similar argentophilic network in Dinoflagellata (for instance in *Polykrikos*, Fig. 70) and in a number of sporozoa (schizogregarines, coccidia, sarcosporidia, Fig. 71). These discoveries are of importance if the 'argyrome' of the flagellates and sporozoa is really homologous with that of the ciliates, since this would indicate the complete independence of the 'argyrome' from the 'kinetome'. Chatton expresses no definite views about the physiological significance of the 'argyrome' but is inclined to attribute to it mainly a supportive function.

In recent years many new data on the subpellicular fibrillar structures of ciliates have accumulated as a result of a wide application of electron microscopy (Metz, Pitelka, and Westfall, 1953; Sedar and Porter, 1955; and others). According to these investigations, a cylindrical basal body or kinetosome lies in the ectoplasm at the base of the cilia. So far the dual nature of the basal apparatus of the cilia, insisted upon by Chatton and Lwoff, has not been confirmed by electron microscopic investigations. A fine fibril, the kinetodesma, runs from the kinetosome, which further unites, but does not fuse, with other kinetodesmata arising from the neighbouring basal granules of the same row of cilia. A bundle of fibrils is thus formed, in which the separate elementary fibrils are in close contact with each other, forming as it were synapses. Each elementary fibril is short, extending only through the length of a few neighbouring cilia of a given row, after which it becomes thinner and dwindles to nothing (Fig. 72). As a result the bundle of fibrils is composed only of a few elementary fibrils. The entire bundle corresponds to the neuronemes or kinetodesmata visible by light microscopy.

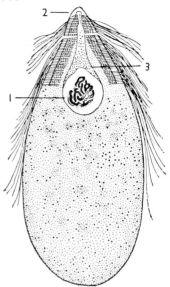

FIG. 70. Argentophile peripheral network in the anterior half of the body of *Polykrikos schwartzi*. 1. nucleus; 2. ostrum; 3. nuclear sac. (After Chatton and Hovasse, 1934.)

Other investigations (Ehret and Powers, 1959; Randall and Jackson, 1958; Yagiu and Shigenaka, 1959) give reason for supposing that the fibrils of the kinetodesma are of considerable length, running, if not throughout the entire length of the body, to a considerable distance; moreover, each fibril of the kinetodesma may be united with many other fibrils, given off from several kinetosomes of a single row. Bonds of the fibrils of the kinetodesmata, of the type of synapses, have not been observed by many authors. In different ciliates a kinetodesma may consist of a varying number of fibrils: in *Colpidium colpoda* there are 2 or 4, in *Paramecium caudatum* 5 or 7 (Ehret and Powers, 1959; Chejsin, 1963), in *Condylostoma* (Yagiu and Shigenaka, 1959) there are a few dozen, and in *Stentor* (Randall and Jackson, 1958) about 500. The character of kinetodesmal bonds probably varies in different ciliates, and further comparative investigations are required to establish the general regularities concerning the connexions between the fibrils of kinetodesmata and the kinetosomes.

As regards the network of fibrils forming Klein's 'indirectly connected system', the results of the electron microscopic investigations are so far

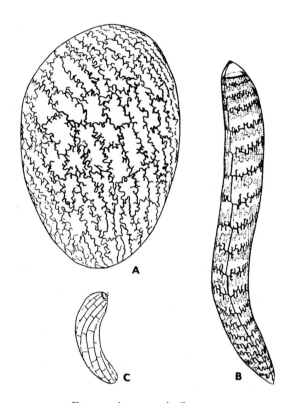

Fig. 71. Argyrome in Sporozoa.

(A) *Klossia helicina*, gamont; (B) *Barrouxia ornata*, merozoite;
(C) *Lankesterella ranarum*, merozoite. (After Chatton, 1937.)

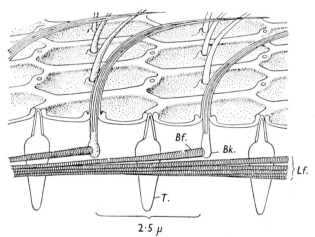

Fig. 72. Diagram of structure of pellicle and kinetodesmal
links in *Paramecium*, based on electron-microscopy.

Bk, basal body; *Bf*, basal fibril; *Lf*, longitudinal fibrils; *T*,
trichocyst. (After Grell, 1956.)

contradictory. Metz, Pitelka, and Westfall (1953) have described in *Paramecium* a peripheral pellicular lattice composed of a network of fibrils lying under the hexagonal thickening of the pellicle. However, Sedar and Porter (1955) have not found a pellicular lattice in this ciliate; they believe that the impression of the presence of a network is created by the surface structure of the pellicle. As to the fibrils of 'direct connexion', Parducz (1962) believes that they correspond to superficial longitudinal septae of paired subpellicular alveoli connected interciliarly. It is these regions which become impregnated with silver and which appear in preparations as fibrils connecting the basal bodies and the trichocysts. Sedar and Porter (1955) have found, in their electron-microscopic examination of *Paramecium*, one more closed fibrillar network on the level of the basal body, which in their opinion corresponds to the third network of the subpellicular fibrils (the infraciliary lattice system), described by G. Gelei. Besides this, on the same level, transverse fibrils are revealed in *P. caudatum*, which connect the kinetodesmata of two adjacent kinetids (Cheissin, 1963).

To form an opinion on the functional significance and role of different fibrillar systems, it is necessary to take into consideration not only morphological characters but also physiological and biochemical data. As shown by observations on living ciliates (*Paramecium*, *Spirostomum*, *Stentor*), and by the method of instantaneous fixation of cilia (Parducz, 1954), the activity of cilia is strictly co-ordinated among themselves. In *Paramecium*, the beating of cilia proceeds in waves from the anterior to the posterior end. The cilia situated on the same level in relation to the longitudinal axis beat simultaneously, while cilia distributed on different levels within the same longitudinal row beat at certain intervals of time from each other.

The occurrence of the above-mentioned metachronism indicates the existence of co-ordination among individual elements of the ciliary apparatus, but does not explain the mechanism of this co-ordination. The direction of the movements of the cilia can be altered or reversed by certain external influences. This takes place for instance under the effect of an electric current or that of univalent cations: the activity of the ciliary covering of the ciliates is then restored, so that it becomes a single, co-ordinated whole.

It has recently been proved that the acetylcholin-cholinesterase (Seaman and Houlihan, 1951) system takes part in the chemical dynamics of the ciliary movement of Protozoa. At the same time it was shown by the method of fractional centrifugation (Seaman, 1951) that in *Tetrahymena* this system and its components (basal granules, fibrillar ectoplasmatic structures) is localized in the pellicle and ectoplasm. As is known, the acetylcholin-cholinesterase system plays an exceptionally important part in the conduction of nervous impulses from the nerve to the working organ (for instance a muscle fibre) or from one neurone through synapses to another. Therefore the discovery of this system in ciliates is most interesting, as it points to a similarity of the biochemical processes forming the basis of the elementary nervous processes. It has been shown that anticholinesterase substances (eserine, diisopropyl-fluorophosphate, and others) have an inhibiting effect on the movements of ciliates. Kostojanc and Kokina (1957) have demonstrated the importance of the system of acetylcholin-cholinesterase for the process of the excitatory summation in *Paramecium*.

The data reviewed in the preceding pages show that many problems connected with the study of the fibrillar apparatus of ciliates are still unsolved and disputable. The problem of the 'nervous system' of Protozoa (chiefly in ciliates) is the most controversial. Perhaps one of the reasons for the failure to solve this problem is the absence of necessary contact between morphological (including electron-microscopy), physiological, and biochemical research.

We shall try to formulate the points which at present are either indisputable or plausible in the problem of the 'nervous system' of ciliates: (1) there is a strict co-ordination in the activity of the separate elements (cilia, membranelles, &c.) of the locomotor apparatus of the ciliates; (2) there is a mechanism for the conduction of stimuli similar to that of the nervous system in multicellular organisms (the acetylcholin-cholinesterase system); (3) the stimulation-wave passes through the ectoplasm. It is probable that the fibrils connecting the basal apparatus of cilia (Gelei's neuronemes, Klein's 'directly connected system', Chatton's kinetodesmese) serve as the material substratum for the passage of impulses. The notion that Klein's 'indirectly connected system' takes part in the conduction of stimuli is improbable. It probably plays a supporting and static role.

IV

PROTOZOAN ORGANOIDS OF
LOCOMOTION

A LL Protozoa are capable of movement, at least at certain stages of
their life. Even the sedentary forms and the intracellular parasites,
immobile by the very way of their life, at some stages of their life
cycle are either motile or the progressive movement of their whole body
is replaced by movements of some of its appendages or its organoids of
locomotion (which in sedentary forms serve to drive food in and capture
it). The Protozoa have different types of locomotion, the structure of their
locomotor apparatus varying accordingly. Three main kinds of organoids
of locomotion may be recognized: flagella, cilia, and pseudopodia. The
classification of protozoa has been based on them for a long time. Apart
from some modifications of these three types of organoids, there are some
particular cases of progressive movement which is accomplished by means
of contraction of special contractile fibrils, or myonemes, which as regards
their physiology correspond to the muscle fibres of Metazoa. The problem
as to which kind of organoids of locomotion is the most primitive one has
not yet been solved. According to a widely accepted view, it is the flagellar
apparatus. Indirect evidence of this is provided by the fact that the class
Mastigophora is considered to be the most ancient among all the Protozoa.
It is also noteworthy that many amoeboid organisms are capable of temporarily reverting to the flagellated state: this phenomenon is regarded
as a recapitulation of previous ancestral organoids. However, there is no
general agreement on this problem, since some investigators interpret the
process of the origin of different kinds of locomotion in the opposite way,
considering flagella as derived from the more definitely localized pseudopodia, the axial filament of which served as a base for the formation of
flagella. This point of view is probably correct.

Flagella and flagellar movement

Flagella represent the most essential systematic character of the class
Mastigophora; though they are occasionally also encountered among vegeta-
tive individuals of other classes, being combined either with pseudopodia
(*Dimorpha mutans* among the Heliozoa; *Mastigina, Mastigamoeba* among
the amoebae) or very rarely with cilia (*Ileonema* or *Monomastix* among the
Holotrichous ciliates).

The arrangement of flagella and their varieties. Flagella represent filamentar processes of the external layer of the cytoplasm, which are very fine and capable of rapid vibration. As a rule, the number of flagella in an animal is not great, varying from one (Euglenida, Protomonadida) (Fig. 73) to two (Cryptomonadida, Dinoflagellata, Phytomonadida) and even eight (Poly-

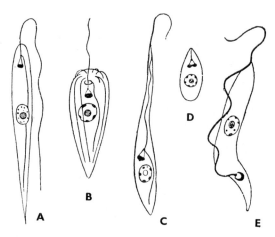

FIG. 73. Locomotor organoids of various trypanosomids (Mastigophora).

(A) *Leptomonas*;   (B) *Strigomonas*;   (C) *Crithidia*;
(D) *Leishmania*; (E) *Trypanosoma*. (After Grassé, 1952.)

mastigida). However, one order of flagellates (Hypermastigida) has a large number of flagella, occupying either only its anterior pole, or covering almost the entire body (Figs. 20, 80).

The microscopic structure of the flagellum is not uniform. A central axis can be distinguished in it, enclosed in a sheath of fluid cytoplasm, which in its turn is covered by a delicate external membrane (Koršikov, 1923). Vlk (1938) and other investigators have detected in flagella, examined in dry smears, numerous filamentar appendages, running in different directions (Fig. 74). Examination by electron microscopy of the flagella of various euglenids in total preparations (Brown, 1945; Foster *et al.*, 1947; Pitelka and Schooley, 1955; and others) has revealed the presence of very fine filaments or mastigonemes, from 1μ to 4μ long and about $10\,m\mu$ thick, running from one or both sides of the flagellar membrane, and representing, in Pitelka and Schooley's opinion, a kind of sheath enclosing the flagellum.

However, such filamentar appendages have not been usually detected in flagella examined in moist smears. Owen (1947, 1949), for instance, denies completely the existence of branched flagella in flagellates, regarding them as artefacts, produced by the dry method of fixation. Having examined more than twenty species of Mastigophora he had encountered only flagella of the usual kind, viz. filamentar with a thinner tip. The apparent branches of the flagellum are produced, according to Owen, as a result of ruptures of its membrane, through which the liquid external plasma of the flagellum is discharged in the form of minute streamlets.

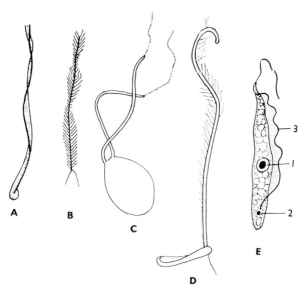

FIG. 74. Flagella of various Mastigophora.

(A) Trachelomonas; *(B) Euglena*: flagellum with mastigonemes; *(C) Polytoma*: whip-like flagella; *(D) Urceolus*, flagellum with mastigonemes; *(E) Trypanosoma*: 1, nucleus; 2, kinetoplast; 3, undulating membrane. (After different authors from Kudo, 1954.)

Recently, however, Roth (1959) has described mastigonemes on the flagella of *Peranema*, examined in ultra-thin sections by electron microscopy (Fig. 75, *A*). In view of these data, it is necessary to reconsider the question of the existence of mastigonemes. Further investigation should show whether they are artefacts or structures that actually exist. Mastigonemes may possibly exist in some flagellates and not in others. They have not been detected by electron microscopy of either total or sectioned preparations of the flagella of *Tritrichomonas* and various Trypanosomidae. An axoneme of complicated structure, a matrix, and a boundary membrane have been detected by electron microscopy in various representatives of the Euglenida, Polymastigida, Hypermastigida, and Trypanosomidae (Grassé, 1956; Pyne, 1958; Anderson and Beams, 1959; and others).

The axoneme always contains eleven longitudinal fibrils, of which nine are situated on its periphery at equal intervals from each other (about 500 Å). They form a kind of cylinder with two more fibrils running through its centre; their diameter varying in different species from 250 to 400 Å. The peripheral fibrils have a diameter of about 250–350 Å; moreover, each of them is doubled. Some additional details of their ultra-fine structure were recently discovered by electron microscopy of the flagella of *Trichonympha* (Gibbons and Grimstone, 1960). Each of the nine peripheral fibrils is composed of two sub-fibrils, with two short processes, called 'arms' (Fig. 75, *B*), running from the side of one of them. The fibrils thus acquire a certain asymmetry. Each of the sub-fibrils, as well as the two central fibrils,

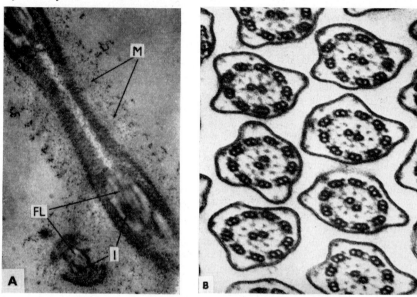

FIG. 75. Electron-micrograph of flagella.

(*A*) longitudinal section of flagellum of *Peranema*: *M*, mastigonemes; *Fl*, longitudinal fibrils; *I*, matrix of flagellum (after Roth, 1959); (*B*) transverse section of flagella of *Pseudotrichonympha*, showing peripheral (double) fibrils and central parafibril. (After Gibbons and Grimstone, 1960.)

possesses a dense outer osmiophilic layer and a less dense central shaft. Between the peripheral and central fibrils nine secondary fibrils, about 50 Å in diameter, running along the axonemes, may be observed. At the boundary between the flagellum and the basal body there is a transverse basal plate.

The axoneme is enclosed in a sheath in the form of a matrix. In some, larger flagella filamentar elements are observed in a matrix (e.g. in *Lophomonas*), while transverse striation is visible in the Euglenidæ. The flagellar membrane passes directly into the membrane surrounding the body of the animal (Fig. 76, *B*). It is interesting to note that the tails of spermatozoa of many Metazoa and the flagella of the microgametes of *Eimeria* (unpublished observations by Chejsin) have a structure analogous to that of a flagellum.

In some flagellates (e.g. *Lophomonas*) a large number of flagella at the anterior end of the body forms a single bundle. There is a cementing

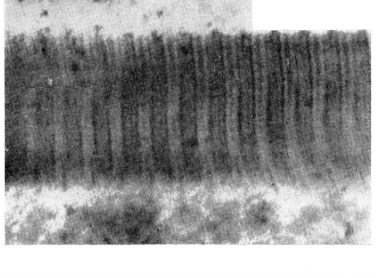

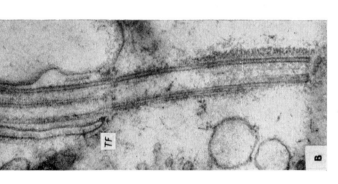

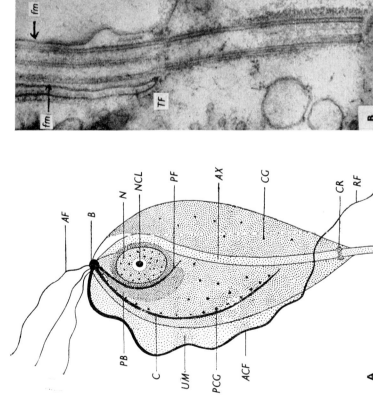

Fig. 76. Structure of locomotor and supporting apparatus in flagellates.

(A) Tritrichomonas muris, diagram. (After Anderson and Beams, 1959.) AF, anterior flagella; B, blepharoplast; N, nucleus; NCL, nucleolus; PF, fibril of parabasal apparatus; AX, axostyle; CG, basophile granules; CR, basophile annulus around axostyle; RF, caudal flagellum; PB, parabasal body; C, costa; UM, undulating membrane; PCG, paraxostyle granules; ACF, marginal fibril of undulating membrane. (B) base of flagellum of Holomastigotoides sp. Electron-micrograph. (After Gibbons and Grimstone, 1960.) fm, sheath of flagellum; TF, boundary between flagellum and basal body (C) Tritrichomonas muris, electron-micrograph of costa, showing alternating brighter and darker rings. (After Anderson and Beams, 1959.)

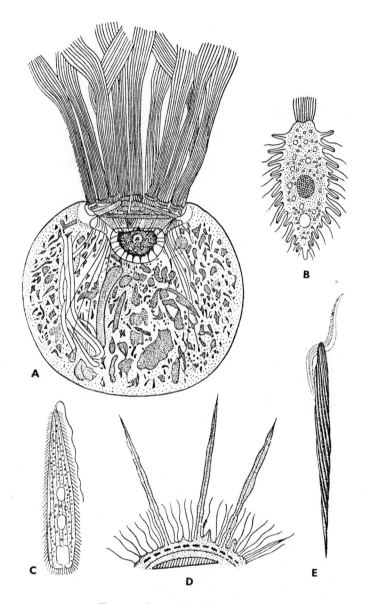

Fig. 77. Organoids of locomotion.

(A) *Kofoidia loriculata*, bundles of flagella united into special loriculae; (B) *Dactylochlamys* (Holotricha Gymnostomata): combination of rows of cilia and trichocyst-bearing tentacles; (C) *Ileonema ciliata*, combination of cilia with flagella; (D) *Myriophrys paradoxa* (Heliozoa), combination of flagella with axopodia; (E) *Haplonympha natator* (Polymastigina) with two bundles of flagella. (After various authors, from Dogiel, 1951.)

substance between the separate flagella of which it is composed binding them together. Flagella stuck together into units of larger size are observed among certain Hypermastigida. Thus in *Kofoidia loriculata* (Fig. 77) the anterior end of the body is surrounded by a corona of 8–16 bundles of flagella, or, as Light (1927) calls them, loriculae. Loriculae form a laevo-rotatory spiral, each of them consisting of about 30 large bunches up to 100μ long. During the animal's life all the loriculae of a bunch are closely joined to each other right down to their tips; but after fixation their distal parts split into separate flagella, while their basal part remained intact. The movement of loriculae consists of pronounced beats in one direction and a straightening up in the reverse one; moreover, the movement of all the loriculae is not synchronized; they contract consecutively from the left end of the spiral to the right.

From this description it may be seen that the loriculae of *Kofoidia* resemble in their structure and even in their distribution the so-called cirri of many ciliates, especially of the Entodiniomorpha from the intestine of hoofed animals.

A pair of loriculae at the anterior end of the body of another flagellate of termites, *Hoplonympha natator*, have an even more peculiar appearance than those of *Kofoidia*. Two bunches, each consisting of approximately thirty flagella, protrude in all directions from the anterior end of the body, to which they are attached laterally; thus producing the effect of a bilateral symmetry. The movements of the two loriculae alternate: while one of them extends far forward for a beat, the other strikes backwards, until it touches the body; then this loriculae draws forward, and the first strikes backwards and touches the body. The beats of loriculae are very frequent; they are an example of an intensification of the work of the flagella.

Apart from loriculae Mastigophora possess another apparatus for the intensification of the activity of their flagella, which does not require any increase in their number; it is known as the undulating membrane. In some Protomonadida, namely in certain Trypanosomidae, the single flagellum is attached to the outer edge of a thin pellicular fold of its body, extending for a considerable distance from its anterior end backwards. The flagellum starts from a blepharoplast in the middle (*Crithidia*) or posterior end (*Trypanosoma*) of the body, after which it runs along the outer margin of the undulating membrane and typically terminates in the anterior end as a free flagellum. Many Polymastigida (*Trichomonas*, *Gigantomonas*, and others) possess, apart from the undulating membrane, also 2–5 free flagella arising from the anterior end of the body, while the attached flagellum emerges at the end of the membrane as a free tail-like flagellum (Fig. 76).

Sometimes there is a supporting fibril—the costa (Polymastigida)—situated at the base of the undulating membrane and running parallel to the base (Fig. 73, *A*, *C*). As has been revealed by electron microscopy, the costa of *Trichomonas muris* consists of alternating transverse rings of varying densities (Anderson and Beams, 1959b). The membrane itself, as shown by some investigators, consists of fine longitudinal fibrils, while an elastic accessory filament runs along its edge together with the flagellum. These elements of the membrane (recurrent flagellum and accessory filament) appear in the light microscope as a single marginal filament. In trypanosomes (e.g. *Trypanosoma equiperdum*), however, the membrane does not display a fibrillar structure (Anderson, Saxe, and Beams, 1956).

The undulating membrane serves either only for locomotion or, in forms possessing a mouth (*Trichomonas*), also helps to some extent in capturing food. In some flagellates (Dinoflagellata and certain Polymastigida) the flagellum is band-shaped, with one thickened edge, resembling in this respect the undulating membrane.

Where there are two flagella they may both be directed forward and have an equal length (Phytomonadida) or else one short flagellum directed forward, while the other longer one, known as the trailing flagellum, trails behind the moving animal (various species of *Bodo*). Finally, flagella of the Dinoflagellata, which were originally at the anterior end, had shifted to the equator of the body, and only one of them is directed forward, while the other encircles the body along a special transverse groove.

Mode of attachment of flagella to the body of Protozoa. The flagellum starts from the basal granule, or blepharoplast, which lies either near the surface of the body (Fig. 76, *B*) or is buried deep inside. The walls of the basal granule (blepharoplast) are limited by nine longitudinal fibrils representing the continuation of the peripheral fibrils of the axoneme of the flagellum, while the two central fibrils terminate in the flagellum before reaching the blepharoplast (Roth, 1959). In *Trichonympha* the outer wall of the blepharoplast consists of nine triplet densely cemented fibrils connected by fine filaments with other similar triplet fibrils. Through the centre of the blepharoplast of *Trichonympha* runs a cylinder connected with the outer fibrils by fine (20 Å) transverse filaments (Gibbons and Grimstone, 1960). In a number of cases the base of flagellum extends into the body in the form of a special root filament or a rhizoplast, which either ends freely in the cytoplasm or reaches the nucleus and is attached to its membrane.

Among the members of the family Trypanosomidae, behind the blepharoplast (Fig. 73), which is usually hardly visible, there lies a larger body, staining with nuclear stains and giving a positive Fuelgen reaction, usually called the kinetoplast (Hoare, 1949). This structure is known under different names: blepharoplast, centrosome, parabasal body, and kinetonucleus. Its terminology has been comprehensively discussed by Hoare (1938) and Kirby (1944). The positive Fuelgen reaction of the kinetoplast indica·es the presence of DNA therein. This is confirmed also by the fact that deoxyribonuclease treatment of the preparation makes the kinetoplast Fuelgen negative. Moreover, tritium-labelled thymidine becomes incorporated into the deoxyribonuclease-removable substrate of the kinetoplast

(G. Steinert, Firket, and M. Steinert, 1958). Thus, DNA synthesis occurs in the kinetonucleus.

The data on the structure of the kinetoplast accumulated considerably after the application of electron microscopy of ultra-thin sections to various Trypanosomidae. For example, *Trypanosoma equiperdum* (Anderson, Saxe, and Beams, 1956), *T. cruzi* (Meyer and others, 1958; Meyer and Queiroga,

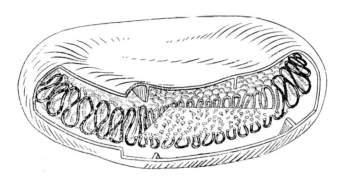

FIG. 78. Three-dimensional scheme of the kinetoplast in *Trypanosoma cruzi*. (After Schulz and MacClure, 1961.)

1960; Schulz and MacClure, 1961), *T. mega* (Steinert, 1960), *T. lewisi* (Clark and Wallace, 1960), *Leishmania donovani* (Pyne and Chakraborty, 1958), *L. tropica* (Pyne, 1960), *Strigomonas oncopelti* (Horne and Newton, 1958), and other forms were studied.

The structure of the kinetoplast is more or less alike in all species studied. This organoid, about $2\,\mu$ large, is covered with a double osmiophilic envelope identical to a mitochondrial membrane. Short cristae protrude from the inner sheet of the envelope. The central part of the kinetoplast is occupied by a network of long twisted fibrils, 125 Å thick, with an inner clear space of 35 Å. A scheme of such a kinetoplast is given in Fig. 78. It is interesting to note that in *T. cruzi* and *T. mega* the kinetoplast is intimately associated with a mitochondrion adjacent to it (Fig. 79), and because of this both organoids form, in fact, one unit (Steinert, 1960; Schulz and MacClure, 1961). It is still difficult to estimate the significance of this fact, but probably such a complex organoid, containing DNA, lipoproteids, and respiratory enzymes, may play an important role in the metabolism and energy conversion of the trypanosomids. The function of this structure is not yet clear, and in the opinion of Hoare and other authors the kinetoplast may play a role in the metabolism of the monosaccharides, which are utilized by blood flagellates during their life processes.

The basal granule (or blepharoplast *sensu stricto*) of a flagellum has a double significance. On the one hand, it is the central constituent of the whole supporting locomotor apparatus, to which is added in some special and fairly frequent cases a special parabasal body (see below) with its supporting suspension filament and the axostyle. On the other hand, the basal granule corresponds to the centriole of metazoan cells, controlling the process of karyokinetic division of the cell as does the latter. Which of these

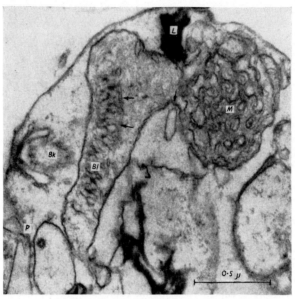

FIG. 79. Electron-micrograph of a section of the body of *Trypanosoma cruzi*, showing kinetoplast (*Bl*) connected with a large mitochondrion (*M*). (After Schulz and MacClure, 1961.)

Bk, basal body; *P*, periplast; *L*, fat droplet. *Vertical arrow* indicates point of junction of the surface membrane of the kinetoplast with that of the mitochondrion; *horizontal arrows* show the double membrane of the fibrils in the kinetoplast.

is its main function is a problem that is still unsolved. It may be noted, however, that among Protozoa karyokinesis may take place without the participation of a centriole (e.g. in ciliates). Therefore Chatton and Lwoff (1931) consider that the main function of the basal granule (centriole) is the control of the locomotor apparatus; in accordance with this they proposed for all Protozoa equipped with either flagella or cilia a specail concept of kinetid, comprising the entire complex of the supporting-locomotor apparatus of a protozoon closely connected with the nucleus. Chatton and Lwoff include in it (1) the flagellum; (2) the rhizoplast, running from the base of the flagellum to the interior of the body; (3) the centrosome or basal granule; (4) the suspension filament of the parabasal body running from the centriole, and (5) the parabasal body (Fig. 80).

The structure called the parabasal body, which is usually spatially connected with the blepharoplast, varies considerably in shape: it may be represented by a simple, elongated body, a sausage-like form, which when large in size may wind spirally round the base of the axostyle, or there may even be a whole bundle of such forms. They are encountered mostly among Polymastigida and Hypermastigida, and much more rarely in other flagellates. It was also found in Choanoflagellata (Saedeleer, 1930), Dino-

FIG. 80. Electron-micrograph of Golgi apparatus in flagellate Foaina from the gut of termite *Calotermes flavicollis* (×40,000).

S, membrane of osmiophile sacs; Vo, osmiophile vesicles; SC, bubbles of chromo-phobe zone of Golgi apparatus. (Grassé, 1956.)

flagellata (Chatton and Grassé, 1929), *Chilomonas paramecium* (Anderson, 1962), and in certain Euglenidae and Volvocales (Grassé and Hollande, 1941). Since the parabasal apparatus is detected almost exclusively by the osmium method, many investigators identify it with the Golgi apparatus; and it probably plays an important role in metabolism. The similarity between the parabasal body and the Golgi apparatus becomes most evident when it is examined by electron microscopy. This has been established for *Joenia annectens, Foaina dogieli, Trinitus divergens, Trichonympha agilis* (Grassé, 1956), and other species (Grimstone, 1959), and also for *Tricho-monas* (Anderson and Beams, 1959b). The system of membranes, each

60–70 Å thick, is the most characteristic constituent of the Golgi apparatus. They are arranged in pairs parallel to each other, with edges of the membranes of each pair lying close to each other, thus enclosing a small space. Several of such pairs of membranes are closely packed within the zone. On the periphery of each pair of membranes small bubbles with osmiophilic walls are formed.

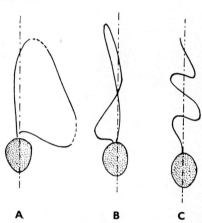

A   **B**   **C**

FIG. 81. Forms of flagellar movement.

(*A*) and (*B*): figures described by the flagellum in its forward movement, shown in two different planes, lying at an angle of 90° to each other; (*C*) bending of the flagellum during the backward movement of the animal. (After Krijgsman, 1925.)

On examination of the parabasal body by light microscopy Grassé (1926) found that it consists, similarly to the dictyosomes of the Golgi apparatus, of two parts: the chromophobe interior and the chromophile exterior parts. The chromophobe part is, according to electron microscopical observations, characterized by the presence of large osmiophilic vacuoles, while the chromophile part has a system of membranes similar to those observed in the corresponding elements of the Golgi apparatus of the metazoan cells. According to Grassé (1956) and other investigators, the membranes of this part of the Golgi apparatus are 70 Å thick and are linked in pairs to form flattened sacs (Fig. 80).

The parabasal bodies probably play a part in metabolism: the periodic changes undergone by them and the fact that sometimes they may partly dissolve in the plasma speak in favour of this interpretation; however, it stands in need of confirmation.

Grimstone (1959) suggested that the membranes of the flattened sacs of the parabasal body might contain enzymes controlling the synthesis of polysaccharides, and that therefore one of its functions is to secrete these substances into the cytoplasm of the flagellate. In the course of division the parabasal body of the daughter-cells is apparently formed anew. In those Hypermastigida in which the spiral rows of flagella encircle the whole body, the parabasal apparatus multiplies, forming a multitude of small osmiophile rings, distributed under the rows of flagella.

Movements of flagella. The delicacy of the flagella and the rapidity of their movements makes a precise examination of the flagellar movements difficult. The basic type of the movement of the flagella is a rotation around the surface of a cone, the apex of which is turned towards the point of flagellar attachment. Simultaneously with this the flagellum also produces undulatory movements. This operation is most efficient when the angle of the cone apex is between 40 and 60 degrees. The speed of the movement is at least 10 revolutions per second, but apparently it may reach as many as 40 revolutions. This rotation of the flagellum produces a current of water directed backwards, which in its turn helps to propel the animal forwards. As a consequence of the flagellar rotation the body of Mastigophora rotates also around its long axis and the path described by the flagellate is not a rigorously straight line. Flagellates moving slowly or creeping along a substratum (*Peranema*) do not rotate round the long axis, since in those cases the flagellum beats from side to side but does not form a cone of rotation. In flagellates with a flattened band-like flagellum the tip draws not a circle but an ellipse. When the ellipse is greatly drawn out the movement of the flagellum recalls a beat, or sweep, going from one extreme point of the ellipse to the other, with a subsequent return of the flagellum towards its starting position. From these examples some investigators are inclined to explain flagellar movement as a series of successive lateral beats: however, in most cases this interpretation is doubtful.

The scheme of flagellar movements described by us is based on those of forms with a single flagellum, but it does not fit even these cases entirely. Thus, for example, we have already mentioned the peculiarities of the movements of *Peranema* in which the bendings of the flagellum affect chiefly its distal part, whereas its proximal part is directed straight forward during its progression, and does not change its position.

The speed of the movement of various flagellates has been calculated only for a few species and is shown in the following table:

Species	Length of flagellata in μ	Speed of movement in μ/sec	Ratio of the path traversed in 1 sec to length of body, which is adopted as a unit
Chromulina rosanoffi	9	35	4
Peridinium sp.	35	125–230	4–7
Menoidium incurvum	15	30	2
Euglena sp.	50	155–235	3–5
Spondylomorum quarternarium	Colony	115	. .
Gonium pectorale	Colony	46	. .
Pandorina morum	Colony	70	. .

Cilia and ciliary movement

Cilia are characteristic of only one class, the Ciliata. In their structure and function they resemble flagella in many respects. They are filamentary processes of the external layer of the cytoplasm, usually shorter than the flagella. All ciliates possess them either throughout life, or only at some stages of their life-cycle, as in Suctoria.

Arrangement and structure of cilia. Cilia are comparatively short (usually 10–15 μ) structures perforating the pellicle and protruding outside it. Unlike flagella, cilia are always encountered in large numbers. Thus in *Paramecium* there are 10,000–14,000 cilia and in *Prorodon* 11,000–12,000. However, some forms are known with a much smaller number of cilia, as, for example, members of the family Blepharocoridae from the alimentary tract of hoofed animals, which possess only 3–4 bundles of cilia. As is shown by electron microscopic examination, each cilium—like the flagella—consists of nine double peripheral fibrils with a diameter of 150–350 Å enclosed in a membrane, and two central fibrils 240 Å thick (Fig. 82, *B*). In the cilia of *Colpidium colpoda* it was found that the peripheral fibrils are double, just as in the case of the flagella of *Trichonympha*. Each peripheral fibril consists of two sub-fibrils. From one of the sub-fibrils of each pair are given off two lateral short processes (arms). Between the peripheral fibrils and the central pair of fibrils (Chejsin and Mosevič, 1962) are situated fine (about 30–50 Å) transverse fibrils running throughout the whole length of the cilium.

In Roth's opinion (1959) the cilia differ from the flagella in that their peripheral fibrils lie directly under the membrane; moreover, they do not form with the central fibrils a bundle separated from the membrane by a layer of matric, as is usually observed in flagella. However, this difference is sometimes not very pronounced. The cilium arises from a basal granule or kinetosome, which under an electron microscope looks like a small cylinder, 300–4,000 μ long. Its wall consists of the nine double peripheral fibrils continuing from the cilia. In certain Astomata, the kinetosome wall consists of nine triplet fibrils instead of double ones, thus resembling those in some flagellates (for example, Trichonympha). The central fibrils do not usually run into the basal body, although Roth (1956), who examined the cilia composing the cirri of *Euplotes patella*, found that the two central fibrils are in fact parts of the same filament which enters the basal granule and forms a loop there (Fig. 82, *C*).

On the other hand, Noirot-Timothée (1958) has noted in *Entodinium* and certain Isotricha, and Randall (1956, 1958) in *Stentor* and *Spirostomum*, that there are no central fibrils in their basal body, but they terminate in the distal part of the basal body at the boundary with the external membrane near the axial granule (Fig. 82, *A*). Roth also noted this granule, but according to his observations the central fibril runs through it into the basal body. The axial granule is connected with the peripheral fibrils by a fine filament. A basal plate separating the basal body from the cilium frequently lies beneath the granule on a level with the pellicular membrane. In *Condylostome, Blepharisma,* and *Stentor* there are dense osmiophilic granules, arranged in rows along the basal body (Randall and Jackson, 1958; Yagiu and Shigenaka, 1959; and others), the significance of which is still unknown. In *Colpidium campylum* and *C. colpoda* the pellicle forms a dense ring (or sheath) around the upper part of the basal body, which is connected with the peripheral fibres of the basal body by short filaments (Pitelka, 1961; Chejsin and Mosevič, 1962). This ring apparently serves for the reinforcement

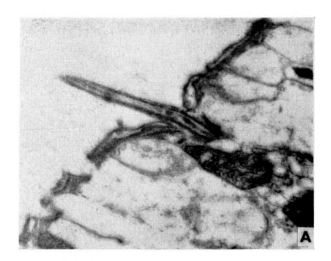

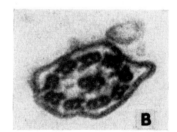

FIG. 82. Electron-micrograph of cilium of *Colpidium colpoda*.

(*A*) longitudinal section (× 40,000); (*B*) transverse section (× 100,000)
(orig.); (*C*) longitudinal section of the basal body of cilium forming
part of cirri of *Euplotes* (× 60,000). (After Roth, 1956.)

of the base of the cilium. However, further investigations are required to elucidate some common features regulating the ultra-fine structure of the cilia and their basal bodies in different ciliates.

So far there are only very few data on the functional significance of the fibrils in flagella and cilia. The movements of cilia are probably due to the

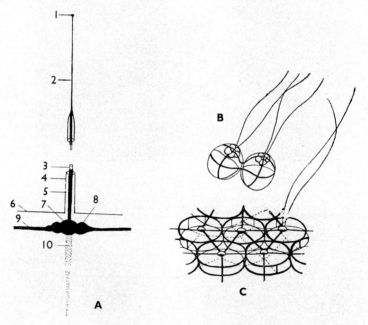

Fig. 83. Supporting locomotor apparatus in Protozoa.

(*A*) diagram of structure of cilia; 1, terminal swelling; 2, terminal part of cilium; 3, axial filament; 4, plasmatic sheath; 5, argentophile membrane of axial filament; 6, pellicle; 7, basal granule; 8, supplementary granule; 9, argentophile line; 10, basal filament of cilium. (*B*), (*C*) scheme of arrangement of argentophile lines in individuals of *Gonium* colony. (After Klein, 1943.)

contraction of the peripheral fibrils, while the direction of ciliary beats is controlled by the central fibrils. The central fibrils may possibly be an elastic shaft.

This structure of cilia and flagella, composed of 9 (or 9 pairs)$+2$ fibrils, represents a pattern common to Protozoa and also to the cells of the ciliated epithelium of Metazoa.

Chatton and Lwoff have introduced a new concept 'infraciliature' (Figs. 83–86) to describe the ciliary apparatus of ciliates, and have extended to each individual cilium the concept of the kinetid, which they had first applied to the flagellar apparatus of Mastigophora.

According to Chatton and Lwoff, each basal granule of a functioning cilium consists of two components. One of them looks like a small granule, strongly blackened when treated with silver, and capable of multiplying by division. Chatton and Lwoff call it the infraciliar granule (kinetosome). The other component is formed from the second granule; silver nitrate has only a weak blackening effect on it. It is not capable of independent

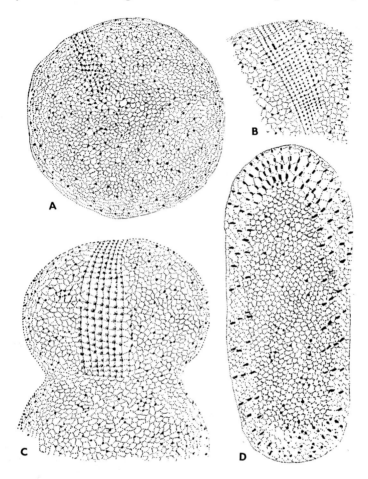

FIG. 84. *Podophrya fixa* (Suctoria); changes in infraciliature during budding.

(*A*) adult suctorian beginning of formation of embryonic field; (*B*), (*C*) organization of kinetosomes and of the system of argentophile filaments in the embryonic field; (*D*) system of kinetosomes of bud. (After Chatton, Lwoff, M. Lwoff, and Tellier, 1929.)

division. Chatton and Lwoff called this the ciliary granule (parabasosome). These additional granules have been described by other investigators as well. As to the morphological significance of the granules, the infraciliary granule corresponds to the centrosome of the kinetid of flagellata. The ciliary granule with its greater liability and its apparent lipoproteid nature is equated by Chatton and Lwoff with the parabasal body of the kinetid of flagellates. The physiological significance of both kinds of granules is revealed most clearly in observations on the loss of the ciliary coating in ciliates (for instance in the course of cyst formation), or on the contrary

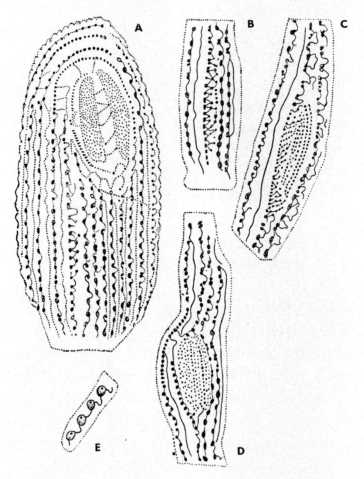

FIG. 85. Anlage of new mouth and adoral apparatus in ciliate *Glaucoma scintillans* during division.

(*A*) area of ventral side of body with old mouth and anlage of new mouth in so-called stomatogenous band; (*B*)–(*D*) successive stages of development of new mouth; (*E*) detail of chain of blepharoplasts showing their double nature. (After Chatton, Lwoff, M. Lwoff, and Monod, 1931.)

during new formation of cilia, as, for example, in the swarmers of Suctoria, or on growth of an aboral ciliary girdle in free-swimming Peritricha. It was demonstrated that at the time of the production of new cilia the animal always contains in its ectoplasm some infraciliary granules, which are either arranged without any regularity (in Suctoria), or occupy the area where the cilia eventually appear (the aboral girdle groove in Peritricha). Moreover, the infraciliary granules undergo heteropolar division, which produces a new infraciliary granule at one end of the short connecting filament, and at the other a ciliary granule, from which there is produced its corresponding cilium. According to this observation, one of the granules, namely the

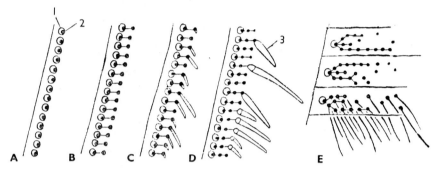

FIG. 86. Process of formation of trichocysts from elements of infraciliature in Aposto-matous ciliates.

(*A*) elements of infraciliature before formation of trichocysts; (*B*) formation of granules from kinetosomes; (*C*) development of trichocysts from specialized granules; (*D*) secondary division of granules; (*E*) formation of 'secondary trichocysts'; 1, basal body; 2, infraciliary body (kinetosome); 3, trichocyst in a state of formation. (After Chatton, Lwoff, and M. Lwoff, 1931.)

infraciliary one, is of main or primary significance, while the ciliary granule is of secondary importance.

In cases of temporary reduction of the ciliary covering, the cilia and their ciliary granules disappear completely, while the infraciliary granules are retained entirely or partially. In the second case they may partially retain their arrangement in rows, or may be disposed irregularly—these, in the expression of Chatton and Lwoff, are wandering infraciliary granules. When the ciliary apparatus is restored, the latter may be shifted, arranged in rows, &c., and may multiply, giving rise either to structures similar to themselves or to ciliary granules, from which cilia grow out.

Hence it is obvious that the kinetid is a permanent element in the organization of the cells of the majority of Protozoa. The flagellar apparatus of the Mastigophora and the ciliary apparatus of the ciliates are structures self-reproducing by division, endowed with genetic continuity from generation to generation, arising from their primordia which are retained continuously in the cells, in the form of centrosomes in Mastigophora and of infraciliary granules in ciliates. Each cilium with its basal apparatus is homologous with the flagellar kinetid of Mastigophora, hence the ciliary kinetids are fully comparable to the flagellar kinetids of those Hypermastigida which possess a large number of flagella. Thus we have a uniform orderly picture of a genetic connexion between the locomotor system of all Flagellata and Ciliata, based on the same initial unit—the kinetid.

Chatton and Lwoff considered that, apart from the nucleus, the main morphogenetic organoid of the cell is the centrosome (centriole) and its derivatives. Like the centriole, these derivatives usually have the shape of a granule, their functions vary, and their names vary accordingly.

In the simplest cases the centriole lying in the immediate vicinity both of the base of the flagellum and of the nucleus situated near the surface has two simultaneous functions: it controls the movement of the flagellum and the division of the nucleus; moreover, both functions are connected with the phenomena of locomotion. This is the case in certain flagellates. In other Mastigophora a special body (mastigosome in Chatton's terminology, or basal granule of the flagellum) is detached from the centriole; it controls the movement of the flagella, while the centriole itself regulates the movement of the nuclear components during division. There can be two very different forms of division of the centriole into centriole proper and mastigosome (or mastigosomes when there are several flagella). In one case the mastigosomes separated from the centriole retain, like the centriole, the very important property of self-reproduction, characteristic of the centriole —these are the autonomous basal granules or mastigosomes (part of the *Mastigophora*). In the other, the mastigosomes lose this ability, and then they have to be periodically restored during the life-cycle, at the expense of the centriole. A very good example of this second kind are certain Hypermastigida, for instance, *Spirotrichonympha africana*, of the Trichonymphidae, observed by Dogiel. This form has at the anterior end of its body a protrusion, the so-called rostrum, covered with a cuticular cap. The elongated nucleus is suspended inside from the rostrum by means of a narrow 'cephalic tube', called by Cleveland the nuclear sleeve. Some spiral bands of flagella run from the anterior pole of the body, each spiral consisting of many dozens of flagella winding round the body from front to back. The flagellar spirals are twisted dextrally. There is a basal granule at the base of each flagellum. The centriole is comparatively large and adjoins the posterior pole of the nucleus from behind, being separated from the anterior end of the body by the whole length of the nucleus and the 'cephalic tube', or the nuclear sleeve. We have also observed numerous dense rows of granules, their number corresponding to that of the flagellar spirals, running from the centriole along the surface of the nucleus in proximal direction. These rows of granules are bent round the nucleus towards the anterior end of the body; moreover, the spiral is coiled in the opposite direction to that of the flagellar spirals, passing from the nucleus to the nuclear sleeve. On reaching the anterior pole of the body the rows of granules bend over the edge of the sleeve and emerge to the surface of the body. At the bend the rows of granules unfold, changing their direction, so that they become twisted dextrally, passing directly into the flagellar spirals, giving rise to new flagella. Such basal granules may be called non-autonomous. As the posterior ends of the spirals wear out they break off approximately at the level of the third quarter of the surface of the body, and new rows of mastigosomes arise at the anterior end of the body from beneath the cuticular cap. They are produced in the depth of the body, under the nucleus, from the single centriole, which was formerly called the centro-blepharoplast. In its significance this is the same important organoid of the kinetid—the centriole.

The extrusion of the same pattern to the ciliates removes the basic difference between Plasmodroma and Ciliophora. And in fact, the infra-ciliar granules (Chatton and Lwoff) can be compared with the autonomous mastigosomes of the flagellates, with this difference, however, that in ciliates they do not pass directly into the basal granules of the cilia, but form separate ciliary granules of a non-autonomous, i.e. of not self-reproducing type.

In general the ideas of Chatton and Lwoff are the most logically worked out; they have been the first to assist in establishing the relationship between the flagella and cilia. However, the harmonic conception of Chatton and Lwoff about the kinetid and the infraciliature has not yet been con-firmed with electron microscopic studies. The data cited above on the electron microscopy of the ciliary basal apparatus failed to confirm up till now its dual nature, which the French authors insist on. Without any doubt, this problem leaves much to be investigated.

A. Lwoff (1950) expressed an original point of view regarding the role of the kinetosome in the morphogenesis of ciliates. He regards it as the cytoplasmic structure common to all Ciliata, which has the ability of self-reproduction and is, therefore, most important in the realization of cyto-plasmic heredity. In Sonneborn's opinion (1950) the kinetosomes may serve as a model of plasmogenes.

Lwoff notes that the kinetosomes do not originate *de novo* but are formed as the result of the division of existing kinetosomes, thereby determining their genetic continuity. At the same time the kinetosome may develop into a trichocyst, trichite, axostyle, or a parabasal body; but primarily they produce cilia. Their different potentialities may probably be connected with mutations.

In Lwoff's opinion the determining factor in the development of the kinetosomes may be the regional difference of material in the body of the ciliate necessary for the synthesis of kinetosomes. In this case their genetic identity must be assumed. On the other hand, if kinetosomes are genetically heterogeneous, which according to Lwoff is more probable, then, owing to different molecular ecology, a selection of diverse genetic types of kineto-somes may take place in various regions of the cell. However, this problem is not clear yet, and its future solution will undoubtedly be of interest for the theory of cytoplasmic heredity.

Fusion of cilia. So far we have discussed the structure and function of single cilia, but apart from them the ciliates are frequently provided with more powerful locomotor apparatus, representing products of fusion of the cilia and their complication. The so-called cirri (syn-cilia) of the Hypotricha (Fig. 87) and Entodiniomorpha are an example of one of the complications. However, in both these groups there are also typical cilia.

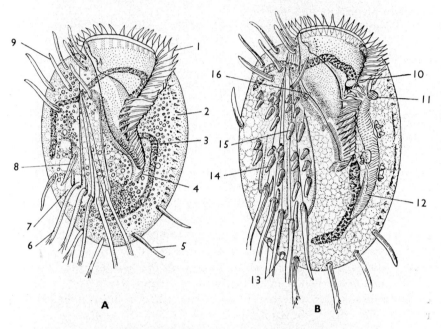

FIG. 87. *Euplotes patella* from ventral side.

(*A*) non-dividing individual; (*B*) dividing individual. 1, adoral membranellae; 2, ventral cilia; 3, macronucleus; 4, cytopharynx; 5, marginal cirri; 6, anal cirri; 7, contractile vacuole; 8, ventral cirri; 9, anterior cirri; 10, reorganization zone of macronucleus; 11, micronucleus; 12, primordium of peristome of the posterior individual; 13, primordium of right marginal cirri of the posterior individual; 14, primordium of anal cirri of the posterior individual; 15, primordium of the anal cirri of the anterior individual; 16, primordium of anterior cirri. (After Dogiel, 1951.)

Each cirrus consists of 2–3 short rows of cilia, fused together into one hooked, or thick, whip-like process. Unlike simple cilia, cirri can bend in different directions. In Hypotricha they are found only on the ventral surface, and are used for creeping over the substratum. As is shown by electron microscopy the cirri of *Euplotes patella* consist of tufts of adjoining cilia lying in rows and not enclosed in a common membrane. According to Roth's data (1956) the cilia in cirri are linked together by means of small extrusions or protrusions of the membrane.

Some modifications of cilia, called membranelles, develop round the mouth of all Euciliata, except for the order Holotricha. Their structure is very similar to that of the cirrus. The membranelles look like flat, thin, triangular plates, consisting of two rows of cilia fused together.

Membranelles serve only for swimming and for driving food into the mouth. They form round the mouth an adoral spiral which descends to the buccal overture.

Furthermore, quite a number of Holotricha and Heterotricha possess so-called undulating membranes situated at the edge of the peristome or in the pharynx, usually more or less parallel to the long axis of the body. They are very delicate, transparent membranes consisting of one or two rows of cilia fused together, the movements of which, depending on their lesser or greater length, are either simple beats or are accompanied by wave-like bending of the whole membrane, hence its name.

Work of the cilia. Cilia operate like oars producing up to 30 beats per second. When striking backwards the cilium is kept straight; at its recovery stroke, i.e. forwards, the tips of the cilia are bent more or less backwards, and their recovery movement is 2–3 times slower than their backward sweep which gives the animal its forward thrust.

The movements of the cilia are related to each other, since as they work they observe a certain rhythm. In fact the beats of the ciliary covering of the body resemble a wave movement; in each longitudinal row the contraction of the cilia starts at the forward end of the row, the undulation proceeding backwards, while each successive cilium of the row starts its beat with a small delay after the preceding one.

In preparations fixed by Gelei's method, it is clearly seen that the ciliary waves run in a dextro-rotatory spiral; as a consequence of this the animal, while advancing, rotates to the left round its long axis. The spirals may wind at steeper or flatter angles, and their coils do not necessarily correspond to the order of the arrangement of the ciliary rows; only round the buccal orifice has a certain order in this respect been observed: here the waves of ciliary beats move in the direction of the buccal orifice. The waves of the ciliary movement may either proceed parallel to each other throughout the whole extent of the body, or in the anterior part they are denser and in a more transverse direction than farther back. When the majority of the waves are moving in a longitudinal direction their forward motion may become a rotation around their long axis. It is interesting to note that in conjugating individuals the direction of the spirals is the same in both. Thus, in ciliates there exists a regulatory apparatus ensuring the co-ordination of the complicated ciliary movement (Worley, 1934; Párducz, 1954). However, there are grounds to believe that each cilium has its own mechanism of beating. Hoffmann-Berling (1955) showed that ATP plays a significant role in the movement of flagella. Serawin (1961) also succeeded in confirming the role of ATP in the ciliary action. He showed on cytolyzed models of the ciliates Spirostomum and Euplotes, prepared by Hoffmann-Berling's method, that addition of ATP in presence of Mg and K ions induces beating of cilia and cirri. Apparently, ATP is the energy source for flagella and cilia, and it causes their contraction and extension.

The frequency of the beats of cilia varies in different ciliates. In *Paramecium* it is 10–11, in *Colpidium* 10 per second; the maximum frequency is taken as about 30 (for instance in the peristomial cilia of *Vorticella*). The speed of locomotion of different ciliates is given below:

Name of species	Speed of locomotion Number of µ per sec	Ratio of path passed per sec to length of body, representing a unit
Prorodon teres . . .	1,066	6
Coleps hirtus . . .	686	10
Didinium nasutum . .	464	4
Colpoda cucullus . . .	310	5·5
Paramaecium caudatum .	2,647	10
Pleuronema chrysalis . .	540	18
Spirostomum ambiguum . .	810	0·8
Stentor coeruleus . . .	1,500	3
Stylonychia mytilus . .	1,400	9
Euplotes charon . . .	1,035	17

In conclusion it may be said that the ciliary movement is a further step in the development of the flagellar motion, carried out by means of basically the same apparatus, that is by flagellar or ciliary kinetids.

Pseudopodia and amoeboid locomotion

Pseudopodia are temporary protrusions of cytoplasm of the body of those protozoa which have a naked body, devoid of a pellicle. In the simplest cases (in amoeba) locomotion by means of pseudopodia consists of a slow flowing over of the body from place to place, which has acquired the special name of amoeboid movement. It is not limited to Protozoa only, but is also observed in phagocytes, leucocytes, and in different amoeboid cells of the body of Metazoa. This type of locomotion is characterized by its apolarity and by the temporary nature of the pseudopodia, as well as by fluctuation in their number and sites of their formation. Pseudopodia and amoeboid locomotion are characteristic of the class Sarcodina; they are, however, also encountered either as an addition to flagella or they temporarily replace flagella in certain flagellata. Some Haemosporidia and Myxosporidia are likewise propelled by means of pseudopodia.

Varieties of pseudopodia. The following main forms of pseudopodia are distinguished.

Lobopodia, or lobed digitiform pseudopodia, are more or less broad and usually rounded at their distal end. Much more rarely they extend considerably and become pointed at the ends, so that the animal acquires a short radial shape (*Amoeba radiosa*). The shapes of lobar pseudopodia depend to a considerable extent on the state of viscosity and gelatinization of the ectoplasm of various species, since it is the ectoplasm which plays the main role in the production of pseudopodia. However, in some species the shape of pseudopodia may easily be influenced by changes in the exterior environment. Thus *Amoeba limax* when in locomotion looks like a short band as it projects in the direction of movement one wide, rounded pseudopodium as wide as its body. However, when a small amount of alkali is added to the water, its body grows shorter, gathers itself together and puts out narrow, pointed pseudopodia in different directions, thus resembling *A. radiosa*.

Lobopodia are widely distributed among Amoebina and Testacea. They are also encountered among many genera of Myxosporidia inhabiting the cavities of the gall and urinary bladders, i.e. in a fluid medium and not inside the tissues.

Filopodia, or filamentar pseudopodia. They may be derived from pseudopodia of the preceding type, which have become considerably extended, but without the formation of anastomoses. Filopodia consist of homogeneous ectoplasm only; they are encountered almost exclusively in Testacea, in which they project in bundles out of the mouth of the shell.

Rhizopodia, or root-like pseudopodia, are widely distributed among Sarcodina, namely in all Foraminifera and Radiolaria; moreover, they are encountered in some Testacea, for instance in *Lieberkühnia* and others. They are thin, branching, and abundantly anastomosing pseudopodia, forming a tangled network spreading in different directions like the roots of a tree. The distribution of rhizopodia over the body of the protozoon usually depends on the construction of its skeleton, and sometimes that of its plasmatic body. In imperforated Foraminifera the rhizopods can emerge from the shell only through the mouth; in perforated ones they issue also through the numerous, thin pores which pierce the walls of the shell. The places of issue of the rhizopodia from the body are most rigidly localized in certain radiolarians. Thus, for example, in the order Phaeodaria the main mass of pseudopodia emerge from the central capsule through three complexly constructed openings, the main (astopyle) and two subsidiary ones (parapyle). The main aperture is covered by a membrane permeable to fluids with a radially striated cap, which has a funnel-like process that opens at the tip, protruding from the middle. This process is usually directed to a special opening in the skeleton, called the pylome. The subsidiary openings are much more simply constructed.

In the order Spumellaria the pseudopodia issue in the majority of cases throughout the whole surface of the central capsule more or less uniformly, but in some families (certain Porodiscidae, Fig. 88) there is a canal-shaped opening in the skeleton, from which protrudes a long and fairly thick tongue of protoplasm or flagellopodium looking like a thick flagellum. This flagellum is apparently a bundle of closely adherent pseudopodia.

Finally, in the order Acantharia, the outer surface of the extra-capsular plasmatic substance, according to Savjakov's data, is divided into polygonal sections, or platforms, surrounding the points of issue of the radial spicules from the body. The number and arrangement of the pseudopodia of Acantharia is so constant that they are used for taxonomic identification of the Protozoa.

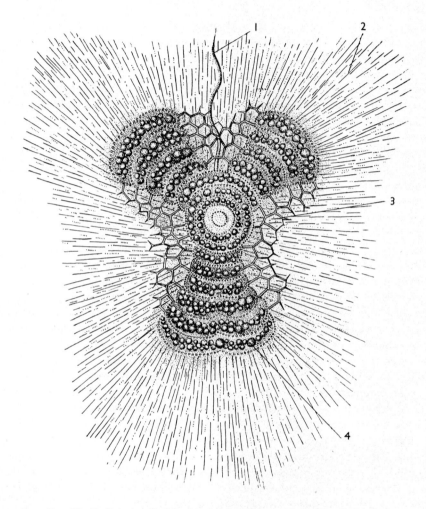

FIG. 88. Radiolarian *Euchitonia virchowii* (Spumellaria, Porodiscidae).

1, Flagellopodium; 2, network of rhizopodia; 3, patagium or accessory peripheral skeleton; 4, internal, more central, part of skeleton. (After Haeckel, 1862.)

Axopodia are straight, radial, fine pseudopodia, not anastomosing with each other, containing inside them a highly refractile axial rod composed of fine fibrils. Owing to the presence of this axial rod, axopodia acquire a certain resilience and permanence.

The Heliozoa, many Acantharia, and possibly one representative of the Radiolaria, *Sticholonche* (Fig. 89), are characterized by the presence of axopods. The sausage-shaped central capsule of *Sticholonche* produces some hundreds of long, straight pseudopodia, distributed in ten dorsal rows and fairly numerous lateral rows, i.e. the number and position of pseudopodia

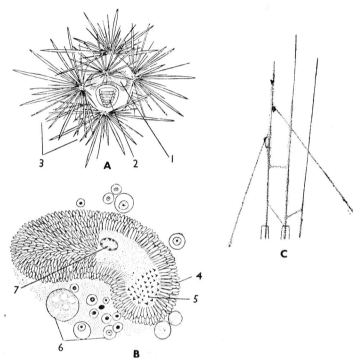

FIG. 89. Radiolarian *Sticholonche*.

(*A*) entire animal inside gelatinous mass; (*B*) central capsule separated from the gelatinous mass with some of it still adhering; (*C*) individual pseudopodia with their axial filament and granular anastomoses. 1, central capsule; 2, parasitic dinoflagellate *Amoebophrya*; 3, bundles of spicules; 4, base of pseudopodia; 5, myonemes; 6, acidophile bubbles; 7, nucleus. (After Hollande and Enjumet, 1954.)

is fixed. The pseudopodia are quite straight, and are, as it were, attached to the outer wall of the capsule by their slightly thickened basal part. The pseudopodia have the ability of retracting slowly to a certain length and then extending just as slowly, growing, as it were, in a radial direction. They are resilient, and in their basal half their walls are so well outlined that they give the impression of small tubes. In animals left for some time under a coverslip the pseudopodia begin to move rhythmically, whole rows of them beating regularly, like the strokes of oars. In general this movement is similar to the lashing of cilia, except that it is much slower. The hinged construction of the pseudopodia noted above is explained by this movement. It is conceivable that at the points of the transition of the pseudopodia to the central capsule there is a mobile connexion between them and the walls of the capsule.

In disturbed *Sticholonche* these beats of the pseudopodia continue until the central capsule with its pseudopodia breaks through the delicate membrane of the ectoplasm; the animal then emerged and continues to move under the coverslip in a straight line, by means of the beats of its pseudopodia. This unique behaviour of *Sticholonche*, which we have frequently observed, is especially interesting since it unites elements both of amoeboid and flagellar movements.

Amoeboid locomotion. In the simplest cases the entire body of an amoeba begins to move as a whole (*Amoeba limax*); the cyclosis of the plasma taking the form of a rotating movement. According to Mast (1926*a*, 1932), an indispensable condition of this movement is the secretion of a sticky substance by the amoeba; this substance remaining effective even on the smooth surface of a quartz glass.

The body of amoeboid organisms, like all fluid substance, is under the influence of surface tension, which tends to turn the body into a sphere. This surface tension changes under the influence of the constantly changing conditions of the fluid medium surrounding the animal and the continuous chemical changes inside its body. Moreover, the fluid protoplasm of the amoeba flows to those points of the body where for any reason the surface tension is lowered, forming at this place a pseudopodium. In conformity with this, a system of protoplasmic currents is observed in a moving amoeba, whose character confirms the foregoing concept. A reversible state of the cytoplasmic colloids is an indispensable condition for the realization of amoeboid movement. Therefore the modern theories regarding the causes of amoeboid locomotion are based on the theory of changes taking place in the viscosity of the cytoplasm.

Pantin (1923) discovered in *Amoeba limax* a local increase of acidity in the cytoplasm at the point of the formation of a pseudopodium. As a consequence water is absorbed from the surrounding medium at this point, and a local swelling of the cytoplasm is produced with the protrusion of a lobed pseudopodium, followed by the gelation of the ectoplasmic layer of the pseudopodium. As the pseudopodium extends farther during progression the gelated section of its ectoplasmic sac is shifted backwards, while its acidity is diminished, and the ectoplasm loses some of its water and contracts. Currents of endoplasm, created by the increasing contraction of the ectoplasmic layer in the posterior half of the body, are directed forward towards the formed pseudopodium. Thus a permanent fountain directed forward is created within the body by the currents of cytoplasm inside the amoeba. On reaching its anterior end this current breaks up into several branches which flow backwards along the periphery and there join the general current which moves forward.

Mast in his numerous papers (1926*a*, 1932, 1941) visualized amoeboid locomotion in approximately the same way. He considers that an amoeba is a sort of elastic sac consisting of a thin surface membrane and a layer of gelated plasma, which cover the internal more fluid mass and are in a state of some tension, pressing upon the contents from all sides. Therefore as soon as the gelated surface layer of plasma becomes thinner somewhere, and the pressure on the inner plasmatic mass decreases, the mass flows in the direction of the thinner section and pushes it out, forming the primordium of a pseudopodium. However, Mast's explanation of the local thinning of the gelated layer of ectoplasm is not very convincing. When the amoeba is ready for locomotion, its plasmagel in contact with plasmasol (the more fluid, inner plasma) undergoes partial dilution, which creates a local decrease of the plasmagel thickness. However, the causes of this primary dilution are not clear.

In Hyman's opinion (1917) solation is the result of some changes in metabolic activity leading to the production of free hydrogen ions, which have a diluting effect on the dense ectoplasm. By means of Child's indicators of metabolic gradient, she has shown the occurrence of local points of higher metabolic activity at certain points of the surface of the body of the amoeba, where pseudopodia are in fact produced later. The very tip of the pseudopodium has the highest gradient.

In the last decade the theory of amoeboid locomotion based on the ability of the cytoplasm and especially its outer layer in the amoeba to perform active contraction has been developed (Goldacre and Lorch, 1950; Allen and Roslansky, 1958; and others). In amoebas, actomyosin-like, ATP-sensitive proteins were discovered, i.e. substances resembling those responsible for muscle contraction. A 1–3 per cent. injection of ATP into a posterior part of the ectoplasm of the amoeba resulted in acceleration of advanced streams of liquid endoplasm leading to pseudopod formation, which confirms the importance of cytoplasm contractility in the mechanism of amoeboid movement. This mechanism is likely to be conditioned not only by the contractility of the ectoplasm of a posterior end but also by that reversible process of transition of sol to gel which appears on the anterior body end.

We do not wish to dwell any longer upon the examination of the problem of amoeboid movement, but refer the reader to the vast and thorough summary devoted to this question by Allen (1961).

Amoeboid locomotion is sometimes most peculiar in its character. Thus Dellinger (1906), while observing *Amoeba proteus* on a specially arranged glass, not from the top but from its profile, noticed that the animal was not creeping on its ventral surface, but was performing some unusual marching movement, touching the substratum only by pseudopodia protruding downwards and moving on them as props.

Amoebae with very dense ectoplasm roll their bodies in a special way along the substratum on very much shortened pseudopodia.

Finally, in forms with rhizopodia the locomotion of the animal under-goes one more modification, as is seen in Foraminifera. Pseudopodia, in the shape of very thin filaments, stretch in a definite direction, adhere to the substratum by their ends, and contract; as a result the animal is pulled forward in the direction of the movement.

The speed of amoeboid locomotion is expressed in the following figures:

Species	Speed in μ/sec
Amoeba limax .	1
Amoeba verrucosa .	0·5
Amoeba geminata	4·5–3
Myxosporidia .	0·33–1·3

The speed of locomotion in amoebae depends on the osmotic pressure of the surrounding medium and on the concentration of hydrogen ions. The optimum for the locomotion of amoebae lies between pH 6·6 and pH 7·6; their movement becoming slower outside this range. Moreover, the rate of their locomotion depends also on a definite ratio of the monovalent and bivalent cations within their environment. The speed of locomotion is affected also by the temperature of the medium. In free-living amoebae the speed reaches a maximum at 24° C. Between this temperature and 28° C. it decreases; but rises again, but not so strongly, at 30° C., dropping down to a complete cessation of movement at 33° C.

Gliding locomotion

Certain sporozoa, namely many gregarines, are endowed with a special gliding kind of locomotion. Without any change in its form and without any visible contraction the animal glides smoothly forward through its environ-ment. Sevjakov (1894) was the first to compare the gliding locomotion of the gregarines with that of diatomous algae; which he explained as follows: the gregarine cuticle is perforated by numerous pores, through which the animal ejects very thin jets of a gelatinous substance, present as a thin layer under the cuticle. This substance flows along longitudinal furrows of the cuticle to the posterior end of the gregarine and there solidifies, forming at the back of the animal a dense stalk composed of fine filaments. As a result of the inflow of further portions of the gelatinous substance the stalk grows at its anterior end, passively pushing the gregarine forward.

Without contesting the factual data of Sevjakov, many later investigators tried to find another explanation for the gliding locomotion. Sokolov (1912) considers the expulsion of mucus as the cause of gregarine locomotion. It is most probable, therefore, that the gliding locomotion is based on the principle of rocket propulsion.

As is shown by the method of time-lapse microsinematography, a large amount of mucus is in fact secreted and left behind as a trace during

locomotion. However, the secretion is not always continuous, though locomotion is uninterrupted. Moreover, at 25° C. the gelatinous filaments are
dissolved, in spite of which the speed of progression remains undiminished.
Therefore the expulsion of mucus should be considered as a consequence
rather than the cause of the gliding locomotion of the gregarines (Beams
and others, 1959).

It was shown by electron microscopy
that a system of very fine contractile
and supporting fibrils is present in
the surface layers of the gregarine.
According to Kümmel (1958), Richter
(1959), and Beams *et al.* (1959) the
gliding locomotion is probably the
result of the action of myonemes
lying under the surface of the ectoplasm. Beams *et al.* note that gliding
is accomplished by a movement of
the body-surface in contact with the
substratum. This movement is facilitated by the mucus, as is the case
in gastropod molluscs moving on
their foot. Therefore gliding is not
a passive act, as has been formerly assumed, but an active one.

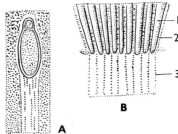

Fig. 90. Gregarine *Clepsidrina munieri*.
(*A*) gregarine during locomotion, leaving
behind it a gelatinous trace in finely powdered Indian ink; (*B*) posterior end of gregarine body; 1, small ridges; 2, furrows on cuticle;
3, rows of granules of Indian ink. (After Sevjakov, 1894.)

The speed of the gliding motion of gregarines reached 5·5 μ per second.

V

IRRITABILITY AND THE RECEPTOR ORGANOIDS OF PROTOZOA

Irritability

THE main characteristic of living matter is its irritability, i.e. its ability to respond by some reaction to stimuli acting upon it in the environment. A change in the external conditions reaching a definite intensity becomes an irritation to the protozoon. The response of the unicellular organism to these irritations serves as indices of irritability which is characteristic of the whole protoplasm of protozoon; but, it is especially manifest in certain organoids playing the part of sensory organs in a unicellular organism.

The responses of Protozoa are manifested first of all in their movements. Therefore irritability is assessed mainly by observing the locomotor reactions rather than others.

The processes of stimulation and inhibition reflected in these reactions are the main physiological processes of cells, tissues, organs, and organisms as a whole. Stimuli provoking response in the protozoon vary in their character—they may be chemical, mechanical, thermal, light, electrical, and others.

In higher animals response to stimuli is affected through their nervous system, their reactions being called reflexes. Organisms devoid of a nervous system have no reflexes, and their responses, which are expressed in alterations of the character of their locomotion and growth, are known as taxes, with the addition of the specification of the nature of the reaction in question: e.g. phototaxis, or taxis in relation to light, galvanotaxis, or taxis in relation to electricity, &c. (Dembowski, 1959). The term 'tropism', which was formerly used to denote orientation to a source of energy, is now restricted to growth responses of organisms.

Each type of taxis may be either positive or negative, depending on whether the stimulus causes attraction or repulsion. However, the reaction to the same taxis may frequently be reversible—sometimes negative, at other times positive—according to the intensity of the stimulus.

The movements of Protozoa brought about by stimuli are in general relatively purposeful, serving in a natural environment to direct the organism to those sections of it where conditions are favourable for its existence, and causing the animal to avoid harmful influences. The activity of certain systems of the organisms or the cell may be either intensified or depressed by an acting stimulus. A depression of vital functions caused by excessive stimulation is called a 'shock' or shock reaction. This depression of the functions corresponds to the state of inhibition—the 'pessimum' reaction described by N. Vvedensky in 1886. These types of reactions are frequently observed in Protozoa.

Chemotaxis

The effect of chemical stimuli upon diverse aspects of protozoan activity is considerable and may manifest itself in most varied ways, such as a change in the intensity of excretion (the effect of different salts on the excretion of neutral red in ciliates), a change in the rate of formation of food vacuoles and defecation (the effect of salts on these processes), and so forth. Changes in protozoan metabolism may take place as a result of their subjection to the action of various chemical substances. Owing to the variety of such observations (Wichterman, 1953), we shall confine our discussion to chemical stimuli which bring about some locomotor reactions in Protozoa, i.e. phenomena directly connected with chemotaxis. The effect of chemical factors on water exchange, digestion, and other functions of the unicellular organisms will be discussed in detail in the corresponding chapters.

Chemotaxis in Sarcodina. In general, the placing—by means of a pipette or in some other way—of a chemical preparation on some point of the surface of amoeba leads to the drawing in of a pseudopod at that point and to a change in the direction of its locomotion. This negative chemotaxis has been observed in response to most diverse substances: vital stains (methylene blue and green), weak alkalis and acids, sugar, distilled and tap water, &c.

Experiments on Sarcodina were carried out with freshwater and marine amoebae. In the case of *Amoeba proteus* it was shown that its rate of locomotion in a neutral hay infusion is not affected by any factors, but the protozoon becomes active when the medium becomes either acid or alkali, the maximum rate of locomotion being observed at pH 6·5–8·8 (Mast, 1932, 1941).

Chemotaxis in ciliates. Ciliates move from one chemical medium to another by means of shock reactions. Paramecia, the favourite objects of experiments, show a negative chemotaxis to all alkalis and all compounds of the alkaline and alkali-earth metals; the more pronounced this reaction, the greater the injury to the animal.

A somewhat different response is observed in paramecia to another group of substances, such as weak acids (organic and inorganic), various alums (with a low metal content), salts of heavy metals, and different sugars. The negative reaction of ciliates to the substances of this group is not proportional to their harmfulness, but is much weaker, with the result that negative chemotaxis to such substances arises when these have already become harmful. Thus, for example, paramecia enter sugar and glycerine solutions, the osmotic pressure of which is much higher than that of common salt solutions avoided by paramecia. Paramecia penetrate into a 20 per cent. solution of sugar and 10 per cent. of glycerine without any sign of negative reaction, although their bodies become flattened and shrivel in the hypertonic medium. The beat of the cilia in a reverse direction, indicating a change in the character of chemotaxis, begins only when shrivelling has already started and it is no longer possible to save ciliates from the effects of the solution.

Acids have a similar effect on paramecia. The ciliates gather together in all weak acid solutions, without any sign of negative reaction, until the harmful effect of the solution begins to manifest itself. Therefore, a drop of a strong acid solution, introduced under the coverslip with the culture, is soon surrounded by a belt of dead ciliates.

The concentration of ciliates round the bubbles of carbon dioxide, introduced into the culture under the coverslip, is also based on the attraction exercised on them by acids.

The most distinct response of ciliates to chemical stimuli consists in a reversal of their ciliary beats, in a direction opposite to the normal one, resulting in a change in the movement of the animal itself. All cilia are subject to such reversal, except the peristomial ones; it continues from a few seconds to a few minutes and is followed by the ciliate turning in the opposite direction and moving in a new direction: this represents the first stage of its avoidance reaction or negative taxis.

Mast and Nadler (1926) have tested the effect of fifty-six different substances on the reversal of ciliary beats. They state that monovalent cations of salts and their hydrates (except for $(NH_4)_2SO_4$ and $NH_4C_2H_3O_2$) cause a reversal, while the bivalent and trivalent ones (except $CaHPO_4$ and $MgHPO_4$) have no such effect. These investigators suggested also that the duration of the reversal stage corresponds to the concentration of the salt acting upon the animal, the exact concentration depending upon the kind of salt used. Moreover, it was found that the effect of movalent cations of salts is neutralized by the bivalent and trivalent ones.

The data of Mast and Nadler have been confirmed by the work of Oliphant (1938); moreover, it has been shown that the reversal effect of the cations proceeds in the following order: $K>Li>Na>NH_4$, whereas the anions play a very insignificant part; the duration of the reversal of the cilia is inversely proportional to the temperature of the experiment. However, according to Eisenberg-Hamburg (1932) bivalent cations also produce a reversal of the beat of cilia in ciliates.

A backward movement of ciliates may be caused by a whole series of factors, such as electric current, concussion, high temperature, ultra-violet light; i.e. it is not the result of the action of a narrow group of agents with a specific effect.

In the light of the investigations of Worley (1934), Párducz (1954, 1955),

Doroszewski (1958), and others, it may be concluded that the reversal of the beating of cilia is a complex phenomenon, which is possibly under the control system of the ciliate. In any case it may be assumed, on the basis of the experiments of Worley, that *Paramecium caudatum* possesses something like a special centre of reversal situated in the anterior part of the body of the ciliate. In fact, surgical removal of the anterior third of the body of the paramecium leads to a loss of the ability of its large posterior fragment to respond to chemical stimuli by reversal of the beat of cilia. We believe that a further study of the backward movement of the ciliate might throw light on the peculiarities of the processes controlling the system of cilia.

The chemotactic reaction is also expressed in changes of progressive and rotation movement (Dryl, 1959).

The majority of investigators are trying to explain a number of phenomena in the life of Protozoa by chemotaxis, such as their search for food and for their mates in the sexual process, &c.

The activity of contractile vacuoles, the rate of the formation of food vacuoles, the rate of ciliary beats, i.e. all the main functions of the ciliates, are influenced by chemical agents. When the active agents are used in non-lethal concentrations and are left to act on the Protozoa for sufficiently long periods, it was found that the ciliates grew accustomed to the new conditions. According to Seravin (1957–60), as a result of such habituation the functions of *Paramecium* (water exchange, phagocytosis, mobility, &c.), which had at first been altered under the effect of the chemical agents, returned almost to the level in the control animals.

The effect of light and phototaxis

Although only some of the flagellates possess special visual organoids, sensitivity to light is observed also among the Sarcodina, and to a much lesser extent in ciliates.

The effect of light on Sarcodina has been investigated mostly on amoebae, especially on *Amoeba proteus* (Mast's works). In Jennings's opinion (1900, 1904) light provokes two phenomena in amoebae: those of shock and of locomotor responses. Shock phenomena caused by a sudden, strong illumination have been noted already by Engelmann (1879), who noted the pronounced contraction of *Pelomyxa* when suddenly exposed to strong light.

Mast (1932, 1941) considered the shock phenomenon in amoebae in greater detail. According to his description, in amoebae sudden exposure to strong light causes either a brief slowing down of the current of plasma in certain definite parts of the pseudopodia or a cessation of the flow of plasma in the whole body, with the resumption of the movement of the current in the opposite direction, after the amoeba recovers from the shock. Intermediate phenomena between these two extremes are also possible. A shock reaction takes place after a certain short period following exposure to light (a few seconds), known as the reaction period. Moreover, a certain time of exposure is required to provoke a shock—the stimulation period. In Mast's opinion light causes the formation of some substance in the cytoplasm, which, independently of light, produces some other substance which evokes a response reaction.

After its response to a rapid increase of illumination the amoeba may repeat the shock reaction only after an interval of time, called the refractory period. During part of this period (1–2 minutes) it makes no difference whether the amoeba is still exposed to light, but during the remainder of the refractory period (10–20 seconds) the amoeba should be either under a weak illumination or in darkness; during this time the amoeba returns to the state preceding the experiment.

In the case of a long exposure to intensified illumination, the state of shock passes gradually and normal locomotion is restored, i.e. adaptation takes place.

Thus the impression is produced that during a shock two opposite, mutually inhibitory, processes take place: a sudden intensification of illumination provokes certain changes (the shock) in the organism, but at the same time further changes tending to counteract the shock and eliminate it take place in the amoeba.

The amount of light energy required to provoke the shock depends also on the composition of the environment. In the presence of traces of hydrochloric acid the amount of light energy required increases, while in the presence of carbon dioxide it decreases. With the increase of the concentration of Cl, $CaCl_2$, $MgCl_2$ in the medium the amount of light energy required to provoke a shock increases, but this regularity is not observed in a corresponding change of the concentration. In general, according to Mast, the amount of energy required is directly proportional to the viscosity of the cytoplasm.

These interpretations of the response of amoebae to illumination are, to a considerable extent, based on the theory of the modifications of cytoplasmic viscosity.

According to the old observations of Rhumbler (1910), an amoeba that had been feeding on filaments of *Oscillaria*, when suddenly exposed to light, not only stopped feeding but even ejected some of the half-ingested filaments. The locomotor reactions in amoeba have the following pattern: when exposed for a long time to weak light, the amoeba becomes inactive, but it regains its activity when light is intensified. In general the changes of its activity correspond to changes due to the effect of temperature. The activity of the locomotion of amoebae previously adapted to darkness increases with the rise in the intensity of illumination up to a certain limit, after which it remains constant.

As is shown by the quantitative data on the changes of the speed of the locomotion of amoebae, the response of Protozoa to irritation is subject to the law of the optimum amount of stimulation required to produce excitation; according to this law, with a progressive intensification of irritation the positive reaction of excitation is replaced by a negative one, i.e. inhibition.

As has already been established by Davenport (1897), amoebae are photonegative. Mast has shown on the same *Amoeba proteus* that during unilateral exposure to light amoebae extend their pseudopodia more actively towards the shadowed side: this results in negative phototaxis. Therefore Mast comes to the conclusion that light has a gelating effect on the cytoplasm on the illuminated side.

The effect of light on Mastigophora. Responses to rapid changes of the intensity of light have been frequently observed in flagellates, and in many of them, as, for example, *Euglena,* the orientation is most precise. However, some forms (for example, *Peranema*) do not orientate to light at all.

Euglena, like most of the chlorophyll-bearing flagellates, is positively phototactic; therefore these forms accumulate in the illuminated parts of the culture, and in vessels containing euglenae they congregate on the side of the vessel turned towards the light. When swimming euglenae rotate round their long axis, while their flagellum bends backwards along its ventral side, i.e. that opposite to its eye-spot or stigma. The shock phenomenon is observed also among the euglenae, but at a pronounced weakening of the illumination. The animals stop suddenly, turn round, and disperse in different directions. That is they reason why euglenae caught in a lighted field appear to be in a trap: when running against the darker areas surrounding them they are thrown by the limits of these areas back to the illuminated field.

The locomotor responses of euglenae are similar to those of amoebae. It has been shown that only the anterior end of *Euglena* is photosensitive. Hence Jennings concluded that, as a result of the turning away from the source of light, less light falls on the photosensitive substance of the euglenae, while their turning towards the light increases the exposure of this substance to light. Consequently positively phototactic forms turn round until they are fully exposed to the source of light, while negative ones turn away so as to be completely out of the light. Once this position is reached the organisms continue to move in the given direction.

The orientation of *Euglena* (Fig. 91) was investigated in detail by Mast (1911, 1927, 1938, 1941) and his pupils. When exposed to a ray of light *Euglena* clearly reveals the part played by the stigma in its orientation. This phenomenon can best be observed by throwing a lateral ray of light on euglenae swimming towards the source of light in a screw-like movement. Moreover, the first source of light should be screened. The behaviour of such laterally illuminated euglenae varies. Those individuals (Fig. 91, *B*) which are turned to this lateral light by their stigmal (dorsal) side are immobilized immediately; then they bend towards their apostigmal (ventral) side, turn, and straighten out to resume their movement. Those whose stigmal side is turned away from the new source of light at the moment of their exposure to the lateral ray (Fig. 91, *A*) continue to move until their apostigmal side is turned to the lateral ray, after which their behaviour

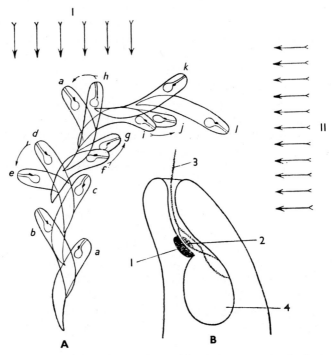

A   **B**

Fig. 91. Orientation of locomotion and locomotor apparatus in *Euglena*.

(*A*) swimming *Euglena*: I and II, the direction of the ray of light falling on *Euglena*; *a–c*, position of *Euglena* when light falls on it only from the direction I; *d–l*, position of *Euglena* when the light falls on it only from the direction II, while the source of light I is covered. (*B*) side view of anterior end of *Euglena*: 1, stigma; 2, thickening of flagellum; 3, flagellum; 4, contractile vacuole. (After Mast, 1927.)

becomes the same as that of those already described. Owing to its incomplete straightening, the anterior end of the *Euglena* is somewhat deflected in the direction of the new source of light at each turning until its anterior end is turned towards it. Under these conditions the stigma remains at the same angle to the rays of light at all positions of its rotation; it is always uniformly illuminated and the organism is orientated directly towards the light. It remains in this position throughout its further movements.

By taking into consideration the structure of the stigma in *Euglena* the process of orientation may be correlated with the influence of the shock phenomenon. The stigma appears as a spoon-shaped accumulation of a red pigment on the dorsal side of the base of the flagellum. One of the two rhizoplasts of the flagellum forms a round thickening in the concavity of this accumulation. When the anterior end of the body or the apostigmal (ventral) side of it is turned towards the source of light the flagellar thickening is completely exposed to the light. However, when the stigmal surface of the body is turned to the light the flagellar thickening is shaded by the pigment covering it. As a result, in lateral light the base of the flagellum is alternately illuminated and darkened. The thickening of the base of the flagellum is most probably photosensitive and at a certain position assumed by the euglenae the pigment serves to reduce the intensity of illumination on the photosensitive section. Each darkening of the latter produces as it were a minor shock leading to the bending of the body at a right angle, followed by an incomplete straightening of the body, thereby bringing about a tendency to move towards lateral light, i.e. to orientation. When the light falls on the illuminated animals directly from the front or from behind, they do not change their orientation, since no shock is produced in such positions.

Flagellates are more sensitive to the short-wave parts of the visible spectrum (violet and blue light). In his comparison of the available data with the distribution of light energy in the spectrum Mast (1917) found that the stimulation effect of light increases from $\lambda = 410$ mμ to $\lambda = 485$ mμ and then decreases completely to $\lambda - 540$ mμ.

Forms of flagellates devoid of stigma and chromatophores, e.g. *Peranema trichophorum*, differ considerably from the Euglena. At a considerable increase of the intensity of illumination *Peranema* suddenly stops and then bends its anterior end to one side. However, there is no response of the organism to a slow increase or decrease of the intensity of light. The whole organism of Peranema is phototactic, but its flagellum is the most sensitive part and its posterior end the least.

As a result of a response to a considerable intensification of light the organism, once it has recovered, changes the direction of its locomotion by approximately 90°.

Stimulation by rays of various wavelengths is manifested in *Peranema* by the occurrence of two maxima. One lies in the ultra-violet part of the spectrum at $\lambda = 302$ mμ, the other in its visible part at $\lambda = 505$ mμ.

The responses of *Peranema* are very precise and constant; its movement is slow, and its time of response is prolonged.

Responses to light in colonial flagellates (Figs. 92, 93) are of interest. What is the behaviour of the thousands of minute individuals of *Volvox* when the colonly is orientated? Do they perform a co-ordinated integrated function, and if so what is the pattern of this remarkable regulation in flagellates with such a simple organization? Is there no general regulation, and does the colony rotate in a disorderly manner? The existence of control integrating the colony into a single whole has been shown by Mast (1917, 1926a, b, 1927) in a series of works.

In spite of its apparently regular spherical form, a *Volvox* colony displays an evident polarity. This polarity is manifested first of all in the presence in the very centre of the physiologically anterior pole of four zooids, differing somewhat from the others, and forming a polyntomic cross.

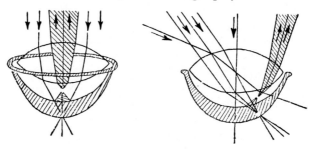

FIG. 92. Path of light rays in the stigma of *Volvox*. Direction of rays shown by arrows. (After Mast, 1926*b*.)

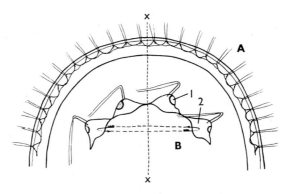

FIG. 93. Diagram of structure of *Volvox* colony.

(*A*) section through anterior hemisphere; (*B*) anterior pole of the colony at high magnification. *X–X*, antero-posterior axis of the colony: 1, stigmata of separate individuals; 2, individuals of the colony: the direction of rotation of the colony is shown by the arrows. (After Mast, 1926*b*.)

Moreover, polarity is also manifested in the structure and arrangement of the stigmata in the zooids of the colony.

According to Mast (1927) the stigmata of *Volvox* consist of a pigment cup, a lens, and a photosensitive substance lying between them. Moreover, apparently, the long waves of light incident on the eye-spot are refracted to the focus situated in the pigment layer, whereas the short waves are deflected to the focus situated in the photosensitive substance. The stigmata of all the zooids are arranged on the side turned to the posterior end of the colony; moreover, the size of the stigmata decreases from the anterior to the posterior poles of the colony. As a result, a kind of morphological gradient is obtained. *Volvox*, rotating around its longitudinal axis, progresses with its anterior end forward. This rotation is produced as a result of the flagella of all the individuals beating backwards not a right angle but obliquely—backwards along the diagonal of the colony. *Volvox* colonies exposed to light move either directly towards the source of light or directly away from it.

In colonies swimming towards the light, when its intensity decreases rapidly, rotation round the long axis ceases, while the rate of locomotion increases as a consequence of the flagella of all the individuals beating directly backwards, not at a diagonal.

With the increase of the intensity of illumination the forward movement of the colony ceases but rotation round its long axis increases, since all the flagella begin to beat not in a diagonal or backward direction but laterally in a direction parallel to the equator of the colony. This movement continues for only a few seconds, and consequently it should be regarded as a shock phenomenon.

Volvoxes become inactive when left in the dark for a few hours, but with the increase of light their activity is resumed. There is no change in the direction of flagellar beats in this case, which distinguishes this phenomenon from that of shock.

When exposed to lateral light the colonies gradually turn either straight to the light or in the reverse direction, i.e away from it. This orientation proceeds in the following manner. Under this kind of light the individuals of the colony are either darkened or lit owing to its rotation around the long axis. At a given moment the zooids on the dark side suffer from a shock and react by energetically beating their flagella backwards. At the same moment the zooids on the side exposed to light suffer from a shock due to this exposure, with the result the flagella beat in a lateral direction. The combination of both these flagellar movements in definite localized points of the colony results in a gradual turning of the colony as a whole either towards the source of light or away from it. When this turning of the long axis of the colony is completed, every eye-spot along the orbit of the colony's rotation is lit alike and therefore the direction of its movement is stabilized for a certain period of time (while the light conditions remain constant). It should be noted that this explanation of phototactic response is a mere hypothesis, since Mast did not carry out any direct observations on the changes of flagellar movement under different illuminations (Gerisch, 1959).

According to Gerisch's observations, the phototactic response in *Volvox aureus* is a result of the inhibition of the activity of the flagella on one side of the colony; moreover, in positively phototactic colonies this inhibition is determined by the intensification of illumination, while in the negatively phototactic colonies it is due to its weakening. In uniform light flagella are directed straight forward, while during the phototactic reaction they are bent owing to irregular contraction of flagellar fibrils.

The stimulating effect of different parts of the spectrum on *Volvox* and *Gonium* is similar to that in *Euglena*, but in *Pandorina* and *Spondylomorum* the area of maximum stimulation lies with the wavelength of 535 mμ instead of 485 mμ, as in the case of *Volvox*.

In general *Volvox* is positively phototactic to weak light and negatively to bright light.

Responses of ciliates to illumination. Most of the ciliates do not respond to illumination at all. More detailed observations on this question have been carried out on *Stentor*, which possesses a certain sensitivity to light. *Stentor* is usually negatively phototactic. At a rapid increase of the intensity of light a swimming *Stentor* stops (shock) and turns the aboral surface of its body to the source of light, and then progresses farther. No response has been observed when the intensity of illumination decreases. The oral edge of the anterior end of the body in *Stentor* is considerably more sensitive to light than its aboral end. As a consequence, under lateral illumination, every time that the oral surface turns to light during rotation of the ciliate the animal bends towards the aboral side. This process is repeated until the ciliate turns its posterior end to the source of light. Then *Stentor* continues to move without changing its direction, i.e. away from the illumination. Hence the light orientation of *Stentor* is based on a series of shock reactions as in the case of *Euglena*. Practically all Protozoa are more or less sensitive to ultra-violet rays. Thus *Paramecium*, which is insensitive to all other rays, evinces a clear, negative reaction to ultra-violet rays of wavelength 280 mμ.

It is most interesting that under certain conditions ciliates normally insensitive to light can be rendered more sensitive to it. We have in view the phenomena of sensibilization. Ciliate cultures placed in a weak solution of fluorescent dyes (eosin, erythrosin) become sensitive to light. Moreover, the resulting irritation depends on the degree of dilution of the vital stains and on the intensity of illumination. Under very weak irritation, *Paramecium*, according to Metzner (1921), is positively phototactic, and at a stronger irritation phototaxis becomes negative, being combined with shock phenomena. In other ciliates (*Spirostomum*) only negative phototaxis was observed. This kind of behaviour in ciliates is called induced phototaxis. It apparently occurs more than had been first thought, since Efimov (1922) found that sensibilization is not restricted to fluorescent dyes, but is provoked by all vital stains (methylene blue, neutral red), although not to the same extent as by the fluorescent ones.

According to some data, the colour of the substratum, i.e. reflected light, may also have an effect on Protozoa, namely on the rate of the division of the ciliates. Dembovskaya (1922) notes that *Paramecium* reproduces most rapidly in cultures placed on a yellow background, and the rate of their division decreases progressively on black, green, red, white, and blue backgrounds. However, these experiments need checking.

Thermotaxis

All the physiological functions of the Protozoa are affected by temperature. Its influence is evident first of all from the fact that the very life of the Protozoa in their active state is possible only within a definite temperature range. Furthermore, the intensity of various functions, both as regards metabolism and the rate of locomotor responses, increases with the rise of temperature up to a certain optimum. Cold and warm torpors and death lie at both ends of the vital temperature range. In Protozoa the optimum is usually nearer to the upper than to the lower temperature limit, though warm torpor and death occur in them at temperatures much lower than that of protein coagulation. Locomotor responses of Protozoa to temperature, or thermotaxis, are orientated in relation to the area of optimum temperature for a given species. As a general rule, in a medium of a uniform temperature Protozoa are distributed uniformly throughout, while in a medium unequally heated in different areas Protozoa congregate in those approaching nearest to optimum temperature.

Thus for paramecia the optimum temperature lies between 24–28° C.; therefore in elongated vessels, with water at one end at a temperature of 25–26° C., and at the other end either heated to 38° C. or cooled to 10° C., the ciliates rapidly concentrate at the end where the temperature approaches the optimum (Mendelssohn, 1902). The orientation of the ciliates proceeds by way of shock reactions of avoidance, which are most easily observed in Hypotricha. When one end of an elongated vessel containing *Oxytricha* is gradually heated to 60° C., the ciliates at this end of the vessel become very mobile, rushing about in all directions. As the temperature of the water rises at this end, *Oxytricha* exhibit avoiding movements, jumping with the posterior end directed forward, and then turning sideways. These reactions alternate with rapid but short forward thrusts of the anterior end. A long series of such movements brings the animal to a position at which it is turned with its anterior end towards the cooler end of the vessel, while continuing its progress in this direction. The animals are then correspondingly orientated.

However, not all the ciliates behave with such a 'purposefulness' as *Paramecium* and Hypotricha. *Bursaria* on heating show a response, but, once turned aside, they do not thrust forward their anterior end, but continue to move with the posterior end forward describing a circle, going round over the same spot until they die.

The response of amoebae to an increase of temperature is investigated by a different method, owing to the slowness of their movements. If the upper part of the coverslip, on the lower side of which amoeba is creeping, is touched by the end of a strongly heated needle, either on the side or in front of the amoeba, the side of the animal turned to the heated point contracts and the amoeba changes the direction of its movement. So far precise responses of amoebae to cooling have not been obtained. Some data indicate the adaptability of Protozoa to new temperature conditions. As has been established already by Mendelssohn (1902), in ciliates adapted to a medium of a higher temperature the optimum is shifted towards the range of higher temperatures. According to Poljanskij (1957, 1959), the resistance of *Paramecium caudatum* depends on the temperature at which these ciliates are cultivated. If the ciliates were cultivated at a temperature of 25–28° C. their resistance at 40° C. was considerably higher than in ciliates kept for a long time at low temperatures. On the other hand, ciliates kept for some time at 2–3° C. could live for a long time at 0° C., whereas the 'warm' ciliates, i.e. those that had been kept at a high temperature, rapidly perish at 0° C.

During the process of adaptation to the conditions of a higher temperature the resistance of *Paramecium* goes through different phases. At first it increases considerably, then it falls gradually until in 2–3 weeks it has settled at a more or less constant level (higher than the resistance of the control individuals).

Mechanical stimuli; thigmotaxis and rheotaxis

The nature of the response of amoebae to mechanical stimuli is quite simple. A sharp touch to some point on the surface of a creeping amoeba provokes contraction, the retraction of pseudopodia at the point of contact, and a change in the direction of the animal's movement. This represents a negative thigmotactic response. A creeping amoeba usually responds to a contact made even with its physiologically anterior tip, by skirting the point of contact at an angle rather than moving in the opposite direction.

An amoeba responds to a touch of its posterior end by a slight acceleration of its movement in the same direction.

However, under certain conditions amoebae may behave differently. When *Amoeba velata* is creeping under a coverslip and accidentally touches the lower surface of the glass with its extended pseudopodium, it will adhere to it by its pseudopodium and crawl on to it. Individual amoebae which are suspended in the culture adhere to the substratum more readily. As shown by the two cases mentioned, amoebae are endowed with positive thigmotaxis as well.

In ciliates reactions to mechanical stimuli are more complex. In the first place, the anterior end of the body of *Paramecium* is considerably more sensitive than the rest of its body, of which only the adoral section has practically the same sensitivity as the anterior part of it.

Mechanical irritation of the whole anterior half of the body provokes a different effect from that of the posterior pole. A typical shock response of avoidance is provoked by touching the anterior part of the body, but when the posterior half of the body of a *Paramecium* at rest is touched, there is either no response or the animal moves forward.

The two processes described have a similar aim—to remove the ciliate from the object with which it has come into contact—i.e. they are reactions of negative thigmotaxis.

However under certain conditions *Paramecium* does not try to avoid the object with which it has collided. These conditions are not easy to define precisely in advance. In general, however, ciliates seem to stop more frequently at objects which they encountered when swimming slowly rather than at those they have collided with at full speed. Moreover, ciliates frequently stop after touching some remains of decayed vegetation or a mass of bacterial zoogloea. Having touched such an object the cilia straighten up and remain immobile, while the adoral cilia often continue their beating rapidly, thereby setting up a current of water which is driven towards the oral aperture.

The other cilia, which are not adoral and which have not touched the object, remain motionless during the whole period of contact. Positive thigmotactic responses may facilitate the capturing of food by the animal.

In many ciliates positive thigmotaxis may have great vital significance. Thus, for example, in the case of many epibionts on the gills of molluscs, in ectoparasitic and endoparasitic ciliates, thigmotaxis serves as one of their methods of fixation to the host, special areas covered with long thigmotactic cilia (ciliated fields) being developed on the body for this purpose. A separate order of Holotricha, named Thigomotricha, characterized by the presence of thigmotactic cilia, has recently been established.

Certain sessile or semi-sessile ciliates, especially Peritricha with a contractile stalk, have a special response to contacts. In spite of their incapacity for free movement, these ciliates show an evident negative thigmotaxis. On contact the whole body of such forms as *Stentor* and Peritricha, possessing non-contractile stalks, contracts and moves away from the object touched. However, in *Vorticella* and closely allied forms, the muscle of the stalk also contracts and the stalk winds up like a corkscrew in response to the contact.

In a number of cases the strength of the positive thigmotaxis is revealed by the fact that it can inhibit or reduce the effects of such stimuli as thermotaxis and galvanotaxis. Thus, paramecia in a state of contact do not move away even under the action of an electric current or of heating. However, at $37°$ C. the extreme intensification of their ciliary activity tears them away, forcing them to swim away from the object of thigmotaxis.

The response of a protozoon to the currents of fluid arising in the surrounding medium, or rheotaxis, may also be included in the category of mechanical stimuli. When a current of water of varying force is passed through a tube containing a *Paramecium* culture, it can be observed that the majority of the ciliates at first stop their movement, then turn their body with its anterior end against the current. The animal remains in this position, either swimming against the current or adhering to the wall of the tube (thigmotaxis). Thus the response to the currents of fluid is positive: the paramecia move to meet the current. Rheotaxis in Sarcodina has the same character, as can be seen from certain experiments with amoebae and particularly clearly in the case of plasmodia of Myxomycetes.

Geotaxis

Response to the force of gravity, or geotaxis, likewise stands closest to responses to mechanical irritation, and consist in the following: many flagellates and ciliates (including *Paramecium*) when placed in vertical tubes do not sink to the bottom, as would have been expected from organisms whose specific gravity is higher than that of the surrounding medium, but, on the contrary, rise upwards and collect in the upper layers of the cultural fluid. The hermetical sealing of the tube containing the ciliates, before the beginning of the experiment, clearly shows that this behaviour of the ciliates does not depend on the presence of a large quantity of oxygen at the upper end of the tube, as might at first have been supposed. Under certain conditions the negative geotaxis described may be changed into a positive one, but this change is only of short duration, and the animal soon returns into the upper layers of the cultural fluid.

Opinions vary as to the causes of negative geotaxis in Protozoa. Jensen (1893) suggested that this phenomenon depends on variation of the hydrostatic pressure of the water column at different levels in the vessel, and on the tendency of the ciliates to find their way to that part where hydrostatic pressure is lowest. Davenport (1897) thought that the reaction is caused by the greater resistance of the medium during the upward than during the downward movement (the specific gravity of the animal being greater than that of the medium). This, however, is not very probable, since in a homogeneous medium its resistance to the beating of the cilia is the same for any direction of the movement of the ciliate.

Lyon (1905) suggested another theory, which seems nearest to the truth. It is based on the fact that Protozoa, and especially ciliates, contain in their cytoplasm some heavier components (for instance, the excretory bodies of ciliates) which by their pressure on the cytoplasm exert on the animal an irritation, due to the effect of gravitation, thereby compelling it to move against the direction of this force, as in the vessels with running water the ciliates move against the pressure of the current of water. Thus the effect of these heavy components of the cytoplasm corresponds to a certain extent to that of statoliths in the statocysts of invertebrates. This explanation is supported by the presence in some ciliates of statocysts, with the excretion bodies serving as statoliths.

This theory is supported also by Koehler's experiments (1925) on feeding paramecia with powdered iron in an electromagnetic field. In these experiments the iron particles were subjected to a magnetic attraction as well as to the effect of gravity, and the animal responded to the increased pressure by a more rapid locomotion in the direction opposite to the magnetic effect.

With the electromagnet in a horizontal position the ciliates gathered at the farthermost end from the pole of the magnet. Therefore the ciliates move in the opposite direction to the pressure of the iron particles attracted by the magnet.

Negative geotaxis is intensified by certain conditions in the medium, namely the concentration in it of hydrogen ions. The higher the saturation of the medium with carbon dioxide the greater is the negative geotaxis of the ciliates. Thus, for example, in a slightly alkaline medium *Spirostomum* keeps to the bottom of the vessel, but at a certain concentration of carbon dioxide (pH 6·5) negative geotaxis becomes apparent, while at pH 5·9 the ciliates swim upwards, stretched out in a vertical direction.

Conditions similar to those of the force of gravity can be produced by centrifuging the ciliates. Jensen (1893) has shown that paramecia, when placed in a horizontal tube rotating at a certain speed in the horizontal plane, try to swim in a centripetal direction. At a certain rate of rotation (4 revolutions per second), at the distal end of the tube where the speed is at its highest, the ciliates are drawn by the force of rotation to the bottom of the tube, in spite of their efforts, while other ciliates, which were located nearer to the middle of the tube, swim actively to its proximal end, i.e. in a central direction. Thus, in general the movements of the ciliates during centrifuging is directed so as to counteract the effect of the rotational force.

Of course, it should be borne in mind that negative geotaxis is not a common phenomenon among Protozoa. Apart from an abundance of bottom-living species, i.e. positively geotactic forms by their very mode of life, many free plankton organisms live at great depths, of thousands of metres, without revealing a negative geotaxis.

Electrical stimuli or galvanotaxis

Experiments on the effect of electric current on Protozoa are almost a hundred years old. Verworn (1903), who had done much work on this subject, gave an account of it in his book *General Physiology*. Since then many investigators have studied electrotaxis in Protozoa (Jennings, 1904; Koehler, 1925; Mast, 1941; Kinosita, 1938, 1939; and others).

The effect of electric current on Protozoa can be easily observed, especially in ciliates. It is revealed primarily in the orientation of the animals in relation to the poles, and in a definite galvanotaxis. Under the action of a comparatively weak current paramecia first of all turn their anterior end to the cathode with their long axis parallel to the line of the current; they then move towards the cathode, forming a dense gathering at the negative pole. At the beginning of the action a reversal of the ciliary beats is observed. When a weak current is used, reversal involves only the anterior cilia, so that in spite of the movement of the animal being directed towards the cathode, at the very anterior end of the animal the cilia beat away from it, towards the anode. With an increase of current reversal spreads farther towards the posterior end of the ciliate, and when more than half of the body is affected by it the animal begins to move towards the anode, without, however, turning to it, but progressing towards the positive pole by its posterior end. With further increase of the current the ciliate begins to disintegrate: its anterior (i.e. cathodic) end swells, but the breaking up starts from the posterior (i.e. anodic) end of its body. When the direction of the current is reversed (i.e. the transformation of the anode into the cathode) a reorientation of the ciliates and their concentration at the new cathode takes place every time.

Jennings suggests that all the responses of ciliates depend on their stimulation at the cathodic side of their body.

This interpretation, however, is contradicted by some facts. If at the closing of the circuit the long axis of the paramecia is arranged obliquely in relation to the direction of the current, the reversal of the cilia may occur not only on the side of ciliate turned towards the cathode but along the whole circumference of the animal, depending on the angle at which the animal is situated in respect to the line of the current and on the strength of the current. This, according to Mast (1941), disagrees with the concept of Verworn and Koehler, who maintain that the current leads only to the division of the surface of the body of the organism into functionally different sections—but supports the idea according to which the action of the current spreads over some system, distributed throughout the body at a certain depth below the surface of the animal. Mast regards the neuromotor apparatus as such a system. However, we do not consider this view to be well founded.

As has been shown by tests on the effect of induction impacts on ciliates, a reversal of the cilia takes place whatever the position of the animal; moreover, there is a contraction of the ectoplasm on the side turned towards the anode, and trichocysts are discharged at these points (Statkevič, 1903, 1907); under a very strong current the discharge of trichocysts spreads over the whole body, after which the body of the ciliate begins to disintegrate.

A paramecium whose anterior end is directed towards the cathode reacts much more readily to a weak current than one in any other position. The response of *Paramecium* is at its weakest when its long axis crosses the line connecting the anode and cathode. Kinosita (1938) has demonstrated the same for *Spirostomum*.

Statkevič (1907) has shown in his experiments on the galvanotaxis of paramecia, stained *in vivo* with neutral red, that the stained granular structure in their plasma turned violet (a colour characteristic for acid medium) under the effect of weak currents and yellow (an indication of alkaline reaction) under strong ones. Kinosita notes that in paramecia stained with neutral red or Nile blue sulphate the cathodic end of the body gave a colouring characteristic for an acid reaction, and the anodic one that of an alkaline one; however, soon the alkaline area began to spread forwards, eventually involving the whole body.

The difference in the behaviour of *Paramecium* under diverse conditions explains the variable effects of the current observed in other ciliates.

Many Hypotricha in contact with the substratum move to the cathode not along a straight line but at a considerable angle to it. *Spirostomum*, at a certain strength of current, take a transverse position to the line of their action, though at a low voltage they behave like *Paramecium*. Grebecki (1961) correlates the galvanotaxis of *Paramecium* with electrophoretic forces caused by electric charge of the cilia.

Galvanotaxis in flagellates has been only slightly investigated. It is known merely that some of them (*Peridinium*, *Trachelomonas*) are cathode-positive, others (*Cryptomonas*, *Polytoma*) are anode-positive, while others again behave according to the environmental conditions.

As to the behaviour of the colonies, some data exist only for *Volvox*. In a direct current the orientation of *Volvox* is most exact but varies under different conditions. Mast (1927) found that in a photopositive state *Volvox* swims to the cathode, and in a photonegative one to the anode; i.e. the response to electricity is linked with a definite response to light.

However, the electrical orientation of *Volvox* is not influenced by the same causes as its light orientation (see above), but on the weakening or cessation of the activity of its flagella on one side of the colony. If the swimming photopositive colonies are rotating around their long axis, then at the moment of switching on the current, the zooids on the cathode side of the colony stop the work of their flagella until the colony turns with its anterior end to the cathode. Then all the flagella begin to beat and the colony swims towards the cathode. Photonegative colonies behave in the opposite way. At the closing of the circuit flagella on the anode side stop beating until the colony turns to the anode and begins to swim towards it.

Mast's theoretical explanations of this phenomenon are not yet sufficiently substantiated.

The data on galvanotaxis in Sarcodina are scarce. *Amoeba proteus*, for instance, when its side is turned towards the anode, contracts under the effect of a weak current and the animal itself moves towards the cathode (Mast, 1941).

When amoebae are exposed to a stronger current, they cease to move (shock?) immediately after the circuit is closed, but after a short interval pseudopodia appear on the cathodic side and the animal continues to move to the cathode.

Under the influence of a still stronger current the anodic end of the amoeba is clearly contracted, and soon afterwards the animal begins to disintegrate, starting from its anodic end.

In Mast's opinion the contraction of amoeba from its anodic end is an indication of the gelation of the anodic surface of the amoeba caused by the electric current.

The action of an alternating current on amoeba produces a completely different picture. First of all it becomes orientated by extending in a direction perpendicular to that of the current (the reverse of what occurs in the case of a direct current); then on those sides of the stretched amoeba which are turned to its poles, i.e. approximately at its equator, there appear bubbles, folds, and small, very fluid pseudopodia; these are followed by ruptures of the surface layer of the animal along its equator and by its breaking up.

Though the factual material on the phenomena of galvanotaxis has recently considerably increased, there is still no well substantiated theory explaining these phenomena.

The observations of B. Klein (1943) on the effect of a current on the system of silver lines in ciliates are also interesting. Klein passed a weak direct current through a culture of *Colpidium* for 20–46 minutes, until the drop of cultural fluid on the glass was dried up. The ciliates were then subjected to dry argentation. It was found that the ciliates at the anode and the cathode were differently stained. The anodic ciliates were black, while the cathodic ones were reddish brown. Moreover, in anodic ciliates the system of lines was impregnated and they were indistinct, whereas in the cathodic ones these lines were most distinctly stained. According to Klein, this difference is due to the fact that at the anode the lines are impregnated with coarsely dispersed silver, while at the cathode they are stained by extremely finely distributed silver. In Klein's opinion this is an indication of the intactness of the silver lines in the area of the cathode, and of their being badly injured in the vicinity of the anode. This could have been obtained only if the silver lines themselves were negatively charged. Klein thought that the large accumulation of ciliates at the anode might also be due to the negative charge of the silver lines, since opposite charges attract each other. We are not in a position to evaluate the correctness of Klein's conclusions, but would say that the facts established by him are interesting and should attract the attention of specialists in galvanotaxis.

Paranecrosis in Protozoa

On the basis of experimental data obtained by them, Nassonov and Alexandrov (1940) have arrived at the conclusion that the protoplasm of plant and animal cells undergoes the same complex of substantial changes when subjected to any stimulants, irrespective of their nature. These changes, called by them paranecrosis, are characterized by the following basic features: a decrease in the degree of dispersion of the cell's colloids; an increase of the viscosity of the cytoplasm, sometimes preceded by a certain decrease; an increase of the sorption properties of the cellular colloids in relation to a number of dyes; a shift of pH of the cellular content towards the acid side.

For a definite dosage of the stimulant all these changes are reversible, and this is particularly characteristic of paranecrosis. Various stimulants provoke typical paranecrotic alterations in Protozoa as well. Thus Makarov (1936, 1940) has established this in experiments on the effect of various narcotics—ether, ethyl alcohol, chloroform, urethan, and other substances —on the ciliates *Paramecium caudatum*, *Colpidium colpoda*, *Vorticella*, and *Pyxidium*. Using the method of vital staining and the examination of objects in a dark field of vision, he has obtained the following main results. Under the influence of narcotics in their effective concentration, which according to this investigator is a dose causing a reversible cessation of the animal's movements, the staining of the cytoplasm becomes diffuse instead of the normal granular, the macronucleus being stained more selectively. A decrease in the degree of colloidal dispersion of the plasma, and particularly of the macronucleus, becomes evident in the dark field; the macronucleus emits a silver light, while the plasma becomes opalescent.

In the dark field, coarse granular bright structures appear in the cytoplasm during reversible changes, and it acquires a coarse coagulated character. No change of oxidation-reduction indicators are observed during the action of narcotics on Protozoa. The same changes of the colloidal state of the Protozoa are produced by acids in concentrations causing a narcotic effect, as in the case of the narcotics themselves: moreover they are as reversible.

The action of carbon monoxide causes the same changes, but in contrast to the narcotics, the influence of this agent is linked with the changes in the conditions of oxidation and reduction in the cell, as is evident in the reduction of the oxidation-reduction indicators, viz. after 25–30 minutes the animal is completely decolorized. However, their colour is immediately restored when a stream of oxygen is passed through. Evidently in the atmosphere of carbon monoxide the dye penetrates into the animal, but there is converted to leuco-form.

The action of all the agents examined which is accompanied by a similar physiological factor, viz. narcosis, is linked with the same type of changes in the state of the cellular colloids, namely with a decrease of their state of dispersion.

From all these facts it can be concluded that the effect of narcotics is closely connected with the changes in the colloidal state of the cells produced by it, manifested by a decrease of the state of dispersion of the cytoplasm and by changes in its sorption properties.

Specific and general features in the response of Protozoa to injuries

Verworn (1903), who studied the responses of Protozoa and tissue cells to the action of various harmful agents, came to the conclusion that in almost every case there is a similar picture of a granular break up. Hence he assumed that the response of the cells was independent of the nature of the active agent.

However, as has been shown by detailed investigations on the process of injury in ciliates, the results of the injury undoubtedly depend on the nature of the harmful agent. Aleksandrov (1948) studied the effect of ethyl alcohol, quinine, methylene blue, heating, and exposure to beta and ultra-violet rays on paramecia. In sufficiently large doses all these agents provoke in the cytoplasm of the ciliates paranecrotic changes like those described by

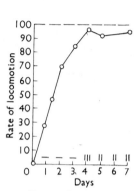

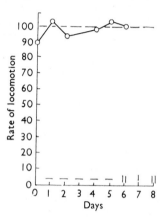

FIG. 94. Rate of locomotion and of division in *Paramecium*, after heating at 38° C. for 22 minutes. Absence of division is indicated by minus signs, number of divisions per day by vertical strokes. (After Aleksandrov, 1948.)

FIG. 95. Rate of locomotion and of division of *Paramecium* after exposure to 0·0005 per cent. methylene blue for 30 minutes. Absence of division designated by minus signs, number of divisions per day by vertical strokes. (After Aleksandrov, 1948.)

Makarov (1938) from his experiments on the effects on these organisms of different narcotics, carbon monoxide and oxygen. However, if the cytological picture of the injury is disregarded, and the behaviour of the injured ciliates is observed for some period of time, the difference in principle between the results of injuries caused by diverse agents becomes evident.

Thus a ciliate injured by a single application of heating (Fig. 94) perishes not later than on the third day, as a result of the after-effect of a minimum lethal dose. However, on heating to lower temperatures the injuries regenerate. A ciliate becomes practically motionless under the effect of a maximum tolerated dose of heating, and typical symptoms of paranecrosis appear in the cytoplasm. However, after being placed in a normal environment, motility is gradually restored after several hours, and by the third day the ciliate returns to normal. Restoration of its motility and of its ability to divide proceed simultaneously (Fig. 94).

A different picture is observed after poisoning with methylene blue (Fig. 95). With maximum doses, the ciliate's power to divide is completely lost in 4–5 days, whereas its locomotor function remains intact throughout the whole course of its disability (Fig. 95). Even after irreversible poisoning with the dye the ciliates move normally during the first few days. Thus, contrary to the heating effect which injures all the main functions of the ciliates, methylene blue has a selective effect on its ability to divide but does not affect the locomotor mechanism.

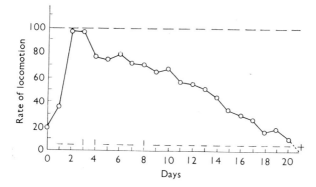

FIG. 96. Rate of locomotion and of division of *Paramecium* after exposure to ultra-violet rays for 33 minutes. Death of ciliates indicated by a cross, other designations same as in Fig. 94. (After Aleksandrov, 1948.)

After a single exposure to ultra-violet light, a peculiar picture of the injury develops in paramecia. Irradiation for 55 minutes caused an almost complete inhibition of all manifestations of life. The only indications of life remaining in the ciliates was the slow pulsation of its contractile vacuoles and the beating of its adoral cilia. Such ciliates perished on the third or fourth day without showing any signs of recovery.

A different result was obtained with smaller doses of irradiation (33 minutes) (Fig. 96). Immediately after the exposure the vital activity of the ciliate was considerably depressed, but within the first two days it was restored in all its functions, including the ability to divide and normal locomotion. However, this recovery was only temporary, for the condition of the ciliates declined steadily during the following days and they died between the seventeenth and twenty-first day. In the case of still smaller doses of ultra-violet irradiation (24 minutes) complete recovery was obtained after a reiterated decrease of the functional activity of the ciliates (Fig. 97).

Thus, a study of the responses of ciliates as a process developing in time has shown the dependence of the result on the quality of the stimulant. The coexistence of general and particular specific features in the responses of the ciliates to each harmful agent may probably be explained by the denaturation theory of injury (Nasonov and Aleksandrov, 1940).

Receptor organoids of Protozoa

Only two classes of Protozoa—Mastigophora and Ciliata—possess special receptor organoids, representing sense organs, as it were; in the other groups the responses if any to outer stimuli are evoked without the aid of special organoids. Mastigophora and Ciliata possess organoids of touch, sight, and equilibrium. The tactile receptors, in the form of sensitive bristles or tentacles, are the most widely distributed.

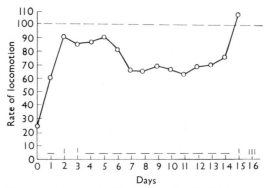

FIG. 97. Rate of locomotion and of division of *Paramecium* after exposure to ultra-violet rays for 24 minutes. Designations same as in Fig. 94. (After Aleksandrov, 1948.)

Tactile receptors. Firstly, every pseudopodium, cilium, and flagellum serves for tactile perception as well as for locomotion. The flagellum of *Peranema*, when feeling the surrounding objects with its tip, exhibits this ability in its very behaviour. In some exceptional cases flagellates also possess some special tactile organoids. In naked Dinoflagellata, like *Erythropsis agilis* (Fig. 98), and in some others a long 'fleshy' tentacle projects from the longitudinal furrow of the posterior end of its body. In some species it is rounded at the tip; in others it terminates in the form of a pointed 'stiletto'. The presence of longitudinal and cross striation inside the tentacle indicates the existence of contractile elements in it, a suggestion confirmed by considerable mobility of the tentacle. In a continuous and rhythmical movement it shortens considerably, being pulled almost into the posterior groove of the body, and then projects far backwards. The precise function of the tentacle is not yet clear. The transversally striated tentacle of *Noctiluca*, and the beak-like anterior process of such flagellates as *Rhynchomonas nasuta*, have apparently some significance as tactile receptors.

In ciliates the role of special tactile organoids is played by certain cilia. One or a few specially long sensitive cilia may be regarded as such in a whole series of Holotricha Hymenostomata (*Loxocephalus, Balanonema, Urozona, Cyclidium*, and others) and in some Trichostomata (*Trimyena, Spirozona*, and others). Among Peritricha the genus *Cyclochaeta* should be noted, the edge of the basal disk of which apparently contains, apart from its circlet of locomotor membranellae, another circlet of sensory cirri which are more widely separated and point resiliently upwards. Finally, in Hypotricha the scanty and motionless cilia of the dorsal surface play the part of sensory filaments. In the genus *Euplotes* the base of these cilia is surrounded by a

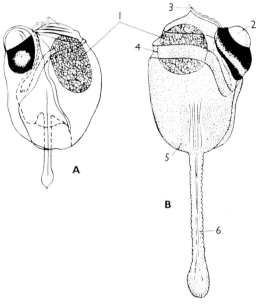

FIG. 98. Dinoflagellate *Erythropsis*, devoid of a skeleton.

(*A*) *E. cornuta* with retracted process; (*B*) *E. pavillardi* with extruded process: 1, nucleus; 2, crystal lens; 3, anterior flagellum; 4, furrow for transverse flagellum; 5, sheath of tentacle; 6, tentacle. (After Kofoid and Swezy, 1921.)

circlet of special plasmatic inclusions which reveal their special function. Gelei (1929) discovered a group of small elongated granules, surrounding the bristle in the form of a circlet at the base of the sensory bristles of *Euplotes* (Fig. 99). When fixed with a mixture of osmic acid, AgnO₃, and formol these elements are blackened from outside, but usually remain light-coloured inside. Gelei regarded them as a sensory apparatus and named them the 'sensucysts'. Similar groups of 'sensucysts' were found at the bases of membranellae (Fauré-Fremiet, 1961). Gelei distinguished in certain Holotricha (*Trachelophyllum*) two kinds of sensory cilia: tactile and chemical. One row of longer cilia running along the whole body are tangoreceptors, while two rows of short cilia in front of its mouth Gelei regards as chemoreceptors.

Photosensitive organoids are of the nature of eye-spots or as they are otherwise called stigmata; they are encountered exclusively in the flagellates Phytomastigina, or in forms genetically related to them—for instance, *Polytoma*. In the simplest case the stigma is a rounded or elongated accumulation of granules of brick-red pigment, of a carotinoid nature.

In *Euglena* this stigma has the following structure. The single flagellum of *Euglena* is inserted at its base into a funnel-shaped invagination at the anterior end of the body, and its base is here doubled, both branches ending at the bottom of the funnel. One of the roots of the flagellum forms a local thickening, while opposite it on the wall of the funnel lies an orange-red

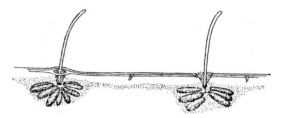

FIG. 99. Two dorsal sensory cilia of *Euplotes* with small sausage-shaped bodies given off from their bases. (After J. Gelei, 1929.)

pigment spot or an eye-spot like a screen. It has been revealed by electron microscopy that the eye-spot consists of forty to fifty minute granules, 100–300 mμ in size, united into several layers (Wolken, 1956). The pigment β-carotene is most probably a component of the eye-spot. This is partly confirmed by the phototactic reaction, which is most clearly manifested at a wavelength of about 465 to 570–600 mμ (Wolken, 1956). Bünning and Schneiderhohn (1956) have found two maxima of positive phototaxis, at the exposure to light of a wavelength of 415–30 mμ and 490–500 mμ. This points to the presence of two adsorbing components, β-carotene and taxantin, in the eye-spot. In Wolken's opinion the eye-spot granules are the sensory photoreceptors which when exposed to light conduct the impulses to the locomotor apparatus, i.e. directly to the flagellum.

In other flagellates (*Chlamydomonas, Pandorina, Eudorina*) the accumulation of stigmatic pigment has a cup-like shape; the cavity of the cup is occupied by a transparent colourless mass, which apparently functions as a lens.

The most complex structure of the stigma is found among some naked Dinoflagellata, in which it might rightly be called the ocellus. The single ocellus of these forms consists of a large accumulation of red or black pigment with a large crystalline lens lying in its concavity. This consists either of one large starch granule composed of concentric layers, or of several granules lying closely one upon another (many-storied). The pigmented mass is capable of a certain amoeboid change of form, with extrusion or retraction of processes. This eye-spot may have an anterior, lateral, or posterior position; and its crystalline lens bulges out the surface of the body (for instance, in *Erythropsis*). The pigmented mass may either envelop almost all the entire crystalline lens, or cover only its inner deep end. An ocellus is present in members of the family Pouchetiidae.

In *Ophryoglena* (Ciliata, Holotricha) there is a so-called 'hour-glass-shaped body'; it probably has a photosensitive function. This body is situated in the upper corner of the mouth and is either greenish or yellowish. It is saucer-shaped, stains deeply by iron haematoxylin and safranin but not by vital stains; it swells slowly in water, and much more readily in 15 per cent. acetic acid (Zinger, 1929). An accumulation of light-refractile granules forming a pigment spot is often adjacent to the convex side of the body. Zinger believed that because of its shape and structure (transparency and density) it may be regarded as an organoid collecting light rays and concentrating them in a definite point of the body.

Organoids of equilibrium

A few (5–8) small Müller's vesicles, with round mineral concretions inside, have been described in the ciliate *Loxodes* as lying along one edge of the body. Penard (1917) suggested that they might be analogous to the statocysts of Coelenterata. However, according to our data, Müller's vesicles are formations connected with water exchange of the ciliate, and are not sensory organelles of the statocyst type. Golgi elements are abundant in the cytoplasm surrounding the vesicles.

The static role of the so-called concrement vacuole (Fig. 100), found among representatives of two families Holotricha (Bütschliidae and Paraisotrichidae), parasitic in the intestine of the horse, and other perissodactyls, is much more substantiated. This vacuole was usually regarded as having an excretory function, until Dogiel's experiments (1929) demonstrated that it is a miniature static apparatus of complex structure. In the genus *Paraisotricha* this statocyst occupies the anterior-most pole of the body, in front of the mouth. In Bütschliidae the anterior pole is occupied by the mouth, but the statocyst still retains its position somewhere within the anterior third of the body. In *Blepharoprosthium* it is a round or oval sac, surrounded by a distinct membrane, and situated directly under the pellicle. The pellicle, which has longitudinal 'ribs', becomes thicker above this sac, forming by a raising of its 'ribs' a bulge, or pellicular cupola, projecting above the surface of the body. In different species the largest diameter of the vacuole varies from 10 to 18 μ. Inside it, there usually lies, in an eccentric position, a group of numerous crystalline granules, very similar to the excretory bodies of ciliates. Moreover, several pairs of thin fibrils extend along the walls of the statocyst from the outer pole adjacent to the cupola in the direction of the inner deep pole, while a thicker fibril may be traced from some way from the centre of the deep pole into the body, where it is lost in the plasma. Its connexion with the meridional fibrils has not been proved. On the other hand, the method of the formation of the vacuole has been established (Fig. 101). In the course of transverse division of Bütschliidae, the anterior individual retains its former concrement vacuole. At a certain stage of division it can be seen that some of the

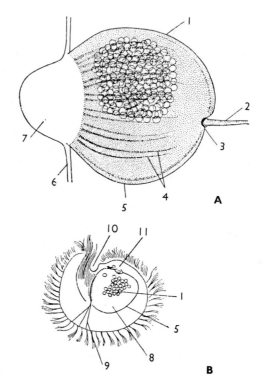

FIG. 100. Concrement vacuole or statocyst in ciliates.

(*A*) vacuole of *Blepharoprosthium pireum*, side view; (*B*) cross-section of anterior end of body with concrement vacuole in *Paraisotricha*: 1, clump of concretions; 2, centripetal fibril; 3, pore; 4, parietal fibrils; 5, vacuole wall; 6, pellicle of body-wall; 7, pellicular cap; 8, vacuole cavity; 9, suspension fibril; 10, peristome; 11, opening for passage of concretions. (After Dogiel, 1929*a*.)

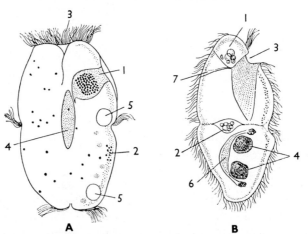

FIG. 101. *Didesmis quadrata* (*A*) and *Paraisotricha colpoidea* (*B*) during division.

1, concrement vacuole of anterior individual; 2, concrement vacuole of posterior individual; 3, cytostome; 4, macronucleus; 5, contractile vacuole; 6, dividing micro-nucleus; 7, suspension fibrils of the concrement vacuole. (After Dogiel, 1929.)

excretory bodies, scattered in the endoplasm, gather behind the initial circular constriction into a clump, which approaches the pellicle. The outline of the membrane of the statocyst is then formed round this group, and the pellicle becomes thicker over it. This is the way the statocyst of the posterior daughter-individual is formed.

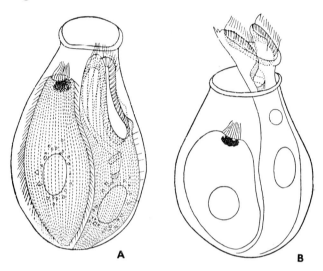

FIG. 102. Division of *Folliculina ampulla*.

(*A*) the swarmer and the individual remaining in the shell have acquired their final structure, showing dimorphism of peristome; (*B*) two ciliates after division; the individual remaining in the shell is represented as being extruded. (Fauré-Fremiet, 1932.)

In *Paraisotricha* the statocyst has on the whole the same structure, but it has fewer granules and they are larger. Moreover, on the posterior wall of the statocyst, which is turned towards the interior of the body, there is an opening with a clear edge around it, through which the cavity of the statocyst is connected with the endoplasm. Taking everything into account, this opening apparently serves to regulate the number of granules within the statocyst: they can leave the statocyst and enter it even after its formation. The statocyst of the posterior individual is formed during division in the same manner as in *Blepharoprosthium*. There is no doubt that here, especially in *Paraisotricha*, we have a complex organized statocyst—in which the excretory bodies of the plasma are successfully used as statoliths. All the 11 genera and about 30 species of the families Bütschliidae and Paraisotrichidae possess a concrement vacuole or statocyst.

Fauré-Fremiet (1932) has made a very interesting observation on dividing *Folliculina ampulla* (Fig. 102). This heterotrichous ciliate lives in a bottle-shaped lorica, through which its broad, extended peristome is protruded. Division takes place inside the shell; moreover, each division gives rise to two individuals of different structure. The posterior individual remains inside the shell and completely reconstructs the structure of the parental organism. The anterior individual, on the other hand, is a swarmer—a founder of a new shell. Before complete division and its emergence from the parent shell, the anterior individual exhibits a simplification of the peristome and a migration of the pigment granules, scattered throughout the plasma, towards the anterior end of the body, where a dense black accumulation of pigment is formed. This accumulation remains during the few hours that the swarmer spends in swimming, but later, after it has settled down, and its peristome assumes its normal extended form, the pigment spot disappears. It seems to us that the pigment spot represents a temporary sense organoid, which is either photosensitive or an organ of equilibrium, reminiscent of the temporarily functioning eye of some larvae, such as miracidia. Its existence is closely connected with the period of free life.

Its pigmentation supports the photosensitive character of the spot, while the absence of refringent devices in it point to its statocyst nature. The second explanation appears more plausible to us.

Organoids of attack and defence

A number of protozoa are supplied with special discharging inclusions in the cytoplasm, which play the part of organoids of attack or defence. They are either simple, rod-like, or complex hollow structures, which the animal shoots out of its body like the nematocysts of coelenterates. These structures are fairly common among Protozoa, especially among ciliates. Besides the ciliates, they are found in many flagellates, as well as in the whole class Cnidosporidia. In the latter, however, their function is somewhat different —they help the sporoplasm or planont to penetrate into the body of the host, but, since we are dealing here with parasites, this act may also be regarded in a broad sense as an attack on the host.

The origin of these sometimes most complex structures may, apparently, be attributed to granular inclusions of tectin (a term introduced by Bresslau) or pseudochitin lying in the surface layer of the body of many protozoa. Tectin inclusions frequently have the shape of oval or somewhat more elongated small bodies, which in the ciliates are cast out of the body on irritation. Owing to their characteristic ability to swell easily in water, the ejected tectin granules are as it were deliquescent in water, forming around the animal a delicate, temporary (but sometimes permanent) protective membrane.

Active means of attack and defence—trichocysts—have developed from this passive protective material by a decrease in the swelling ability and gradual morphological differentiation.

Trichocysts. In accordance with such origin the initial distribution of trichocysts in the body was probably diffuse: they were present everywhere under the pellicle. However, they frequently accumulate at the anterior end of the body. In some cases they form a palisade along the whole anterior margin of the body (*Spathidium*, Fig. 103, *b*), while those left in the endoplasm serve as reserve trichocysts, since those discharged by the animal can no longer be used. In other ciliates extremely long trichocysts

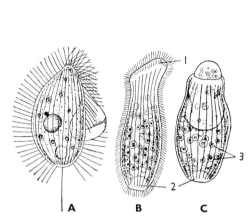

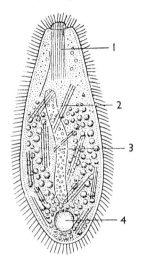

FIG. 103. Tactile organoids and the capture of food in ciliates.

(*A*) *Cyclidium* with its tactile seta; (*B*) *Spathidium spatula* not feeding, and (*C*) swallowing its prey. 1, trichocysts; 2, contractile vacuole; 3, food vacuoles. (After Woodruff and Spencer, 1922.)

FIG. 104. Arrangement of trichites in ciliate *Enchelyodon farctus*.

1, trichites of pharynx; 2, trichites of cytoplasm; 3, macronucleus; 4, contractile vacuole. (After Blochmann and Kirchner, 1895.)

(trichites) form a regular circlet around its buccal aperture and are also scattered throughout the cytoplasm of the body (*Enchelyodon farctus*, Fig. 104).

The orderly arrangement of trichocysts is particulary clearly seen in such ciliates as *Dileptus*, whose buccal aperture is situated at the base of the long motile proboscis, and a strong band of trichocysts extends along its oral side down to the buccal aperture. When the prey touches the oral side of the proboscis, it gives a spasmodic jerk and stops. The significance of the trichocyst is well illustrated by the peculiar gymnostomatous ciliate *Teutophrys*, whose buccal aperture is surrounded by three long ciliated appendages, similar to the arms of an octopus: the side of the arms turned towards the buccal aperture is densely set with trichocysts.

In *Legendrea bellerophora* and *Actinobolus radians* (Fig. 105) the trichocysts occupy the same position, since they are disposed at the ends of special prehensile tentacles in bundles, which may be called trichocyst batteries.

The role of trichocysts in some endoparasitic ciliates, as for example *Entorhipidium*, from the intestine of sea-urchins, and in many Apostomata from the intestine of anemones, remains obscure.

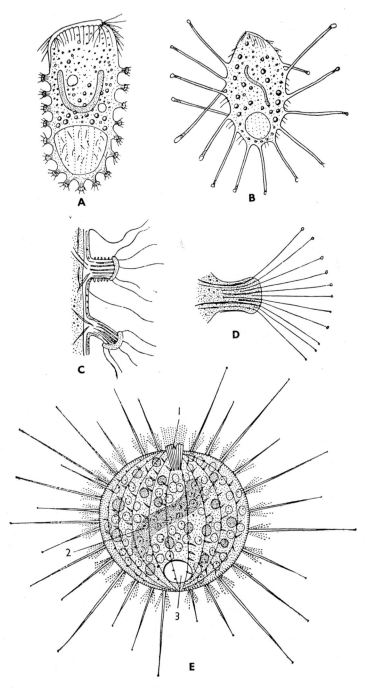

FIG. 105. Tentacles in ciliates.

(A)–(D) *Legendrea bellerophon*: (A) swimming form with tentacles retracted; (B) form with tentacles extended; (C) tentacle with circlet of trichocysts; (D) tentacle with discharged trichocysts; (E) *Actinobolus radians* with extended tentacles, whose base is surrounded by bundles of cilia. 1, cytostome and pharynx; 2, macronucleus; 3, contractile vacuole. ((A–D) from Penard, 1922; (E) from Ševjakov, 1896.)

Trichocysts are widely distributed in almost all the suborders of Holo-tricha, and are found also in some flagellates.

As to the way in which trichocysts originate opinions differ. Mitrofanoff (1903) observed that trichocysts, though situated in the ectoplasm, origi-nate in the endoplasm in the closest vicinity to the macronucleus, at first in the form of short rods (*Paramecium*). Tönniges (1914) thinks that the trichocysts of *Frontonia* originate from the endosomes of the macronucleus and that their development proceeds during their migration into the ecto-plasm. Chatton and Lwoff (1935), having studied the ciliates Apostomata, came to the conclusion that trichocysts are formed from trichocystosomes, i.e. granules formed by the division of the kinetosome (Fig. 86). Conse-quently the trichocysts are produced directly at the site eventually occupied by them. At the point of the formation of the trichocyst one of the infra-ciliary granules divides, whereupon one of the products of the division remains at the same spot, retaining its former function (i.e. that of a true infraciliary granule). The other product of the division, while retaining by means of a fibril (desmose) its connexion with the infraciliary granules, moves somewhat away from it, giving off a rod-like process into the depth of the cytoplasm. When this process reaches its definitive length and comes to the end of its development, it becomes a trichocyst. The opinion of Tönniges as well as that of Chatton and Lwoff do not find any support in the recent investigations. The trichocysts apparently arise in the endoplasm from elements of the endoplasmic reticulum, the ribosomes taking part in this process, and then migrate to the surface of the body (Ehret and Halles, 1961).

The structure of the trichocysts is not uniform among different ciliates. The old opinion that the lengthening of the trichocyst during its discharge depends only on the ejection from the trichocyst sac of a stream of sub-stance which on setting forms a fibril, should be considerably changed at present, mainly on the basis of investigations by Krüger (1934, 1936) who has examined the trichocysts of thirty-six genera of Holotricha in the dark field. He found that there are several types of trichocysts (Fig. 106) and that they have a complex structure. Forms like *Paramecium* and *Frontonia* have a simpler type of trichocysts; Krüger calls them the spindle-shaped trichocysts. A trichocyst at rest contains under its membrane a substance with a strong swelling capacity, owing to which the sac-like trichocyst is extended in the course of extrusion. There is an arrow-like point at the anterior end of the discharged spindle-shaped trichocysts; and sometimes the posterior end of the trichocyst (*Frontonia*) bears a cupola-like thicken-ing. In other ciliates, as for example in *Prorodon, Didinium,* &c., tubular trichocysts, or, as they were called by Kudo (1954), trichites, have the shape of a cylindrical, thick-walled capsule, within which lies a spirally twisted filament, which can shoot out of this capsule. Such trichocysts of *Prorodon* reach the length of 11 μ, while the filament extruded from it reaches 20 μ.

In *Didinium* this thread is 40 μ long and in *Strombidium* even 120 μ. These trichocysts are sometimes called cnidotrichocysts (Krüger, 1936). At present the term 'trichites' is used for the rod-like structures occurring in

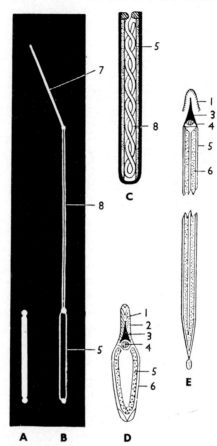

FIG. 106. Different types of ciliate trichocysts (semi-schematic).

(*A*)–(*C*) *Prorodon teres*: (*A*) not discharged; (*B*) discharged trichocyst; (*C*) diagram of structure of trichocyst. (*D*), (*E*) *Paramecium caudatum*; (*D*) not discharged; (*E*) discharged trichocyst. 1, cap; 2, swelling substance; 3, tip of trichocyst; 4, base of the tip; 5, membrane; 6, inner hydrophile layer; 7, end of the filament; 8, trichocyst filament. (After Krüger, 1936.)

the endoplasm or on the boundary between the ecto- and endoplasm. Lwoff (1950) considers that the trichocysts have a tubular structure, and that they are capable of increasing in size, while the trichites are homogeneous and do not change their size.

It has been established by electron micrographs (Jakus, 1945; Jakus and Hall, 1946; Rouiller and Fauré-Fremiet, 1957; and others) that a discharged trichocyst of ciliates (*Paramecium, Frontonia,* and others) consists of a long cross-striated shaft with a short spine at its tip. The shaft is commonly cylindrical in shape, consisting of longitudinal fibrils. The cross-striation of the shaft is due to its surface not being smooth but consisting of transverse thickenings and alternating with the boundaries between them (Fig. 107). The distance between the transverse thickenings is approximately 550 Å, but some even finer transverse structures can sometimes be detected between them. Unextruded trichocysts represent homogeneous bodies without cross-striation. The change in the structure of trichocysts during extrusion is undoubtedly associated with very rapid and pronounced molecular changes leading to an increase in the electron density of the trichocysts, and to a change in their ability to bind heavy metals.

Trichocysts react sharply to external irritations, for example, in *Paramecium* to pressure, to the addition of acids and alkalis, to attacks by *Didinium*. Opinions regarding the function of trichocysts vary. Thus Penard considers that some of the so-called 'trichocysts' are secretory organs providing material for the formation of membranes (an accumulation of tectin). Some authors refer to such trichocysts by the vague term 'protrichocysts' (Bresslau, 1921; Krüger, 1936; and others) or mucous trichocysts (Dragesco, 1952; Fauré-Fremiet, 1953a). However, it still remains uncertain precisely to which of the structures the secretory function is ascribed. Investigations by electron microscopy have shown, for instance, that *Colpidium colpoda* possesses, in addition to a few trichocysts, a large number of vesicles or ampoules lying under the pellicle (Fig. 130) which discharge a gelatinous substance on to the surface of the body (Chejsin and Mosevič, 1961). Bresslau, however (1921, 1928), believed that the gelatinous substance for the membrane was secreted at the expense of the tectin rods or protrichocysts.

Saunders (1925) thinks that the local discharge of trichocysts helps the ciliates to stay in one place (anchoring) when feeding on bacteria. Krüger considers that the discharge of the trichocysts in some ciliates (especially of the long trichocysts of *Strombidium*) represents an additional mode of locomotion, enabling the animal to progress, as it were, by jet propulsion.

However, the main function of the trichocysts is undoubtedly the attack and defence of the animal. No definite pattern has been observed in the distribution of different types of trichocysts in the various Holotricha. It can only be said that species of the same genus possess trichocysts of approximately the same type.

The pre-eminently aggressive or defensive significance of the trichocysts in a given species may be revealed by its position in the body. The uniform distribution of trichocysts throughout the periphery of the body (*Paramecium* and others) clearly indicates their defensive function.

Among the flagellates straight, refringent rods situated partly at the anterior pole, partly in other parts of the body, have been described in some

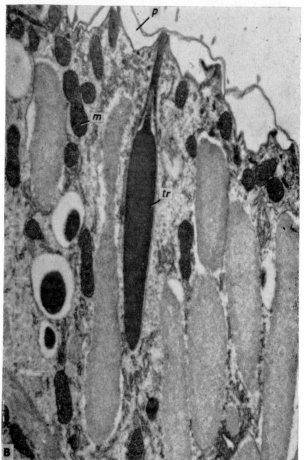

FIG. 107. Fine structure of trichocyst of *Paramecium*.

(*A*) terminal portions of discharged trichocysts of *Paramecium* with solid tips (electron-micrograph, ×16,000: after Jakus, 1945); (*B*) trichocysts under pellicle of *Paramecium caudatum*: *m*, mitochondria; *Tr*, trichocyst, *P*, pellicle. (Ultra-fine section, electron-micrograph, ×30,000: Original.)

species of *Gymnodinium*, *Gyrodinium*, *Nematodinium*, and *Polykrikos*, while Fauré-Fremiet and Chatton regarded them definitely as trichocysts.

Apart from Dinoflagellata, trichocysts occur also in other orders of flagellates, namely in Chloromonadida, Euglenida, and Cryptomonadida. The problem of trichocysts in these groups is especially fully treated in a series of papers by Chadefaud (1936). He considers that all trichocyst-bearing flagellates are characterized by the presence, in addition to trichocysts, of a special vestibular depression; moreover, in those forms that have a mouth, it is situated at the bottom of this depression; the author uses the term 'vestibular depression' for a structure which in flagellates is often, but not quite correctly, called the gullet. Among Chloromonadida the trichocysts have been best described for *Goniostomum*, where they are distributed throughout the surface of the body in the form of elongated spindle-shaped rods arranged perpendicularly to its surface. After extrusion from the body they discharge a long sticky filament; they are readily stained *in vivo* by neutral red and cresyl blue, like the trichocysts of the ciliate *Conchophthirus*.

In some species of Cryptomonadida the trichocysts are oval bodies, lying in the walls of the vestibular depression; moreover, Krüger (1934) has observed the extrusion of the sticky thread by *Chilomonas*. The electron microscope reveals that the anatomy of these trichocysts is unlike that of the classical trichocysts of ciliates. Since these structures can be extruded from the body of the organism, they have been called 'ejectisomes' (Anderson, 1962). The ejectisomes have a regular geometrical shape and a complex internal structure. They consist of two unequal components. Morphological polarity is established by a 'trapezoidal' smaller anterior unit and a 'hexagonal' posterior larger unit. Nothing can be said for the present about the function of the ejectisomes.

In Euglenida trichocysts were, according to Chadefaud, described as 'muciferous bodies', but in some species they are spindle-shaped and Chadefaud regards them also as trichocysts. Considering everything, the above-mentioned flagellates do in fact possess trichites and trichocysts, but Chadefaud's attempts to connect their origin with the kinetid have remained so far unconvincing.

Cnidocysts or *nematocysts*. Dogiel has found them in *Nematodinium*, and Chatton (1914) described them for *Polykrikos*. *Polykrikos* is a linear colony of naked Dinoflagellata consisting usually of four individuals lying in one longitudinal row and not completely separated from each other. Cnidocysts are permanent organoids of *Polykrikos* (Fig. 108). Each individual has about ten of them.

A fully developed cnidocyst has the shape of a capitated flask; its hollow head or cap has a deep invagination or ampulla into the cavity of the flask or capsule. From the thickened bottom of this invagination a short point protrudes towards the head; this is the striking pin, while a spirally twisted stinging filament goes down to the bottom of the capsule.

There is a small opening at the top of the head closed by a mucous plug. The extrusion is instantaneous and apparently takes place in the following manner. The spiral filament is in a state of tension; moreover, it is not hollow (as in Coelenterata) but solid. The cause of the discharge of the cnidocyst,

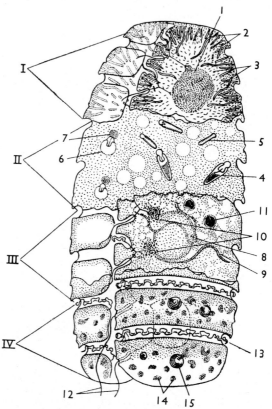

FIG. 108. *Polykrikos schwartzi,* diagram of structure of dinoflagellate with 4 energids and 8 kinetids.

I, II, III, IV: separate energids, nucleus with two kinetids given off; 2, trichocysts; 3, mitochondria; 4, cnidocysts; 5, cnidoplast; 6, cnidogen; 7, cnidosphere; 8, nucleus; 9, kinetids with their parabasal apparatus; 10, Golgi apparatus; 11, fat; 12, flagella; 13, flagellar groove; 14, glycogen; 15, vacuoles. (After Chatton and Grassé, 1929.)

according to Chatton, is an increase in the volume of the capsule's content; this causes the turning of the ampoule inside out into the cavity of the cap, to rupture the latter and to the tearing of the bottom of the ampoule, whereupon the striking pin falls to the side and the stinging filament shoots out through the opening formed at the bottom. Thus the discharge is the result of a simple unbending of the filament caused by the forces of elasticity. The development of these complex formations in the cytoplasm of *Polykrikos*

(Fig. 109) is preceded by two stages: the cnidoplast and cnidogen. The cnidoplasts are homogeneous cylinders with rounded ends, one of which is in contact with the capitated end of developed cnidocyst; this cnidoplast is covered by a pellicular cap. This cap gives rise to that of the future cnido-

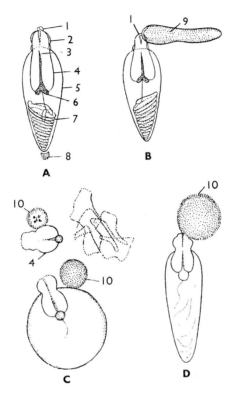

FIG. 109. Cnidocysts of *Polykrikos schwartzi.*

(A) fully developed cnidocyst; (B) cnidocyst and its cnidoplast; (C), (D) cnidogens at different stages of development; 1, mucous plug; 2, cap; 3, striking pin; 4, ampoule; 5, capsule; 6, base of striking pin; 7, nematocyst; 8, cap; 9, cnidogen; 10, sphere of future cnidogen or cnidoblast. (After Dogiel, 1951.)

cyst, to its ampoule and striking pin, while the rest of the cnidoplast remains undifferentiated. Later this undifferentiated part of the cylinder dissolves and a clear vacuole appears in its place, while one end of the primordium of the head and ampoule of the future cnidocyst is embedded in it. Chatton regards the moment described as the transition between the stages of cnidoplast and cnidogen.

This is followed by two simultaneous processes. First a cuticular membrane, at first very delicate, then more solid, begins to be formed around the vacuole; this is the primordium of the capsule of the cnidocyst, while a

spiral thread penetrates into it from the bottom of the ampoule; the formation of the new cnidocyst is thus completed. At the same time a plasmatic
ball, the so-called cnidosphere, reaching 8 μ in diameter, appears on the
convex top of the tap. In the centre of the sphere is a siderophile granule

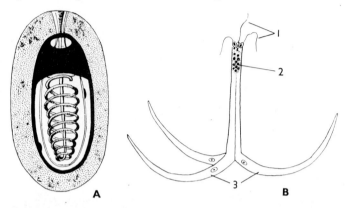

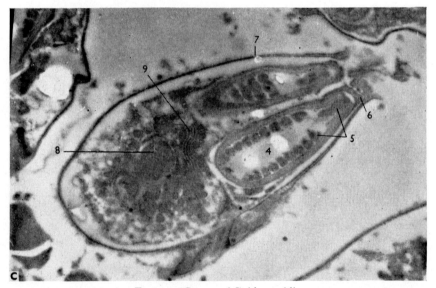

FIG. 110. Spores of Cnidosporidia.

(*A*) spore of Microsporidian *Nosema*; (*B*) spore of Actinomyxidian *Triactinomyxon* (after Léger
from Kudo, 1954); (*C*) spore of *Myxidium* sp. (electron-micrograph, at ×16,000: Original). 1,
three extruded filaments; 2, group of amoeboid cells; 3, trivalve spore membrane; 4, polar capsule;
5, section of polar filament; 6, lid of capsule; 7, wall of spore; 8, nucleus; 9, Golgi apparatus.

connected by a thin thread with the top of the cap of the cnidocyst so
formed. The sphere is gradually extended and converted into the cnidoplast while the first primordium cap of the new cnidoplast is differentiated
at the end farthest from the cap of the extended sphere. The biological

significance of the cnidocysts of *Polykrikos* is still unknown. It is very interesting from the morphological point of view that these cnidocysts originate from pre-existing cnidocysts, and are not formed anew in the plasma. According to Hovasse (1951) the Golgi apparatus plays an important part in the formation of cnidocysts.

The three orders of the class Cnidosporidia—Myxosporidia, Actinomyxidia, and Microsporidia (Figs. 110, 111), whose spores have one to four polar capsules—are the last representatives of Protozoa possessing cnidocysts. These capsules are in fact cnidocysts. Their structure has not been sufficiently investigated, but it is known that each capsule is formed at the expense of a separate portion of the plasma with a nucleus, the latter degenerating more or less after the formation of the capsule. The capsule is an oval sac suspended by one somewhat narrowed end to one end of the spore. Within each capsule there is a filament twisted spirally in smaller or larger coils. It is possible by means of various agents (tincture

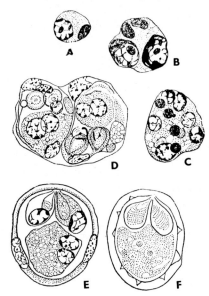

FIG. 111. Sporogony in *Myxosoma catostomi*.
(*A*) pansporoblast; (*B*), (*C*) formation of two sporoblasts; (*D*) formation of two spores; (*E*), (*F*) final formation of spores with polar capsules. (After Kudo, 1926.)

of iodine, sulphuric acid, and others) to cause an artificial discharge of the filament, which when extruded straightens out. This filament in some Myxosporidia reaches 500 μ, while the spore itself measures 10–20 μ. The polar capsules of these parasitic Protozoa serve for temporary attachment of the spores to the body of the host, thereby allowing the embryo enclosed in the spore to penetrate into the tissues of the host.

Morphologically the organoids of the Protozoa described by us belong to two main types.

The first type is composed of spindle-shaped trichocysts which are shot out by a simple stretching out of the organoid.

The cnidocysts of *Polykrikos* and *Nematodinium*, the cnidotrichocysts of ciliates, and the polar capsules of Cnidosporidia belong to the second type, their extrusion being effected by the uncoiling and straightening out of a tightly coiled dense spiral filament.

VI

PHYSIOLOGY OF METABOLISM OF THE PROTOZOA

Captured food and digestion

ALL living processes are based on metabolism, which depends on substances taken in from outside and used to build up the cytoplasm. Metabolism is manifested first of all by the processes of the capture and assimilation of food, processes which are secured by appropriate morphological adjustments, the combination of which in the most highly organised protozoa acquire the character of a special 'alimentary system'.

The modes of nutrition of Protozoa vary greatly, the following being the main types of feeding: holophytic, saprozoic, and holozoic; moreover, a mixed type of nutrition, which is called mixotrophic, is observed among a whole series of Protozoa.

Holophytic nutrition

Holophytic or autotrophic nutrition is accomplished by the type of photosynthesis characteristic of vegetative organisms and is therefore sometimes called phototrophic. It is characteristic of only one group of flagellates, the Phytomastigina, possessing special coloured plastid, the chromatophores. The chromatophores contain very labile coloured substances of the chlorophyll type, by means of which they are able to absorb carbon dioxide from the atmosphere in the presence of sunlight, and to synthesize various carbohydrates from it, and from water which enters their body by osmosis. The proteins of the cytoplasm are built from these carbohydrates and from salts (including nitrogen compounds) absorbed from the surrounding medium as a result of osmosis. Since many autotrophic and saprozoic organisms absorb their food through the surface of the body, by means of osmosis, there are no manifestations of either active capture of food, or its digestion or defecation, which are associated with the ingestion of solid food, and organoids controlling these processes are also absent. Therefore in such cases there is no question of a special alimentary system. However, in forms possessing chromatophores, these play an essential role in metabolism, on account of which they may be included in the category of organoids serving the function of nutrition. The chromatophores of Protozoa are very similar to those of plants, being intracellular structures of most varied shapes, round or oval plates, bands, spindles, saucers, and reticular bodies. There may be a single chromatophore or many. The colour of the chromatophores depends on the amount and type of pigments associated with the chlorophyll. Therefore in various orders of Mastigophora the coloured substances of the chromatophores are represented by diverse chemical substances.

In the orders Phytomonadida and Euglenida it is a typical chlorophyll extractable with alcohol. It has a definite absorption spectrum; it contains large amounts of carbon and hydrogen and only small amounts of nitrogen and magnesium. Thus the crystals of chlorophyll (type b) contain $C_{55}H_{70}O_6N_4Mg$. The chlorophyll of higher plants is usually accompanied by an admixture of a number of other pigments, among which the most widespread are the red-orange carotene ($C_{40}H_{56}$) and the product of its oxidation, the yellow xanthophyll ($C_{40}H_{56}O_2$).

It has been found that, apart from chlorophyll, Mastigophora may contain other pigments.

The orders Chrysomonadida and Cryptomonadida have brown-grey, yellow, or olive-coloured chromatophores due to the presence of pigments related to carotene and xanthophyll. Members of the small order Chloromonadida are coloured grass-green, and contain an excess of xanthophyll. The chromatophores of the Dinoflagellata are dark yellow or brown-grey owing to the presence of phycopyrrin, which too belongs to the carotenoids. However, apart from these forms some Dinoflagellata have a green, blue-green, and even cornflower-blue colour; the latter was observed by Dogiel (1907) in one member of Gymnodiniaceae.

Apart from the pigments localized in the chromatophores, some carotinoid pigments, not linked with the chromatophores, may be present in the cytoplasm of flagellates. Thus, for example, there is the black melanine (in some Dinoflagellata) and the red haematochrome, belonging to the carotenoid group. Apart from Dinoflagellata haematochrome is present in other orders of flagellates: *Chlamydomonas nivalis*, *Dunaliella salina*, *Haematococcus* (Fig. 112), *Euglena sanguinea*, and others. The large accumulation of haematochrome in these flagellates was found to be associated with the scarcity of nitrogen and phosphorous in their environment as, for example, when they were grown in cultures deficient in these substances. Haematochrome disappears on artificial enrichment of the culture with nitrogen and phosphorus, and the normal green colour of the chromatophores is restored. In some cases haematochrome performs a special function. There are some small red granules of haematochrome in the plasma of *Euglena rubra*. When these flagellates are grown in the shade the granules move nearer to the centre of the body, being covered from the outside by a layer of green chromatophores; and, on the other hand, when exposed to direct sunlight the haematophores become arranged on the surface of the body, covering the chloroplasts. This apparatus works with such precision that 15 minutes in the shade are enough for the euglena to turn from red to green. In this case the function of the haematophores consists in protecting the organism from the harmful effect of ultra-violet rays. However, the mechanism of this phenomenon is still unknown.

In coloured flagellates, apart from the chromatophores, some special organoids—the pyrenoids—take a certain part in the assimilation and accumulation of food. These special inclusions are closely connected with the chromatophores, being either directly embedded in the chromatophores or closely adjacent to them. The pyrenoids have a round or ellipsoidal form and a homogeneous structure; they also have a certain affinity to nuclear stains. Pyrenoids are either naked or enclosed in a more or less thick starch membrane. The pyrenoid consists of a viscous structureless mass of protein substance. On reaching a certain size, the pyrenoid divides, its division in most cases coinciding with that of the flagellate itself. The function of the pyrenoids consists in the formation of starch and other related products of photosynthesis.

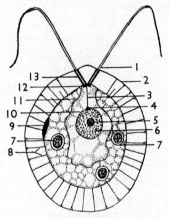

Fig. 112.   *Haematococcus pluvialis* (Phytomonadina).

1, flagellum; 2, surface of body; 3, rhizoplast; 4, centriole; 5, karyosome; 6, nucleus; 7, pyrenoids; 8, cellulose membrane; 9, stigma; 10, nuclear membrane; 11, cytoplasm; 12, basal granules; 13, points of passage of flagella through cellular membrane. (After Reichenow, 1909.)

Our present conception of the food requirements of autotrophic Mastigophora has been considerably modified and has become more precise thanks to the method of pure cultures of one species in a medium free of other micro-organisms (axenic culture). Thus, it has been shown that at least in artificial media, by no means all Mastigophora formerly regarded as autotrophic are able to survive in a purely mineral medium. A number of authors (Hall, 1941*a*; Pringsheim, 1937, 1946; Lwoff, 1951) have tried to classify various types of nutrition. Thus Hall (1941*a, b, c*) uses the following classification for the types of nutrition of different phototrophic and heterotrophic Protozoa in pure cultures. He divides the phototrophic and autotrophic Protozoa into three categories, according to their food requirements in pure cultures, mainly in relation to their source of nitrogen.

(1) Photoautotrophic forms, which can live in purely inorganic media (*Chlorogonium euchlorum, Euglena gracilis*, and some others).

The best known mixture adequate for the maintenance of a culture of these organisms must contain carbon, hydrogen, oxygen, nitrogen, phosphorus, potassium, magnesium, sulphur, calcium, chlorine, and traces of copper, barium, iron, arsenic, manganese, zinc, and lead. Doyle (1943) notes the great importance of certain substances required by the Protozoa in oligodynamic doses; these substances may differ for various species.

Moreover it has been proved that some species require certain specific elements. Thus *Euglena stellata* has a particular need for calcium and *Euglena anabena* for manganese. Photoautotrophs assimilate the mineral compounds of nitrogen while using light energy.

(2) Photomesotrophic forms that grow in media containing, in addition to inorganic substances, one or several amino acids, and consequently are utilizing the nitrogen from simple organic compounds, *Euglena deses*, for instance, is an obligatory photomesotroph.

(3) Photometatrophic forms that grow in peptones and in certain other protein media, but neither in amino acids nor in a mineral medium. *Euglena pisciformis* is regarded as an obligatory photometatroph. The preceding categories can also feed according to this type.

Heterotrophic organisms grown in artificial media are, according to Hall, also divided into three categories.

(1) Heteroautotrophs, utilizing inorganic nitrogen in the presence of an organic source of carbon. Colourless *Polytoma uvella* and *Astasia* may serve as examples of such forms. Optionally *Chilomonas paramecium* may likewise be referred to this category, but under these conditions this species requires an additional growth-factor (e.g. thiamine).

(2) Heteromesotrophs, that grow on various amino acids, as sources of supply of nitrogenous and carbohydrate food (*Chilomonas paramecium*, *Polytomella caeca*, and others belong to this category).

(3) Heterometatrophs that grow on peptones, utilizing the nitrogen from complex organic compounds, but do not grow on amino acids. On such media it has been possible to grow *Hyalogonium klebsii*, *Strigomonas*, the ciliates *Colpidium*, *Glaucoma*, the amoeba *Acanthamoeba*, and others. Owing to the absence of chlorophyll, they are incapable of photosynthesis, thereby differing from the photometatrophs.

Thus it is evident that in pure bacteria-free cultures both pigmented and non-pigmented Protozoa manifest to a greater or smaller extent their ability to utilize organic and inorganic substances as sources of food. Moreover, they form definite groups, ranging from the complete autotrophs to typical saprozoic forms.

All the diverse types of nutrition are in fact encountered among different Protozoa; moreover, it is interesting to note that taxonomically related forms sometimes (as is shown by the foregoing examples) differ essentially in the manner of their nutrition.

Certain flagellates can feed either as plants or as animals, i.e. they represent mixotrophic forms. Such are, for example, the Chrysomonadida, with their well-developed chromatophores, which at the same time feed like animals with the aid of pseudopodia. Thus, Dinoflagellata and especially some naked Gymnodiniaceae readily revert to animal nutrition. They sometimes swallow large lumps of unicellular algae through their flagella groove. In armoured species the non-pigmented variety *Ceratium hirundinella austriacum* has the same ability to swallow solid food. We shall not consider the problems of the biochemistry of the nutrition of phytoflagellates in greater detail but shall refer the reader to the treatise *Biochemistry and Physiology of Protozoa*, edited by Lwoff (1951) and Hutner and Lwoff (1955), where these questions are dealt with comprehensively.

Saprozoic (saprophytic) nutrition

Saprozoic nutrition is closest to autotrophic nutrition, and strictly speaking it may be regarded as one of the categories of heterotrophic nutrition, but in the method of obtaining nourishment it is similar to autotrophic nutrition, since, as in pigmented flagellates, food is absorbed by osmosis, i.e. through the walls of the body. However, the composition of food is different, since it consists mainly of organic substances dissolved in water, which are more or less decomposed (amino acids and peptones). Parasitic saprozoic forms may also use directly the serum of their host's blood. Among free-living Protozoa this method of nutrition is encountered in its pure form among non-pigmented flagellates, which are, however, closely related to the pigmented Phytomastigina. Examples of these are *Chilomonas* among the Cryptomonadida, *Astasia* among the Euglenida, *Polytoma* among Phytomonadida, and a number of others. In such forms their origin from plant flagellates may be traced in the retention of the stigma (*Polytoma*) and in other characteristics. According to the observations of Pascher, Lwoff, and others, the plant characteristics of such non-pigmented Mastigophora are gradually lost. Some flagellates have distinct but reduced chromatophores with no power of functioning effectively. In others the chromatophores have disappeared, but the pyrenoids, characteristic of the pigmented forms related to them (*Tetrablepharis*), are still preserved; while the third kind, as noted above, have not retained either the chromatophores or the pyrenoids, but have preserved the stigmata. Finally, the fourth kind have lost all the morphological characteristics of plants but have retained the ability to form products of assimilation peculiar to plants (starch)—*Chilomonas*, *Polytoma*, and others.

This process can be partly reproduced experimentally in artificial cultures. When grown in the presence of light, *Euglena mesnili* has up to a hundred chromatophores. However, their number decreases to 20–15 after 6 months in darkness; after 15 months most of the individuals lose all but two of their chromatophores, while some individuals are entirely devoid of them and are incapable of synthesizing starch. It may therefore be assumed that some non-pigmented Mastigophora have evolved from pigmented ancestors.

Saprozoic nutrition is characteristic of many parasitic Protozoa. In fact most of them, except for the intestinal flagellates and amoebae, many ciliates and perhaps some coelozoic Myxosporidia, which form long pseudopodia, represent saprozoic forms. In the parasitic mode of life the transition to saprozoic nutrition is preceded by the loss of mouth and gullet in Opalinata and Astomata. Another prerequisite for the transition to saprozoic nutrition is a tendency to increase the absorbing surface of the body (coelozoic Myxosporidia and gregarines: *Urospora maldaneorum, Aikinetocystis* (Fig. 113), the slender ribbon-like trypanosomes).

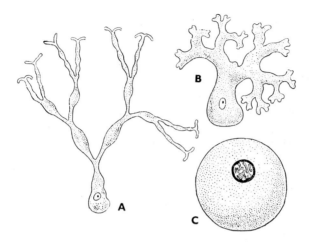

FIG. 113. Shape of body in coelozoic gregarines.

(*A*) the gregarine *Aikinetocystis* from the body-cavity of tropical oligochaetes; (*B*) *Urospora maldaneorum* from the body-cavity of polychaetes; (*C*) *Diplocystis phryganea* from the body-cavity of caddis-flies. (From Dogiel, 1951, after various authors.)

An interesting modification of saprozoic nutrition has been observed in certain ecto- and endoparasitic Dinoflagellata (Blastodinidae, *Haplozoon*). From their feeding cell or trophocyte emerged a ramifying plasmatic pedicle, representing as it were a bundle of solidified thickened pseudopodia, which penetrates into the tissues of the host. Osmotic nutrition by means of the pedicles is effected at the expense of the cells and tissues within which they ramify. Some of the intestinal parasites (*Giardia, Streblo mastix*, and others) absorb the products of the digested food intended for the host and transformed by its digestive ferments into a soluble and readily assimilated state. Intracellular tissue parasites (various Sporozoa and others) obtain nourishment in a similar manner. However, in the case of the erythrocyte stages of the malaria parasite (*Plasmodium lophurae* and *P. Cezghei*) Rudzinska and Trager (1957, 1959) have established by means of electron microscopy the interesting fact that the parasites are intracellular phagotrophs and engulf a large portion of the cytoplasm of their host cell; they may in this way obtain not only haemoglobin as their bulk source of nitrogen, but also proteins and other high molecular-weight compounds required as growth factors in small amounts. Haemoglobin is actually digested in food vacuoles, and this process is accompanied by the formation of a pigment.

Independently of the type of their diet, Protozoa require for normal existence certain inorganic and organic substances, especially mineral salts and vitamins. The study of the food requirements makes it possible to determine the character of the metabolism of a parasite to a considerable degree.

As has been shown by investigations which are far from complete, some Protozoa require for growth in cultures, apart from carbon, hydrogen, oxygen and nitrogen, at least twelve more elements: calcium, copper, cobalt, iron, manganese, magnesium, phosphorus, potassium, silicon, sodium, sulphur, and vanadium. Probably zinc and molybdenum may also be of considerable importance (Hall, 1953).

The majority of Protozoa require, for instance, iron, which is a constituent of the prosthetic group of cytochromes. Phosphorus and potassium are required by *Chilomonas paramecium* and *Tetrahymena*, obviously for the phosphilation of metabolites and vitamins. These organisms also require sulphur, a component of some vitamins which are synthesized by protozoa. Silicon and vanadium promote the growth of *Chilomonas paramecium* in culture, while cobalt, as a component of vitamin B_{12}, is required for the growth of *Euglena gracilis* and probably for some other Protozoa (Hutner et al., 1956).

Active research is being carried out at present on the requirements of Protozoa in vitamins, but comparatively few protozoa have so far been examined.

It has been shown for some members of the Phytomastigina group that for the growth of, for instance, *Chilomonas, Euglena pisciformis, Polytoma oceleatum*, and others thiamine is indispensable, while for *Haematococcus fluvialis* ascorbic acid is also essential. Thiamine is also necessary for *Acanthamoeba castellanii*. On the other hand, representatives of Zoomastigina, such as *Leishmania, Leptomonas*, and *Strigomonas* and a number of species of *Trypanosoma*, require for their growth in culture haematin, which contains their growth factor, and ascorbic acid. As has been shown by a detailed investigation (Trager, 1957a) the leptomonad stage of *Leishmania tarentolae* requires for its nutrition, apart from inorganic salts, also sources of purine and pyrimidine, at least some fifteen to seventeen amino acids, and, among the vitamins, folic acid, biotin, pantothenic acid, nicotinic acid, riboflavin, thiamine pyridoxine choline or its combination with pyridoxal and pyridoxamine.

Trichomonas foetus (Weiss and Ball, 1947) has similar requirements. Moreover, ascorbic acid is necessary for various species of *Trichomonas*, while *T. vaginalis* also requires some sterols (Sprince and Kupferberg, 1947). Thus cholesterol is important for the growth of not only *T. vaginalis* but also of *Entamoeba histolytica* (Snyder and Meleney, 1943).

Among the ciliates *Tetrachymena pyroformis* (Elliot, 1949; Kidder and Dewey, 1949; and others) has been studied in greatest detail: it requires for its growth thiamine, nicotinic acid, pantothenic acid, pyridoxine, riboflavin, and other substances.

The food requirements—in particular the importance of vitamins—have been studied in detail in certain species of malaria parasites (Ball, 1946; Trager, 1947, 1957a, b, 1958; and others) both *in vivo* and *in vitro*. In the case of *Plasmodium lophurae* and *P. knowlesi* it has been shown that para-aminobenzoic acid and folic acid, and in the case of *P. falciparum* only the latter, favourably affect the development of the parasites in erythrocytes *in vitro*. The same can be said also about pantothenic acid as a growth factor (Glenn and Manwell, 1956). Its deficiency in chicks decreases the severity of infection with *P. gallinaceum*. Moreover, it has been established that the growth of the plasmodium *in vivo* is stimulated by pyridoxine and biotin. It has been shown that para-aminobenzoic acid in the host's diet is also an essential factor for the development of *P. berghei* in the body of the rat (Hawking, 1954). On the other hand, the development of a malaria parasite is inhibited by the deficiency of ascorbic acid, thiamine, riboflavin, or biotin in the diet of the host (Seeler and Ott, 1944; Trager, 1947; and others). In the case of deficiency in pantothenic acid the schizonts of *P. gallinaceum* divided into fewer merozoites than the number produced in the presence of a normal content of this acid. For more detailed data on the food requirements of the malarial plasmodium see Moulder (1962).

There are data regarding the synthesis of vitamins by Protozoa. It has been shown indirectly for example that thiamine may be synthesized from simpler compounds by *Chilomonas paramecium* and *Polytoma caudata*. The growth of these flagellates is stimulated by thiazole instead of by thiamine, while in *P. caeca* the same effect is obtained with thiazole+pyrimidine. It has been proved that *Chilomonas paramecium* is able to synthesize nicotinic acid, pyridoxal, and riboflavin (Holz, 1950). It has been also shown that *Tetrahymena* can synthesize riboflavin (Kidder and Dewey, 1945).

Holozoic nutrition

Holozoic or animal nutrition is the second method of heterotrophic nutrition; by this method the protozoon obtains the raw material for its cytoplasm, i.e. proteins, carbohydrates, and fats, by ingesting other organisms, both vegetable and animal. This method of nutrition in its turn involves the development of organoids for food capture, ingestion, digestion, and the rejection of indigestible residues. All these devices eventually develop into a special alimentary system, which has a particularly complex structure in the case of ciliates.

Holozoic nutrition of Mastigophora. The first stages of the development of an alimentary apparatus may be traced in holozoic Mastigophora, i.e. in flagellates which have lost their chromatophores. They capture their solid food by means of the same organoids which serve them for locomotion, i.e. flagella, but the food enters their body to be digested. Since the body of the flagellates is covered by a more or less tough pellicle, the formation of an area of soft or liquid cytoplasm on the surface of the body is essential in order that solid food may penetrate into the body. In such flagellates as *Bodo* the construction of the site for the reception of food is very simple. It is situated at the base of the flagellum where there is an area of naked cytoplasm rising slightly above the pellicle as a slight tubercle. The lashing of the flagellum creates a current which drives food particles (bacteria and others) to the anterior end of the body where the tubercle is located. When the food particles come in contact with the soft tubercle, they at once stick to it, and enter the food vacuole which is being formed in the cytoplasm to meet them. The vacuole gradually slides backwards under the surface of the body, sinking into the endoplasm. The receptive tubercle may some-times be formed at some distance from the base of the flagellum, in the middle of the body, as in *Bodo jaculans*.

A whole series of colourless flagellates have at the base of their flagella a small depression, which may be called the oral groove. As it deepens and assumes the form of a duct, having definite and permanent shape, it is said that the oral aperture leads to the gullet or pharynx. It is interesting but difficult to account for the fact that a well-developed pharynx is sometimes encountered in purely saprozoic species, as for example in *Chilomonas*, *Cyathomonas*, and others. In *Chilomonas* the internal walls of the pharynx bear several circlets of small trichocysts, so that this depression may play a defensive role.

In some Euglenida, which have lost their chromatophores, as for example in *Entosiphon* and *Urceolus*, the buccal apparatus is provided with a special rod-shaped organ, lying inside the body, which probably helps to capture food. Sometimes the oral aperture is very extensible, allowing the Protozoa to ingest even such large objects as granules of starch and various protists (Fig. 114).

Choanoflagellata (Fig. 115) have an interesting superstructure to their receptive tubercle. In them a receptive vacuole rises in the form of a tubercle from a slight depression behind the base of the flagellum; the food particles enter this vacuole, while around the base of the flagellum a delicate plas-matic collar is formed. Driven by the flagellum the minute food particles glide backwards over the outer surface of the collar to its base, and thus find their way into the receptive vacuole. The vacuoles with food enter the endoplasm of the flagellates, and once the food is digested, they are expelled from the body somewhere in the posterior half of the animal. In flagellates a special and strictly localized anal aperture is still absent.

The intestinal flagellates of termites, belonging to the order Hyper-mastigida, have a method of capturing solid food, namely pieces of cellulose,

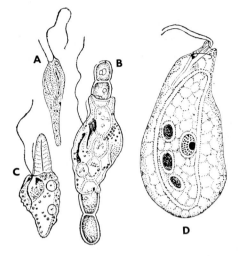

FIG. 114. Capture of food by flagellates.

(A) *Chlorochromonas ocellata*; (B) same, swallowing 7-cellular hypha of a fungus; (C) same, swallowing a diatom; (D) *Heteronema acus* containing an ingested *Euglena* (From Dogiel, 1951, after various authors.)

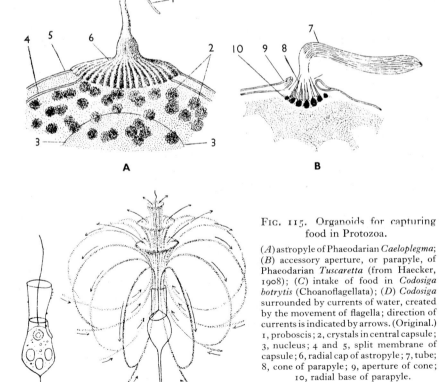

A

B

C

D

FIG. 115. Organoids for capturing food in Protozoa.

(A) astropyle of Phaeodarian *Caeloplegma*; (B) accessory aperture, or parapyle, of Phaeodarian *Tuscaretta* (from Haecker, 1908); (C) intake of food in *Codosiga botrytis* (Choanoflagellata); (D) *Codosiga* surrounded by currents of water, created by the movement of flagella; direction of currents is indicated by arrows. (Original.)
1, proboscis; 2, crystals in central capsule; 3, nucleus; 4 and 5, split membrane of capsule; 6, radial cap of astropyle; 7, tube; 8, cone of parapyle; 9, aperture of cone; 10, radial base of parapyle.

which is quite different from that of all other flagellates (Fig. 116). Most of their body, except for its posterior end which remains naked, is covered by flagella. When this end of the animal comes in contact with bits of food, it either draws them into the body, or pushes out local pseudopodia, with

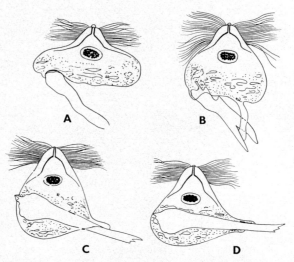

FIG. 116. *Trichonympha* from termite *Zootermopsis*; phagocytosis of food particles through posterior end of its body.

(*A*) beginning of food ingestion; (*B*) formation of pseudopodia at posterior end of body; (*C*), (*D*) food completely engulfed into the endoplasm, and beginning of digestion. (After Swezy, 1923.)

which it seizes the pieces of food. This is a case of transition to amoeboid feeding.

The exceptionally large vacuoles of certain marine Dinoflagellata, known as pusules (see p. 233), probably have a digestive function. Apparently they serve for the swallowing of the decaying organic substances dissolved in water through the duct connecting the pusule with the external medium.

Holozoic nutrition of Sarcodina. All Sarcodina, as a rule, eat solid food. The method of capturing food moreover depends on two morphological elements: on the arrangement of the pseudopodia and on the presence or absence and type of the skeleton. The absence of a skeleton gives full freedom to amoeboid nutrition, while its presence on the contrary restricts and localizes in various degrees the ingestive and defecatory surface of the body.

The most typical forms of amoeboid nutrition are encountered in Amoebina (Fig. 117). The amoebae, with naked body, which readily changes its shape, and pseudopodia extending from any point of it, capture their food with any part of the body by circumfluence. The catching of a motile prey sometimes takes place by so-called circumvallation, when the amoeba, without touching its prey, encircles it at a certain distance, and then by enclosing it with the ends of its body catches it alive together with a certain amount of the water surrounding the prey.

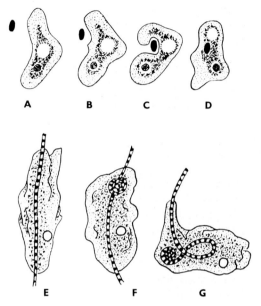

FIG. 117. Ingestion of food particles by amoebae.

(*A*)–(*D*) ingestion of food by encirclement of solid food particle (after Verworn, 1897, from Lang, 1913); (*E*)–(*G*) amoeba ingesting a filamentar algae (from Rhumbler, 1910).

Amoebae can swallow objects much longer than their own body: thus *Amoeba verrucosa*, measuring 90 μ in diameter, swallowed within an hour a filament of algae 540 μ long.

Amoebae with a very thick pellicle display another modification of the act of swallowing—invagination. Thus *A. terricola* forms over its prey an invagination of its ectoplasm penetrating deep into the endoplasm, into which its prey is as it were engulfed or sucked in.

By means of circumvallation amoebae are capable of catching even such rapidly moving ciliates as paramecia.

The capturing of food is somewhat different in forms with long, fine anastomosing pseudopodia, i.e. Foraminifera and Radiolaria. Unlike amoebae, these Protozoa feed mainly on motile protozoa: flagellates, ciliates, or bacteria. This type of prey stops immediately on coming in contact with the network of pseudopodia. Apparently, apart from simply sticking to the gluey surface of the pseudopodia, this effect is partly due to the secretion of some substances paralysing the prey. In Foraminifera the presence of only small pores in the shell prevents the ingestion of prey as a whole; therefore the food is often digested outside the shell. Once a small ciliate or some other food particle adheres to the pseudopodia, an increased inflow of granular cytoplasm along the pseudopodia and directed towards the prey is observed, so that it is gradually enclosed in a small island of plasma. The prey is dissolved inside it, while the plasma with the products of assimilation gradually moves along the pseudopodia towards the body of the rhizopod.

In other cases, especially in Phaeodaria, the prey is drawn towards the body of the rhizopod and into the cytoplasm, where it is digested. An accumulation of pigment granules, tiny lumps of secretion and remnants of the prey, known as phaeodium, gathers inside the ectoplasm at the chief aperture to the central capsule of Phaeodaria. In some Phaeodaria the skeletons of its prey are usually retained in the ectoplasm and are arranged there in a more or less orderly manner. The armour of *Silicoflagellata* swallowed by Phaeodaria were considered by former investigators to be parts of the skeleton of the Phaeodaria themselves. A food-vacuole is formed round the swallowed food, its reaction being acid at the first moment but later becoming alkaline, i.e. it passes through the same phases as in ciliates.

The axopodia of some peculiar Heliozoa (*Camptonema nutans*) may perform some special, brisk flagellar movements when capturing food. It may be noted that in some heliozoans digestion is effected by the combined efforts of several individuals, which encircle some large food object, for instance the crustacean *Bosmina*, their bodies fusing together; after this co-operative digestion of the prey they part company again.

In completely naked forms—Amoebina, Heliozoa, and many Radiolaria— the elimination of undigested food remnants proceeds at any point of their body.

In testaceous amoebae (Testacea) the aperture of the shell is used for the elimination of excreta, while in *Foraminifera* excreta are expelled from the pseudopodia network outside the shell. Finally, in Phaeodaria excreta are apparently not eliminated, and during the life of the individual a large phaeodium accumulates, consisting of remnants of food, digestive secretions, &c.

Holozoic nutrition of ciliates. The construction of the digestive system of the ciliates represents, as it were, a further development of the type of structure which originated in flagellates. Food is taken in at the oral aperture and carried into the body through the pharyngeal duct; it is driven towards the mouth by cilia; excreta are eliminated through the cytopyge, which in distinction from the flagellates is strictly localized.

Alimentary system. As a rule the ciliates have a round, buccal orifice or mouth; only in some Holotricha, namely in Pleurostomata, the mouth lying on one side of the flattened body is extended lengthwise and is slit-like. The most primitive position and structure of the mouth and adoral apparatus is encountered in some Holotricha and Gymnostomata, for instance in *Holophrya*. The round mouth or cytostome lies in the centre of the anterior pole, with rows of cilia running from it in meridional rows to the posterior end. In many parasitic Gymnostomata from the intestines of hoofed animals (*Bütschlia* and others) the mouth-opening and cilia have the same arrangement. All the chief complications of the buccal apparatus are already found within the limits of the order Holotricha.

In its simplest type the mouth or cytostome lies at the level of the surface of the body. The first complication consists in the sinking of the mouth into the body and the formation in front of it of a small depression, the so-called vestibulum (Corliss, 1959), while at the other end of the mouth a tubular cytopharynx runs into the endoplasm (Fig. 118). In this stage the ciliary apparatus does not undergo any modifications around the mouth: the anterior cilia of the meridional rows, serving to drive the food in, have the usual appearance and size. In certain forms (*Ichthyophthirius* and others) this arrangement is somewhat complicated by the formation of a thickened ectoplasmic border around the mouth. The necessity for this device is obvious in the case of ciliates, which swallow their large prey whole: the presence of a lip allows the mouth to stretch without tearing its edges. Further complication may proceed in different directions: first, the mouth is deepened and a peristome is formed; secondly, supporting structures appear round the pharynx (for instance the rod apparatus and others); and, thirdly, the differentiation of the adoral ciliary apparatus takes place. Moreover, in ciliates a displacement of the mouth from the anterior end to the ventral surface often takes place.

The development of the peristome or buccal cavity is of importance for the establishment of a regular current of water carrying food particles to the mouth. Among the Holotricha the formation of the peristome is usually associated with the shifting of the mouth backwards along one of the sides of the body: the peristome usually has a boat-like shape and the cytostome lies at its bottom. The shifting of the mouth proceeds along one definite row of cilia; this line of displacement is known as the buccal meridian. This displacement may be more or less considerable. Sometimes, for example in many Thigmotricha, the mouth moves almost to the very posterior pole of the body.

In other groups (Heterotricha, Peritricha) the peristome occupies the anterior pole of the body in the form of a somewhat asymmetrical funnel; the neck of the funnel corresponds to the cytostome, followed by the pharynx.

In Holotricha the peristome is frequently covered by the same kind of cilia as the rest of its body. In certain Holotricha, however, there is a distinct band or a spiral row of more powerful cilia in the neighbourhood of the mouth; they lead to the cytostome and are called adoral cilia (*Chilodon* and others).

The buccal armature of many Holotricha is still more complicated by the fact that the ciliary cover is continued beyond the edge of the cytostome into the pharynx, while sometimes there is a special part of the peristome in front of the gullet, known as the vestibulum.

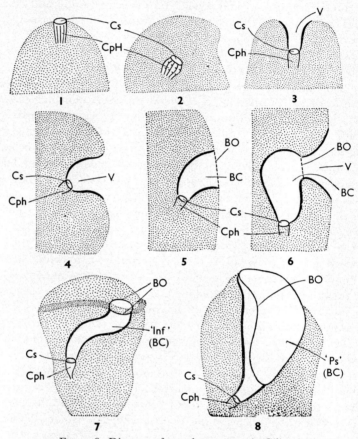

FIG. 118. Diagram of mouth apparatus in Ciliates.

1, buccal apparatus of order Gymnostomatida, suborder Rhabdophorina; 2, oral complex typical of Gymnostomatida, suborder Cyrtophorina; 3, buccal apparatus in lower Trichostomatida and Chonotrichida; 4, position of mouth in many Trichostomatida; 5, oral complex in Hymenostomatida, suborder Tetrahymenina; 6, same in Hymenostomatida, suborder Peniculina; 7, oral area in Peritricha; 8, buccal apparatus in Hypotricha. Whole ciliature is omitted, while body of ciliate is shown by stippling. *BC*, preoral (buccal) cavity; *BO*, edges of the preoral cavity (buccal overture); *Cs*, cytostome; *Cph*, cytopharynx; *Inf*, infundibulum (preoral cavity); *Ps*, peristome (circumoral cavity); *V*, vestibulum (preoral depression). (After Corliss, 1959.)

In Hymenostomata, among the Holotricha, part of the adoral cilia coalesce to form one, two, or more undulating membranes. These membranes are particularly strongly developed in such forms as *Pleuronema* and *Lembadion*, where they project beyond the peristome, forming, as it were, a sail flapping over water. In the undulating membranes and pharyngeal cilia only the function of capturing food is retained, while their purely locomotory function has disappeared.

Finally, in other subclasses of ciliates, apart from Holotricha, the adoral cilia may coalesce into rows of spirally arranged membranelles driving food more energetically towards the mouth.

The construction of the adoral apparatus corresponds more or less to the method of capturing food, especially in Holotricha. Among them the forms devoid of undulating membranes, but equipped with rod-like bodies, represent so-called 'swallowers', which swallow smaller or larger prey and which keep their mouth shut when at rest. On the other hand, Hymeno-stomata continuously swallow their food, bacteria, and detritus through a permanently open mouth. As a result of this manner of feeding the diameter of the mouth of such 'drivers' of food remains unaltered, whereas in the 'swallowers' the mouth is extensible.

In the Spirotricha adoral membranelles rather than undulating mem-branes are especially developed. The arrangement of membranelles, in-variably along a spiral leading to the mouth, is apparently the most effective way for driving the food. The direction of the coils of the spiral is apparently unimportant: in the Chonotricha, Hypotricha, Entodiniomorpha, and Heterotricha the spiral of membranelles is coiled clockwise, while in Peri-tricha it winds anti-clockwise. The spiral structure of the adoral apparatus in the small group Chonotricha is particularly accentuated. They have not only a spiral membrane at the anterior end but also a fold of ectoplasm edging it, or a lip, forming in different genera of Chonotricha from $2\frac{1}{2}$ to 5 coils.

Unlike the 'drivers of food', in the 'swallowers' of bulky food there appear special devices facilitating the capture of food by the mouth and its pro-pulsion through the pharynx. Such devices are of two types: (1) supporting rods in the walls of the pharynx (Holotricha); (2) supporting plates in the pharynx (Entodiniomorpha).

Apparently the starting-point for the formation of the rod-like apparatus are the trichites present in the plasma of many Holotricha and Gymnostomata. The trichites are first arranged without any order, but later they apparently begin to be localized along the walls of the pharynx and may project beyond the mouth when attacking prey. They represent as it were stabilized trichites which have altered their function. In the simplest cases they retain their appearance of simple, straight rods directed from front to back. With the increase of their supporting function the rods of the apparatus wind round the pharynx into an extended spiral. They dissolve in weak alkalis and acids. We think that rods of this apparatus might have been formed as local, longitudinal thickenings of the pharyngeal wall. Weinreb (1955) has dis-covered that in the ciliate *Homalozoon vermiculare*, the trichites, surround-ing the cytostome, are formed not in the ectoplasm but in the endoplasm, and that they migrate to the anterior end of the body where the cytostome is situated.

The supporting apparatus of the pharynx of Entodiniomorpha formed by flat, skeletal plates of hemicellulose is of quite a different nature. The strong development of these plates in the higher and larger Entodiniomorpha is explained by the fact that when very large pieces of cellulose are swallowed by them, the plates protect the walls of the pharynx from rupture. In general the alimentary apparatus of Entodiniomorpha has a much more complicated structure than that of all the other ciliates. Their mouth, surrounded by a spiral of adoral cirri, lies at the anterior end of the body and leads to the pharynx, which runs backwards almost to the posterior end of the body. The pharynx adjoins the right side of the body, which is covered by skeletal plates, while on the left side there is a longitudinal furrow leading to the so-called endoplasmic sac, i.e. a portion of the plasma, centrally situated and clearly demarcated from the ectoplasm by a layer of fibrils, into which the food passes from the pharynx for digestion. There is a deep, funnel-shaped invagination into the endoplasmic sac at the posterior end of the body, representing the hindgut. There is a layer of longitudinal supporting or muscular fibrils in the walls of the pharynx, while the hindgut is encircled by a muscle—the sphincter. In other words the digestive system of Entodiniomorpha is quite comparable to that of some higher worms.

The nature of food. The ciliates with a buccal apparatus may be classified according to the nature of their food as (1) bacteriophages and detritophages, and (2) predators or forms with a mixed diet, since some forms while feeding on microplankton also eat unicellular algae.

The bacteriophages include first of all Holotricha, Hymenostomata, and almost all the Peritricha, while Holotricha, Gymnostomata, Heterotrica, and Hypotricha are predators or semi-predators. Often, however, they do not keep to strictly one diet. It is sufficient to note that such a typical bacteriophage as *Paramecium caudatum* sometimes ingests unicellular algae.

The question of the existence of true monophages among the ciliates and of the ability of the ciliates to distinguish food from substances unsuitable for nutrition has arisen more than once. The tendency to monophagy is observed in certain predators. Thus *Didinium* (Fig. 119) is best cultivated on populations of *Paramecium* giving a normal daily ration of twelve paramecia. This amount of food is determined by the fact that about two hours are required by *Didinium* to digest one swallowed *Paramecium*.

As is shown by some data on the interesting predatory ciliate *Actinobolus* (see Fig. 105), it thrives preferentially if not exclusively on the ciliate *Halteria*. The long-living cultures of *Actinobolus*—about 400 generations in 8 months—could be grown only on *Halteria* cultures, the predators ingesting 25–35 individuals in 24 hours.

Chlamydodontidae (Holotricha, Gymnostomata), which feed on different blue-green algae, are less discriminating. *Amphileptus claparedei* eats *Vorticella* exclusively.

Sometimes it is possible to observe a gradual specialization as regards food within the same systematic group of ciliates, for instance a family. Thus the most primitive members of the family Ophryoscolecidae are the least discriminating, feeding like many free-living ciliates partly on bacteria and mould spores and only much more rarely (*Entodinium vorax*) on smaller species of its own kind. With the increase of their size and the development of the pharyngeal lamelliferous skeleton (*Epidinium, Ostracodinium, Eudiplodinium*), Ophryoscolecidae begin to ingest large fragments of grass (Fig. 120) and in spite of the larger size of the ciliates they cease to be predators. However, even as regards their vegetative food a certain differentiation according to genus is observed. Thus the genus *Ostracodinium*

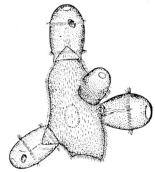

FIG. 119. Four individuals of *Didinium nasutum* attacking a *Paramecium*. (After Mast, 1909.)

readily ingests long vegetable fibrils, twisting them into several coils inside its body. On the other hand, *Eudiplodinium* can cope with large and massive fragments of grass, rarely ingesting fibrils.

The question arises, what determines the choice of food in such and similar cases?

There is first of all the size of the food particles in relation to that of the ciliate body, and to its shape. Evidently the ciliates are usually able to ingest particles considerably smaller than their own body (however, there are some exceptions: e.g. *Eudiplodinium*). Therefore in the genus *Entodinium* only its largest species *E. vorax* turns to predatory feeding. The capture of food is greatly facilitated in the ciliates by a strongly developed thigmotaxis. The choice of food may be conditioned not so much by the size of the animal as by that of its mouth and the construction of its adoral apparatus: the difference between the 'swallowers' and the 'drivers' of food is apparently based on this. In other cases their relation to food is determined by the chemical and physical properties of the latter. This difference in their response to food is readily observed in ciliates, owing to the reversibility of the beating of the cilia, which push away unsuitable food. It has been observed, for instance, that *Stentor* push away carmine, starch, and ground glass, but swallow *Euglena* and *Phacus*. *Stentor* swallow these flagellates not only when they are alive but even when they have been killed, for instance by high temperature provided their shape remains unchanged. Therefore, in this case, it appears that the choice is influenced by thigmotactic impressions of the shape of the object or its surface.

On the other hand, *Bursaria* reacts differently to particles similar in form

(yolk granules) but stained by different chemical dyes. Moreover, the acceptance or refusal of food is not always determined by the greater or lesser
toxicity of the dye. For instance, granules strongly stained with safranin
were more readily accepted than those faintly stained with Janus green,

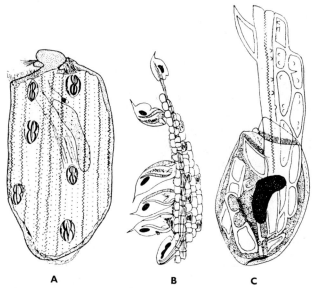

A   **B**   **C**

FIG. 120. Ingestion of food particles by ciliates from the rumen of cattle.

(*A*) *Eudiplodinium bubalidis* taking in a piece of grass with 6 stomata;
(*B*) piece of grass eaten around by *Opisthotrichum janus* and
Ostracodinium gracile nibbling at a blade of grass; (*C*) *Eudiplodinium
bubalidis* ingesting a piece of grass. (After Dogiel, 1925*a*.)

although safranin is considerably more poisonous. This difference is even
more clear in Metalnikov's experiments on feeding of *Paramecium* on yeast
cells, stained either with poisonous thionine (blue) or with harmless Congo
red. A great majority of the food-vacuoles in these ciliates was stained red,
even when the number of blue yeast cells in the suspension was five times
greater than that of the red ones. Consequently here the choice of food is
affected by the toxicity of the substance swallowed.

Metalnikov's experiments on *Paramecium* (1912) on the ability of ciliates
to choose their food led to considerable discussion. Metalnikov tried to
prove that this ciliate grows accustomed to distinguish indigestible particles
from acceptable food; he found that those ciliates which have lived for
some time in a suspension of carmine begin to refuse the dye so readily
accepted by them before, but accept Indian ink as readily, though it is as
indigestible as carmine. He considered it as an indication that paramecium
could 'learn' to distinguish carmine, and of the existence in them of, as it
were, a cellular 'memory'. Though not contradicting the facts, Vladimirskij
(1916) strongly criticized their interpretation. He regarded the refusal of

carmine as a sign of depression arising as a result of the population of paramecia remaining for a long time in the same culture fluid. And indeed, if the carmine mixture is changed daily, the dye is absorbed for months. On the other hand, when kept in the same culture fluid, *Paramecium* finally ceases to accept other substances, apart from carmine, Vladimirskij categorically refuted the 'learning' theory. Bozler (1924) took up an intermediate position. While recognizing the accuracy of Vladimirskij's experiments, he had found that the ability of ciliates to distinguish food was gradually lowered if the same food entered their mouth all the time; and, on the contrary, when the ciliates were fed on varied food this ability increased. As a consequence of diverse particles touching the cilia, these respond to various stimuli more and more rapidly. In his opinion the discriminating ability develops with the exercise of it. It seems to us that Calkin's (1933) explanation of the facts as indicating a certain degree of 'learning' is the most correct. He suggests that these phenomena point to a kind of fatigue, connected with the loss of irritability by a chemically definite type of extraneous particles, while a certain period of rest is required for the restoration of irritability. This neuro-physiological interpretation may be the most acceptable. Lozina-Lozinskij (1931) considers that chemotaxis plays a role in the choice of food.

Processes of food digestion. In forms ingesting small particles of food, it always enters a receptive food-vacuole, formed at the base of the pharynx. In bacteriophages this has been investigated best of all in *Paramecium* (Fig. 121). Every $1\frac{1}{2}$ minutes at room temperature the vacuole formed at the base of the pharynx is detached from it and moves backwards as a result of cytoplasmic cyclosis.

The further progress of the food-vacuole inside the plasm is frequently irregular, but in some cases (including *Paramecium*) its path in the body is fairly definite. In *Paramecium* there are the so-called 'short' and 'long' circuits of digestion. Its rate of progress is not uniform: the vacuoles are retarded in the area directly behind the nucleus; this is thought to be due to the special importance of the secretion of digestive ferments by the nucleus. At room temperature the whole circulation of the vacuole is completed in 1 to 3 hours. Finally, the vacuoles approach the cytopyge, which is usually a permanent aperture, occupying a definite position in the ectoplasmic cellular network of fibrils. Dogiel (1927) has noted that in *Paramecium* the number of defecations does not correspond to the rate of the development of new food-vacuoles. At room temperature defecation takes place once every 7 minutes, and it has been established that the vacuoles approaching the anal area are not discharged at once but accumulate and coalesce into one general 'faecal vacuole'. This is later violently ejected. Judging from this, there would appear to be a kind of sphincter around the cytopyge yielding only under the pressure of several vacuoles.

The permanence of the path traversed by the vacuole in the endoplasm of a number of ciliates raised the question as to whether there was some kind of a preformed digestive duct in the plasm, along which the vacuole travels. Dogiel's observations on the influence of some salts on the acceptance of dye suspensions by paramecium seem to support this view.

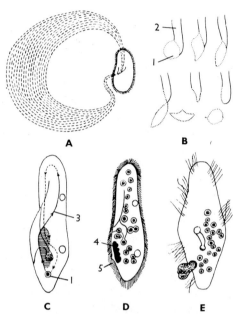

FIG. 121. Ingestion and digestion of food in *Paramecium*.

(*A*) current of water induced by the work of ciliary apparatus of *P. putrinum*; (*B*) different stages of formation of food-vacuole in *Paramecium caudatum*; (*C*) path followed by food-vacuole in endoplasm of *P. caudatum*; (*D*) accumulation of vacuoles in area of anus in *P. caudatum* fed on Indian ink; (*E*) moment of defecation in *P. caudatum*; 1, food-vacuole; 2, pharynx; 3, large circle of digestion (small circle of digestion is cross-hatched, direction of movement of vacuole indicated by arrow); 4, accumulation of food-vacuoles; 5, anus. (From Dogiel, 1951, after various authors.)

Dogiel observed that, on addition of sublethal doses of magnesium chloride to the Indian-ink mixture, the latter was taken in so rapidly that the food-vacuoles passed, as it were, one into another, so that Indian ink flowed through the endoplasm in a continuous current. The mass of Indian ink invaginated into the plasm formed inside it up to $2\frac{1}{2}$ coils, similar to the 'short' digestive circuit; however, normal defecation was not attained, and eventually the entrance of new portions of Indian ink ceased and the 'digestive tract' thus formed either remained inside the body or was rejected through the mouth.

The food-vacuoles undergo a whole series of changes during their progress through the body.

1. On becoming detached from the pharynx the vacuole still retains the alkaline reaction characteristic of its environment (first alkaline phase).

2. In the posterior end of the body of the ciliate the reaction of the vacuole soon becomes acid, and the bacteria inside it, which had remained alive while the vacuole was moving from the pharynx to the posterior end, are killed by acid in 30 seconds, but in some cases more slowly. At this period the acidity of the vacuole contents is pH $1 \cdot 4-3 \cdot 4$. These figures are approximately the same as the acidity of $0 \cdot 3$ per cent. hydrochloric acid, i.e. like that of the gastric juice of a dog.

This acid period of the reaction of the vacuole is needed as a preliminary to further digestion and assimilation of food; it lasts in different species from 4 to 60 minutes. The volume of the vacuole becomes somewhat smaller during this period.

3. Eventually, as the vacuole carried by the cyclosis of the plasm travels forward, the reaction inside it becomes alkaline, remaining alkaline until defecation. During the alkaline period, or the second alkaline phase, lasting several hours, granules staining deeply with neutral red appear around the vacuole. They penetrate inside the vacuole and, in the opinion of Nirenstein (1925), represent accumulations of a tryptic ferment. Roskin and Levinson (1926) have detected a reaction to oxidase in these granules, i.e. an enzyme stimulating the oxidation reaction in the plasma in the presence of molecular oxygen.

By this time the contents of the vacuoles are compressed into one lump while their volume increases as a result of liquid from the plasma entering into them. Proteins are gradually dissolved and absorbed and granular disintegration of the contents of the vacuoles takes place.

4. Vacuoles containing indigestible residue travel towards the cytopyge aperture, coalesce with the common 'faecal vacuole', and defecation takes place. Such is the process of digestion which has been studied in detail in Peritricha.

In ciliates feeding on larger food, this is usually not enclosed by a distinct vacuole, nor does it undergo a regular cyclosis in the plasm.

In the Suctoria the buccal apparatus undergoes secondary reduction and no trace of it is left. However, it is replaced by new organoids, adapted to predatory feeding—sucking tentacles. These tentacles are usually extensible plasmatic tubes with a knob at the end, where the duct of the tentacle opens outwards. In the genus *Dendrocometes*, living on the gills of beach fleas (Fig. 122) or Amphipods with very large, massive tentacles, their ends may be branched. In some Suctoria, for instance *Ephelota*, there is a differentiation of tentacles into common suctorial and special prehensile ones. The latter are much longer and gradually become thinner at the end. In *Ephelota* these long tentacles serve only for capturing their prey, but not for sucking it. Having captured a ciliate these tentacles contract, pulling the prey within the sphere of action of the shorter sucking tentacles, which then begin sucking out the prey.

Sucking tentacles have a central canal, lined with a thin membrane, containing longitudinal fibrils, similar to myofibrils, and also radially arranged lamellae extending into the lumen of the canal; prehensile tentacles, however, have no canal, but internally it is divided by thin membranes into longitudinal compartments, down the middle of each of which

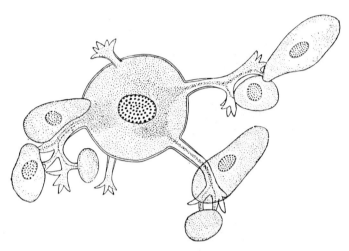

FIG. 122. *Dendrocometes paradoxus* (Suctoria) sucking its prey (From Pestel, 1931.)

runs a thick birefringent protein fibre. In the electron microscope each of these appears to be composed of a network of delicate fibrils (Rouiller, Fauré-Fremiet, and Gauchery, 1956).

There are different accounts of the effect of the tentacles on the prey. According to some data, they have a paralysing effect; according to others, they merely suck out the contents of the prey.

Apparently the effect may depend upon the relative size of the predator and the prey. Thus the large *Dendrocometes paradoxus* requires only two minutes to suck out a *Paramecium caudatum*, whereas the small *Podophrya collini* needs four hours for the same procedure.

In general, however, the toxic action of the tentacles on the prey is practically proved, the more so since the experiments of Izyumov (1947) on *Tocophrya*. Izyumov has shown by intravital staining of feeding suctorians that the tentacles not only draw in the endoplasm of the prey through their canal but that they secrete acid into its body. Congo red produces a blue-violet coloration in the protoplasm of the ciliate at the point where the knob of the tentacle adheres to its prey, while the rest of the plasm of the latter acquires a brick-red alkaline colour. This observation indicates that the predator secretes an acid into its prey. In the majority of cases only the liquid endoplasm of the prey is sucked out, while the covering of denser ectoplasm shrivels and falls off. Sometimes, however, the entire body becomes deliquescent before it is completely sucked in. The mechanism of the sucking itself and the forces which provoke a very intensive pumping action of the tentacles are not fully understood.

From the morphological point of view it may be said that the alimentary apparatus of *Suctoria* consists of several secondary mouths which are not homologous to the mouth of other ciliates.

There is a unique case of multiple mouths in the Gymnostomata —*Pycnothrix monocystoides*—an intestinal parasite of hyraxes. Its mouth is displaced far backwards along the ventral side of its body but is connected with the anterior pole by means of the so-called oral groove. However, in this species not only is the mouth located at the very end of the furrow, which bends forward along the dorsal side of the body, but along the course of the groove there are numerous small apertures which also serve for ingestion of food. The origin of these apertures has so far not been sufficiently studied; it is possible, however, that they represent parts of the true oral aperture, which had separated from it as it moved backwards with the development of the furrow. In that case the small apertures are homologous with the true mouth, which had multiplied in this curious ciliate.

Various types of digestive enzymes have been found in a number of Protozoa. Thus the proteolytic enzymes (peptidase, proteinase, pepsin-like enzyme) have been detected in *Amoeba proteus, Pelomyxa, Tetrahymena, Paramecium, Colpidium,* and *Frontonia*. In the food-vacuoles of *Paramecium multimicronucleatum, Tetrahymena pyriformis, T. corlissi,* and *Amoeba proteus* non-specific esterases and acid phosphatases were revealed which seemed to play a significant role in the intracellular digestion (Seaman, 1961; Holter and Lowy, 1959; Müller and Törö, 1962; Müller, Toth, and Törö, 1962; and others). The presence of such hydrolytic enzymes in the food-vacuoles of Protozoa allowed some authors (Müller, Toth, and Törö, 1961; Müller and Törö, 1962) to consider these vacuoles, on certain stages of digestion, as lysosomes in the broad sense of the word. According to Novikoff (1959, 1961), lysosomes are cytoplasmic structures which are bounded by a unit membrane and contain a wide array of acid hydrolases. Their main function is the storage and breakdown of material ingested by cells. Diastase has been found in *Balantidium,* some Ophryoscolecidae (Fig. 123), and other ciliates; and in amoebae and Foraminifera, which therefore are able to utilize some polysaccharides, for example, starch, for their growth. Isotricha from the rumen of the ruminants also ingest starch; they can therefore be maintained in a culture not only on glucose but also on starch (Sugden and Oxford, 1952). However, *Dasytricha* does not feed on starch, and probably does not contain diastase.

As has been noted from fermentation reactions of extracts obtained from Protozoa, some of them may utilize disaccharides. Thus *Leishmania* consume saccharose, while *Trichomonas* also utilizes maltose and lactose.

Cleveland (1924, 1925) has found in Polymastigida and Hypermastigida cellulase and cellobiase which act on cellulose. These two enzymes are secreted by a vast majority of the flagellates inhabiting the digestive tract of termites in such quantities that they may provide enough products of decomposition of cellulose for the nutrition not only of themselves but also of their hosts.

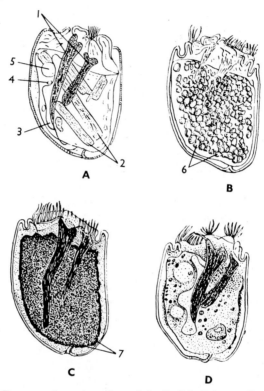

FIG. 123.   Ingestion of starch in *Eudiplodinium medium*.

(*A*) ciliate beginning to feed; (*B*) 10 minutes after start of feeding; cytoplasm is filled with starch; (*C*) 2½ hours later, the cytoplasm is filled with glycogen; (*D*) 16 hours later, only residues of glycogen are left. 1, skeletal plates; 2, fragments of grass; 3, macronucleus; 4, micronucleus; 5, vacuole; 6, starch; 7, glycogen. (After Westphal, 1934.)

In the same way cellulose in the digestive tract of the ungulates is assimilated mainly as a result of the enzyme activity of bacteria and some of the ciliates Entodiniomorpha which break up the cellulose, since the digestive juices of the ungulates have no enzymes acting on cellulose. Cellulase was found in *Diplodinium neglectum*, *D. magii*, and *D. multivesiculatum*, and cellobiase, hydrolyzing disaccharides, was detected also in *Dasytricha*. However, these enzymes were not found in *Entodinium caudatum* (Hungate, 1955).

It should be noted that *Diplodium* grows in cultures only in the presence of dried grass and pure cellulose (Hungate, 1942), and the duration of life of these ciliates, for instance *D. medium*, in cultures is greatly increased in the presence of an adequate amount of cellulose (Sugden and Oxford, 1952).

Fats are also digested by Protozoa; Dawson and Belkin (1928) have injected various oils into *Amoeba dubia* and have found that 1·4 to 8·3 per cent. of the fats introduced into them were digested by the amoebae. The possibility of digestion of neutral fat by amoebae is stated by Mast (1938). The ciliates probably also possess some lipatic enzymes, as shown indirectly by changes in the fat content of the cytoplasm at different periods of the ciliate's life.

Pinocytosis

In addition to phagocytosis, observed among the Protozoa in the members of the Rhizopoda and of certain Flagellata, there exists also a process of ingestion of liquid food through the surface of the body called pinocytosis. This term is derived from the Greek word πίνειν meaning 'drink'. Lewis (1931) was the first to discover this phenomenon of active drinking by cells in a tissue culture and proposed that it should be called pinocytosis. A similar process in unicellular organisms was first noted by Mast and Doyle (1934), who investigated the behaviour of *Amoeba proteus* in a protein solution. In subsequent years pinocytosis was closely investigated not only in the Metazoan cells, but mainly in unicellular organisms, such as various amoebae (*Amoeba, Pelomyxa (Chaos)*) and ciliates (*Paramecium* and others) (Chapman-Andresen and Holter, 1955; Brandt, 1958; Holter, 1959; Roth, 1960, and others). In the former pinocytosis was observed to take place mainly through the surface of the body, while in the latter it proceeded only from food-vacuoles directly into the cytoplasm.

During pinocytosis the liquid is imbibed by a cell intermittently, through definite parts of the body, and not continuously as in the case of diffusion through the whole surface of the body. In fact, pinocytosis represents a mechanism by means of which solutions are conveyed through the cellular membrane (Brandt, 1958).

Pinocytosis is stimulated by the presence of various active substances in the medium surrounding the cell, such as some proteins and many salts. In amoeba, for instance, pinocytosis is intensified under the action of gamma-globulin in a 0·01 M solution of NaCl; whereas sugars do not induce pinocytosis and do not enter the cytoplasm through the surface of the body. Amoebae immersed in a solution of glucose do not absorb it, but if the amoeba *Chaos chaos* (*Pelomyxa carolinensis*) is immersed in a medium containing labelled glucose mixed with gamma-globulin, which induces pinocytosis, then the labelled glucose penetrates into the cytoplasm through the plasmolemma comparatively rapidly (in 45 minutes) and accumulates in the pinocytic vacuoles (Chapman-Andresen and Holter, 1955). The activation of pinocytosis is apparently associated with the adsorption on the surface of charged molecules and a change of the surface tension of the cellular membrane.

Substances activating pinocytosis in amoeba cause the formation of folds of plasmolemma on separate parts of the body, in which it sinks into the cytoplasm. Such an invagination of the plasmolemma leads in various amoeba (*Amoeba proteus, Chaos chaos*) to the formation of a thin tubular canal running from the periphery to the inside of the body. Minute drops of protein or of other liquid substances, present in the nutritive medium, are engulfed by the small folds of the plasmolemma and enter the canal. The liquid moves along the canal and at its end it is surrounded by a vacuole the wall of which represents part of the invaginated external cell membrane. This vacuole at the end of the canal is called the pinocytic vacuole. Its diameter is approximately 1 μ. The pinocytic canals formed in amoeba usually become separated from the plasmolemma and frequently break up into small droplets or vacuoles. By means of gamma-globulin labelled with fluorescein it is possible not only to determine the rate of pinocytosis (the rate of the formation of pinocytic vacuoles does not exceed 30–50 minutes), but also to calculate the amount of liquid consumed (Holter and Marshall, 1954). The labelled albumen present in the medium in which the amoeba were cultivated was later detected in the pinocytic vacuoles. Holter and Marshall (1954) established that after 3 hours the quantity of labelled gamma-globulin attains 30 per cent. of the original cell volume.

It has been established that pinocytosis does not take place through the entire surface of the body of the amoeba, but occurs only in certain parts of it.

The physiological significance of pinocytosis apparently consists of the ability of the cell to absorb high molecular compounds from the external medium in this way. However, the problem of how these substances overcome the membranous barrier and emerge from the pinocytic vacuoles into the cytoplasm remains unsolved. In other words, it is not quite clear how the protozoal cell utilizes these high-molecular substances. Holter (1955) had suggested that the membrane of the pinocytic vacuole is digested by the enzymes present in the cytoplasm and that in this way the contents of the vacuole are discharged into the cytoplasm. This opinion is based on the assumed instability of cytoplasmic structures in relation to their own enzymes. Holter also considers another possibility, namely an alteration in the permeability of the membrane of the pinocytic vacuole, resulting in its content being discharged into the cytoplasm. However, this problem is still unsolved and in need of further investigation.

An investigation of the process of digestion in various species of *Pelomyxa* by electron microscopy has shown that the liquid products of digestion are removed from the food-vacuole by pinocytosis. The membrane of the food-vacuole forms in different places small protrusions into the surrounding cytoplasm, which become detached from the vacuole in the form of small bubbles, and as a result of this minute pinocytic vacuoles filled with liquid are formed. Since these vacuoles are extremely small, the process of their formation is known as micro-pinocytosis (Roth, 1960). A similar process has also been observed in *Paramecium aurelia* (Jurand, 1961), in which minute secondary vacuoles are formed around the old food-vacuoles by means of a process very similar to pinocytosis. The formation of such secondary vacuoles, the walls of which are formed from the membrane of the old vacuole, probably leads to an increase of the surface of absorption, thereby creating conditions for a more rapid assimilation by the organism of large amounts of products of digestion.

Excretion and secretion

The function of the excretory apparatus is to free the organism from an excess of water absorbed by it and from the products of metabolism accumulated in its plasm. This apparatus as a specific structure is absent in many Protozoa and the excretion of the final products of metabolism, apparently, takes place by osmosis through the whole surface of the body. This diffusion type of excretion is characteristic mainly for those Protozoa which do not require any special elimination of water from their body since they live in media with a higher osmotic pressure. Therefore excretion by diffusion takes place almost exclusively in marine or endoparasitic organisms: in all Foraminifera and Radiolaria and all Sporozoa, in endo-parasitic amoebae and flagellates, and in some (but not all) endoparasitic ciliates. In cases where the function of excretion is combined with that of osmo-regulation, it is effected by a special apparatus—contractile vacuoles or diverse modifications of them.

Contractile vacuoles

The morphology of contractile vacuoles. The majority of Protozoa (except Sporozoa) have a special, more or less strictly localized, and some-times very complex excretory apparatus, in most cases in the form of the so-called contractile or pulsating vacuoles.

As a general rule all freshwater Mastigophora, Sarcodina, and all ciliates possess vacuoles. Mastigophora have in most cases only one contractile vacuole, rarely two (Phytomastigina).

Certain forms of flagellates may possess up to sixteen vacuoles (*Chloro-gonium*). The majority of freshwater Amoebina also have one vacuole, ex-cept the large, multinucleate forms, for instance *Pelomyxa*, which have a considerable number of small vacuoles. Testacea usually have one vacuole, Heliozoa one, two, or several. The greatest variety in the number of vacuoles is observed in ciliates, where the excretory apparatus in general reaches its highest development. It may be assumed, however, that here, too, the original number was one vacuole, and the increase in their number may be regarded as a result of polymerization, which finds expression in a whole series of organoids in the course of the evolution of the phylum Protozoa (see p. 549). The number of vacuoles varies from 1 to 100 in different ciliates. The greatest variety in number is observed in Holotricha, while Peritricha, Heterotricha, and Hypotricha have usually 1 vacuole each. The increase in the number of vacuoles is easily observed in the suborder Entodiniomorpha, of the family Ophryoscolecidae. The genus *Entodinium*, which is the most primitive and the smallest in size, has only 1 vacuole, the genera *Anoplodinium* and *Eudiplodinium*, characterized by 2 vacuoles, have a more complex structure, the genus *Ostracodinium* has 2–4 vacuoles, and, finally, the most highly differentiated and more recently developed genera *Caloscolex* and *Ophryoscolex* are provided with 10–15 vacuoles. Moreover, the increase in the number of vacuoles coincides with the increase in the size of the body in Ophryoscolecidae. In the large Ophryoscolecidae, *Polydinium* and *Elephantophilus*, parasitic in the alimentary tract of elephants, the number of vacuoles reaches 30 and more. The number of vacuoles may frequently serve as a reliable criterion of species. Thus in the genus *Paramecium* 7 species have 2 vacuoles each, 1 species has only 1 (*P. putrinum*), and 1 species from 3 to 4 vacuoles (*P. multimicronucleatum*).

The size of the vacuole apparatus is in general proportional to that of the body and inversely proportional to the number of vacuoles in the body of the animal. Thus the large Heterotricha (*Stentor*, *Spirostomum*) have only one vacuole, but (together with its canals) it attains a very large size. *Trachelius ovum* has up to 30 vacuoles, but they are very small.

In some cases there is an increase in the number of vacuoles with the growth of the animal, as for example in *Collinia branchiarum* and some other Astomata. This increase in the number of vacuoles, which in *Collinia* (*Anoplophrya*) occurs during its individual life, apparently took place during the evolution of the whole group Astomata (Fig. 124). And indeed, among them may be noted a whole series of forms in which the vacuole apparatus becomes more and more complex. Thus in *Dogielella* there is only one subterminally situated vacuole; the genus *Anoplophrya* has one longitudinal row of a small number of vacuoles; in the general *Bütschliella* and *Monodontophrya* the number of vacuoles in this row is greatly increased, while in *Radiophrya* the vacuoles form two longitudinal rows. Finally, in the genus *Haptophrya* the numerous vacuoles of a row coalesce into one common longitudinal vacuolar canal, a row of separate efferent apertures bearing evidence of its origin.

In the Sarcodina and Mastigophora the entire excretory apparatus is limited to the vacuole only. In a few flagellates (for instance *Euglena*) the contractile vacuole is surrounded by a circlet of small collecting vacuoles which are connected with it by means of fine canals. Papas and Brandt (1958) believe that in *Amoeba* water enters the vacuole as the result of the discharge into it of small vesicles lying round it, by the coalescence of the membranes of these vesicles with the central vacuole. The collecting vacuoles in ciliates are usually equipped with one or several afferent pulsating canals: *Spirostomum* has one such canal, *Stentor* two, *Frontonia* ten long ones, &c. The canals apparently radiate to a much greater distance in the cytoplasm than is visible under the microscope. At least when *Paramecium* is treated with osmic acid, the continuation of the peripheral ends into long, fine, terminal branches becomes visible. Fluid (i.e. mainly water) is taken in by the collecting vacuoles and the afferent canals from the cytoplasm and transported to the contractile vacuole. The entire vacuolar apparatus of the ciliates lies within the endoplasm and does not change its position in the body. Some interesting data on the electron-microscopical structure of the contractile vacuole and of the afferent canals of *Paramecium caudatum* were published by Schneider (1960). According to Nassonov (1924) the afferent canals are surrounded by an osmiophilic muff, and according to Gelei (1925) by sponge-like plasm (Nierenplasma or Nephridialplasma).

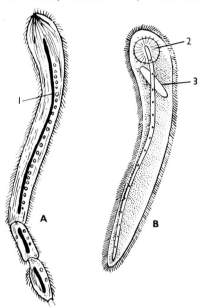

FIG. 124. Contractile vacuole in stomatous ciliates.

(*A*) *Radiophyra hoplites* with numerous vacuoles arranged in one row; (*B*) *Haptophrya gigantea* with a contractile canal and multitude of pores. 1, 3, macronucleus; 2, sucker. (After Chejsin, 1930.)

According to Schneider's investigations, this region of the plasm surrounding the afferent canals (nephridial canals) is composed of numerous fine, convoluted tubes with osmiophilic walls (Fig. 125). The lumen of these tubes during systole is equal to 100 Å, and during diastole to 150 Å. The whole layer of nephridial plasm is $1-1·5 \mu$ thick. On its periphery the tubes pass directly into the small canals of the endoplasmic reticulum, which penetrate the whole body of *Paramecium* (Fig. 125). Moreover, the nephridial plasm is also surrounded by special tubules with osmiophilic walls, which are sometimes arranged in bundles. Their diameter attains 500 Å, while their length is about 1μ.

The afferent canals have an osmiophilic membrane. During systole this canal becomes slit-like, with a lumen of about 300 Å, while during diastole it widens up to 4000 Å. The small tubules surrounding the afferent canal open into it only during diastole, when they increase in diameter, whereas during systole these tubules are closed and are not connected with the canal. The afferent canal at its proximal end passes directly into the ampulla, which opens into the reservoir of the vacuole through the small terminal canal. Within the walls of the ampulla and the terminal canal there are tubular contractile fibrils arranged in several bundles. From the walls of the

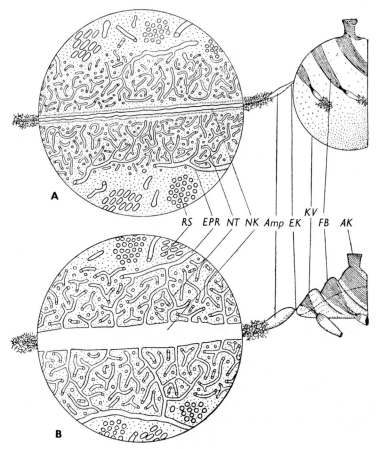

RS EPR NT NK Amp EK KV FB AK

FIG. 125. Diagram of contractile vacuole with collecting canal and surrounding cytoplasm in *Paramecium*: as revealed by electron-microscopy. (After Schneider, 1960.)

(*A*) radial canal in stage of systole; contractile vacuole at stage of diastole. (*B*) radial canal in diastole, contractile vacuole in systole. *AK*, efferent canal of vacuole; *Amp*, ampulla of peripheral canal; *EK*, canal connecting ampulla with contractile vacuole; *EPR*, canals.

terminal canal they pass directly to the wall of the reservoir of the contractile vacuole, where they are also distributed in separate bundles (Fig. 125).

According to Rudzinska (1957), in *Tokophrya infusionum* in the cytoplasm around the vacuoles are concentrated minute vesicles of ergastoplasm and accumulations of mitochondria. Moreover, structures comparable to dictyosomes were found round the vacuole. They apparently take part in the secretion and accumulation of fluid entering from the cytoplasm.

Some differences in the structure of the vacuolar apparatus are found in certain endoparasitic ciliates whose vacuoles have a delayed rate of action. Contractile vacuoles in Ophryoscolecidae from the stomach of ruminants have, according to MacLennan (1933), no walls of their own: they are formed by a simple fusion of small collecting vacuoles, which in their turn are formed anew at every pulsation within the granular area of the ectoplasm surrounding the contractile vacuole (Fig. 126). The interior end of the

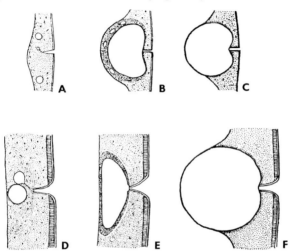

FIG. 126. Diagram of pulsation of a contractile vacuole of *Ophryoscolecidae.*

(*A*)–(*C*) in *Polyplastron multivesiculatum*; (*D*)–(*F*) in *Eudiplodinium maggii*. (After MacLennan, 1933.)

efferent duct of the vacuole is closed by a thin membrane during systole. Strelkov (1939) has found around the efferent canal of *Cycloposthium* a distinct annular fibril, probably representing a myoneme, which regulates the elimination of the fluid through the canal to the exterior. In all the ciliates the excretory aperture of the contractile vacuole is a preformed pore. It is usually round or oval and has a constant position among the rows of cilia, which is characteristic for every species. In the genus *Conchophthirus* the opening has the form of a narrow slit with a thickened margin. Possibly this shape of pore in *Conchophthirus* has a certain functional significance connected with its closing. Namely here its closing is probably effected by the edges of the slit coming together, like two lips, rather than by annular constriction of the efferent canal. The pore opens into the efferent canal, which is usually very short but sometimes (*Paramecium putrinum*) forms several looplike coils. The presence of a permanent pore and excretory canal surrounded by fibrils (180 Å thick) which cause it to contract (Rudzinska, 1957) was confirmed by electron-microscopic examination of the contractile vacuole of *Tokophrya infusionum*. Similar fibrils were detected in *Paramecium* by Schneider (1960).

The functional significance of contractile vacuoles

The process of contraction of pulsating vacuoles. Vacuoles operate rhythmically, alternately dilating (diastole stage) and being gradually filled with fluid, and then suddenly contracting (systole stage) and expelling their contents through the efferent canal to the exterior. Where special afferent canals are present, the contraction cycles of the whole apparatus become more complicated; namely, the cycle begins with the dilatation of the canals, while the vacuole is at the systole stage (diastole of the canals); this is followed by contraction of the canals (systole) and a discharge of their contents into the contractile vacuole, causing its systole; at the same time the canals begin to dilate again. Actually, corresponding stages also exist in vacuoles devoid of a system of canals, but there they are either not well marked or not all noticeable, since during diastole of the vacuole minute vesicles which are irregularly distributed in the surrounding medium pour out their contents into the vacuole (see Ophryoscolecidae, Fig. 126).

The rate of pulsation varies in different Protozoa, and it also changes in the same species as a result of a change in the factors of the environment. Thus in various freshwater Protozoa the intervals (in seconds) between the pulsations at different temperatures are as follows:

Name of organism	3° C.	5° C.	8° C.	10° C.	14° C.	18–20° C.	24–25° C.	27° C.	30–32° C.
Euglena	..	..	..	..	..	30	..	..	22
Vorticella	..	60	..	..	23	..	8	..	..
Euplotes charon	..	61	..	48	..	..	..	..	23
Stylonychia pustulata	18	..	..	14	6	..	23	4	4
Chilodonella cucullulus	9	..	..	7	..	4	4	..	..
Glaucoma colpidium	110	..	50	..	..	19	..	6·5	5·5

The pulsation of contractile vacuoles in marine ciliates which possess them is slower than in freshwater ones. Thus in the marine ciliate *Acineria* the interval between two pulsations is equal to 6–12 minutes at room temperature. Among the freshwater ciliates *Spirostomum* is notable for the slow pulsation-rate at room temperature, the interval between two pulsations reaching 30–40 minutes. Chejsin (1952) has noted a remarkable dependence of the rhythm of pulsation of the contractile vacuole in the parasitic ciliates *Astomata* on the host's habitat. He studied the rate of pulsation of the vacuoles in Astomata of the alimentary tract of oligochaetes living in different biotopes, namely in freshwater, marine, and soil oligochaetes. It was established that the rate of pulsation of the contractile vacuole is not uniform in all Astomata, but depends on the osmotic conditions of the medium inhabited by the host. Thus in *Mesnilella clavata* and *Haptophrya secans* from freshwater oligochaetes the pulsation is just as frequent as in free-living freshwater ciliates, viz. the pulsation does not exceed one per minute (20–30 sec.).

In *Radiophrya*, from the marine oligochaete *Enchytraeus* sp., observed in the littoral zone of the Barents Sea, pulsation takes place every 6–8 minutes.

Finally, in *Metaradiophrya lumbrici* and *Anoplophrya lumbrici* from the alimentary tract of the soil oligochaete *Eisenia foetida* and in *Mesnilella fastigata* and *Radiophrya prolifera* from soil oligochaete *Enchytraeus* sp. the rate of pulsation is slower (1·5–4 minutes) than in freshwater ciliates, and somewhat more rapid than in Astomata from marine oligochaetes. Thus in related species of the ciliates Astomata there is an essential physiological difference in the adaptation to environments varying in osmotic conditions. The isotonic medium for ciliates from freshwater worms is 0·4 per cent. Ringer's solution, while for ciliates from the alimentary tract of soil worms it is 0·75–0·8 per cent. Ringer's solution, and for marine forms 3 per cent. of the solution.

In general the pulsation of vacuoles in parasitic ciliates from marine and terrestrial hosts is considerably retarded. In a number of ciliates from the intestines of sea urchins the intervals vary from 5 to 20 minutes; in *Entodinium* from the stomach of ruminants this interval is 6 minutes; in *Epidinium* from ruminants the intervals vary from 2 to 45 minutes; in *Cycloposthium* from the alimentary tract of horses from 25 seconds to 2 minutes.

These wide variations in parasitic ciliates depend, probably, partly on the fact that the animals are observed under conditions not quite normal for them.

As early as 1910 Zuelzer demonstrated the influence of changes of the amount of salts in the surrounding medium on the rate of vacuolar pulsations. She showed that in the course of adaptation to sea water *Amoeba verrucosa* exhibits a gradual retardation of the pulsation of its vacuole when starting from a salt concentration of 0·3 per cent., the vacuole disappearing completely at a salt concentration of 1·5 per cent., and reappearing on a gradual dilution of the culture with fresh water. Similarly Herfs (1922) obtained for *Paramecium*, in the course of adaptation to life in sodium chloride solutions and in fresh water, the following data:

		0	0·25	0·5	9·75	1
Percentage of salt in water		0	0·25	0·5	9·75	1
Interval between pulsations in seconds . .		6·2	9·3	18·4	24·8	163
Amount of fluid expelled in an hour, in volumes of the body		4·8	2·82	1·38	1·08	0·16

In general the amount of fluid expelled through the vacuoles during definite period, other conditions being equal, is proportional to the rate of pulsation and may differ greatly in various Protozoa. For instance, the contractile vacuole of *Uronema nigricans* at a temperature of 28° expels in 2 minutes a volume of water equal to that of the body of the ciliate, while *Euplotes patella* requires 14 minutes for this operation, and *Paramecium aurelia* 46 minutes.

The physiological significance of contractile vacuoles

The vacuoles apparently have multiple functions. First of all, there are reasons to believe that the vacuoles serve for the elimination of the final products of metabolism accumulated in the body. This was suggested in the last century by Stein (1878) and others, but Howland (1924) was the first to demonstrate indirectly the excretion of uric acid by Protozoa. She found uric acid in cultures of paramecia and amoebae, its concentration increasing approximately proportionately to the time of maintenance of the culture. Novikov (1908), Shumwey (1917), and Flather (1919) have shown the increase of frequency in the rhythm of pulsation of the vacuoles in ciliates fed on thyroid gland, under the effect of epinephrine or extract of epiphysis, while the vacuoles themselves increased in size, i.e. a stimulation of excretion was obtained under the effect of the same substances which cause diuresis in vertebrates.

Weatherby (1927) detected urea in the fluid of the contractile vacuole of *Spirostomum*, obtained by means of a micropipette. However, according to calculations made by this investigator, only one per cent. of the urea excreted by mass cultures of *Spirostomum* is expelled by the vacuole.

In general, however, the data on the nature of the nitrogen products excreted are most contradictory. Apart from uric acid and urea, some investigators detected, instead of these substances, ammonia as a product of excretion (for instance in *Glaucoma* and *Spirostomum*). However, the fact that intravital stains introduced into the plasm are not excreted by contractile vacuoles does not wholly support their excretory function; in this respect they differ from the higher animals, since in the latter intravital stains are frequently eliminated through the kidneys and other excretory organs.

It has been repeatedly suggested that the contractile vacuoles have something to do with the respiratory metabolism of Protozoa in helping to remove carbon dioxide from the cytoplasm; however, there is no direct evidence of a specific activity of this kind on the part of the vacuole. Only the indirect data obtained by Ludwig (1928) on the correlation between the actual amount of carbonic acid excreted through the vacuole and the estimated amount discharged by the animal led this investigator to postulate the respiratory function of the vacuole.

At present most authors insist on the significance of the contractile vacuole as an osmoregulating apparatus. As early as 1905 Degen demonstrated that the cytoplasm of freshwater Protozoa has, owing to the presence in it of salts, a higher osmotic pressure than the surrounding medium; this leads to a continuous imbibition of water by the cytoplasm. The expulsion of the continuously absorbed excess of water by the plasm is a function of the contractile vacuole. Were it not for this expulsion of water by the vacuolar apparatus, it is possible that the body of freshwater Protozoa would be dissolved in the surrounding water. The correctness of this view was confirmed both by the character of the distribution of the contractile vacuoles among the Protozoa and by experiments on the adaptation of freshwater Protozoa to water with an increasing salt concentration (Loefer, 1939; Finley, 1930; and others). In an experimental investigation on the pulsation of the vacuole of *Paramecium caudatum*, Seravin (1958) has shown that during the first 15–30 minutes after the transfer of ciliates into salt solutions of increased concentration the rate of pulsation of the vacuoles is decreased many times, after which it is gradually accelerated, approaching that of the control ciliates, though usually not reaching this level. For instance in 0·2 per cent. sodium chloride the rate of pulsation after 30 minutes was on the average 40·5 sec., and after 48 hours it had reached 13·1 sec.; while in the control ciliates the pulsation proceeded at a rate of 10·3 sec. The same was observed in solutions of 0·1 per cent. lithium chloride, 0·5 per cent. calcium chloride, and 1 per cent. saccharose in urea solution. There was a retardation of 7–15 times, but in 2 days the rate of pulsation in these solutions was slowed down only by 1·5–3 times. In lower salt concentrations a complete restoration of the rate of pulsation of the vacuole was observed. Substances like hydrochloric acid, sodium hydroxide, cadmium chloride, and formalin in very low concentrations caused slight retardation of pulsation, which soon returned to normal. Adrenalin in 0·0005 per cent. concentration even caused an increase of water exchange, but eventually the pulsation likewise returned to normal. Thus similar alterations in the activity of the contractile vacuole are caused by osmotically active and non-active substances. There is thus a general tendency to control the water current passing through the cytoplasm of ciliates by an alteration in the rate of the pulsation of the contractile vacuole. Moreover, the ciliates adapt themselves to changing conditions in the osmotic pressure of their environment. This has been noted by Kitching (1952) for *Carchesium* and *Podophrya*, in which at high concentrations of ethylene-glycol and saccharose there is a complete cessation of the activity of the vacuole, but after a while its pulsation and water exchange are restored.

All this points to a complex mechanism of activity on the part of the contractile vacuole, which plays an essential role in the water exchange of ciliates. Seravin thinks, however, that since osmotically inactive substances cause a retardation in the pulsation of the vacuoles it is possible that water exchange in ciliates is not determined by osmosis, and therefore the role of the contractile vacuole in osmoregulation cannot be considered as proved.

The function of the vacuole cannot be understood without a proper understanding of the mechanism of the circulation of water from the cytoplasm into the reservoir of the vacuole and of the mechanism of contraction of the vacuole itself. Gelei, J. and G. (1928, 1939), and many other investigators believe that the contraction of the reservoir of the vacuole is determined only by turgor tension developing in the cytoplasm and, consequently, by the osmotic conditions. It is also conceivable that there is an active mechanism for the secretion of water into the vacuole (Kitching, 1956). According to Schneider (1960) the pulsation of the vacuole is caused by the activity of contractile fibrils lying in the wall of the vacuole, while the filling of the afferent canals with water proceeds in the following way. The fluid is collected into the canals of the endoplasmic reticulum and then, owing to the diameter of these canals being larger than that of the tubules of the nephridial plasm, a current of water is created flowing from the canals of the endoplasmic reticulum into the tubules of nephridial plasm and from them into the lumen of the canal. Further investigations are, of course, required to obtain a more precise knowledge of the mechanism of these processes. It is possible that the contractile vacuoles have excretory and respiratory functions, but this has not been finally proved.

Contractile vacuole and Golgi apparatus. The problem of the morphological significance of the contractile vacuole entered a new phase after the work of Nasonov (1924, 1925), who expressed the view that the contractile vacuole of the Protozoa is homologous to the Golgi apparatus in the cells of Metazoa. By using the osmium technique on ciliates, Nasonov (1924) and almost simultaneously Gelei, J. (1925), detected important new features in the structure of contractile vacuoles (Fig. 127). Nasonov found that the contractile vacuoles of many ciliates (*Campanella, Lionotus, Paramecium, Nassula*), and of *Chilomonas*, are enclosed in a membrane strongly blackened by reduced osmium. The surface of this membrane is either smooth or is surrounded by a layer of minute granules, stained grey with osmium. The membrane either encloses the whole vacuole (in species mentioned above) or appears like a reticulated ring encircling the vacuole around its equator (*Chilodon, Dogielella*). In forms with a system of afferent canals (*Paramecium*) the membrane extends over these; moreover, the canals can be traced in the endoplasm much further than by any other method of examination, and their distal parts are enclosed in a reticulated, grey muff. Nasonov regards this portion of the canals as the actual excretory part of the apparatus, while the proximal part of the canals and the vacuole itself represent only the efferent part of the vacuolar system. In *Dogielella* Nasonov found that during the systole of the vacuole the back ring encircling it does not follow its contraction, but remains in its previous position. Gelei, J. (1925), attempted to compare it with the nephridial system of Metazoa, equating the contractile vacuole itself with the urinary bladder and other parts of the apparatus with other sections of the nephridia. However, Nasonov merely emphasized the similarity between the osmiophilic membrane of the vacuoles and the Golgi apparatus in Metazoa. In fact, his figures showing various types of contractile vacuoles and Golgi apparatus, taken from diverse types of cells in Metazoa, are most convincing in their similarity.

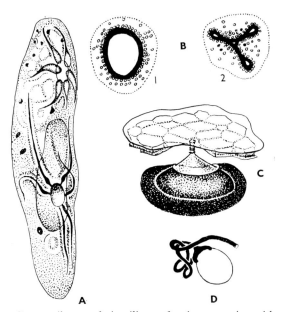

FIG. 127. Contractile vacuole in ciliates after impregnation with osmium.

(A) *Paramecium caudatum*, total preparation; (B) *Campanella* (1, diastole; 2, systole) (after Nasonov, 1924); (C) *Cycloposthium*, showing external pore, efferent canal, and sphincter (from Strelkov, 1939); (D) efferent canal of vacuole in *Paramecium trichium* (after King, 1928).

Therefore Nasonov considers it possible to detect in the osmiophilic spongy membrane of the afferent canals of *Paramecium* and reticular ring of *Dogielella* not only a morphological but also a functional analogy between these structures and the Golgi apparatus. The reticular nature of the substance of the ring is due to the presence in it of small collecting vacuoles —the stage of bound secretion. These small vacuoles then coalesce to form the central vacuole in the middle of the ring—the stage of free secretion, discharged to the exterior. In Nasonov's opinion, the Golgi apparatus serves for the collection of certain substances from the plasm, which accumulate in it and are then expelled from the body through the vacuole. The data obtained by Nasonov were later confirmed by a number of investigators (Strelkov, 1939, on Cycloposthiidae; Fauré-Fremiet, 1925, on *Verticella*; King, 1928, on *Paramecium multimicronucleatum, Euplotes*, and others). It is true, that in some Protozoa no special osmiophilic membrane was detected around the vacuole, but this might have been due to differences in the method used.

Many authors have accepted Nasonov's point of view, but there are also not a few opponents of his concept.

If the osmiophilic cover round the contractile vacuole is considered as a homologue of the Golgi apparatus, the question arises as to what form the latter takes in Protozoa without vacuoles, such as many Sporozoa, the parasitic Sarcodina, and Flagellata. The Golgi apparatus is encountered in all metazoan cells either as a reticulate structure or as one consisting of separate dictyosomes. Therefore it may be assumed that it also occurs in all unicellular organisms. And, indeed, the investigations by Hirschler (1927), Hovasse (1937), Joyet-Lavergne (1926), and others have shown that the cytoplasm of many Protozoa (Gregarines, Coccidia, Flagellata, Sarcodina) contains minute rods, rings, and spheres with a strongly osmiophilic margin which are very similar to the dictyosomes of metazoan cells.

In Metazoa the characteristic features of the Golgi apparatus are its ability to reduce specifically some compounds of heavy metals—silver and osmium—which is manifested in the blackening of the structures of the apparatus. These structures are not intravitally stained by neutral red or methylene blue. Dictyosomes, composed of two parts, chromophobe and chromophile, are frequently characteristic features of the Golgi apparatus. The secretion granules are usually embedded in the chromophobe part. As a rule, the Golgi apparatus is located in the secretory zone of the cell.

The structural unity of the Golgi apparatus in various metazoan cells has been demonstrated by electron microscopy. Double membranes (or γ-cyto-membranes according to Sjöstrand) arranged parallel to each other and forming a system of 3–7 or more pairs were found in all the cells examined. Each pair delimits a lighter space 50–200 Å wide, forming as it were a flat sac. Sometimes it is dilated to the size of a large vacuole. The membranes are embedded in a finely granular basic substance. In a number of cases membranes may surround vacuoles of various sizes. All these structures are fairly stable.

It is significant that the patterns of the Golgi apparatus obtained by light microscopy in metazoan cells by Nasonov and other investigators and the patterns obtained recently by electron microscopy are in complete conformity.

Dalton and Felix (1957) note also that the contractile vacuole of *Chlamydomonas* is limited by membranes similar to those of the Golgi apparatus metazoan cells; thus they support Nasonov's hypothesis regarding the homology of these organelles. Round the contractile vacuole of the ciliates *Campanella* and *Ophridium* are situated numerous tubules with dense osmiophilic walls, which may to a certain extent be compared with the ultra-structures of the Golgi apparatus (Fauré-Fremiet and Rouiller, 1959). However, Schneider's data mentioned above, regarding the structure of the nephridial plasma surrounding the afferent canals of the contractile vacuole of *Paramecium*, make it difficult to homologize its structure with the ultra-structure of the dictyosomes.

The homology of the osmiophilic membranes of the contractile vacuoles and the Golgi apparatus had already been denied earlier by French authors (Duboscq and Grassé, 1933; Grassé and Hollande, 1941), who thought that the osmiophilic walls of the vacuoles and the contractile vacuoles themselves are structures completely independent of the Golgi apparatus.

It should be noted that some ciliates, for example *Balantidium elongatum*, possess crescentic or ring-shaped dictyosomes which are not connected with the vacuoles (Villeneuve-Brachon, 1940). Noirot-Timothée (1957) has established by electron microscopy the presence in the endoplasm of certain Ophryoscolecidae of typical Golgi apparatus not linked with a contractile vacuole.

French investigators consider the parabasal body as a homologue of Golgi apparatus (see p. 133) because this structure, especially when examined by an electron microscope, proved to be similar to dictyosomes in cells of Metazoa (Fig. 81).

However, further comparative investigations are required to solve the problem regarding the homology of various structures of Protozoa with the Golgi apparatus in metazoan cells.

Other excretory organoids of protozoa

Pusules of dinoflagellates. All Dinoflagellata sometimes possess a most complicated system of special large vacuoles, called pusules by Schütt. In their appearance they are somewhat like a system of contractile vacuoles, but they do not display regular pulsation, but only rare, non-periodical changes in volume. This apparatus reaches an exceptional complexity in those dinoflagellates which are provided with a cellulose membrane and are at the same time devoid of chromatophores. The pusule apparatus in them is composed of several parts: the sac-like pusule, the collecting pusule, small supplementary pusules, and one or two efferent canals.

The canals open at the crossing of the longitudinal and transverse furrows apparently near the base of the flagella. The pusules contain a pinkish fluid. Kofoid and Swezy (1921) deny any similarity between the pusules and the contractile vacuoles, not only in their structure but also in their function. They have observed in *Gymnodinium* that the function of the pusules is to absorb water into the body. This does not take place gradually, but by a sudden inflow of water into the pusules. This is facilitated by a definite direction of the flagellar movement. Therefore Kofoid suggests that the pusules represent an apparatus concerned with saprophitic nutrition, especially in zones of mass destruction of plankton, resulting in the accumulation of large amounts of organic substances dissolved in water. However, these observations are in need of verification, especially in view of the fact that the structure of the pusules is in many ways similar to that of the contractile vacuoles.

Canal system of Opalinata. A long, irregularly convoluted canal, passing through the whole body in the endoplasm and opening at the posterior end of it, has been found in *Protoopalina intestinalis* (Fig. 128). This canal does not pulsate.

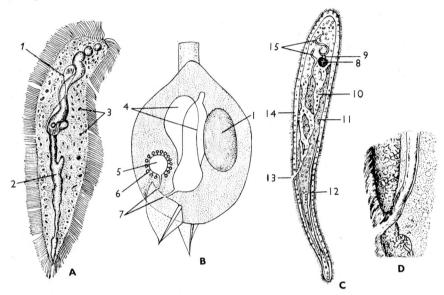

FIG. 128. Excretory apparatus in Protozoa.

(*A*) *Protoopalina intestinalis* (from Metcalf, 1923); (*B*) *Peridinium michaelis* (from Schütt, 1895); (*C*) *Pycnothrix monocystoides* (whole ciliate); (*D*) longitudinal section through the same ciliate at the opening of the ciliated duct of the canal system. 1, nucleus; 2, excretory apparatus; 3, granules of glycogen; 4, sac-like pusule; 5, collecting pusule; 6, afferent vacuoles; 7, efferent ducts of pusules; 8, macronucleus; 9, micronucleus; 10, canal system; 11, endoplasm; 12, ciliated furrow; 13, exterior opening of canal system; 14, ectoplasm; 15, parasitic nematodes. (*C*), (*D*) (from Lühe, 1913).

A system of non-pulsating canals similar to those of the Opalinata is present in a large ciliate from the alimentary tract of hyrax—*Pycnothrix monocystoides* (Fig. 128). These canals branch in the endoplasm and open to the exterior through a common ciliated pore.

Secretory structures are of different character. We have already seen that the Golgi apparatus and the parabasal body have at least partly a secretory function.

Some Protozoa also possess certain structures which apparently perform purely secretory functions, representing a kind of intracellular gland.

Fauré-Fremiet (1925) and Fursenko (1929) describe in swarmers of *Zoothamnium arbuscula* before their attachment an accumulation at the posterior pole of the body of numerous special secretory granules, which serve for the formation of the stalk as they settle down. This structure is particularly pronounced in the swarmer of macrozoid, even before its separation from the colony, when the granules occupy in the body a sharply circumscribed space.

Dogiel (1922) found in *Pseudotrichonympha* a sharply restricted area of the cytoplasm at the base of the tube of the rostrum packed with large round granules. Part of the granules penetrate also into the tube of the rostrum

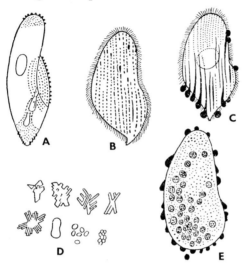

FIG. 129. Process of secretion in ciliates.

(*A*) *Paramecium caudatum*: discharge of neutral red on to surface of body; (*B*) same in *Cryptochilum echini*; (*C*) same in *C. echini* in weak solution of LiCl; (*D*) crystals of calcium phosphate in *P. caudatum*; (*E*) *Glaucoma* sp. discharge of neutral red in weak solution of Li$_2$SO$_4$. (After Dogiel, 1927*b*, and other authors.)

and in certain cases they are expelled from the body through the anterior aperture of the tube, while the cuticular cap of this latter is discarded. The mass of granules discharged outside looks like slime. Thus the area of the granular plasm described represents a kind of gland, the tube of the rostrum serving as its efferent duct.

In some ciliates certain secretions may be discharged through the whole surface of the body. Thus, for example, Nirenstein (1925) observed in *Paramecium*, placed in a dilute solution of neutral red, the appearance after a few hours of minute red drops of the substance secreted throughout the surface of the whole body. Dogiel (1927) described a similar secretion in the parasitic ciliate *Cryptochilum echini*, and its increase under the effect of certain salts (Li$_2$SO$_4$). Moreover, the secretion of the drops stained with neutral red becomes so copious that whole streams of the stained secretion run down the longitudinal furrows of the body (Fig. 129). Andreeva (1929) records similar observations on *Glaucoma* and others, in which the secretion, intensified by the action of salts, appears at first in the form of minute excretory 'pearls', described by Nirenstein, and then as large stained drops. According to the intensity of their effect on the secretion of the 'pearls' the anions and cations of different electrolytes are arranged in the following lyotropic series:

$$J < NO_3 < Cl < SO_4,$$
$$Ca < Mg < K < Na < Li.$$

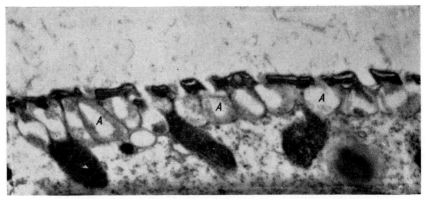

FIG. 130. Secretory ampules (A) under pellicle of *Colpidium colpoda*, secreting tectin from which the gelatinous membrane is formed. (Electron-micrograph × 40,000.)

On the contrary, in the secretion of large drops the lyotropic series are arranged in the reverse order, according to the intensity of their action:

$$SO_4 < Cl < NO_3 < I,$$
$$Li < Na < K < Mg < Ca,$$

i.e. they are arranged in the same order in which these salts cause the haemolysis of erythrocytes or the secretion of pigment from the eggs of the sea-urchin *Arbacia*. The substance which is secreted to form the jelly envelope of *Colpidium colpoda* is shed from special ampulae situated beneath the pellicle and visible only in the electron microscope (Fig. 130).

Respiration of Protozoa. During the process of respiration of a cell metabolites are oxidized, leading to the liberation of energy, which can be used either for synthetic processes or for the accumulation of substances with macro-energetic links.

Some species of Protozoa are obligatory aerobes, others can exist in the presence of a small access of oxygen, and finally a third kind can be either obligatory or facultative anaerobes.

In Protozoa the process of the consumption of oxygen from the external environment does not require the development of complex respiratory mechanisms. Diffusion through the walls of the body, an intensive water exchange, and the movement of the cytoplasm seem to supply adequate amounts of oxygen to the plasm to satisfy the requirements of these organisms. It is probable that their contractile vacuoles take part in the respiratory exchange only indirectly, through frequent water exchange.

Since 1895 numerous papers on the intensity and the level of the absorption of oxygen by different representatives of Protozoa have been published (see Table I).

The intensity of respiration varies in different groups of Protozoa. Thus, for example, it is lower in amoebae than in the ciliates (Vinberg, 1949). By comparing the data obtained by various investigators, Vinberg came to the conclusion that the intensity of respiration in free-living Protozoa is equal to or even higher than that of worms and crustacea (comparable in size with the unicellular organisms). Quantitatively the respiration of amoebae is comparable to tissue respiration of invertebrates and poikilothermic vertebrates. It is interesting to note that the basal metabolism in mice is 2·6 mm.^{3} of oxygen per 1 mg. of live weight per hour, i.e. even at 37° C. it is approximately twice as low as the intensity of the exchange in *Paramecium* at 20° (calculated per 1 mg. of the weight of these ciliates: Vinberg, 1949).

Many parasitic Protozoa, for example malaria parasites, the respiration of which has been studied in sufficient detail, have the same high rate of oxygen consumption (Maier and Coggeshall, 1941; Wendel, 1943; Speck and Evans, 1945; and others).

The rate of oxygen consumption in Protozoa is apparently influenced by a whole series of factors.

Their rate of respiration increases with the rise of temperature of the surrounding medium, i.e. they are typical poikilothermic organisms (Barrat, 1905; Leichsehring, 1925; Pace and Kimura, 1944; Brand, 1946; Pace and Lyman, 1947; and others).

As has been shown by Root (1930), changes in the active reaction of the medium over a wide range do not affect the respiration of *Paramecium caudatum*. Similar data were obtained by Dach (1942) for *Astasia klebsii* and by Reich (1945) for the amoebae *Mayorella palestinensis*. Hall (1941), however, has shown that the rate of respiration in *Colpidium campylum* reaches a maximum at pH 5·5, while in more acid or alkaline solutions a pronounced decrease of oxygen consumption is observed. According to B. Humphrey and G. Humphrey (1948), the respiration of *Paramecium caudatum* depends on the active reaction of the medium, being most intensive at pH 6·6–7·6. A pronounced fall in respiration takes place in the alkaline zone, while in the acid one (up to pH 3·7) it decreases slowly.

The independence of the intensity of respiratory exchange of various Protozoa from the partial pressure of oxygen in the medium has been established by a number of investigators (Lund, 1918; Amberson, 1928; Brand, 1946). A decrease of oxygen consumption was observed only for very low partial pressures of oxygen. However, Specht (1935) has shown that the respiration of *Spirostomum ambiguum* decreases with the diminution of the amount of O_2 contained in the cultural fluid.

Additional investigations are required to explain these contradictions in the available data; and to decide whether they are due to an error in the methods used by some investigators or to the difference in the sensibility of various species of unicellular organisms to pH and to the partial pressure of O_2.

A number of investigators have pointed out that the energy of oxygen consumption depends on the physiological state of the organism.

Lund (1918), having made paramecia starve, observed a lowering of the intensity of their respiration during the first twenty hours of the experiment. In *Bursaria truncatella*, according to the data of Barbarin and Solovjeva (1941, 1948), a pronounced lowering of respiration is observed only during the first 24 hours of their starvation, after which its intensity gradually begins to increase, reaching a maximum on the second or third day. At that time respiration is even more intense than in normally fed individuals.

A considerable decrease in the consumption of oxygen by Protozoa with the age of the culture has been noted by some investigators (Hutchens, 1939; Dach, 1942; Pace, 1945; and others).

Zweibaum (1922) has found that during conjugation the rate of respiration in *Paramecium* increases four times, but after the end of conjugation the rate of oxygen consumption by the ciliates rapidly returns to normal.

As has been established by Boell and Woodruff (1941) respiration of *Paramecium caudatum* is lowered during the period preceding conjugation.

Particularly full data on alterations in the respiratory exchange of ciliates at different stages of their life-cycle are given by Barbarin and Solovjeva (1947, 1948) and Barbarin (1954) in their works on *Bursaria truncatella*. The intervals between two divisions in these ciliates last 26–30 hours. A hundred of these large ciliates were used for each experiment. The oxygen uptake was determined by means of the Warburg apparatus after 6, 18, and 26–30 hours. It was shown that the maximum rate of respiration occurred 18–20 hours after division. Soon after one division and shortly before a new one the rate of respiration fell sharply. Therefore, in the opinion of these authors there is, as it were, an 'ontogenesis' of the cell and one can speak of 'young' and 'old' ciliates.

According to the data of Barbarin and Solovjeva, respiration in *Bursaria* is lowered during the first period of conjugation (3–5 hours) and then rises again, reaching its maximum in exconjugants. During the encystment of *Bursaria* the rate of respiration at first remains unaltered, but twenty-four hours after encystment the absorption of oxygen falls considerably, while two days later it cannot even be recorded by Warburg's respirometer. On the other hand, during the first hours after excystation respiration in *Bursaria* is more intensive than in ordinary individuals.

Biochemical processes connected with aerobic respiration of Protozoa have been comprehensively studied, and at present its main stages, connected with the cytochrome–cytochrome-oxidase system, are known.

The first investigators to study the action on Protozoa of potassium cyanide which, as is well known, inhibits the metal-containing respiratory enzymes (the cytochromes) came to the conclusion that oxygen respiration of unicellular organisms is insensitive to cyanides (Lund, 1918, 1921; Peters, 1929; Gerard and Hyman, 1931; Pitts, 1932; A. Lwoff, 1934; Kitching, 1939; Jahn, 1941). Hence there arose the idea that the catalysis of oxidation proceeds in them according to a quite different scheme than that of metazoan cells. However, it was later proved that the experimental methods used by these investigators were faulty. In the presence of potassium hydroxide the cyanide in the respirometer is distilled from the experimental solution and this leads finally to a rapid restoration of the respiration of the Protozoa, which had fallen at the beginning of the experiment, up to the control level or even higher. By adding small amounts of potassium cyanide to potassium hydroxide, thereby preventing the evaporation of the former first from the experimental solution, Hall (1941) has proved that potassium cyanide in a 0·001 N concentration exerts a strong inhibitory effect on the respiration of *Colpidium campylum*. Earlier, Christophers and Fulton (1938) demonstrated the inhibitory effect of cyanides on the consumption of oxygen by *Plasmodium knowlesi*. The presence of the cytochrome–cytochrome-oxidase system in Protozoa was subsequently proved in numerous investigations on various species, which established the cyanide-sensitivity of aerobic respiration. This was simultaneously demonstrated in 1945 for different species of *Paramecium* by Boell and Pace.

According to Barbarin and Solovjeva (1948) the fluctuations of the rate of respiration, characteristic of different stages of the life-cycle and of various physiological states, are due only to respiration inhibited by cyanides, whereas 'residual respiration' remains at the same level.

Saito and Tamiya (1937) have shown by means of spectrographic analysis the presence of cytochromes *a* and *c* in the cytoplasm of paramecia. By the same method, Baker and Baumberger (1941) have demonstrated the presence of cytochromes a_1, a_2, c, and b in *Tetrahymena pyriformis*. Later it was shown that Protozoa exhibited a high cytochrome-oxidase activity (Boell, 1945; Seaman, 1953).

In this connexion it is interesting to note that haemoglobin was also found in certain ciliates. Its content was found to be very high in the cytoplasm: thus in *Paramecium caudatum* it amounts to 1·12–1·72 per cent., and in *Tetrahymena* to 0·22–0·3 per cent. of their dry weight (Keilin and Ryley, 1953). Keilin (1953) thinks that haemoglobin is included in some aerobic respiratory processes, which have so far not been studied.

In the process of respiration sugars are oxidized to carbon dioxide and water. It is generally accepted (Lardy, 1949; James, 1953) that the first stage of aerobic respiration is a typical glycolysis, as the result of which glucose is converted into two molecules of lactic acid. Only after this does the aerobic process itself begin, during which lactic acid is converted into pyruvic acid (pyruvate) and later into carbon dioxide and water.

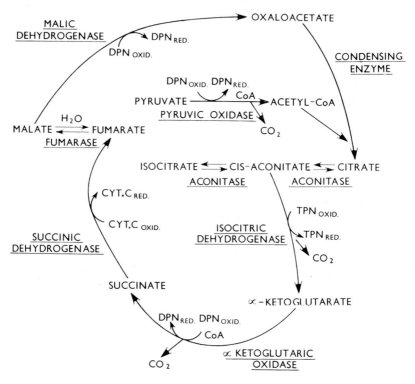

FIG. 131. Cycle of tricarboxylic acids, according to Krebs. Enzymes observed in ciliates are underlined. (After Seaman, 1955.)

Pyruvate is not directly split into carbon dioxide and water but undergoes a series of chemical changes. Pyruvate is only partly oxidized to carbon dioxide and water on condensation with oxaloacetic acid, while its non-oxidized part is used in the formation of citric acid. The further breakdown occurs as a result of the action of a series of special enzymes, which convert citric acid into cis-aconitic and then consecutively into α-ketuglutaric, succinic, fumaric, and malonic acids. The last gives rise to oxalo-acetic acid which can condense with new molecules of pyruvic acid, &c. (Fig. 131). Thus the breakdown of pyruvate into carbon dioxide and water proceeds according to the Krebs cycle of tricarboxylic acids, the occurrence of which was proved for the cells of Metazoa (Lardy, 1949). B. Humphrey and G. Humphrey (1947, 1948) have carried out some experiments on protozoan homogenates, proving the existence of some links of the Krebs cycle in *Paramecium caudatum*. Important investigations on this question have been carried out by Seaman (1955) on *Tetrahymena pyriformis*, who proved most convincingly that in the case of *Tetrahymena* oxidation of the pyruvate proceeds according to the Krebs cycle. As has been demonstrated by the investigations of Speck, Moulder, and Evans (1946), the erythrocytic stages of *Plasmodium gallinaceum* can utilize as a substratum all the acids included in the tricarboxyl acids of the Krebs cycle, except citric and cis-aconitic acids.

The cytochrome–cytochrome-oxidase system is connected with the cycle of the tricarboxylic acids. It should be noted, however, that although KCN inhibits aerobic respiration, it does not stop it completely. Thus in *Paramecium caudatum* the intensity of aerobic respiration is lowered by 40–60 per cent. by the cyanide (Boell, 1946, Nelson and Krueger, 1950); in *Tetrahymena pyriformis* by 18 per cent. in the absence of glucose and by 34 per cent. when it is present in the medium (Ryley, 1953); in amoeba *Mayorella palestinensis* by 47 per cent. (Reich, 1948). This indicates the presence in the cytoplasm of Protozoa of a system (or systems) of aerobic respiration not connected with oxidases containing metals. In this respect also the Protozoa reveal a similarity to multicellular organisms.

Simonsen and Wagtendonk (1952) have found that the respiration of the 'killer' *Paramecium aurelia*, in contrast to that of the 'sensitive' ciliate (see below, p. 502), is not decreased by the action of potassium cyanide. In their opinion, this is due to the fact that the cytochrome system in the 'killer' does not play an essential role and is completely replaced by the flavoprotein system.

In *Tetrahymena pyriformis* respiration is considerably reduced by urethane (M. Lwoff, 1934; Ormsbee and Fisher, 1944). As is known, respiration is lowered by urethane when its mediator is not cytochrome but glutathione. However, the mechanism of aerobic oxidation connected with flavo-proteins and glutathione has not yet been sufficiently investigated in Protozoa. Ball and his collaborators (1945) have discovered in the ery-throcytes of monkeys infected with *Plasmodium knowlesi*, flavinadenin-nucleotid; therefore it may be assumed that *Plasmodium* possess a respiratory enzyme of the flavoprotein type.

Leichsehring (1925) noted that the respiration of *Paramecium caudatum* was more strongly stimulated by proteins and amino-acids than by carbohydrates. Later, Boell (1946) found that the consumption of oxygen by *Paramecium* is invariably linked with the formation of ammonia. As a result of his experiments he concluded that the greater part of aerobic respiration in *Paramecium* (75 per cent.) is effected by the oxidation of proteins, and not of carbohydrates. Humphrey and Humphrey (1948) consider that the whole of the cyanide-insensitive part of the aerobic respiration in *Paramecium caudatum* is connected with proteins as a substratum of respiration and with flavo-proteins as mediators of their oxidation.

Unfortunately the role of proteins as a respiration substratum has not been sufficiently investigated in Protozoa.

Irlina (1963) studied the mechanism of respiration in *Paramecium caudatum* adapted to various temperatures (4–5° C., 14–15° C., and 27–29° C.). Utilizing various inhibitors of respiration and of glycolysis (cyanide, malonate, monoiodacetate), she showed that at high temperatures oxydative processes are supported mainly by enzymes of the cytochrome oxidase group, whereas at medium ones by flavoproteins. At low temperatures, the processes of glycolysis acquire the leading role. Thus, the mechanism of respiratory processes and its relation to glycolysis may change even within one species, depending on the factors of the medium (in this case on the temperature).

Summing up, it can be said that according to the data available at present, aerobic respiration of Protozoa does not differ in principle from that of the tissues of higher animals.

Most Protozoa are obligatory aerobes. However, polysaprobic Protozoa, living in sewage affluents, or in waters rich in products of decomposition and in ooze, can exist in the absence of free oxygen. Thus Noland (1927) has found the ciliate *Metopus* in a water-tank with decaying leaves, the water of which smelled of hydrogen sulphide and contained no free oxygen. It contained 14·9 cm.^{3} of free carbon dioxide per litre and 78·7 cm.^{3} of fixed carbon dioxide. However, ciliates were living quite well in this environment.

Certain Protozoa, for instance *Trepomonas agilis*, are obligatory anaerobes, and perish rapidly in the presence of oxygen. The parasitic ciliates Ophryoscolecidae, inhabiting the rumen of ruminants, are apparently obligatory anaerobes (Brand, 1946). The same can also be said of the flagellates from termites (Trager, 1934, and others). *Entamoeba histolytica* and *Balantidium coli*, parasites of the human alimentary tract, are optional anaerobes. When these Protozoa penetrate from the lumen of the intestine into the mucous membrane, they gain access to molecular oxygen and probably under such conditions they become aerobic. *Giardia intestinalis*, which attaches itself to the epithelial cells of the wall of the duodenum in man, requires, in Brand's opinion (1939), more oxygen than the Protozoa living in the lumen of the intestine (Brand, 1946). Whereas a high oxygen content is not required for the reproduction of malaria parasites in cultures, they need much more oxygen when living in the blood of the host. At low oxygen content in cultures (0·37 per cent.) these parasites grew and multiplied well, while at a 95 per cent. content of oxygen in the gas mixture the parasites ceased to multiply and degenerated (Ball, 1946).

In anaerobic conditions the Protozoa respire at the expense of carbohydrates. M. Lwoff (1934) notes that *Glaucoma* can live for three days in the absence of oxygen, provided there is some sugar in the culture.

It has been proved now that various genera, species, and even strains of the same species of ciliates differ in their ability to utilize various carbohydrates. The most detailed research on this problem was carried out on *Tetrahymena pyriformis* (see Table II). Loefer and McDaniel (1950) consider it possible to distinguish separate strains of *T. pyriformis* according to their relation to sugars.

In anaerobic conditions *Paramecium, Stentor*, and other ciliates utilize for their respiration polysaccharides contained in the endoplasm (Pütter, 1905; Galadžiev and Malm, 1929; Zinkin, 1930; Barbarin, 1938). Geddes and Humphrey (1951) have proved the formation of lactic acid during anaerobic incubation of extracts of *Paramecium caudatum* in a medium containing such carbohydrates as glucose, fructose, or glycogen.

Lactic fermentation, or glycolysis, is one of the best-known anaerobic processes taking place in animals. There are reasons for thinking that true glycolysis proceeds in some trypanosomes (Fenjvessy and Reiner, 1928; Brand, 1946; and others) and in different species of *Plasmodium* (*P. gallinaceum, P. knowlesi*) (Wendel, 1943; Silverman, Geithaml, Taliaferro, and Evans, 1944; Moulder, 1962; and others).

Certain stages of the anaerobic fermentation of sugars in *Tetrahymena* have been studied by Seaman (1951, 1952), Ryley (1952), and others, who demonstrated the presence in Protozoa of such enzymes as hexokinase, phospho-gluco-mutase, isomerase, aldolase, and others. Phosphorylation of sugars by these ciliates during anaerobic utilization has been proved.

As was shown by Thomas (1942), the end-products of anaerobic carbohydrate metabolism in *Tetrahymena geleii* are lactic, acetic, and succinic acids. According to Ryley (1953), apart from these substances small amounts of ethyl alcohol are also formed in *Tetrahymena pyriformis*.

In *Trypanosoma equiperdum* in the absence of oxygen the decomposition of sugars leads to the formation of glycerine and pyruvic acid, while in *T. lewisi* succinic and acetic acids are also formed (Brand, 1946). Anaerobic decomposition of polysaccharides in flagellates from the intestine of termites leads to the formation of carbon dioxide, hydrogen, and organic acids (acetic acid) (Hungate, 1939, 1950). Brand suggests that anaerobic respiratory processes leading to the formation of a whole series of organic acids should be called 'mixed fermentation' processes. Such processes are presumably often observed in Protozoa. In any case it is clear from the available data that in different Protozoa the forms of anaerobic respiration are not similar and that they lead to the formation of diverse end products. Apparently, as regards the variety of methods of anaerobic respiration, the Protozoa are second only to bacteria.

A number of interesting data on comparative biochemistry would no doubt be revealed by further investigation of the processes of respiration in Protozoa.

TABLE I

Aerobic consumption of oxygen by various Protozoa. (From Dogiel, 1951.)

Species	Amount of oxygen mm.^{3} per hour for million individuals	Presence (+) or absence (−) of bacteria in experimental fluid solution	$t°$
Paramecium caudatum . . .	2250	+	23
	3300	+	19
	5600	+	22
	3500	+	23
	2100	+	20
Paramecium aurelia . . .	350	+	20
Paramecium multimicronucleatum .	1000	+	25
	600	+	25
Paramecium calkinsi . . .	450	+	25
Tetrahymena geleii 'young' . .	396	+	25
,, ,, 'old' . .	222	+	25
Spirostomum ambiguum . . .	2590	+	25
Strigomonas oncopelti . . .	0·4	−	28
Leptomonas ctenocephali . . .	0·3	−	28
Trypanosoma equiperdum . .	0·05	−	37
Chilomonas paramecium . . .	17–26	−	25
Khawkinea halli	2050	−	—
Astasia sp.	2400	−	—
Actinosphaerium eichhornii . .	1100	+	20

TABLE II

Utilization of carbohydrates by different strains of Tetrahymena pyriformis.
(After Seaman, 1955.)

Strain	Carbohydrates			
	Galactose	Mannose	Lactose	Cellulose
GL	{ +		−	
	{ +	−		
Gf–I	+	−		
E	{ +	+	−	
	{ −	+	−	−
H	{ −	+	−	
	{ +	+	−	−
W	{ −		−	+
	{ −	+	−	−
S	+	+		
GC			+	

Consumption of oxygen obtained from symbionts. A fairly large number of Protozoa make use of plant symbionts present in their body for their respiratory exchange. The nature of these symbionts known, since the first half of the nineteenth century, was established by Zenkovski in 1871, who identified them as unicellular algae. Since then such symbiotic algae have been found not only in Protozoa but in many higher invertebrates; depending on their colour they were given the common name of zoochlorellae and zooxanthellae. The former are commonly encountered in freshwater Protozoa and are referred to Protococcales, mainly to the genus *Chlorella*. Zooxanthellae have yellow or greyish-brown chromotophores, and are really Cryptomanadina of the genus *Chrysidella*. Zoochlorellae are encountered in some amoebae (*Amoebae viridis*), Testacea (*Difflugia pyriformis*), Heliozoa, and in many ciliates, as well as among the marine flagellates *Noctiluca* and *Leptodiscus*. Zooxanthellae were detected in foraminifera (*Trichospaerium*, *Peneroplis*), and are also widely distributed among radiolarians. They are found among practically all radiolarians, except the deep-water ones, where their presence is excluded by the absence of light. In *Mesodinium rubrum* (Holotricha), a red-coloured ciliate, the symbionts are represented by the Chrysomonad *Erythromonas haltericola*, which possesses a single flagellum in the free motile state.

The symbionts appear like small spherical inclusions measuring from 3 to 10 μ in diameter, scattered in the cytoplasm of the host. They usually lie in the endoplasm; among the radiolarians only Acantharia have symbionts inside the central capsule, while all the other orders contain them outside the capsular substance, i.e. in the ectoplasm.

The number of symbionts in a single individual host varies considerably. This number depends mainly on the relation between the sizes of the symbiont and the host. Sometimes one individual of the host contains only 6–8 zooxanthellae (in the ciliate *Spastostyla*); in other cases more than 100,000 (large specimens of *Peneroplis*).

The stability and permanence of symbiosis differs in various Protozoa. Thus many Protozoa harbouring symbionts, such as *Actinosphaerium*, *Actinophrys*, *Coleps*, *Euplotes patella*, *Frontonia leucas*, *Spirostomum ambiguum*, are more frequently found free of them than infected. Others are usually infected with zoochlorellae, but from time to time are encountered without the symbionts *Paramecium bursaria*, *Stentor polymorphus*. Some species, however (*Rhaphidiophrys viridis*, certain *Difflugia*), are so far known only as individuals containing zoochlorellae.

On the other hand, the symbiotic algae are apparently also able to lead a free-living existence. At any rate they can live for a long time outside their host. The host can be artificially freed of symbionts by keeping it for a long time in the darkness, when the algae are gradually expelled from the body of the protozoon.

According to some data, Protozoa can be artificially infected with symbionts. Thus Ševjakov (1896) had succeeded in infecting colourless *Frontonia* by feeding it on a crushed individual containing symbionts. Colourless *Paramecium bursaria* swallowed zoochlorellae, which not only remained undigested inside the ciliate but multiplied in it by successive division into four rounded cells. In a few days the colourless ciliate acquired a green colour.

During division of Protozoa infected with zoochlorellae, the latter are usually simply distributed between both the daughter individuals. However, when the products of division are very small (for instance the gametes of Foraminifera and Radiolaria) the infection of the adult individuals of the host apparently takes place only anew and at a later period. In such cases the new symbionts are probably swallowed in the course of artificial infection, i.e. with food.

During encystation of the host the symbionts in some cases (*Actinosphaerium*) perish, and infection has to proceed anew.

Zooxanthellae are encountered mostly in transparent, very frequently pelagic, animals (Radiolaria, Heliozoa, and others). In such organisms the symbionts are protected by the host; they get sufficient light and at the same time they can utilize the carbon dioxide given off by the animal during respiration to build up their plasm. On the other hand, they give off abundant oxygen which is required for the respiration of the host. It is possible that part of the nitrogen products excreted by the host can be utilized for the metabolism of the symbionts.

A rare case of the formation of red pigment in the body of the ciliate *Stentor igneus* should be noted. Small granules of red pigment, apparently haematochrome, accumulate in such stentors in the cytoplasm itself, and not inside the zoochlorellae. Moreover, the distribution of the pigment is affected by light. Thus, in day-time the accumulations of haematochrome lies outside the chlorelae and as a consequence the ciliate has a red appearance; by the evening, when the intensity of light is decreased, the pigment withdraws deeper into the cytoplasm and the ciliate becomes green.

VII

REPRODUCTION OF PROTOZOA

REPRODUCTION AND REGENERATION

THERE are two aspects to be distinguished in the problem of the reproduction of Protozoa. On the one hand, the reproduction as such, which consists in a multiplication of the number of individuals of a given species; this may take place in a great variety of ways but its result is always the same, namely an increase of the number of individuals by means of nuclear and cellular division. The further development of these products of reproduction varies considerably: in some cases they grow directly and assume the appearance of the maternal vegetative individual (amoebae), in others they undergo a kind of metamorphosis into the maternal individual (Suctorian swarmers), or they are entirely transformed into a sexual individual (the gamete, for instance, in *Polytoma*, in pre-conjugants of certain ciliates), and, finally, they may first produce gameto-cytes (sporozoites of gregarines). Thus different forms of the same process lead to various forms of the same structure—the unicellular organism.

Under certain conditions and at a definite period a completely different phenomenon is interpolated into the life-cycle of a protozoon—the sexual process—the main feature of which is a profound reconstruction of the nuclear apparatus and of the plasmatic composition of the organism as well as a modification of its hereditary properties. This is a special process associated with the formation of special stages of development, the gametes, which arise by different methods of reproduction: gametes may be produced by means of a simple, equal division (*Actinophrys, Trichonympha, Oxymonas*), by unequal division (*Opisthotichrum*), by palintomy, or by multiple division or syntomy. It may be associated with the reproduction of gametes of both sexes, or of one sex (male), or it may not be associated with reproduction (conjugation, autogamy, parthenogenesis). Moreover, the nuclear composition of the vegetative stages of the life-cycle is not essential for the sexual process: both the haploid and diploid protozoa (Trichonymphidae, Ophryoscolecidae) can grow equally well, reproduce, and reach the highest stages of perfection of cellular structure. The essential part of the sexual process is not reproduction, nor the original composition of the nuclear apparatus (haploid or diploid), or even the fusion of sexual individuals of dual origin, since in autotomy this may not occur. The important aspect here is the reconstruction of the nucleus and of certain plasmatic components of the organism, proceeding through a series of consecutive phases to the formation of a new generation differing from the previous ones in its viability and its hereditary properties. Therefore in our opinion it is more correct to speak not of two modes of reproduction in Protozoa, asexual and sexual—since reproduction always consists in one form or another of some kind of cellular division (binary or multiple)—but of two types of different generations, asexual and sexual, which may alternate either regularly or irregularly or, finally, constitute the whole life-cycle of a given protozoon in its pure form. Thus, in Eugregarinida each sporozoite is the result of a preceding sexual process, while in the majority of Mastigophora the sexual process is generally absent.

Hence we prefer, in the case of Protozoa, to refrain from classifying reproduction into sexual and asexual, but to consider separately, on the one hand reproduction in general and on the other the sexual process. This is to be seen most clearly in ciliates, since their sexual process is in general not associated with reproduction, while their reproduction itself bears the same morphological pattern of uniform division throughout the whole life-cycle.

The combination and correlation of these two phenomena in the life cycle of different Protozoa will be considered below.

Binary fission

Simple binary fission or monotomy. This type of reproduction is the most widely distributed both among Protozoa and the tissue cells of Metazoa. Typical binary fission is a regular, uniform division of the body of the protozoon into two identical daughter individuals, the division being preceded by a certain period of nutrition and growth. This occurrence of a period of nutrition and growth is of great importance, since it serves to distinguish a simple binary division from a repeated division or palintomy (see p. 257).

A classical example of a binary fission proceeding in its simplest form is the reproduction of amoebae (Fig. 132). In amoebae, whose body has an asymmetrical, irregular shape, division is not strictly orientated, but takes place in any direction. The body is formed on the equator, deepening gradually, until finally it splits the animal into two approximately equal halves, which start their independent existence at once. The fission of the cytoplasm is accompanied by karyokinetic division of the nucleus. In *Amoeba proteus* (Fig. 133) there is a definite correlation between the stages of nuclear division and the exterior morphological changes of the body. During prophase the amoeba becomes rounded, its whole surface becomes densely covered with short, fine pseudopodia, and a hyaline area appears in the centre of its body, which disappears during metaphase. During anaphase pseudopodia become rapidly coarser and thicker; only during telophase does the body expand and become constricted, after which the pseudopodia return to the shape typical of *A. proteus*.

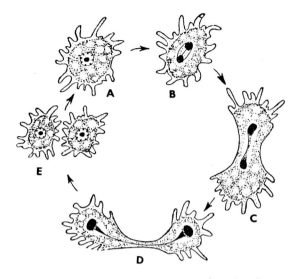

FIG. 132. Agamous division in *Amoeba polypodia.*

(*A*)–(*E*) successive phases of division. (From Lühe, 1913.)

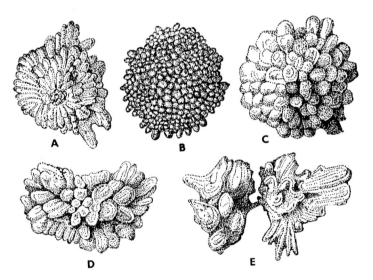

FIG. 133. External morphological changes in *Amoeba proteus* during fission (low magnification).

(*A*), (*B*) beginning of division; (*C*), (*D*) middle stage of division; (*E*) completion of fission. (From Dogiel, 1951.)

During division of amoebae the organoids present in the parental organism either divide themselves (nucleus, mitochondria) or are simply distributed between the two daughter individuals, while the organoids lacking in one of the individuals are formed anew (contractile vacuoles).

Non-orientated fission similar to that of the amoebae is also observed in naked radiolarians (*Thalassicolla* and others) and in some heliozoans (*Actinosphaerium*).

The development of a skeleton in Sarcodina introduces some complications in the process of fission, owing partly to difficulty in the division of the skeletal elements; this often leads to the establishment of a definite plane of division most suitable for the distribution of the skeletal elements between both daughter individuals.

Testaceous amoebae (Testacea) may serve as a first example of such complications; the process of their division has been thoroughly studied by Ševjakov (1887) in Euglypha (Fig. 26) which possesses a sac-like shell consisting of overlapping siliceous platelets. Before division a certain reorganization of the cytoplasm takes place; it consists in the lying down of primordial reserve siliceous platelets within special small vacuoles which appear at that time in the cytoplasm. The plane of division then becomes definitely reorientated, this orientation again depending on the skeleton, and not on the plasmatic body: the plane of division lies perpendicularly to the longitudinal axis of the shell.

During division of *Euglypha*, *Arcella*, and other Testacea, the nucleus also divides, and about half the cytoplasm with one of the daughter nuclei and some reserve test platelets emerges from the aperture to the exterior and is surrounded by a new test easily distinguishable by its clean appearance and lighter colour.

The extent to which the presence of skeletal elements determines the orientation of division may be seen in radiolarians. Thus, for example, the skeleton of some Phaeodaria is composed of a pair of siliceous valves, provided with a complex system of processes arranged on the sides along the longitudinal axis. During the division of such radiolarians (for example *Coelospathis* and others) the valves move away from each other with half the living content of the shell, which restores the opposite valve, lost during the process. In this case, owing to the position of the valves, division takes place in the plane parallel to the longitudinal axis.

The direction of the division is much more constant and stabilized during the simple uniform fission in the classes Mastigophora and Ciliata.

In flagellates division, as a rule, proceeds in longitudinal direction (Fig. 134), in ciliates in a transverse one. Moreover, in Mastigophora division begins at the anterior pole progressing from there to the posterior end of its body. Sometimes in the course of fission the two halves of the body become bent in opposite directions, which produces a false impression of transverse division.

In some cases, however, namely almost exclusively in the order Dino-flagellata, deflexion of the plane of division from the longitudinal axis actually takes place, so that division proceeds in an oblique direction—for

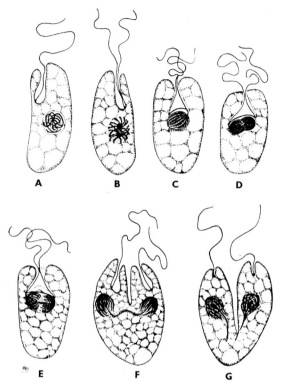

FIG. 134. Division of flagellate *Meoidium incurvum* (Euglenida).

(*A*) nucleus in prophase; (*B*) prometaphase; (*C*) metaphase;
(*D*) early anaphase; (*E*), (*F*) stage of anaphase and beginning
of division of body; (*G*) telophase. (After R. Hall, 1923.)

example in *Ceratium hirundinella* (Fig. 135) and many others. In *Oxyrrhis marina* (Fig. 30) division is even more oblique, almost transverse. The transition from the oblique to the strictly transverse division is clearly seen in certain greatly modified parasitic Dinoflagellata of the genus *Haplozoon*: in some species of the genus the partitions between cells run obliquely (*H. armatum*), in others transversely (*H. lineare*).

In flagellates division is initiated by that of the basal body (blepharoplast) of the flagellum. When a single flagellum is present it often remains with one of the individuals, while in the other a new flagellum develops either from its basal body (blepharoplast) or from a centriole. When there is a pair of flagella, each daughter individual sometimes receives one, its second one being formed anew.

It is an interesting fact that each fission—especially in the most complex Mastigophora—is accompanied by a series of reorganization phenomena. This reorganization consists in the absorption of many organoids of the mother individual either during or directly after fission and their replacement by newly formed ones. Periodical renewal of organoids is thus obtained.

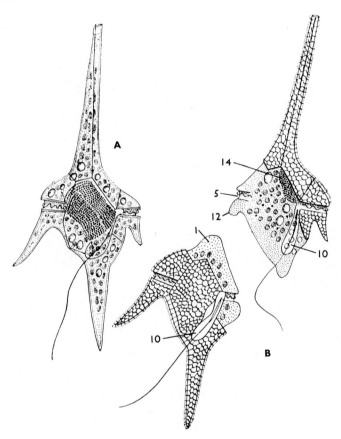

FIG. 135. Division of *Ceratium hirundinella*.

(*A*) beginning of division; (*B*) two individuals immediately after division.
(After Lauterborn, 1895.)

Thus in flagellates with a simple structure (*Spongomonas, Polytoma,* and others) there has been often observed the absorption of both flagella of the mother individual and their formation anew from the basal granules of both daughters.

This process, however, is most clearly marked in the highly organized Polymastigida and Hypermastigida from the intestine of termites and cockroaches. Thus in *Oxymonas dimorpha* (Fig. 58) the nucleus leaves its normal position at the anterior end of the body before the beginning of fission and loses all connexion with the supporting locomotor apparatus. The axostyle, the attachment stalk or rostellum, and the flagella are absorbed during fission. In *Macrotrichomonas* from termites the old costa (i.e. the base of the undulating membrane), the flagella, axostyle, and the coiled parabasal body are absorbed during fission. All these organoids are formed anew in both daughter individuals.

Reorganization is most clearly marked in the Hypermastigida *Lophomonas* from the intestine of cockroaches. The nucleus with a small paradesmose leaves the complex supporting locomotor apparatus encircling it and moves to the opposite end of the body, where a new supporting locomotor apparatus is formed from the centrioles of the paradesmose while the old one, consisting of a flagellar plume, parabasal body, a special cup encircling the nucleus, and the axostyle, is dissolved in the cytoplasm.

Contrary to the flagellates, the ciliates always divide transversely into two approximately equal halves. Certain sessile forms, namely Peritricha, are exceptional in having a longitudinal fission, caused by the change in the position of the longitudinal axis of the body of these ciliates. This change in the direction of fission should, probably, be regarded as an adaptation to a sessile mode of life. Owing to longitudinal fission, both resulting daughter individuals retain their connexion with the stalk, by means of which they are attached to the substratum. It is in this way that colonies are formed.

Complete reorganization of both individuals either during or after fission is even more clearly expressed in ciliates than in flagellates. This process is especially pronounced in Hypotricha, where it was first discovered by Wallengren (1901). However, a reconstruction of the organism during fission takes place to a greater or lesser extent in all ciliates. In Hypotricha the old adoral membranelles of the anterior daughter individual are gradually reduced in size, while at the same time miniature plasmatic buds— primordia of new membranelles—appear at their bases. They grow as the old ones are absorbed. Each ventral cirrus is replaced in exactly the same way by a new bud in each half of the dividing individual. The undulating membranes are also retracted and replaced by new ones, so that both daughter individuals obtain a complete new set of all locomotor organoids. In Chlamydodontidae the old rod apparatus is dissolved and replaced, and so on. It is interesting to note that a similar complete replacement of the locomotor apparatus occurs during experimental regeneration in Hypotricha. Even at the removal of only one of the large ventral cirri in Hypotricha, complete reconstruction takes place (Dembowska, 1925, 1926). This confirms the identity of the stimulus causing reorganization, on the one hand, during regeneration, on the other, during fission of ciliates; thus the process of reorganization can be compared with physiological regeneration.

In some rare cases binary fission may be distinctly unequal, as for instance during the preconjugation division in the ciliate *Opisthotrichum* (Fig. 136) from the rumen of the antelope *Bubalis*. In *Opisthotrichum* the strong skeletal platelet remains in the anterior individual while the posterior one has no skeleton and is about half the size of the other. Nevertheless, the size of both individuals remains unchanged, and in this form they proceed to conjugate. Such patterns resemble the budding processes.

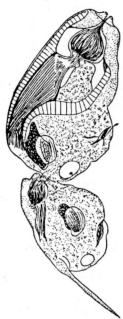

Only in some rare cases are the sexual individuals, or gametocytes, produced by simple, monotomic binary fission. Paedogamic copulation in *Actinophrys* and hologamic copulation in *Copromonas subtilis*, *Trichonympha*, *Saccinobaculus*, and others, described by Cleveland (1949*b*, 1956*a*, *b*), may serve as good examples.

Moreover, the preconjugants of ciliates are usually formed by simple transverse division of neutral individuals; however, this division is followed not by feeding but by conjugation.

Repeated binary fission or palintomy. As has been mentioned above, palintomy denotes binary fission repeated over and over again, without the intermediate stage of nutrition and growth. At a first glance there seems to be no difference in principle between monotomic and palintomic fissions; yet these two types of agamic reproduction differ in some essential features. These

FIG. 136. Progamous, unequal fission of ciliate *Opisthotrichum janus* (Ophryoscolecidae). (After Dogiel, 1925.)

differences consist both in the process of their fission itself and in the position palintomy occupies in the life-cycle of Protozoa.

Thus, first of all palintomy is frequently preceded by a hypertrophic growth of the parental individual, which enables it to divide without excessive diminution in size of the products of division. Moreover, in accordance with this palintomy often occurs during the periods of the life-cycle preceded by increased nutrition. In addition, palintomy is usually characterized by a temporary dedifferentiation of the products of division, since the resulting individuals have no time for reorganization during the short intervals between the divisions. As a consquence of dedifferentiation of the products of division during palintomy, in the vast majority of cases this process takes place in an encysted state, under the protection of the cyst wall. All these factors together make palintomy similar to cleavage of the ovum in Metazoa, while the cyst wall can be likened functionally to the egg membrane of many Metazoa.

We shall use below the classification of the forms of palintomy proposed by Sachwatkin (1949) in his interesting book on reproduction of Protozoa and embryology of the lowest multicellular organisms.

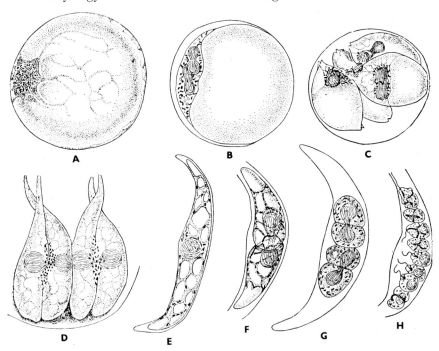

FIG. 137. Palintomy of *Dissodinium lunula* (Dinoflagellata).

(*A*) maternal cyst before division; (*B*) division of nucleus into 4; (*C*) formation of sporocysts within maternal cyst; (*D*) third division of nucleus, leading to the formation of horned cysts; (*E*) horned cyst; (*F*)–(*H*) division inside horned cyst with formation of eight gymnodinia. (After Dogiel, 1906.)

Typical palintomy consists of a series of repeated equal divisions leading to the formation of completely identical products of reproduction. The productivity of palintomic reproduction varies according to the systematic position of the Protozoa and to whether the resulting organisms are solitary or colonial. Typical palintomy is encountered among flagellates (especially in parasitic forms) and ciliates.

As regards the pattern in which the products of division are arranged two main types may be distinguished among Protozoa; linear and tabular.

In linear palintomy its products are arranged in the form of a chain, with their opposite poles alternating; the chain is formed as the result of repeated transverse or pseudo-transverse (oblique), but actually longitudinal, divisions. This type of palintomy occurs widely among many free and parasitic Dinoflagellata. In some forms the animals first encyst and then divide repeatedly. If the cyst is elongated (*Cochlodinium*, horned cysts of *Dissodinium lunula*, Fig. 137) the products of division are arranged in one row. But if the cyst is rounded (*Gyrodinium* sp., according to Kofoid) the sixteen products of division lose their linear arrangement, forming a rounded bundle lying in the centre of the cyst.

The same type of palintomy is observed in many parasitic ciliates, especially in Apostomata, for example in Gymnodinioides, Polyspira, and others, except that here we have linear palintomy resulting from true

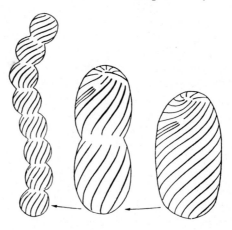

FIG. 138. Linear palintomy of tomont in *Polyspira delagei* (Aposto-mata). (After Chatton and Lwoff, 1935.)

transverse divisions. Linear palintomy is clearly seen in such forms as *Gymnodinioides* (Ciliata Apostomata), where it takes place in the cyst and leads to the formation of a chain of sixteen products of division (tomites) (Fig. 138).

It has recently been discovered that palintomy occurs commonly also among free-living ciliates, especially among those which, according to Mugard (1948), are 'histiophages', i.e. feed on tissues of dying or decaying aquatic arthropods. Thus among Holotricha Hymenostomata there is a whole group of more or less related forms in which palintomy is a necessary stage in their life-cycle. These are, first of all, the representatives of the family Ophryoglenidae. In their active stage the members of this family are in the 'tomont' stage, when they feed intensively and reach large dimensions. An adult tomont does not divide in its motile state, but first encysts and produces a varying number of smaller tomites inside the cyst by successive division (palintomy). The tomites leave the cyst, feed, and each again becomes a tomont. The number of tomites in a cyst varies greatly in different species: from 4 in *Protophryoglena* to 128 in *Ophryoglena flava*.

The subcutaneous parasite of fish, *Ichthyophthirius multifiliis* (Fig. 139), is now also referred to the family Ophryoglenidae. The tomont of this species, which is parasitic in the subcutaneous connective tissue of the host, increases considerably in size (up to 650 μ), leaves the host, and encysts.

Inside the cyst up to 2,000 minute tomites are produced by palintomy; they leave the cyst and set off in search of a host.

Tabular palintomy arises as a result of the alternation of longitudinal divisions in two planes perpendicular to each other, as a consequence of which the products of fission are arranged with their main axes parallel to each other in the form of a flat table, their poles being turned in one

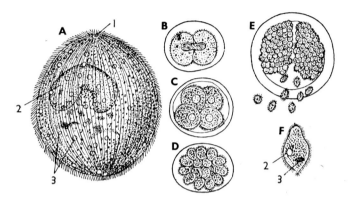

FIG. 139. Multiplication of *Ichthyophthirius multifiliis*—a parasitic ciliate from skin of fish.

(*A*) adult form; (*B*)–(*E*) encystment and palintomy inside cyst; (*F*) young ciliate emerging from cyst. 1, mouth; 2, macronucleus; 3, contractile vacuole. (After Bütschi, 1889.)

direction. This type of palintomy is characteristic of the order Phytomonadida, and for some Dinoflagellata (the first stages of division inside the cyst of *Dissodinium*), Euglenida (*Euglena gracilis*), and choanoflagellates. It is also common among the lower algae, especially in the palmella stage. In many of these forms palintomy terminates at the stage of four tomites, the resulting individuals being grouped in two intersecting pairs, to form a characteristic figure of a 'cross'. This stage closely resembles the stage of four blastomers in the development of certain Metazoa with complete cleavage (for instance in crayfish, Pantopoda, and others). Palintomy is often observed during the formation of gametes in the majority of Volvocidae, for example, of male gametes in *Volvox*. The microconjugants in many Peritricha are also formed in this way.

Modified palintomy (*palinsporogenesis*). This peculiar modification is characteristic of many parasitic Dinoflagellata (Fig. 140). It is based on a combination of repeated pseudo-transverse division with a trophic differentiation into two unequal daughter individuals: the trophocyte, which remains associated with the host, continuing to feed and to grow, and the gonocyte, which continues to divide by linear palintomy; while the trophocyte continues to give off new gonocytes. The gonocytes, continuing to divide, eventually form numerous flagellated zoospores. Each individual trophocyte may produce up to 6–7 gonocytes, while each gonocyte gives rise to 64–128 or more zoospores, so that the total productivity is very high. The repetition of heteronomic simple divisions takes place usually much earlier than the completion of palintomic division of the first gonocytes, and all the products of sporogony remain for a long time connected with each other and with the parent individual, i.e. the trophocyte. This connexion is due to the fact that the separation of each new gonocyte is accompanied by 'ecdysis', that is by the formation around the trophocyte of a new, thin membrane, within which all further divisions of the corresponding gonocyte takes place, with the result that the dividing individual is surrounded by several concentric membranes enclosed one within another, each of which contains the descendants of one gonocyte.

This process leads to the formation of extremely peculiar temporary aggregates of cells, consisting of the parent individual—trophocyte—and a whole complex of gonocytes, successively formed by it and in different stages of palintomy. This complex process has apparently evolved through a series of phases, which may be seen from a comparison of different representatives of the family Blastodinidae. The first phase is illustrated by the genus *Oodinium*, parasitic on various plankton animals (salpids, *Alciope*, and others). This parasite is a pyriform uninucleate organism, which attaches itself to the outer epithelium of its host by means of a special pseudopodial stalk. During reproduction *Oodinium* detaches itself from its stalk, becomes surrounded by a membrane, and breaks up successively into smaller and smaller oval units, which in their turn become invested with membranes. Thus, in this case the trophocyte acts also as a gonocyte, and the products of palintomy do not retain their connexion with each other during the process.

The next phase of this process can be observed in the genus *Apodinium*— an ectoparasite of the appendicularian *Fritillaria*. It is very similar to *Oodinium*, but has a much longer stalk and the body to which the latter is attached divides periodically into two cells: the proximal, trophocyte, and the distal, gonocyte. The gonocyte at once begins to divide into two cells, which were called sporocytes by Chatton (1920a, b), who carried out a detailed study of Blastodinidae. Further, the trophocyte produces a second gonocyte, which at once begins to divide. The first gonocyte continues to divide, while the trophocyte prepares for the detachment of a new gonocyte, and so on. At the separation of every new gonocyte a membrane formed, which encloses the trophocyte and the latest gonocyte. Thus a many-layered system of membranes is formed around the whole cluster of sporocytes undergoing palintomy; the membranes are inserted into each other and gradually rupture at their distal end, releasing the mature sporocytes.

The third phase is represented by the genus *Blastodinium*, inhabiting the intestine of marine Copepoda (Fig. 140).

An adult *Blastodinium* is elongated, its shape being like that of a grain of oats; it has a thin membrane and is very similar to the so-called horned cysts of many Gymnodiniaceae. Its later development is at first somewhat reminiscent of them too. It divides by binary fission, the anterior individual becoming a trophocyte, and the posterior one the first gonocyte. The gonocyte divides into sporocytes; the trophocyte slowly gives off new gonocytes, which vigorously divide in their turn, so that ultimately a large oblong trophocyte, surrounded by several concentric layers of minute sporocytes, is produced inside the extended membrane, each layer being produced by one gonocyte and separated from the others by its own thin membrane. Then the common membrane of the whole complex bursts, the sporocytes are eliminated from the intestine and are transformed into zoospores, while the trophocyte remains in the host's intestine and, apparently, can give rise to new batches of sporocytes. *Blastodinium* lies free in the intestine.

The genus *Haplozoon*, discovered by Dogiel (1906a) in the intestine of Polychaeta, the last member of the series formed by the family Blastodinidae, is best adapted to intestinal parasitism. Its high degree of adaptation is manifest first of all in the fact that the cephalic cell of this multicellular organism, or its trophocyst, is attached to the intestinal epithelium by a pseudopodial stalk (compare *Oodinium*); furthermore the trophocyst of *Haplozoon* is supplied with a mobile stylet and a series of reserve stylets, which are derived from the trichocyst of certain free-living Dinoflagellata; finally, owing to the presence of contractile fibrils, the trophocyte itself

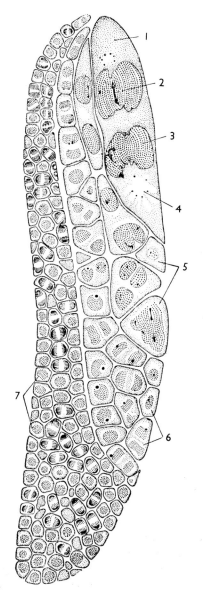

FIG. 140. Multiplication of *Blastodinium pruvoti* (Dinoflagellata), longitudinal section.

1, trophocyte; 2, dividing nucleolus; 3, chromatin; 4, centrosphere; 5, gonocytes of 3rd order; 6, gonocytes of 2nd order; 7, gonocytes of 1st order. (After Chatton, 1920b.)

may bend and straighten out. From the trophocyte is successively detached a row of gonocytes (six to seven) which, however, remain closely associated with it by means of small intercellular portae, uniting the trophocyte with the anterior gonocyte and other gonocytes with each other. The gonocytes divide into sporocytes mostly in an oblique direction, which is reminiscent of the fission of free-living Dinoflagellata, and form rows of sporocytes, arranged in one plane, and varying in length, according to the order of the gonocyte which gave rise to them. In this way a multicellular plate is formed. At their posterior end, approximately beginning from the 13th sporocyte in order from the cephalic cell (in *Haplozoon armatum*), the sporocytes begin to be rounded, while their nuclear division becomes quarternary (simultaneously into four lying in the same plane), which points to an acceleration of nuclear division. These posterior sporocytes are detached from the body of the *Haplozoon* either in pairs or in fours and carried out of the intestine into the water to produce minute zoospores, the further development of which is unknown (as in all Blastodinidae).

In larger species of *Haplozoon* (*H. macrostylum*) division of sporocytes in the posterior third of the body is especially rapid, taking place not in one plane, but in two, so that the posterior third of the body has not one but many layers.

Thus we see that the family Blastodinidae forms a compact group of parasitic organisms, which have evolved from a planktonic mode of life to being ectoparasitic on planktonts (*Oodinium, Apodinium*), thence to being endoparasitic in planktonts (*Blastodinium*), and finally to endoparasitic existence in bottom-dwelling annelids (*Haplozoon*).

A similar palintomy is observed in the unusual family of ciliates Pilisuctoridae (Holotricha, Trishostomata), namely in the genus *Conidiophrys* (Fig. 141). These ciliates attach themselves to the secretory setae of marine crustaceans, Amphipods (Chatton and Lwoff, 1934, 1936a), in the form of a motile, flat, disk-like swarmer or tomite. Having settled down the ciliate loses its cilia, becomes sausage-shaped, and secretes around itself and around the end of the seta a continuous sac-like cuticle. Under the protection of the cuticle the trophont formed detaches by successive transverse constrictions from two to twelve tomites, which are gradually supplied with cilia, are transformed into swarmers, and, tearing themselves away from the trophont, escape through the ruptured cuticle, and swim away, while the trophont continues to grow. The trophont, apparently, feeds on a secretion of the glandular setae of the host.

In all the forms discussed the repeated fission is a special modification of linear palintomy in which the parent organism does not cease its vegetative activity (except *Oodinium*), but continues to feed and grow. Therefore it is capable of producing not a single but several broods of sporocytes and zoospores, attaining by this unusual method a high degree of multiplication which is a feature characteristic of parasites.

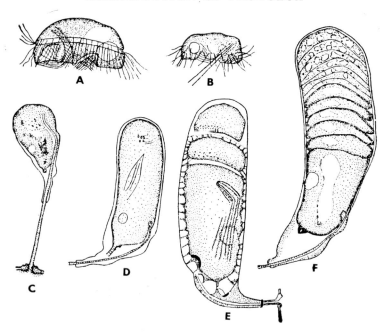

FIG. 141. Multiplication by palintomy of ciliate *Conidiophrys pilisuctor* (fam. Pilisuctoridae).

(*A*) swarmer or tomite; (*B*) tomite attached by its mouth to hair on carapace of crustacean *Corophium;* (*C*) transformation of tomite into trophont; (*D*) growing trophont before reproduction; (*E*) formation of two tomites by division; (*F*) trophont with 11 tomites, terminal tomites are vacuolated and degenerating. (After Chatton and Lwoff, 1936*a*.)

Budding

Budding processes in their simplest form may be likened to a form of irregular fission, in which the inequality is more sharply marked, so that the larger parent individual can be easily distinguished from the budded-off daughter ones.

In simple, or monotomic, budding, one daughter individual is produced, while in multiple budding several buds are formed simultaneously. Finally, there exists a third type—linear budding.

Simple budding is common among Suctoria, a group in which various types of budding are represented. In some more rare cases (*Podophrya*) all the tentacles are retracted, the whole organism becomes covered with cilia, detaches itself away from its stalk, and swims away as a swarmer. There is actually no budding here, but only dispersal, which to a certain extent foretells the direction to be followed in the course of adaptation of Suctoria along the line of asexual reproduction. In other Suctoria, for example *Paracineta* (Fig. 142), true budding is observed, during which the macro- and micronuclei of the ciliate divide, while the distal part of the animal becomes covered with cilia and swims away with one set of daughter nuclei. Later it settles down on the bottom, loses its cilia, and develops tentacles. In this case the bud is almost of the same size as the individual remaining on the stalk, but differing from its parent in the absence of tentacles and in the development of cilia. As an interesting improvement of such a type of budding it should be pointed out that in some species the bud begins to

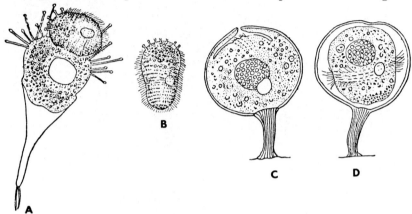

FIG. 142. Vegetative reproduction of Suctoria.

(*A*), (*B*) *Paracineta patula*, exogenous budding and separation of bud; (*C*), (*D*) *Tokophrya cyclopum*, transformation of whole ciliate into a swarmer. (After Collin, 1912.)

form at its distal end tentacles in the shape of small protuberances, before it completely breaks away from its mother's body. In this way the transformation of the bud in complete functional readiness for the capture of food is accelerated.

This simple exogenous budding has undergone modifications in two directions: firstly to monotomic but endogenous budding, when at the distal pole of a suctorian a deep depression was formed, from the bottom of which a plasmatic knob—the primordial bud—protrudes into the depression; the nuclear apparatus which had divided in the process of budding enters into it and the depression serves as a brood chamber; the bud then develops its cilia after which it escapes outside through the opening of the depression and swims away as a swarmer (*Tokophrya*, Fig. 143).

The other modification leads from simple exogenous to multiple exogenous budding, which is especially well developed in *Ephelota* (Fig. 144). Here a whole circle of four to twelve protuberances arises on the distal surface of the animal; they represent buds containing the branched macronucleus and small micronuclei produced by division of the mother macronucleus. The buds then develop cilia and simultaneously break away from the mother's body. Finally, side by side with endogenous budding in certain *Suctoria*, for instance *Acineta tuberosa* and *Trichophrya*, an endogenous multiple budding is developed which differs from the simple one

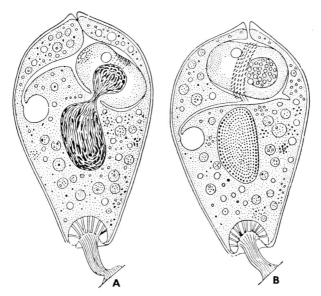

FIG. 143. Endogenous budding in *Tokophrya cyclopum*.

(*A*) beginning of budding; (*B*) fully developed swarmer. (After Collin, 1912.)

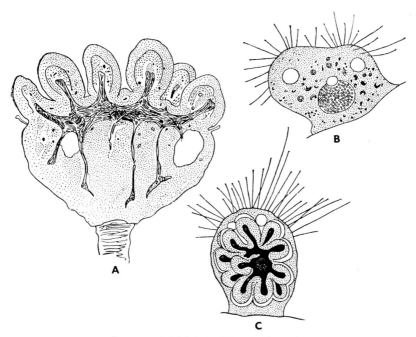

FIG. 144. Multiple budding in Suctoria.

(*A*) *Ephelota gemmipara*, exogenous budding; (*B*), (*C*) *Trichophrya salparum*, endogenous budding. (After Collin, 1912.)

only in the fact that not one but several buds eventually covered with cilia grow out from the walls of the brood chamber into its cavity.

The formation of non-ciliated exogenous buds by certain Suctoria (*Anarma, Ophryodendron*) is of quite a different biological significance. Thus, *Anarma* may, in addition to its endogenous ciliated buds, produce from its basal part protuberances bearing tentacles but no cilia, which at

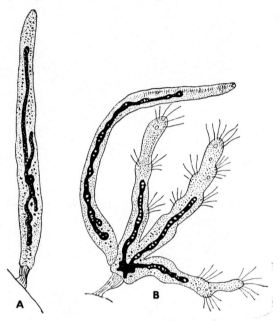

FIG. 145. Budding in *Dendrosomides paguri*.

(*A*) separation of a vermiform embryo; (*B*) detached embryo.
(After Collin, 1912.)

once settle down to the bottom. The same pattern is observed in *Ophryo-dendron* and *Dendrosomides* (Fig. 145). *Dendrosomides* has a branchcd body, some of its branches being vermicular and devoid of tentacles; they are able to detach themselves from the mother individual. Evidently, in forms like *Anarma* and others the basal budding is not intended for a wide dispersal of the species, but for a local increase of population, which might be situated in favourable conditions of nutrition.

Finally, apart from the methods of budding mentioned, some Suctoria reproduce by means of simple, binary fission. Thus the group Suctoria exhibits the great variety of types of asexual reproduction.

Except for binary fission, in all these cases the products of multiplication are swarmers bearing cilia. It is interesting, moreover, that some epibionts, for instance *Dendrocometes* from the gills of Amphipods, have also another method of formation of swarmers, which does not include reproduction.

Namely, when the entire chitinous shell to which the ciliates are attached is shed during ecdysis, like an empty skin, the adult ciliates form in the interior of the body a large brood chamber, into which about half of the contents of the body and the whole nucleus protrude; this evagination is then covered with ciliary circlets arranged as in swarmers, detaches itself from the large residual body, and is transformed into a swarmer. This

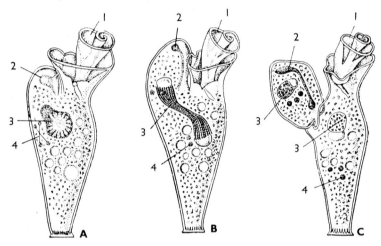

FIG. 146. Budding in *Spirochona gemmipara*.

(*A*) and (*B*) beginning of budding; (*C*) termination of budding process. 1, adoral funnel; 2, primordium of funnel in bud; 3, macronucleus; 4, micronucleus. (After Hertwig 1877.)

process is somewhat like that mentioned above in *Podophrya*. Hence in this case the stimulus for this unusual budding is provided by the behaviour of the host, i.e. its ecdysis.

Among other ciliates, a pattern of budding very similar to that of Suctoria is found in members of the small order Chonotricha (Fig. 146). These animals attach themselves to various crustacea by means of a plantar disk, while at their free end there is an intricately arranged ectoplasmatic funnel, at the bottom of which lies the mouth, surrounded by rows of cilia. The rest of their body is covered with a pellicle and is devoid of cilia.

Asexual reproduction takes place by exogenous budding, either single or multiple, in which the buds, first naked, as in Suctoria, are later transformed into ciliated swarmers. The latter swim away, settle down, and are transformed into adults.

Members of the small family Sphaenophryidae (suborder Thigmotricha, Fig. 147) possess the same type of budding, except that it is single and simple, not multiple; these animals attach themselves to the gills of molluscs by their flat lower side. The adult animal is devoid of cilia, but develops a special sucking proboscis, but during the asexual reproduction a protuberant exogenous bud develops on its dorsal side, becomes covered with cilia, and swims away as a swarmer. Similar swarmers are formed by sessile Peritricha—for example, by *Ellobiophrya*.

There is an essential difference between the budding of ciliates and their binary fission to which up to the present no attention has been paid.

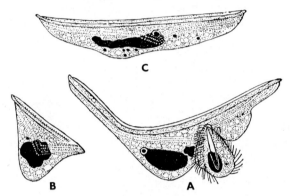

FIG. 147. Budding of ciliate *Sphenophrya dosiniae*.

(*A*) adult individual; (*B*) ciliate with bud covered with cilia;
(*C*) young individual. (After Chatton and Lwoff, 1921.)

In both cases the process consists of the detachment from the organism of a certain portion of it, which is capable of living independently and consists of cytoplasm and nucleus. Differences in the size of the part detached may not be particularly great. However, in simple fission this process strongly affects the whole of the body of the dividing ciliate, which is manifested in the complete reorganization of the whole locomotor apparatus, experienced by both individuals in division. On the other hand, all processes of reorganization are absent during the formation of buds. Thus in Suctoria the mother organism retains its former tentacles, and in Peritricha its ciliary apparatus. Hence the ciliate reacts to the process of fission as if it were an injury (see p. 286), while the mother organism does not react at all to the process of budding. The causes of this important difference are not yet clear, and are in need of experimental investigation.

Among Mastigophora the process of budding is observed only as an exception. Although the so-called 'budding' in Cystoflagellata (*Noctiluca*) is well known and has been investigated in detail, this case should in fact be referred, as we shall see below, to another category of reproductive processes.

Thus at present two or three cases of budding in Mastigophora can be mentioned; and apparently only one case of simple exogenous budding exists in the genus of Blastodinidae, namely in *Haplozoon*, in which the growth of a protuberant bud from the cephalic cell or trophocyte has been observed; however, this process has not been followed to the moment of the detachment of the bud.

Besides this, simple exogenous budding has been described for some sessile freshwater Chrysomonadida (*Palatinella, Cyrtophora, Pedinella*).

Among heliozoans multiple exogenous budding is known in *Acantho-cystis*, where it is found side by side with simple fission. The nucleus divides once or several times and one of the daughter nuclei remains inside the mother individual, while the others approach its periphery, and are

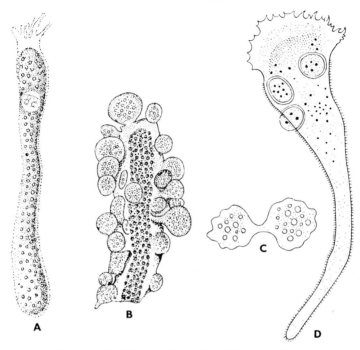

FIG. 148. Budding of plasmodia of Myxosporidia.

(*A*) plasmodium of *Myxidium lieberkühni*; (*B*) plasmodium of same species in stage of multiple budding; (*C*) endogenous budding in *Sphaerospora*; (*D*) plasmotomy in *Chloromyxum leidigi*. (After Doflein and Reichenow, 1953.)

detached from it with small portions of the cytoplasm, and with part of the siliceous skeletal spicules. Up to twenty-four buds may be detached from one animal, which sometimes retain a temporary connexion with the large mother organism.

The question of budding in radiolarians is in need of revision, since Chatton and his pupils have made it clear that some processes of reproduction, which were supposed to be connected with that of the radiolarians themselves, actually belonged to their endoparasites, namely the Dinoflagellata. In general budding is rare among the Sporozoa and Cnidosporidia. Two forms of it have been described in certain Myxosporidia. Thus in the plasmodium of *Myxidium lieberkühni* (Fig. 148) from the urinary bladder of pike, multinucleate portions of the cytoplasm evaginate from the wall of the plasmodium, and then detach themselves from it and lead an independent existence. In distinction from this species in another microsporidium, *Sphaerospora dimorpha*, multinucleate portions of the cytoplasm are separated within the plasmodium, after which they escape to the exterior as small round buds. These processes produced the impression of exogenous and endogenous multiple budding. However, since we are dealing here with amoeboid and multinucleate organisms, with a highly extensible plastic cytoplasm, the question arises whether, especially in the case of exogenous 'budding', this represents true budding or plasmotomy. In fact, observation of living plasmodia of coelomic myxosporidia under the coverslip has shown that they have an extremely extensible cytoplasm, which readily assumes most varied outlines, stretching into very long cords, &c. On account of this, under different accidental conditions, the same species may either detach from itself small portions (buds), or become constricted into large plasmatic pieces (plasmotomy). Although Myxosporidia are said to be capable of budding, we are rather inclined to regard the cases described as plasmotomy.

Linear budding in its typical form is observed only in one group of ciliates, namely in Astomata, which live in various invertebrates, mainly in the alimentary tract of Oligochaetea, temporarily attaching themselves to the walls of the intestine by means of hooks or cuticular ribs situated at the anterior end of the body. Asexual reproduction in these ciliates is either by simple division, or, more frequently, by linear or terminal budding.

The simplest case is represented by simple budding when the ciliate divides into a large anterior and a smaller posterior individual, or bud. Here both individuals are similarly orientated and in the same way, moreover, as in binary fission (monotomy), which clearly indicates a close connexion between the processes of monotomy and of simple linear budding. This type of budding is common in the family Anoplophryidae.

Chain linear budding occurring in many Astomata is a complication of simple budding (Fig. 149). In this case a single primary individual gives rise to a whole chain, in which one can distinguish the initial front link of the chain, or primite, which is often equipped with an attachment apparatus, as well as the other links of the chain, or satellites, The first transverse cleavage divides the single individual into a primite and a first satellite, which remain connected with each other.

Subsequent linear budding may proceed according to two different types.

First type—palintomic chain-budding or the *Haptophrya* type (so far known only for this genus). In this type the first satellite formed is not detached from the primite, but both continue to divide synchronously, the products of division remaining connected with each other. Thus, the two-cellular stage is followed by the four-cellular one, consisting of the primite, the second satellite, and the two products of division of the first satellite. A new division of all the four members of the chain then occurs, and an eight-cellular stage is produced, which is composed of the primite, the third satellite, two descendants of the second satellite, and four products of division of the first satellite.

Apart from its organoids of attachment, the primite also differs from the

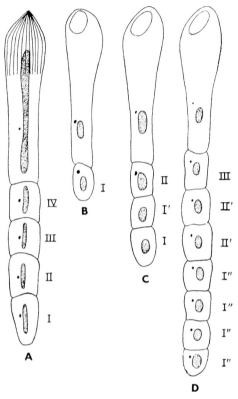

FIG. 149. Two types of linear budding in astomatous ciliates.

(A) *Radiophrya* type; (B)–(D) *Haptophrya* type; order of formation of buds designated by roman figures, order of division of buds given by primes. (After Chejsin, 1930.)

satellites by its somewhat larger size, and sometimes by its different shape. The resulting temporary colony is later separated into independent individuals. As may be seen, this type of division is very similar to linear palintomy in Dinoflagellata and the ciliates Pilisuctoridae. However, in this case both the primite and the satellites continue to grow during the existence of the colony.

The second type may be called strobilation, or the *Radiophrya* type; it is much more widely spread among Astomata, and its characteristic feature is that the satellites given off from the primite retain their link with it but do not themselves divide. Consequently in this type of chain formation the links (as in the strobilae of Cestodes) are formed only by budding of the primite, and they are arranged in the chain so that the older the segment (i.e. satellite) the closer it lies to the posterior end of the strobila.

According to Cépède (1910) the significance of linear chain budding consists not only in the acceleration of reproduction and auto-infection, but also in the fact that chain formation of the complex of individuals is better protected against possible rupture by a current of food moving through the alimentary tract than a single individual growing in length.

THE DISTRIBUTION OF VARIOUS TYPES OF BUDDING IN PROTOZOA

Name of organism	Simple exogenous	Multiple exogenous	Simple endogenous	Multiple endogenous	Chain linear
Astromata	I	I	I	I	I
Suctoria	I	I	..	..	..
Chonotricha	I	..	..	..	I
Shaenophryidae	I	..	..	..	..
Peritricha	I	..	..	..	..
Chrysomonadide	I	..	..	..	..
Blastodinidae	..	..	..	..	..
Heliozoa	..	I	..	..	..
Myxosporidia	..	I	..	I	..

Multiple division (syntomy)

In this type of reproduction the animal experiences a repeated division of its nucleus at a certain stage of its life-cycle (usually after a period of nutrition and growth), when it becomes temporarily multinucleate and then undergoes fission into as many daughter individuals as the number of its nuclei. According to their further fate, the discrete units are known under different names. As has been mentioned above, the entire plasmatic body is commonly used up in the formation of these daughter individuals. Sometimes, however, a certain portion of the body remains unused in reproduction, forming the so-called 'residual body'. This residue is non-viable and eventually always perishes. The stage is called either a schizont or a gamont, depending on whether vegetative individuals or sexual cells are produced by its multiple division, but when multiple division completes a sexual process this stage may be referred to as a sporont. In accordance with this, the products of the fission of a schizont are called merozoites and those of a gamont gametes, while the products of the division of a sporont are referred to as sporozoites, if this term is being used for Sporozoa; in other classes the result of sexual reproduction may be zoospores, pseudopodiospores, &c.

Multiple division is widely spread among Sporozoa, Sarcodina, and less so among Mastigophora, and is absent only in ciliates. Without dwelling on numerous examples, we shall note only the main varieties of syntomy.

The division of the individual in which the whole body is used up in the formation of the products of schizogony should be regarded as the original and primary method of multiple division. The schizonts of coccidia Eimeriidae, which usually break up completely into a bundle of vermicular merozoites arranged like orange lobules, is a good example of this type. In certain schizonts, however, a very small, purely plasmatic residual body may be left over. The method of formation of merozoites in the malaria parasites *Plasmodium* is on the whole similar except that the merozoites have a shorter, irregular shape; moreover, in this case there remains a small residue of the schizont body; it consists mainly of the products of excretion in the form of pigment (haematin) granules, which are not used in reproduction.

Trypanosoma lewisi, which undergoes schizogony in the cells of the alimentary tract of the rat flea, is completely divided into a group of vegetative individuals, &c.

In Gregarinida the development of gametes and their copulation takes place inside a cyst, each of the two partners forming the cyst being a gamont which gives rise to a large number of oval gametocytes, usually arranged in one layer on the surface of the irregularly bent large residual body of each partner. In certain gregarines (among Polycystidea) a small number of residual nuclei is retained in the cytoplasm of this body, while the residual body itself remains very motile for some time, bending inside the cyst and assisting in the mixing of the gametes belonging to both partners. The gametes unite in pairs, while the residual body disintegrates. Thus in this case gametocytes of both sexes are formed by multiple syntomy. In most gregarines the residual body does not display any activity.

Multiple division frequently takes place during the development of male gametes in Sporozoa (Coccidiida, Haemosporidia), the nucleus of the spherical microgametocytes dividing into numerous small nuclei (from ten to a thousand in certain *Eimeria*).

The nuclei, which are at first scattered in the cytoplasm of the microgametocyte, migrate to the periphery, where they are arranged in one layer, while the main central mass of the cytoplasm forms an enormous residual body. Microgametes enclosed in small amounts of cytoplasm later detach themselves from the surface of this body. In some species of this group the residual body breaks up during syntomy into separate islets, while microgametes are formed on their surface. The shape of the residual body, is, apparently, in this case a function of the size of the mother cell and of the number of the independent units produced. Thus in species of *Plasmodium* multiple division gives rise, on the one hand, to microgametes from a microgametocyte and, on the other, to sporozoites from the encysted zygote. Moreover, the microgametocyte is very small, producing only a small number of microgametes (six to ten), whereas the oocyst developed from the zygote (ookinete) is much larger, giving rise to thousands of thin filamentar sporozoites. In the microgametocyte the gametes are arranged around one central residual body; while in the oocyst the latter is either twisted into coils within the cyst, or it breaks up into separate islets, surrounded by a layer of sporozoites in a state of formation. Evidently the complication of the shape of the residual body during sporogony is due to the fact that this shape (provided the sporozoites are arranged in one layer

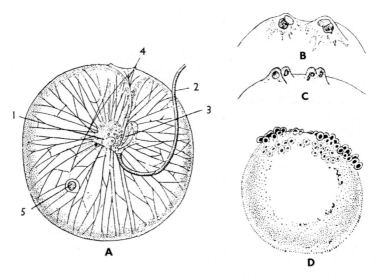

FIG. 150. Budding of *Noctiluca miliaris*.

(*A*) trophozoite; (*B*)–(*D*) budding on surface of body. 1, nucleus; 2, tentacle; 3, flagellum; 4, sulcus; 5, food. (From Doflein and Reichenow, 1929.)

on the surface of the plasma) facilitates the formation of a large number of sporozoites: on a regular, spherical surface a much smaller number of them could have developed than on a residual body with a fantastically coiled contour.

Finally, in exceptional cases of multiple division (*Noctiluca miliaris*, Fig. 150), the daughter individuals are formed only on a small area of the surface of the spherical schizont. In fact, in *Noctiluca* the nucleus approaches the very surface of the body during its so-called 'budding', pushing it out like a protuberance and dividing into numerous small nuclei, which in their turn push out the wall of the body in one area of the surface of the sphere. Each of these nuclei becomes surrounded by a small portion of the cytoplasm, and is transformed into a flagellate gamete; the gametes themselves then detach from the body of *Noctiluca*, which perishes after this. Hence in *Noctiluca* multiple fission leads to the formation of a swarm of gametes and the corpse of the parental organism. Such reproduction could hardly be called budding, since during budding one or several individuals of somewhat smaller size are separated from the living mother organism; whereas in *Noctiluca*, apart from the residual body, the whole of the mother individual is used up in the formation of gametes.

An analogous picture but of a somewhat different pattern is obtained during sexual reproduction of certain Schizogregarines, viz. in *Schizocystis sipunculi* (Fig. 151).

This gregarine was discovered by Dogiel (1907) in the alimentary tract of the gephyrean *Sipunculus*. In contrast to all the cases described by us, it multiplies by endogenous schizogony. A group of twenty to thirty merozoites is differentiated in the posterior half of the body, and a clearly outlined cavity, the 'brood chamber', is formed round them, opening at the posterior pole of the body through a special aperture with smooth edges, which obviously serves for the emergence of merozoites. The mother gregarine itself develops round the merozoites a kind of plasmatic cyst, composed of a large amount of cytoplasm and even of the residue of the vesicular nucleus.

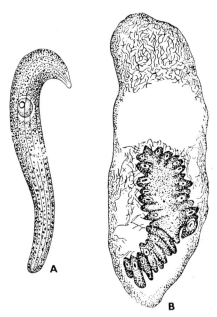

Fig. 151. Endogenous schizogony in gregarines *Schizocystis sipunculi*.

(*A*) adult gregarine; (*B*) formation of group of merozoites inside body. (After Dogiel, 1907.)

Certain types of multiple fission closely resemble the well-known forms of cleavage of eggs in Metazoa. Thus the total multiple fission in the schizonts of Coccidia is reminiscent of complete cleavage, in the form met with in a Ctenophora; then there is the surface multiple fission, analogous to the surface cleavage of eggs in insects (compare microgametocytes of Coccidiida); while in *Noctiluca* we have a process parallel to the discoidal cleavage of cephalopods. Finally, there exist the most unusual forms of multiple division, as, for example, endogenous schizogony. Obviously this similarity has no phylogenetic significance. However, they are of interest as evidence that some processes of evolution are limited in the number of ways by which they can be effected. Hence the inevitability and frequency of convergence of similar pathways for processes, which have an analogous physiological significance in diverse organisms; such convergences proceed along paths easiest for realization.

The other principle used for the classification of types of multiple fission is based on the further destiny of the products of fission and on the place of schizogony in the life-cycle of the protozoon. According to this character three types of multiple fission may be distinguished.

1. *Multiple fission is a stage of asexual reproduction, its products being called merozoites.* This type is observed among Sarcodina and Sporozoa. Among Sarcodina this type is observed first of all among parasitic amoebae (*Endamoeba blattae, Entamoeba*); the segmentation of the animal into merozoites takes place when the animal leaves the multinucleate cyst, and the merozoites have the characteristics of either pseudopodiospores or amoebospores. Furthermore, schizogony of this type represents an obligatory stage of asexual reproduction in the complex cycle of all Foraminifera, and as a result of it pseudopodiospores are produced, developing into the megalospheric asexual generation of foraminifera.

Unfortunately the developmental cycle of radiolarians has not been sufficiently studied. This cycle includes multiple fission, giving rise to the biflagellate zoospores. However, the fate of these zoospores has in most cases remained unexplained. In Acantharia they copulate in pairs and represent gametes, i.e. they do not belong to the category being considered by us at the moment.

Schizogony is widely distributed among Sporozoa: it occurs during asexual reproduction of Schizogregarinida (Fig. 151), Coccidiida, and Haemosporidia, being sometimes repeated for a number of generations until the sexual process intervenes. There are some data on the occurrence of schizogony in Microsporidia.

An examination of the nature of merozoites, produced in asexual reproduction, reveals that they differ, and the merozoites reflect in their structure the structural type of the given class: thus in Sarcodina merozoites repeat the amoeboid type (pseudopodiospores), in Sporozoa the gregarinoid type, i.e. of a small heteropolar vermicule with a definite permanent shape. In the rare cases of schizogony in Mastigophora (certain *Trypanosoma, Dinamoebidium*) the merozoites repeat the form of their vegetative stage (*Trypanosoma*) or the ancestral group of the given order (gymnodinium-like merozoites of *Dinamoebidium*).

The complete absence of schizogony in ciliates is most interesting. In our opinion it is due to the higher organization and nuclear dimorphism of this class of Protozoa.

2. *Multiple fission represents a stage of sexual reproduction; its products being called gametes.* This category includes the founders of the microspheric generation of many foraminiferes, viz. flagellated gametes and the isospores of the radiolarians Acantharia, the copulation of which was observed by Ševjakov (1926). When the sexual individuals are anisogametes, the male gametes bear flagella (the majority of Coccidiida and Haemosporidia). In general, flagellospores form the predominant type of the products of syntomy, and exceptions to this rule have to be specially indicated. Thus in certain Schizogregarinida (*Lipocystis*) isogametes produced by syntomy

have the appearance of round, naked bodies, whose origin from flagello-spores is evident from the presence in them of a centriole and of the base of a flagellum. Oval or round gametes without flagella are formed in certain Eugregarinida (*Actinocephalus, Lankesteria,* and others). Gametes of both sexes in the coccidian *Hepatozoon* are of gregarinoid character and are devoid of flagella. It is interesting that the microgametocytes produced by syntomy retain their gregarine form much more often (for example in coccidia *Orcheobius, Adelina, Karyolysus*), but when repeated fission of a microgametocyte gives rise to four microgametes they exhibit, to a certain extent, the characters of zoospores.

3. *Multiple fission takes place after a sexual process, giving rise to sporo-zoites.* This type of syntomy is often encountered among Sporozoa, and it commonly takes place under the protection of the spore membrane at the expense of the zygotes present in the spores. In Haemosporidia, where the spores are absent, sporozoites develop directly in the cyst formed by the zygote. The sporozoites never have flagella; they are of gregarinoid type.

Plasmotomy

The necessity of distinguishing plasmotomy as a special type of asexual reproduction seems doubtful. This is the name usually applied to the division of multinucleate Protozoa into two or more smaller multinucleate individuals; during this the fission of the cytoplasm proceeds independently and is not co-ordinated with nuclear division. Depending on the size of the parts that are being detached, all transitions from divisions to simple or multiple budding are represented here. Asexual reproduction by plasmo-tomy occurs in Mycetozoa, certain coelomic Myxosporidia, Haplosporidia, and some amoebae (*Pelomyxa*)—in other words among plasmodial organ-isms.

Colony formation as a result of asexual reproduction

It is perfectly natural to consider the tendency to form colonies after asexual reproduction, since the formation of these is a result of incomplete agamic reproduction. Colonies deserve careful attention, as one of the phases in the development of higher forms of individuality.

True colonies are encountered in all classes of Protozoa, except Sporozoa. Three different criteria may be applied for the classification of various types of colonies in Protozoa. They may be distinguished by the length of time during which members of the colony remain in a colonial state, or by the morphological structure of the colony, or finally by the method by which the colony was formed. These three methods of assessment throw light on various aspects of the problem of colonial organisms.

According to the duration of the colonial state, colonies may be either temporary or permanent. Temporary colonies provide a good illustration of the process of the origin of permanent colonies from forms reproducing by simple transverse (or pseudo-transverse) division. All temporary colonies are linear or catenoid colonies. Such are the temporary linear colonies of free-living Dinoflagellata (*Ceratium* and others), the temporary chains of the ciliates Astomata, and a few others.

The duration of the connexion between the members of such colonies varies considerably, depending probably on different conditions of the environment, for example in Dinoflagellata on the calm or disturbed state of the water.

There are some data on the influence of the conditions of the environment on the very formation of temporary colonies. Evidence of this is given by Chatton's observations (1921), which show that in cultures of *Colpidium* with *Bacterium coli* dividing individuals form chains of two or even four individuals.

Permanent colonies may have diverse structures. First of all they are sometimes arranged according to the linear type. *Polykrikos*, a remarkable representative of marine dinoflagellates, may serve as an example of such a colony. Constructed according to the type of linear colonies of armoured dinoflagellates, like *Ceratium*, this naked flagellate forms permanent complexes of four individuals permanently connected with each other in a row and in a state of broad communication with each other. Since it is equivalent to four undivided individuals, *Polykrikos* contains 4 nuclei and 8 of each set of other organoids, namely transverse grooves, flagella, centrioles, &c. Unfortunately the cycle of development of *Polykrikos* remains so far unknown. In this case all the individuals of the colony are so closely united together that they form as it were one organism of a higher order.

Dendritic colonies, encountered among the flagellates and ciliates, are much more widely distributed. In dendritic colonies, in contrast to *Polykrikos*, an alloplasmatic substance, secreted by the components of the colony as gelatinous, mucous, or chitinoid membranes, frequently plays an important part in the formation of the colony.

From the ecological point of view, dendritic colonies are usually associated with a sessile mode of life. Only in exceptional cases (*Dinobryon*, Fig. 152, and *Epistylis rotans*), and apparently as a secondary adaptation, some of them pass over into the plankton.

In the overwhelming majority of dendritic Mastigophora the connexion between the individuals of the colony is secured by means of alloplasmatic stalks and loricae of the components of the colony. Such is the case of colonies of the type of *Dinobryon*, *Hyalobryon*, *Poteriodendron*, and others, in which the parent individual is situated inside a chitinoid lorica, while the products of division (one or both) build new loricae adhering to the free margin of the maternal one. In others, as in *Colacium*, the parent simply sits on a mucilaginous stalk; when it divides the end of the former stalk is prolonged into two short branches, at the ends of which are situated the daughter individuals. During the thickening and shortening of the alloplasmatic stalks, the individuals resulting from repeated longitudinal division form at the end of the stalk of the branches clusters with adjacent bases, as in *Cephalothamnium*, *Anthophysa* (Fig. 152), *Spongomonas*, and *Diplosiga*. Organic (cytoplasmatic) connexion between the individuals of this kind

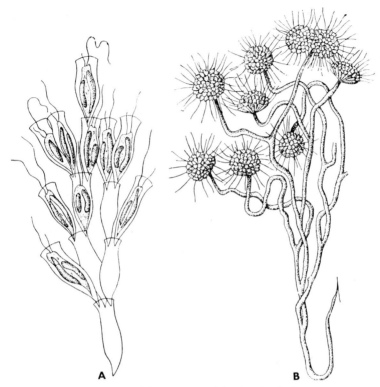

FIG. 152. Different types of dendroid colonies.

(A) *Dinobron*; (B) *Anthophysa*. (Modified, after Grassé, 1952.)

of colony is absent, so that the only useful interaction between the components of the colony is due to the increased current of water circulating round the colonial flagellates.

Dendritic colonies of peritrichous ciliates resemble in many respects the flagellate colonies in appearance. In some of them all the individuals of the colony are enclosed in a common mucilaginous mass, as, for example, in *Ophrydium*. In the majority of cases the colonies have the appearance of dichotomously branching trees, exhibiting different kinds of connexions between the components of the colony and various degrees of polymorphism. The family Epistylidae manifest the weakest connexion and the least differentiation. Its representatives form fairly large, bushy, dichotomously branching colonies seated on cuticular, hollow, non-contractile stalks. The next phase in the development of the colonial association is represented by the colonies of certain Vorticellidae, for instance in *Carchesium*. In these forms, a contractile myoneme is present inside the stalks, the myonemes of separate individuals joining each other at the points of the branching of the stalk; however, they are not directly connected with each other, therefore the individual stalks contract independently of each other.

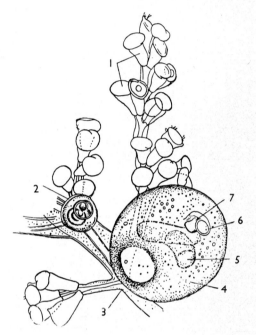

FIG. 153. *Zoöthamnium arbuscula*; part of branch of colony with macrozooids.

1, microzooids; 2, growing macrozooid; 3, scopula; 4, fully-grown macrozooid; 5, macronucleus; 6, peristome; 7, contractile vacuole. (After Fursenko, 1929.)

Finally, in species of the genus *Zoothamnium* the stalks of separate individuals of the dendroid colony are directly connected and the colony contracts as a whole. The highest degree of connexion and integration of a colony into a peculiar multicellular whole is attained by the beautiful palm-like colony of *Zoothamnium arbuscula*, exhaustively studied by Fursenko (1929) (Figs. 153, 154).

The founder of the colony *Zoothamnium arbuscula* is a large hyper-trophied individual—a macrozooid (Fig. 154), which breaks away from its paternal colony. After a swimming period the macrozooid attaches itself to the substratum by its posterior end and develops a long stalk. Simultaneously the macrozooid divides repeatedly by multiple longitudinal (pseudo-longitudinal) and not quite uniform fission, proceeding in precise successive stages. Eventually on the originally common stalk a colony of nine branches is produced, orientated in a very definite manner, two of the

branches being the main ones. In the early stages of the development of
the colony the individuals composing it are all completely equivalent and of

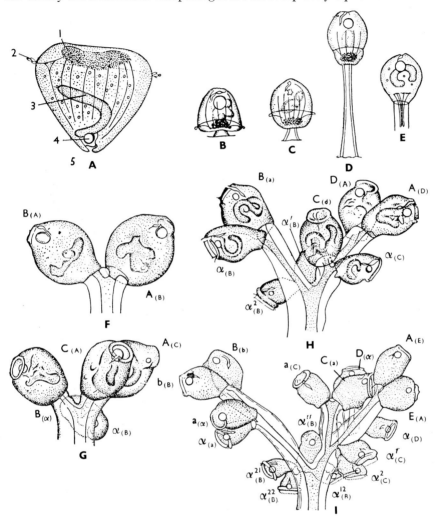

FIG. 154. Development of colony of *Zoothamnium arbuscula*.

(*A*) macrozooid (swarmer) broken away; (*B*)–(*E*) growth of stalk of colony after attachment of
swarmer (fig. (*E*) shows growth of scopula into stalk); (*F*)–(*I*) development of colony after stalk
had grown to full length. 1, scopula; 2, circlet of aboral cilia; 3, macronucleus; 4, contractile
vacuole; 5, peristome; sequence of formation of cells indicated by letters. (After Fursenko,
1929.)

the same size. But at a definite moment some of them, located at well-defined
points, begin to grow intensively, to distend, and are transformed into
macrozooids, which break away from the colony when their development is
completed. Asexual reproduction of the colony is carried out exclusively

by these swarmers. Moreover, under certain conditions special sexual individuals are formed on the colony of *Z. arbuscula* at precisely fixed points: two macroconjugants at the bases of both main branches, and numerous microconjugants at the ends of all the branches.

The high level of the integration of the colony is evident from the fact that the hypertrophic growth of macrozooids proceeds at the expense of the small individuals surrounding them (the mouth of the macrozooids themselves is somewhat reduced) and also that the small individuals die when the existence of the colony comes to an end. Thus the colonies of *Z. arbuscula* are in no way inferior to the *Volvox* colonies either in the permanency of their form, or the regularity of their morphogenesis, or the polymorphism of the individuals, as well as in the presence of plasmatic bridges and in the division of labour between them, nor, finally, in the differentiation of the individuals into somatic and reproductive forms.

Discoid colonies, composed of a group of individuals, arranged in one plane as a single-layered plate, mostly round, more rarely of some other shape, represent the rarest type of colonies. They include only certain species of flagellates, such as *Cyclonexis* (among Chrysomonadida), *Bicosoeca* among choanoflagellates, as well as *Gonium* and *Platydorina* (among the Phytomonadida). The individuals of these colonies are united with each other by a gelatinous matrix.

On the other hand, spheroid, sub-spheroid, or ellipsoid colonies are common among the flagellates. Among Sarcodina, certain radiolarian Spumellaria, such as *Sphaerozoum* (spheroid colony) and *Collozoum* (a sausage-shaped ellipsoid colony) belong to this type. These radiolarian colonies develop as a result of a repeated division of the central capsule of the parent individual, while the gelatinous extracapsular mass remains undivided. In this way dozens of separate central capsules with nuclei are embedded in the common greatly expanded gelatinous mass. Spheroid colonies are encountered much more frequently among flagellates; they are known among Chrysomonadida (Fig. 155), and especially among Phytomonadida (family Volvocidae). The connexion is at its weakest in such colonies as *Synura*, where several dozens of individuals are distributed radially around a common centre, converging on it by their posterior ends; while in *Uroglenopsis* and *Chrysosphaerella* (Fig. 155) the individuals are arranged radially in the peripheral layer of the gelatinous sphere without any closer union between them. The union is closer in *Uroglena*, where from the posterior ends of the individuals arranged in the same way as in *Uroglenopsis*, slender cords of a denser gelatinous substance run to the centre of the gelatinous sphere, where they unite in a common gelatinous mass.

A long list of species forming spheroid colonies are known for the family Volvocidae (Fig. 156). These colonies vary considerably in their form, the number of individuals, and the degree of integration. At the beginning of

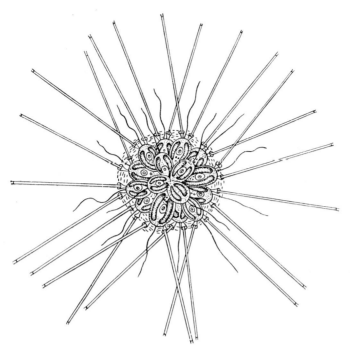

FIG. 155. Colonial Chrysomonadine *Chrysosphaerella* with long siliceous needles; a nucleus and two chromatophores are seen inside the
individuals. (After Doflein and Reichenow, 1929.)

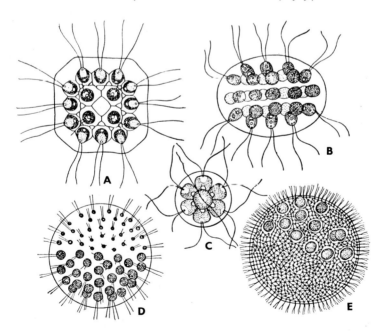

FIG. 156. Colonies of various Volvocales.

(*A*) *Gonium pectorale*; (*B*) *Eudorina elegans*; (*C*) *Pandorina morum*; (*D*) *Pleudo-
rina californica*; (*E*) *Volvox aureus*. (After Fott, 1959.)

the series are colonies with few members, consisting of 4 (*Conium sociale*) or 8 (*Stephanosphaera*) individuals arranged in the form of a cross or a ring along the equator of a gelatinous sphere. All the individuals of these species, when separated from the body of the colony by division, may give rise to a new colony.

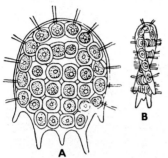

FIG. 157. *Platydorina* colony viewed (*A*) from its flat side and (*B*) from its edge. (After Kofoid, 1899.)

The 16-membered colonies of *Pandorina* and 32-membered colonies of *Eudorina elegans* and *Platydorina* (Fig. 157) represent the next step in the increase of a colony. However, in *Eudorina* and *Platydorina* there are indications of a main axis: moreover the stigmata of the component individuals of the colony diminish progressively from the anterior to the posterior end of the latter. Furthermore, in *Eudorina*, and in still more complexly organized colonies, the individual cells, when separated from the body of the colony, lose their ability to restore the whole colony. Thus potential morphogenetic property of the separate components decreases with the complication of the structure of the colony.

In another species of *Eudorina*, *E. Illinoisensis*, there is a further differentiation of the cells of the colony, namely the 'distribution of labour'; thus 4 cells of the anterior circlet of individuals lose their ability to reproduce, being transformed into sterile somatic cells, which differ also from the other 28 reproductive cells by their small size.

In *Pleodorina californica* this process of differentiation of the individuals proceeds still further. The anterior half of the spheroid colony of *Pleodorina* is composed of 32–64 small sterile cells, while the posterior half consists of the same number of large reproductive deep green gonidia.

Finally, in the genus *Volvox*, at present separated into several genera, colonial formation reaches the highest degree of complication and integration. The total number of individuals reaches, in various species of this type, from 512 to 16,000–20,000 in the largest species of *Volvox*. It therefore corresponds to a number of descendants produced by 9–10 and even 15 synchronous repeated divisions. The number of the component individuals is as constant as in the colonies previously described, but their differentiation into somatic and reproductive forms proceeds much further. In the first place, the great majority of individuals are somatic, only 6–30 individuals being hypertrophied gonidia; the latter are situated only in the posterior half of the sphere. Secondly, the axial orientation of the somatic individuals bears a pronouncedly graduated character. Individuals of the anterior pole are smaller than the rest and of paler colour, but then they possess larger stigmata. These characters are reversed as one moves backwards. Finally, in the majority of the species of *Volvox* the components of the colony are connected with each other by plasmatic bridges or plasmodesmata, which radiate from each cell and bind all members of the colony into a kind of syncytium. This type of connexion between the individuals of the colony creates a physiological unity between them, one of its characteristics being the hypertrophical growth of gonidia at the expense of somatic individuals. When new, young colonies are formed at the expense of the gonidia the parent colony perishes.

In general the series of varying forms of Volvocidae demonstrate with wonderful clarity the progressive evolution of the initially small and simple colonies into highly differentiated organisms, which have strictly speaking no longer a polyzooidal but a multicellular organization.

According to Zachvatkin (1949) another criterion which may be used for the separation of the colonies into various categories is their mode of formation. Zachvatkin recognizes two such modes and accordingly establishes two types of colonies:

1. *Monotomic colonies*, developed step by step by repeated multiplication by simple division, with zooids performing their vegetative functions uninterruptedly. In this type he places the majority of dendroid colonies, apart from *Zoothamnium arbuscula* (see p. 278) and all the spheroid colonies, except for those of Volvocidae.

2. *Palintomic colonies*, originating as a result of palintomy. Zachvatkin refers to this type the Volvocidae and *Zoothamnium arbuscula* as well as a few Peritricha. The method of their development is very similar to the process of cleavage of the egg of Metazoa, in that the cells formed as a result of division do not grow and the products of division (cleavage) are arranged in a strictly regular pattern relatively to each other. For instance, in *Eudorina* (Fig. 158) this process proceeds according to the type of tabular palintomy and leads first to the development of a disk composed of 8 cells, 4 of which form in the centre a characteristic figure of a cross. As a result of a further cleavage the number of cells increases to 32. The cellular disk formed as the result of palintomy is first bent towards the side where the flagella and stigmata are situated. This process is called 'incurvation'. It is followed by the opposite process called 'excurvation', when the cellular disks are turned inside out in the opposite direction, after which flagella and stigmata are facing outwards and the colony becomes spheroid.

The process of palintomy during development of the *Volvox* colony is still more complicated; here it bears a considerable resemblance in the arrangement of individual cells with the arrangement of blastomeres during the spiral cleavage in Annelides and Mollusca. The processes of 'incurvation' and 'excurvation' are also well marked during the development of *Volvox* (Fig. 159).

The classification into monotomic and palintomic division has certain

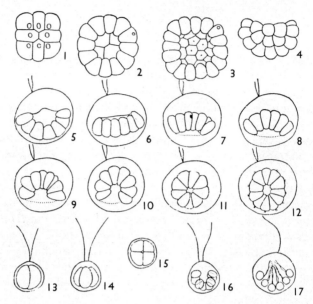

FIG. 158. Development of colonies of various Eudorinidae.

1–4, *Eudorina illinoisensis*: 1, tabular 8-cell stage; 2, 16-cell stage; 3, calyciform 32-cell stage from above, and 4 from side; 5–12, *Eudorina elegans*: 5, incurvation; 6–11, successive stages of excurvation; 12, beginning of differentiation of blastula of *Eudorina elegans*; 13–17, cleavage and incurvation of *Gonium pectorale*. (From Zachvatkin, 1949.)

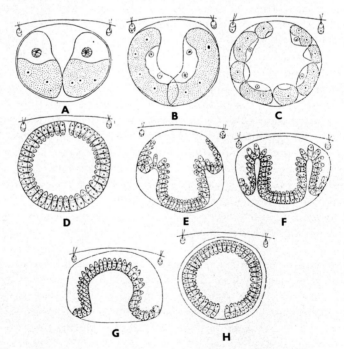

FIG. 159. Development of colony of *Volvox* (schematized).

(*A*) 2-cell stage; (*B*) 4-cell stage; (*C*), (*D*) first vesicular phase; (*E*)–(*G*) excurvation of first vesicular phase; (*H*) young colony after excurvation. (After Zimmermann, 1921.)

drawbacks, since not all the organisms referred to the second category conform to the criteria postulated for palintomy.

In fact, although colonies in Peritricha, in particular *Zoothamnium*, originate from one hypertrophied individual, the individuals produced as a result of fission of the sessile macrozooid feed and reach normal size from the stage of forty-eight cells, while all the numerous further fissions represent ordinary monotomy; apart from this the *Zoothamnium* colony, though very regular in structure, does not manifest the permanency of cellular composition, which according to Zachvatkin characterizes palintomic colonies. It would rather seem that the difference between the colonies of the type of Volvocidae and those of Peritricha and colonies of the type of *Uroglena*, *Synura*, and others is of the same order as the difference between Metazoa with a permanent cellular composition (Rotatoria, Nematodes, Appendiculariae) and those without it.

Finally, in addition to the types of formation of colonies established by Zachvatkin, there should also be added the symplasmatic type, characteristic of the radiolarians; in this case the division into unicellular individuals does not take place at all during the formation of the colony; only the nucleus and central capsule of the parent individual divide, whereas the whole of the extracapsular cytoplasm remains common throughout. This type is found in the radiolarian colonies of the type of *Collozoum*, *Sphaerozoum*, and others of the order Spumellaria.

Multiplication of colonies

This section does not deal with the asexual reproduction of separate individuals of Protozoa, but with the methods whereby the number of their multicellular complexes, that is colonies taken as a whole, multiplies. There are altogether three such methods.

The first method consists in division of the whole colony into two halves, as a result of which two colonies are produced of half the size of the original one. This method is characteristic of colonial radiolarians and free-swimming spheroid colonies in Chrysomonadida (*Synura*, *Uroglenopsis*, and others). Among the sessile ones, a somewhat similar phenomenon is observed during the process of the subdivision of *Anthophysa* colonies (see Fig. 152), when new branches of the stalk of the complex colony are formed by division into two of the globular groups of individuals.

The second method consists in the emigration of separate individuals from the body of the colony and in the foundation by them of new colonies. This method is common among sessile colonies, both of flagellates and of Peritricha. The emigrating individuals represent swarmer-parents of new colonies. In some cases (the flagellates) the swarmers do not differ in any respect from the other individuals of the colony; in others (Peritricha) the swarmers develop before breaking away from the colony additional locomotor organoids (a circlet of cilia round the aboral pole); furthermore, sometimes (*Zoothamnium arbuscula*) they undergo hypertrophic growth at the expense of the other individuals of the colony.

The third method is effected among the spheroid and other colonies in Phytomonadida (*Pandorina, Eudorina,* and others) and is in some respects essentially similar to the second method. In this case all the individuals of the colony simultaneously become in effect homologous to swarmers of the colonies of the previous category. Here, however, each equivalent of a swarmer remains immobile until a whole new colony develops under its cellular membrane by repeated divisions. Then flagella develop on the individual organisms and the colony frees itself from the membrane of the parent cell and swims away.

Regeneration in Protozoa and its connexion with asexual reproduction. Regeneration in some of its aspects reveals a close relationship with the phenomena of asexual reproduction. Regeneration is natural to the majority of Protozoa, and this phenomenon can be investigated by two methods which are complementary to each other. One of these is experimental regeneration produced artificially by surgical intervention; the other method consists in observations on natural or physiological regeneration during division, conjugation, or encystment in various Protozoa.

Natural regeneration, connected with the peculiarities of the life-cycle, is especially widely spread among ciliates (during division, Fig. 160, conjugation, encystment), in flagellates (during division and encystment), and among Sarcodina (during division and encystment). Natural regeneration is not usually observed in Sporozoa.

Experimental regeneration is very easily produced among a variety of Protozoa, except Sporozoa. Dembowski (1913) and Sokolov (1924) failed to obtain regeneration of Sporozoa in cases of injury.

Experimental regeneration is of great importance, since it allows conclusions to be drawn on the comparative importance of various organoids of a protozoon both for its existence in general and for the fulfilment of certain of its physiological functions.

One of the first experiments of this type is the elucidation of the significance of the nucleus in the life of a protozoon. If an amoeba is cut in half, the portions containing the nucleus retain all their vital functions, among them that of growth and reproduction, so that they soon restore a perfectly normal appearance. On the other hand, the enucleate portions of an amoeba behave quite differently. They retain, it is true, their ability to form pseudopodia, their contractile vacuole continues to pulsate for a certain time, but they either do not ingest food, or, if they do, they do not digest it. The swallowing of food which has already commenced as well as defecation proceed to the end, but the discharge of mucus essential in the life of amoebae ceases in portions deprived of a nucleus.

However, strictly speaking there is no true regeneration in amoebae, since they do not possess organoids to be restored after the dissection: there is a regeneration only of the substance, but not of the organoids. Nuclei removed from the body of Protozoa are also unable to regenerate the

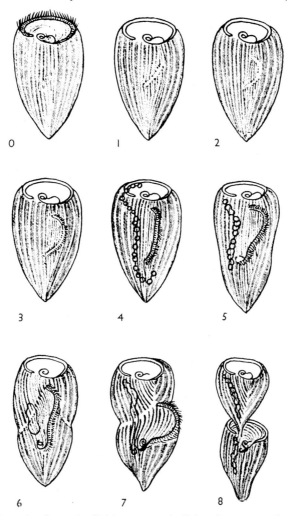

FIG. 160. Stages in division as seen in living *Stentor coeruleus*.

Stage 0. First indication of fission: a splitting of granular bands at the bulk-centre of the cell on the oral side. (Fine striping of frontal field and ciliary membranelles shown here, but omitted in remaining sketches.)

plasmatic components of the body, and they perish. Regeneration of various organoids is more pronounced in the higher Protozoa possessing a more complex structure, especially in ciliates.

Among the ciliates, *Stentor* and various Hypotricha were found to be the most suitable objects for regeneration experiments; *Stentor* owing to its large size and the long, segmented macronucleus; Hypotricha owing to the pronounced morphological and physiological differentiation of its locomotor organoids (cirri), which makes it possible to follow the changes taking place when the locomotor apparatus is restored.

As in the case of Sarcodina, the nucleus has a decisive influence on the further fate of the dissected fragments in ciliates.

Fragments of *Stentor* devoid of a nucleus are able to restore or to re-differentiate the lost parts only to a very small extent. However, when a fragment contains a section of the peristome it is regenerated. Even so, the loss of their ability to capture food soon cause these segments to degenerate and disintegrate.

The role played by the micronucleus and macronucleus in the regeneration of ciliates has been much discussed, but the problem has not been fully solved. According to some investigators, both nuclei are required for the restoration of a normal individual; while others believe that regeneration takes place also in segments devoid of a micronucleus.

Thus Calkins (1911*a*, *b*) and later Young (1922) found that in *Uronychia* (Hypotricha, Fig. 161) regeneration takes place in amicronucleate fragments, but that in 3–4 days they become abnormal and perish, as a result, apparently, of starvation. If *Uronychia* were cut in two halves, one with the micronucleus and the other without, only the former was capable of fission, although both had completely regenerated their outward shape. Hence in this species regeneration of the external form is possible without the micronucleus, but the final, physiological regeneration cannot be attained without it.

On the other hand, the possibility of regeneration without the participation of a micronucleus is supported both by the existence of amicronucleate strains of ciliates, and by the capacity of such strains for normal regeneration. Thus a strain *Oxytricha fallax*, which did not possess a micronucleus and was cultivated in this state for two years, manifested completely normal regeneration after dissections.

It has been observed that the ciliate *Blepharisma* (Heterotricha) is unable to regenerate when the macronucleus is completely absent. However, when the operation is performed in the early stages of division, such fragments sometimes regenerate; but later they perish in spite of the presence of a micronucleus.

Schwartz (1935) has demonstrated that in *Stentor* regeneration is considerably dependent on the macronucleus; fragments of the body devoid of the macronucleus but retaining their micronuclei behave in the same manner as completely enucleate fragments. They control the external shape of their body, but are unable to digest food and are doomed to perish.

In some cases the ability to regenerate depends not only on the presence of a fragment of the nucleus, but also on the adequacy of the size of the portion of the body left after the operation. Thus Lilly as early as 1896 obtained regeneration of pieces of Stentor measuring 70–80 μ in diameter which were equal to 1/30 of the volume of the whole body. B. Sokolov (1924) refers to his experiments in which complete regeneration was obtained with portions of *Spirostomum* of 1/57, 1/69 and portions of *Dileptus* of 1/70, 1/75 of the total volume of the body.

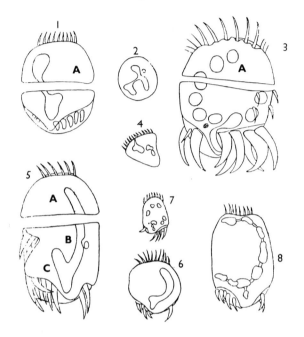

FIG. 161. Regeneration of injuries in *Uronychia transfuga*.

1, individual operated immediately after division; 2, segment *A*, 3 days later: no regeneration has taken place; 3, individual cut across 5 hours after division; 4, segment *A*, 3 days after operation: no regeneration; 5, individual cut into 3 fragments *A*, *B*, and *C* at beginning of fission; 6, fragment *A* has regenerated 24 hours after the operation into a normal individual but devoid of micronucleus; 7, *B* has regenerated into a normal miniature individual; 8, *C* has regenerated into a normal individual. (After Calkins, 1911b.)

As regards the nuclei themselves, in *Stentor* one or two segments of their moniliform macronucleus are able to restore the whole nucleus. Hence the impression of a more or less homogeneous structure of the macronucleus.

When some of the micronuclei are removed in ciliates possessing a multiple set of them, the number of micronuclei missing from the complete set is made up by division of the single remaining micronucleus.

Weisz's investigations on *Stentor* and *Blepharisma* (1948a, b, 1949a, b, c, 1950a, b, 1951a, 1954) have thrown new light on the course of regeneration and regulatory processes in ciliates.

Are all the segments of the moniliform macronucleus of *Stentor* equipotential in determining the regeneration process? Weisz has demonstrated that the answer to this question will differ according to whether it is a case of a ciliate just divided, and half-way between two divisions, or a ciliate which must soon proceed to its next fission. It is known that during the process of division the segments of the macronucleus are concentrated into one non-segmented nucleus, which extends in the form of a ribbon, is constricted, and later regains its characteristic moniliform structure. Weisz demonstrated that in young, i.e. recently divided *Stentor*, all the segments of the nucleus are equipotential, for each of them can ensure the normal course of regeneration. Later there is a gradual change in the potentiality of separate segments of the macronucleus, which becomes the more pronounced the closer the next division: while the anterior segments retain their ability to ensure regeneration, the posterior ones lose it, whereas the central segments secure only partial regeneration. Weisz (1950) has demonstrated by special cytochemical methods that this change in the potentialities of the parts of the macronucleus proceeds parallel with alterations in the content of a polymerized form of DNA. In 'young' macronuclei DNA is uniformly distributed in all the segments and its content becomes considerably reduced in the posterior ones. During the process of division of the macronucleus the content of DNA in different parts of it again becomes uniform.

In *Blepharisma undulans*, as well as in *Stentor*, the potentialities of the macronucleus undergo a change in the interval between two divisions (Weisz, 1949c). In this case, however, these changes are of a somewhat different character. The anterior and posterior segments of the macronucleus are able to regenerate whereas the intermediate ones are not.

It should be noted, however, that Tartar (1957), who had worked on the regeneration of *Stentor* and *Condylostoma*, could not confirm Weisz's data regarding the potentialities of the segments of macronucleus during regeneration. This problem is obviously in need of further investigation.

The change in the regenerative ability according to the stage of the life-cycle has previously been established by Calkins (1911b) in the hypotrichous ciliate *Uronychia*.

The dependence of regeneration from different phases of life-cycle. Independently of Weisz, and much earlier, Calkins (1911) demonstrated on *Uronychia* that the regenerative ability of these ciliates was weak when the operation is performed soon after the division, and that regeneration takes place only in the presence of the micro- and macronucleus. Half-way between two divisions the regenerative capacity is slightly increased: such fragments are sometimes capable of regenerating in the complete absence of the micronucleus. Regeneration proceeds most readily when the ciliate is in the pre-division stage. When the cut was made somewhat in front of the 'projected plane of transverse division, three well-formed but small individuals were obtained: one small, one produced from the anterior amicronucleate fragment, and two others produced as a result of the vegetative division commenced before the operation, but completed after it; one of these individuals corresponded to the separated posterior daughter individual of the parent, the other from the remaining portion—the prospective anterior daughter individual. Both individuals possessed a micronucleus and were completely developed, but the anterior individual was, in conformity with its origin, of a very small size. Calkins's experiments were checked many times and confirmed on *Uronychia* as well as on other Hypotricha.

In some other ciliates (*Spathidium, Paramecium*) the regularity discovered by Calkins was not observed, so Tartar (1939) doubted the correctness of the interpretation of Calkins's experiments.

The state of conjugation does not deprive the ciliates of their ability to regenerate. In this respect the clearest results were obtained by Calkins (1921), which were facilitated by a fortunate choice of the object of research, namely the ciliate *Uroleptus mobilis*. The body of this species is extended in length and ribbon-like; furthermore in mating the animals unite by the anterior ends; the exchange of the migrating pronuclei also takes place through the coalesced anterior ends, while the stationary pronuclei move far away to the centre of the body. Consequently the separation of pairs and the removal of the anterior ends of the body with the male pronuclei are much facilitated. It was found that the members of a conjugating pair may be cut from each other, and that in general this does not disturb the further course of the process of reorganization. When the anterior ends of the body are cut away together with the male pronuclei, large posterior fragments remain, each containing only a female pronucleus and the remnants of the disintegrating macronucleus. Nevertheless, the cut individuals obtained in this way regenerate completely and all their vegetative and reproductive functions are restored.

Poljanskij (1938) has separated by bisection conjugating pairs of *Bursaria*. In most individuals separated from each other the process of the reconstruction of the nuclear apparatus is continued 4–6 hours after separation, but is replaced by autogamy, in the course of which fusion of pronuclei belonging to the same individual takes place, and the resulting autogamous synkaryon restores the complete nuclear apparatus.

Numerous experiments have been carried out in recent years on the separation of conjugating *Paramecium*, with comparable results, except for the experiments on *Spathidium* (Moore, 1924), which apparently differs from the others by its much lower regenerative capacity.

In the process of regeneration in ciliates, in addition to the nuclear apparatus, an important part is played by the ectoplasm and the infraciliature associated with it (Weisz, 1951, 1954; Lwoff, 1950; Tartar, 1961). The presence of the ectoplasm is essential for the satisfactory progress of regeneration in ciliates. In the basal apparatus of the ciliates (infraciliature) there are certain areas which play an organizing role during morphogenesis of the locomotor organoids. In *Stentor* this area of infraciliature is represented by the first longitudinal row of kinetosomes, situated in the area of the suture, where the longitudinally running rows of cilia meet at an acute angle; this suture is known as the left boundary stripe. The distances between the ciliary rows and granular stripes, situated to right and left of the suture, are different. Those to the left are arranged far more closely to one another than those to the right. These distances gradually become wider from left to right. The region where narrow and wide stripes come into contact plays the role of an organizing centre, inducing formation of the primordium of the oral complex of organoids during physiological as well as traumatic regeneration. This question was especially thoroughly studied by Weisz and Tartar, and is discussed in detail in Tartar's interesting book *The Biology of Stentor* (1961). For studying the morphogenetic role of the boundary region between wide and narrow granular stripes, Tartar widely used regeneration methods as well as transplantation and grafting of *Stentors*. During the early stages of primordium formation the determination of its parts (the future mouth apparatus and the adoral zone of membranelles) is not yet definitive, and regulation occurs after disturbances of the primordium integrity. During the later stages the determination becomes more strong, and damaging of certain parts of the primordium results in *Stentors* with abnormal peristomal and oral apparatus. Tartar formulates this regularity as follows:

'Hence there is good evidence that the oral anlage is induced to form mouthparts by its normal surrounding. Once this interaction has taken place and although there are yet no beginnings of mouthparts, the primordium is then determined and can develop completely regardless of where it is placed' (Tartar, 1961, p. 176).

Tartar finds that the complex interaction of parts during physiological (at asexual reproduction) and traumatic regeneration in *Stentor* (and, probably, other ciliates) has analogies with the embryonal development of Metazoa, and particularly of Amphibia. These analogies are doubtlessly of great biological interest, because they indicate the existence of general regularities of animal morphogenesis at the unicellular as well as at the multicellular level. Tartar writes the following about it:

'It is therefore remarkable that on the cell level in *Stentor* we find something very much like induction as manifested in the embryogenesis of Amphibia. In both cases there is the evocation of a major elaboration determining the principal axis of the organism—neural tube in salamander and feeding organelles in *Stentor*—around which a new individuality can be organized' (Tartar, 1961, p. 194).

Hence in the phenomena of regeneration and reorganization of ciliates an important part is played, on the one hand, by the macronucleus, on the other, by the ectoplasmic structures—two independent systems which interact physiologically during the processes of morphogenesis.

The dependence of regeneration on the race to which the animal under experiment belongs. The most reliable work on this problem belongs to Tartar (1939), who studied regeneration in 25 races, belonging to 7 different species of the genus *Paramecium*, and carried out about 900 operations.

Tartar distinguishes two steps in the process of regeneration; first the healing from the trauma and then complete regeneration. At first, when examining the regeneration processes after minor injuries, he came to the conclusion that each *Paramecium* that is capable of recovery from the injury caused by the operation possesses the power of complete regeneration. Then Tartar carried out more serious operations, cutting off the greater part of the posterior end of the body. Complete regeneration took place in 93 per cent. of the individuals which recovered from the operation. Judging from this, the power of regeneration in *Paramecium* is much stronger than was formerly thought. Hence, the author concluded that he was unable to distinguish any special racial or species peculiarities within the genus *Paramecium*.

Dependence of regeneration on extent of injury. There is considerable evidence of the dependence of regeneration on the extent of the injury of the organism, but the nature of the dependence varies very much and is sometimes even unexpected. Thus in a number of cases regeneration is accompanied by the phenomena of preliminary dedifferentiation, which is especially evident in the order Hypotricha; moreover, according to the extent of the injury, the animal may either manage without dedifferentiation or may undergo it. Taylor and Farber (1924) have removed small globules of cytoplasm from the body of *Euplotes*, without observing any dedifferentiation. Similarly, shallow marginal cuts heal almost instantaneously; on the other hand, serious operations affecting some locomotor organoids provoke dedifferentiation and the resorption of the whole ciliary apparatus. The behaviour of various species of Hypotricha differs greatly in this respect. The extreme case as regards exceptional sensitivity to injury is represented, according to Dembowska (1925, 1926), by *Stylonychia* (Fig. 162) and *Uronychia*, in which the removal of a single cirrus or even injury of its basal plate is sufficient to cause dedifferentiation, followed by the reorganization of the whole ciliary apparatus.

In these Hypotricha the duration of the regenerative process does not depend on the extent of the injury suffered, taking invariably 3–4 hours to restore the normal structure completely.

Dembowska (1925) describes the process of regeneration in *Stylonychia* (see Fig. 162) in the following manner. When both the nuclei are intact regeneration proceeds by means of one regeneration area which appears on the ventral side, near the anterior macronucleus. Six longitudinal clefts, arranged in the shape of a rhombus, appear on the pellicle of this area. The ectoplasm emerged to the exterior through these clefts, giving rise to the primordia of eighteen future cirri. These primordia gradually diverge in different directions along the lower side of the body and are arranged at the bases of the former cirri undergoing reabsorption and at those of the cirri that had been removed. Moreover, two more bands of primordia producing two series of marginal cirri are formed at the flanks of the ventral side of the body, while a primordium of a new peristome emerges through the pellicle closer to the anterior edge. All the old cirri and membranelles, without exception, are reabsorbed, and replaced by new ones; moreover, the

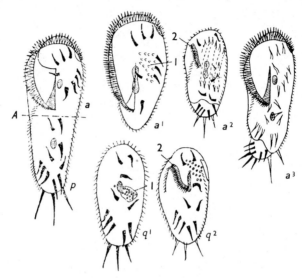

FIG. 162. Regeneration in *Stylonychia*.

The ciliate has been cut along line *A*. a^1–a^3, regeneration of anterior half of body; q^1 and q^2, regeneration of posterior half of body. 1, formation of new cirri; 2, foundation of new adoral zone. (After Dembowska, 1925.)

process of restoration proceeds in the same order as during the process of normal division, long ago described by Stein. The only difference is that in normal division there are formed not one but two regeneration areas, in accordance with the fact that in the process of division two, instead of one, ciliary apparatus (for the anterior and posterior daughter individuals) are restored.

When the ciliate is operated on during division, any injury to one half does not affect the other half of the dividing individual. It is noteworthy that, in contrast to the cirri, the cutting off of the three caudal setae, present in *Stylonychia*, does not lead to the regeneration of the ciliary apparatus. This difference is probably due to the fact that the setae are inert, immobile structures, serving merely for the transfer of tactile sensations.

Injuries to *Uroleptus mobilis* caused by a high voltage current also lead to regeneration. Moreover, in ciliates moving from the anode to the cathode it is the posterior end of the body that is usually injured, being either vacuolized, deformed, or casting off pieces of cytoplasm. Complete regeneration, accompanied by the reconstruction of ciliary apparatus, takes place.

Hyper-regeneration and heteromorphoses. As has already been shown, the processes of regeneration resemble in many respects analogous phenomena in multicellular organisms. The similarity is expressed, among other things, by the regenerating ciliates producing a picture of hyper-regenerations and

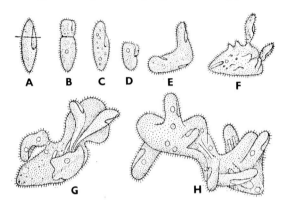

FIG. 163. Hyper-regeneration of *Paramecium caudatum.*

(*A*) individual cut transversely along horizontal line; (*B*) division of posterior fragment of individual (*A*); (*B*)–(*D*) individuals formed from posterior fragment; (*E*)–(*H*) gradually complicating hyper-regeneration of individual developed from individual (*D*), which regenerated various organoids but did not reproduce. (After Calkins, 1911*a*.)

heteromorphoses. Hyper-regeneration has been particularly clearly demonstrated in the experiments of Calkins (1911*a*) on *Paramecium*. After a transverse bisection of *Paramecium* closer to the anterior or the posterior end, the animal does not regenerate the lost part of its body, but becomes rounded at the cut end and then divides not at the middle of the body of the resulting individual but at the level of the division zone of the individual present before the operation. The resulting two individuals differ in size and shape. Furthermore, the division frequently becomes irregular: thus subsequent divisions are initiated but are not brought to an end, and complex polymeric monsters arise in the shape of irregular protuberant masses containing up to sixteen mouths scattered on the surface of the body. Calkins (1934) connects this variety of patterns produced during the regeneration of *Paramecium* with an intensification of the vital energy associated with the reorganization process during division, encystation, endomixis, and conjugation.

Regeneration and division. As has been noted by a number of authors, the initial stages of regeneration and of division have some common features. Hence division may be regarded as a physiological regeneration

(Weisz), when restoration and reorganization proceed without the infliction of injuries (Fig. 160): the more so since replacement of membranelles was observed in *Stentor* without division and without injuries. Moreover, it is possible to a certain extent to substitute the process of reproduction by repeated regeneration, as has been done by Hartmann (1924, 1928) with *Stentor* and *Amoeba*. By repeated dissections of this ciliate and amoebae in a state of regeneration, Hartmann prevented them from bringing to an end the course of division, thereby placing the animals in a condition of an artificially prolonged individual life. Hartmann repeatedly cut *Amoeba polypodia* every time it reached a size which indicated the imminent occurrence of division. By cutting off every time about one-third of its body, Hartmann arrested division, and thus prolonged the personal life of a given individual. In this way he succeeded by 32 repeated operations in preventing one amoeba from dividing for 42 days, while later (1928) by means of 130 repeated dissections he kept one specimen of *Amoeba proteus* without division for as long as 4 months, during which time the control individual divided 65 times.

Although Hartmann's experiments provide no proof of the possibility of continuing this process indefinitely, they do indicate that the normal life-cycle may be changed to a great extent by regeneration and that the latter may be substituted for asexual reproduction.

It is noteworthy that Luntz (1936) had succeeded in suppressing division by other methods as well, namely by subjecting *Stylonychia* every day to the action of a weak electric current. Luntz was able in this way to prolong the individual existence of *Stylonychia* for the duration of 27 consecutive divisions of the control individuals.

The sexual process

We have already mentioned that the life-cycle of the majority of Protozoa, apart from the processes of growth and periodically repeated reproduction, is accompanied also by a periodically repeated process of fertilization, which is interpolated into the cycle. However, the periodical recurrence of reproduction and the sexual process in the majority of cases differ in their tempo. The processes of the usual, asexual reproduction, which in all Protozoa proceed at a more or less rapid rate, are in most cases only comparatively rarely interrupted by the sexual process, which is followed again by a long series of asexual generations. The rate of the alternation of asexual reproduction and the sexual process may vary greatly not only in different species of Protozoa but even within the same species, according to changes in the environment and the corresponding physiological state of the animal. This is particularly well proved by experiments on induced conjugation in ciliate cultures and copulation in chlamydomonads.

The sexual processes in Protozoa correspond in their main features completely to the process of fertilization in multicellular organisms; they are also accompanied by the formation of sexual cells or sexually differentiated individuals; furthermore, these cells, in all Protozoa, except the ciliates, fuse with each other, or undergo copulation. Only in all the ciliates the sexual process proceeds differently, namely the individuals entering upon a sexual process do not fuse with each other, but are merely temporarily united to each other, exchanging parts of their nuclear apparatus, then separating again and returning to an independent existence. This peculiar form of sexual process, known as conjugation, undoubtedly represents a secondary modification of a more ancient type of the sexual process. Both types of the process, i.e. copulation and conjugation, which are interpolated into a series of asexual reproductions, pass through several consecutive stages. These stages may vary in detail, but they are in general similar and consist in a preparation for the sexual process, the actual sexual process, and a gradual return of the animal to the usual pattern of asexual reproduction.

In copulation the different periods of the sexual process may be divided into those preceding copulation, or progamous including the act of copulation itself, the eugamous and finally the metagamous periods, which follows directly after copulation, and returns the organism of the protozoon to the state of a vegetative or neutral individual. In conjugation the corresponding periods can be called preconjugational, conjugational, and exconjugational. When passing through various phases of the sexual process an individual experiences a series of changes, which bear corresponding names. The progamic period corresponds to the stage of gametocytes, the eugamous to gametes, the metagamous to the stage of zygote. In conjugation the analogous periods correspond to the preconjugant, conjugant, and exconjugant stages.

In all Protozoa possessing a sexual process, the latter is reduced to the fusion of two gametes and the formation of a zygote. This process is completed by the fusion of the two nuclei (karyogamy), as a result of which a nucleus of a dual nature, the synkaryon, is formed in the zygote. The nuclei of the gametes always have a set of single chromosomes—haploid-n—while a zygote as a rule has a set of double chromosomes—diploid-$2n$, in which each chromosome is represented by a pair (one from each gamete). During the sexual process of the conjugation type, copulation of the gametes is replaced by the fusion of the haploid nuclei, which likewise leads to the formation of a diploid synkaryon, fully corresponding to the diploid nucleus of a zygote.

During the further development of the zygote in various Protozoa, at different stages of their life-cycle a reduction of the number of chromosomes invariably takes place which again brings about a halving of their number, i.e. to transformation of the diploid complex into haploid.

The Meiosis

Reduction of the number of chromosomes is effected by special divisions of the nucleus, called *meiosis*.

According to the stage in the life-cycle of Protozoa, when meiosis occurs (and correspondingly, the reduction in the number of chromosomes) there are three types of this process. The first (Fig. 164) is zygotic reduction, when meiosis occurs during the very first division of the zygote, so that the zygote is the only diploid phase in the life-cycle. This type is observed,

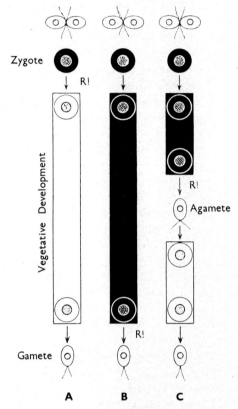

FIG. 164. Diagram showing relationship between haploid (white) and diploid (black) phases in life-cycles of Protozoa.

R1, position of meiosis in the cycle of development: (A) haplont with zygotic meiosis; (B) diplont with gametic meiosis; (C) heterophasic alternation of generations with intermediate meiosis. (After Grell, 1956a.)

apparently, in all Sporozoa, and the majority of Mastigophora (except for some Polymastigida and Hypermastigida) in which there is a sexual process.

The second type, which is also common among the Protozoa, is gametic reduction (Fig. 164), when the number of chromosomes is reduced during the process of formation of gametes (or of pro-nuclei in the case of conjugation) which represent the only haploid phase of the life-cycle, whereas in all other stages of its life-cycle the protozoon is diploid.

This type of reduction corresponds to that in Metazoa, where likewise only the gametes are haploid. A similar type of this process is observed in Heliozoa (*Actinophrys*), and some Polymastigida (*Notila, Urinympha, Rhynchonympha, Macrospironympha*), and in all ciliates.

Fairly recently, mainly as a result of investigations by Le Calvez (1950) and Grell (1954, 1956*a, b*, 1957, 1958*a, b, c*) the occurrence of an 'intermediate meiosis' has been established for many species of Foraminifera. In this case some of the stages of the cycle (agamont) possess diploid nuclei (from the zygote to the formation of agametes), others haploid ones. This is a generation developing from the agametes and later producing gametes (gamont) (Fig. 164). This type of relationship between the haplo- and diplophases is reminiscent of some groups of plants (mosses and ferns) where there is a regular alternation of a haploid gametophyte and diploid sporophyte. These types of life-cycles will be discussed in greater detail in a special chapter below.

Meiosis represents a special form of the nuclear and cell division, as a result of which the number of chromosomes is halved. This process, which has been studied in great detail in the case of the sexual cell of Metazoa, is still far from sufficiently investigated in Protozoa. We can now consider briefly the general plan of the course of meiosis as it proceeds in most Metazoa and, apparently, in a considerable number of Protozoa (Fig. 165).

The diploid complex of chromosomes is formed as a result of the union of two haploid sets of gametes in the zygote (Fig. 165). Each category of chromosomes of the diploid set is always represented by a pair.[1] In the course of further development the constant number of chromosomes is maintained by mitotic divisions in the course of which each chromosome is split longitudinally (see p. 42). Meiosis is composed of two divisions which usually follow each other rapidly. During prophase of the first meiotic division there takes place a temporary, longitudinal union (conjugation) of the paired (homologous) chromosomes, the chromosomes adhering to each other at precisely corresponding areas (Fig. 165); this is most clearly visible in those cases when the chromosomes display chromomere structure. The number of chromosome pairs (bivalents) corresponds to the haploid number. At the beginning of the conjugation of chromosomes, they are long and thin, and are frequently coiled round each other (zygotene and pachytene stages); later they become shorter as a result of the increase of chromosomal spiralization (the diplotene stage and diakinesis).

Chromosomes united in pairs in their turn split longitudinally, each being divided into two chromatids. This longitudinal division of each chromosome usually takes place at the zygotene stage. Thus every bivalent is transformed into a quadrivalent group (the tetrad), composed of two conjugating homologous chromosomes, each of which had split longitudinally

---

[1] Except the sexual chromosomes (heterochromosome), which will not be considered here.

into two chromatids. During this splitting the centromeres (kinetochores) of each chromosome are not doubled, but remain single.

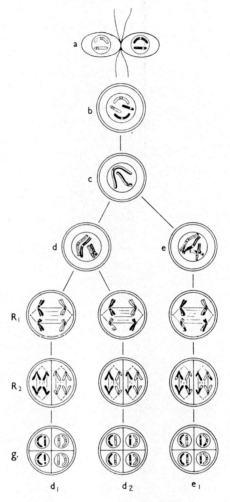

FIG 165. Diagram of zygotic meiosis.

(*a*) copulation of gametes; (*b*) zygote; (*c*) fusion of homologous chromosomes; (*d*)–(*d₁*) and (*d*)–(*d₂*) various combinations in the distribution of paternal and maternal chromosomes during meiosis, showing position of the kinetochore during first division; (*e*)–(*e₁*), exchange of parts of chromatids; R_1 first meiotic division; R_2, second meiotic division; *g*, haploid cells. (After Grell, 1956*a*.)

During conjugation of homologous chromosomes there is a mutual exchange of corresponding (homologous) portions between some of them, a process known in genetics as 'crossing-over' (Fig. 165).

Cytologically this process finds its expression in the close contact between some points of the chromatids pertaining to the homologous chromosomes.

These points of contact, where the crossing-over of the portions of chromatids probably takes place, are called chiasmata. There may be from one to several chiasmata within the area of one bivalent.

The transition from prophase to metaphase of the first meiotic division is characterized by a pronounced shortening of the chromosomes (diakinesis stage). During this process the homologous chromosomes belonging to one pair begin to part and move away from each other. However, within the area of chiasmata the link between them is maintained for some time. As a result during diakinesis the bivalents frequently form characteristic figures, in the form of a ring (if the chiasmata are terminal), a cross, &c. Homologous chromosomes diverge to the opposite poles during the anaphase of the first meiotic division; in multicellular organisms their divergence is usually accompanied by cell division, whereas, as will be shown further in detail, in Protozoa the cytoplasm does not divide during this process.

After a short period of rest, during which the structure of the interkinetic nucleus is frequently not restored, the second meiotic division begins. As it proceeds the centromeres (kinetochores) divide, while the chromatids, already formed during the prophase of the first meiotic division, diverge to the opposite poles of the achromatic spindle. In this way, as a result of meiosis four nuclei are formed from a single one, each with a haploid set of chromosomes. During maturation of the sexual cells in Metazoa the meiotic division of the nucleus is accompanied by the fission of the cytoplasm, giving rise to four cells, each of which is transformed into a gamete (spermatozoon). In ovogenesis, of the four nuclei and cells that are formed, three, as is known, are abortive (polar bodies) and only one produces an egg cell.

The process of meiosis described briefly above is thus characterized by two maturation divisions. It may be called, as suggested by Cleveland, two-division meiosis (the 'Zwei-Schritt-Meiose' of Grell). Meiosis, apparently, proceeds according to this scheme in many Protozoa; however, in most cases its details have not yet been studied sufficiently.

We can now consider some examples of meiosis in Protozoa, proceeding according to the 'two-division meiosis' type. The heliozoan *Actinophrys* is one of the objects best studied in this respect (Bělăr, 1922). The sexual process proceeds here according to the type of paired merogamy (see Fig. 166). The heliozoan undergoing the sexual process draws in its axopodia and encysts. Then it divides into two cells inside the cyst. The nucleus of each of them undergoes typical meiosis (Fig. 166) consisting of two nuclear divisions (not accompanied by fission of the cytoplasm). After each division one of the nuclei undergoes pycnosis and perishes. As a result of meiosis each cell becomes a gamete. The two gametes fuse, forming a zygote, which develops axopodia, and in its turn is transformed into the vegetative form of heliozoan. *Actinophrys* is thus a form with gametic reduction. The diploid number of its chromosomes is 44. During the prophase of the first meiotic division 22 bivalents are formed. All the changes of chromosomes characteristic of meiosis proceed in a most typical way (Fig. 166)—from the stage of fine filaments to diakinesis; and the pachytene stage with long chromosomes coiled round each other is clearly exhibited (Fig. 166), while

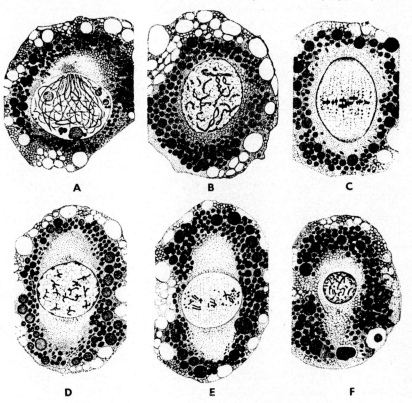

FIG. 166. Stages of meiosis in *Actinophrys sol* (Heliozoa).

(*A*) bunch stage; (*B*) union of homologous chromosomes: strepsitene stage; (*C*) metaphase I; (*D*) interkinesis; (*E*) metaphase II; (*F*) nucleus of gamete. (After Bělǎr, 1922.)

in some places the chiasmata are visible. As is shown by the study of meiosis in *Actinophrys*, this process proceeds in some Protozoa in exactly the same way as during gametogenesis in Metazoa.

A more or less typical course of meiosis has been described also in some Polymastigida or Hypermastigida from the alimentary tract of cockroaches, *Cryptocercus punctulatus* (Cleveland, 1949*a*, *b*, 1950*c*, 1954*a*, *b*, *c*), and in the genera *Trichonympha, Barbulanympha, Eucomonympha*. In distinction from *Actinophrys*, in *Trichonympha* the reduction is zygotic (Fig. 167).

The splitting of chromosomes into chromatids takes place before their conjugation—before the formation of bivalents. After the union of homologous chromosomes typical tetrads are formed (Fig. 167). The reduction of the number of chromosomes is brought about as a result of two divisions rapidly following each other.

According to Grell's investigations (1954, 1956a, b, 1958c), the two-division-meiosis occurs also in Foraminifera, in which an 'intermediate meiosis' is observed, and reduction takes place when the agametes are

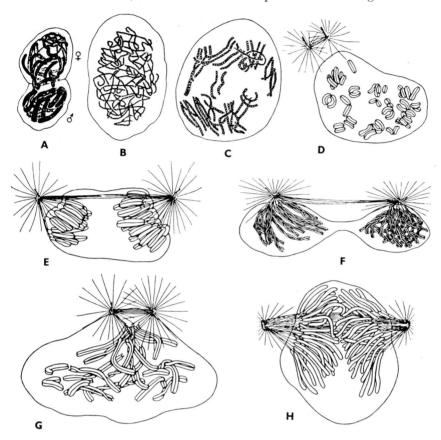

FIG. 167. Meiosis of *Trichonympha* (Polymastigida).

(*A*) karyogamy; (*B*) synkaryon (chromatids strongly coiled); (*C*) beginning of fusion of homologous chromosomes; (*D*) formation of tetrads; (*E*) anaphase I; (*F*) telophase I; (*G*) prophase II; (*H*) anaphase II. (After Cleveland, 1949a.)

formed (Fig. 164). A fairly typical pattern of meiosis with the formation of bivalents, tetrads, and even clearly defined chiasmata is observed in the one-chambered rhizopod *Myxotheca arenilega* (Fig. 168). This process is less clearly exhibited in *Rotaliella heterocaryotica* (Fig. 169) and some other Foraminifera.

It has been proved beyond doubt for many species of Ciliata and Suctoria that during conjugation meiosis occurs at the time of the first two divisions

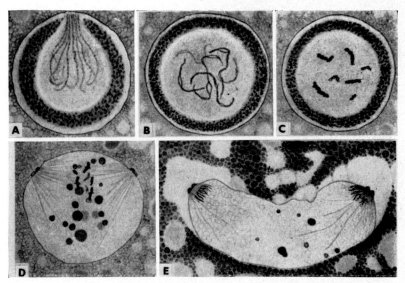

FIG. 168. Separate stages of the first mitotic division in *Myxotheca arenilega* (Foraminifera).

(*A*)–(*C*) prophase; (*D*) metaphase (combined from two sections); (*E*) telophase. (After Grell, 1956.)

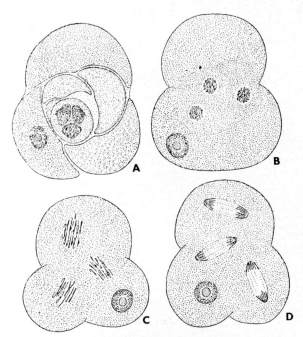

FIG. 169. Stages of first meiotic division in *Rotaliella heterocaryotica* (Foraminifera).

(*A*) early, and (*B*) late prophase; (*C*) prometaphase; (*D*) anaphase. (After Grell, 1954.)

of the micronucleus (see also the section 'Conjugation', p. 356). However, the cytological pattern of meiosis is still not sufficiently investigated, owing to the small size and frequent great number of chromosomes in ciliates. During prophase of the first meiotic division in ciliates a considerable elongation of the micronucleus is frequently observed leading to the for-

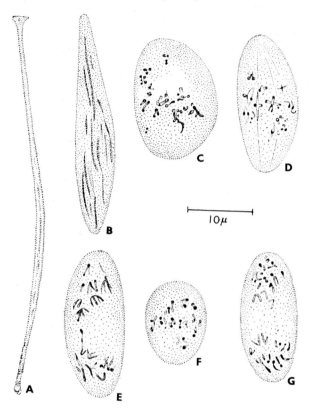

FIG. 170. Meiosis and first maturation division of micronucleus in *Colpidium campylum*.

(*A*) prophase (sickle like stage), (*B*) transition to metaphase I;
(*C*) prometaphase; (*D*) metaphase I; (*E*) anaphase I; (*F*) prometaphase II; (*G*) anaphase II. (After Devidé and Geitler, 1947.)

mation of the so-called 'Sichelstadium' (Fig. 170). In others (many Hypotricha and Heterotricha) there is a corresponding stage known as the 'parachute-stage' ('Paraschutstadium'), during which the chromosome material of the micronucleus is concentrated at one of the poles of the inflated nucleus. This stage corresponds probably to the 'bouquet' observed during the early prophase in the meiosis of many Metazoa. So far the conjugation of chromosomes and the formation of typical tetrads have been observed only in comparatively few ciliates. Devidé and Geitler (1947) have described tetrads in the diakinesis of *Colpidium campylum*. Ray (1956) has observed tetrads during the first and diads during the second meiotic divisions in *Tetrahymena pyriformis*. Mügge (1957) describes tetrads in *Vorticella campanula*, although in this case they are not well pronounced. Rajkov (1958*a*, *b*) has observed a very clear pattern of tetrads during the first meiotic division and of diads during the second in the course of conjuga-

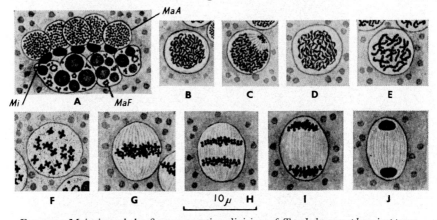

FIG. 171. Meiosis and the first maturation division of *Trachelocerca phoenicopterus*.

(*A*) nuclear apparatus of preconjugant; (*B*) leptothene stage; (*C*) 'parachute' stage; (*D*) spireme; (*E*) pachytene stage; (*F*) diakinesis; (*G*) metaphase; (*H*) and (*I*) anaphase; (*J*) telophase; *MaA*, primordium of macronucleus; *MaF*, fragments of micronucleus; *Mi*, micronucleus. (After Rajkov, 1958*b*.)

tion of *Trachelocerca phoenicopterus* (Fig. 171). These observations leave no doubt that in ciliates the first two divisions of the micronucleus during conjugation, leading to a reduction of the number of chromosomes, represent typical meiosis.

In principle all the forms of meiosis described above for different groups of Protozoa differ but little from the meiosis during gametogenesis in Metazoa.

In both cases the process is effected by two divisions, in the course of which first conjugation takes place and then the reduction of the number of chromosomes, and the transformation of the diploid complex into a haploid one. However, in some Protozoa, as has been pointed out by Grell (1952), meiosis may consist only of one reduction division. In these cases there is probably no mutual exchange of portions of homologous chromosomes, which is possible only at the stage of four parallel filaments (chromatids), and correspondingly no chiasmata are formed. Cleveland calls this type of meiosis and reduction 'one-division meiosis' (the 'Einschritt Meiose' of Grell).

Apparently a process of this type takes place in all the Sporozoa, which are characterized by zygotic reduction. As an example, let us consider the course of the reduction in *Eucoccidium dinophili* (Grell, 1953). During the process of reduction division a considerable extension of the diploid nucleus is observed in the zygote (Fig. 172). This stage has usually been referred to as 'Befruchtungsspindel', but actually it represents the prophase of meiotic division. Later the bivalents are formed and their shortening takes place. During anaphase one chromosome is given off from each bivalent

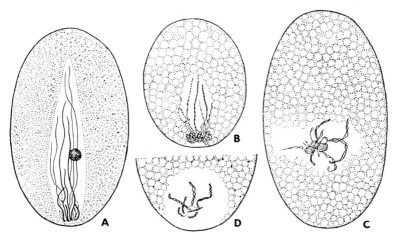

FIG. 172. Separate stages of prophase of meiotic division in *Eucoccidium dino-phili* (Coccidia).

(A)–(C) general view of oocyst; (D) part of oocyst. (After Grell, 1957.)

and passes into the daughter nuclei, and this brings meiosis to an end. In this process, the type of nuclear division is similar to paramitosis (see p. 50). The formation of a long 'Befruchtungsspindel' is not obligatory during 'one-division meiosis'; thus in gregarines it does not take place, although meiosis proceeds according to the same pattern.

It is noteworthy that 'one-division meiosis' occurs also in some genera of Polymastigida and Hypermastigida, parasites of the alimentary tract of the cockroach *Cryptocercus*. It is observed both during zygotic reduction—*Oxymonas* (Fig. 173) (Cleveland, 1950a), *Saccinobaculus* (Cleveland, 1950b), and during gametic reduction *Notila* (Cleveland, 1950c), *Urinympha* (Cleveland, 1951).

Thus in a number of cases a definite type of meiosis is characteristic of certain taxonomic groups. We have seen that in Heliozoa, Foraminifera, and Ciliates 'two-division meiosis' is observed, whereas, for example, 'one-division meiosis' is characteristic for Sporozoa. However, among the various Mastigophora living in the alimentary tract of *Cryptocercus* both types of meiosis takes place. As will be shown below, these peculiar Protozoa also reveal a most exceptionally wide variability in other phases of their life-cycle.

The solution of the problem of the correlation of both types of meiosis requires further detailed cyto-karyological investigation in various groups of Protozoa. In the meantime one can accept as a preliminary hyopthesis the views of Grell (1952) that the 'one-division meiosis' represents a more

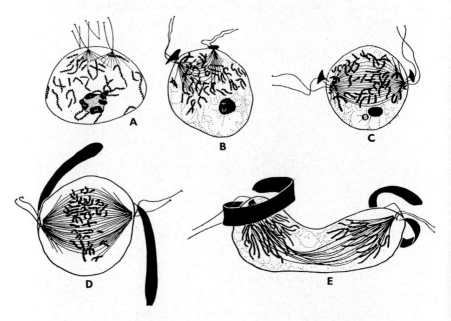

FIG. 173. Meiosis in *Oxymonas doroaxostylus* (Polymastigidae).

(*A*) early; (*B*), (*C*) late prophase; (*D*) metaphase; (*E*) early telophase, centrioles lying inside nucleus, afterwards emerging on to surface and acquiring ribbon-like shape (black in figure). (After Cleveland, 1950*a*.)

primitive and probably the initial form of meiosis and reduction of the number of chromosomes.

Copulation

The sexual process of the copulation type consists of a complete fusion of two gametes which results in the formation of a zygote.

Hologamous copulation. This form of copulation is regarded as the simplest form of the sexual process. Its simplicity is reflected mainly in the progamous period of the sexual process. In fact, hologamy is characterized by an almost complete absence of the preparatory stage of gameto-cytes, since in this case the gametes do not differ at all morphologically, or only slightly, from each other or from the ordinary vegetative individuals. A vegetative individual apparently becomes a gamete (in particular an isogamete) directly, without undergoing any special changes and omitting the stage of a typical gametocyte. This type is very rarely found among the Protozoa.

Among the Mastigophora an example of hologamy is presented by the colourless form of the Chlamydomonad *Polytoma uvella* (Fig. 174) (Dogiel, 1935). In this case the copulating individuals have the same form and size as the vegetative individuals, but during transformation into gametes they undergo certain physiological changes, since they are filled with granules of starch, which distinguishes them from the more transparent neutral individuals. Moreover, both in *Chlamydomonas* and *Polytoma* the zygote produced after copulation immediately encysts (cystozygote). The encystment of the zygote is frequently observed in Protozoa. The zygote does not produce free vegetative individuals directly after its first division, but first undergoes inside the cyst two consecutive divisions, which represent meiotic divisions, i.e. zygotic reduction. As a result of these divisions four small vegetative individuals are formed inside the cyst. These are vegetative zoospores, which, emerging from the cyst, feed, grow, and give rise to the first vegetative individuals of the new vegetative period of the life-cycle.

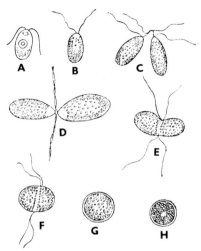

FIG. 174. Stages of copulation in *Polytoma uvella*.

(*A*) vegetative individual; (*B*) gamete; (*C*)–(*F*) various stages of fusion of gametes; (*G*) zygote; (*H*) encysted zygote. (After Dogiel, 1951.)

Hologamous copulation takes place also in some Phytomonadina belonging to the genus *Chlamydomonas*. In some species of *Chlamydomonas* the vegetative individuals are directly transformed into gametes, without going through special progamous divisions. In *Chlamydomonas* the zygote usually encysts and then undergoes two divisions (meiosis) within the cyst, giving rise to four vegetative individuals.

Finally, apart from certain minor differences, copulation of amoebae of the family Vahlkampfiidae, namely *Amoeba* (*Sappinia*) *diploidea* (Fig. 175), should be referred to the hologamy group. The originality of this organism consists first of all in the fact that its gametes retain the amoeboid form of the vegetative individual. The other peculiarity of *Sappinia diploidea* consists in the retention by its vegetative individuals of nuclei obtained by them during the preceding copulation of the two gametes. These nuclei remain separated from each other right up to the beginning of the next copulation, when fusion of nuclei obtained from the previous sexual act at last takes place. As a result *Sappinia* remains throughout the entire vegetative period of its life and during its period of reproduction in a binucleate state, and these two nuclei have arisen not by nuclear division, but as a result of a prolonged non-fusion of the nuclei of the two gametes, from which the individual originated.

At the beginning of the copulation two ordinary, vegetative, mature binucleate amoebae meet and are enclosed in a membrane (i.e. they encyst); at the same time the two nuclei in each amoeba finally fuse. The single nucleus of each gamete now undergoes two heteropolar maturation divisions

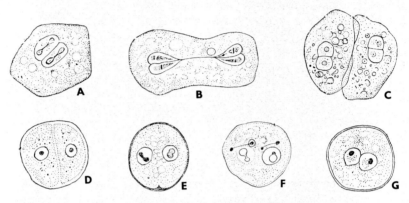

FIG. 175. Sexual process in *Amoeba diploidea*.

(*A*), (*B*) binary fission; (*C*) copulation; (*D*) encystment of copulating individuals; (*E*), (*F*) reduction division; (*G*) encysted zygote. (After Hartmann and Nägler, from Doflein and Reichenow, 1929.)

(meiosis), during which the protoplasts of the mature gametes fuse, while the nuclei retain their independence, with the result that a larger amoeba with two nuclei is produced in the cyst. In the meantime the reduction bodies of both exgametes are absorbed in the cytoplasm. After a time, under favourable conditions, the cyst ruptures, the amoeba inside it crawls out and gives rise to a new series of vegetative individuals. In assessing this cycle we note a certain shifting of the stages as compared to *Chlamydomonas* and *Polytoma*; namely the stage of encystment, which usually represents a transition to the metagamous period of copulation, takes place earlier here, and is replaced by the stage preceding the fusion of gametes, i.e. to the very beginning of the eugamous period. However, the significance of encystment remains the same: in both cases a resting cyst is produced, which in *Chlamydomonas* also serves at the same time for metagamous reproduction. The morphology and number of chromosomes in *Sappinia* have not been studied.

Merogamous copulation. This name is given to copulation in which the gametes are produced not by simple transformation from vegetative individuals but by means of special processes of reproduction (and sometimes also of differentiation) of these. In this case the number of gametes arising from the vegetative forms may vary from two (paired merogamy) to several hundred (multiple merogamy). Since the first type differs from the second in certain essential characteristics, the two types will be considered separately.

1. *Paired merogamy*. In the last few years numerous cases of paired merogamy in the parasitic flagellates Polymastigida and Hypermastigida, inhabiting the alimentary tract of the cockroach *Cryptocercus*, have been described. It is noteworthy that many representatives of this group of flagellates, parasitic in the alimentary tract of termites, reproduce only asexually, whereas in the cockroaches they pass periodically through a sexual process that is strictly correlated with definite periods in the host's life-cycle, namely with its moulting period. This last problem will be discussed in more detail below.

We can now consider several examples of the course of sexual processes in these most peculiar flagellates, which have a very complicated structure, on the basis of Cleveland's detailed investigations. A typical pattern of paired merogamy is observed in the genus *Trichonympha* (Cleveland, 1949*a*, 1956*a*) (Fig. 176). These are very large members of the Hypermastigida with a most complicated structure. Their elongated body, pointed at the anterior end, is composed of an anterior portion or rostrum covered by a cuticular cap, of a postrostrum lying farther back and gradually widening, and of a posterior oval portion with a rounded end. The rostrum and the anterior part of the postrostrum bear several hundreds of long flagella directed backwards, while the rest of the body is naked. In the rostrum are situated the centrioles and a thin-walled sac or sleeve is suspended there; it holds the nucleus, which lies somewhat below the rostrum at the end of the anterior fourth of the body. In its vegetative state *Trichonympha* represents a haploid organism containing twenty-four chromosomes. The commencement of the progamous period is marked by the beginning of nuclear division in the course of which the chromosomes split and form two groups. It is of special interest that one of the chromosome groups differs from the other in its deeper staining by iron haematoxylin. At this stage the gametocyte becomes somewhat shorter and is invested in a thin-walled membrane, when it is transformed into a gametocyst, under the protection of which the sexual process continues. The division of the nucleus and of the whole body of *Trichonympha* continues; as in the case of all flagellates, the fission proceeds in a longitudinal direction from the anterior to the posterior end. As a result, the cyst contains a pair of smaller individuals of the trichonymphid type of structure, differing from each other in several well-defined characters, i.e. they are dimorphic. At first dimorphism is restricted to the nucleus, since one of the individuals acquires a haploid set of chromosomes which stain deeper, and the other a paler set. The cyst then ruptures and both individuals emerge from it, while the differences between them are intensified. The individual with a dark-stained nucleus remains unchanged, while the other individual reveals in its cytoplasm after excystment an accumulation of siderophilic granules, i.e. granules

TRICHONYMPHA

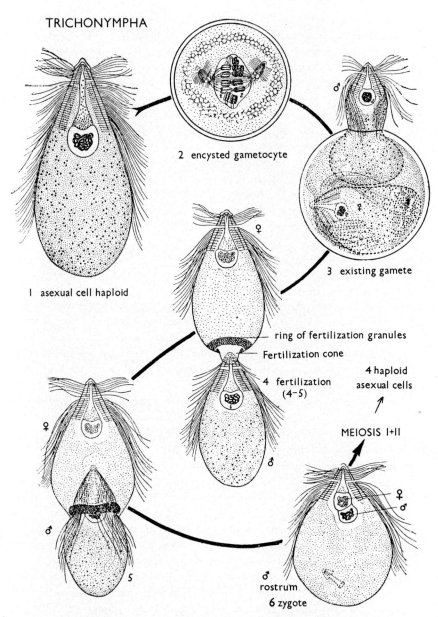

2 encysted gametocyte

1 asexual cell haploid

3 existing gamete

ring of fertilization granules

Fertilization cone

4 fertilization
(4-5)

4 haploid
asexual cells

MEIOSIS I+II

rostrum

6 zygote

5

FIG. 176. Sexual process in *Trichonympha*. (After Cleveland, 1956a.)

staining deeply with iron haematoxylin. These granules accumulate, forming a dense siderophilic ring round the posterior pole. The centre of the
posterior pole of the body remains light and from there a cone of transparent cytoplasm protrudes slightly into the lumen of the siderophilic
ring of granules. Thus the difference between the two excysted individuals
becomes very pronounced, and the individuals themselves reveal by their
further behaviour that they represent gametes. In fact, in the intestine containing such individuals a mass copulation begins, in the course of which
individuals with dark chromosomes always couple with individuals of a
different structure. The active role which they play in this process reveals
their male nature.

The male gamete approaches the posterior pole of the female and inserts
its rostrum into the light protuberance of the latter, known as the fertilization cone. Gradually the whole male gamete penetrates through the siderophilic ring of fertilization granules into the female gamete, where there is
hardly enough room for its bent body. Then the cytoplasm of both individuals mixes until it is indistinguishable and various organoids of the
male individual (flagella, cap, nuclear sleeve, and some others) are absorbed
in the common cytoplasm. The male nucleus then gradually moves towards
the anterior end of the female gamete, where its nucleus lies, and fuses with it.
The resulting motile diploid zygote increases considerably in size, after
which it divides twice within a short interval (24 hours), giving rise to four
vegetative individuals. These two divisions represent meiosis and lead to
the reduction of the number of chromosomes.

Apart from *Trichonympha*, haploids with a zygotic reduction are represented also by a number of genera of Mastigophora from *Cryptocercus*,
namely *Eucomonympha, Saccinobaculus, Barbulanympha*(Cleveland, 1950b,d,
1953).

Since the course of the sexual process in all these forms cannot be dealt
with here, we shall restrict ourselves to certain essential characteristics of
some species. As has been mentioned above, in *Trichonympha* zygotic
reduction proceeds as a two-division meiosis, whereas in some genera,
such as *Oxymonas*, a one-division meiosis is observed (Fig. 173). Among
the genera of Polymastigida and Hypermastigida mentioned above, one-
division meiosis also takes place, apart from *Oxymonas*, in *Saccinobaculus*
and *Leptospironympha*.

In contrast to those listed above, some genera of flagellates parasitic in
Cryptocercus are diplonts with gametic reduction. In these forms a haploid
complex of chromosomes is found only in the gametes; whereas the other
stages of their life-cycle, beginning from the zygote, are diploid. According
to Cleveland, the genera *Notila, Urinympha, Rhynchonympha*, and *Macrospironympha* are diplonts.

As an example let us consider the course of the sexual process in *Macrospironympha zylopletha* (Cleveland, 1956a, b). This is a large flagellate

(Fig. 177) equipped with two spirally arranged rows of flagella, a rostrum at the anterior end, with a centriole situated inside it, one nucleus, and an axostyle consisting of 36–50 separate filaments. The general scheme of the sexual process is represented in Fig. 178. The vegetative forms are diplonts. At the beginning of the sexual process two meiotic divisions take place accompanied by division of the cell. The first takes place in the free motile

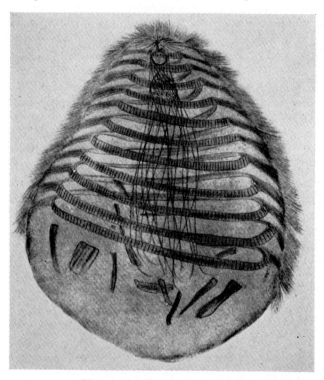

FIG. 177. *Macrospironympha zylopletha*, general view of trophozoite. (After Cleveland, 1956a.)

state (Fig. 178), the second in the encysted state within the gametocyte. A partial destruction of spiral flagellar bands takes place during the second division; the bands are later regenerated at the expense of their remaining anterior part. After the second meiotic division the gametes leave the cyst and restore the flagellar apparatus. The gametes possess haploid nuclei. Thus meiosis proceeds here according to the two-division type, and each individual undergoing meiosis gives rise to four gametes. These are actively motile, and later they are fused in pairs and a zygote is formed. At this period differentiation into male and female gametes takes place. The flagellar bands and the rostrum of the male gamete are absorbed in the cytoplasm of the developing zygote. Soon after this the fusion of the nuclei of the gametes takes place and the diploid structure of the chromosome

complex is restored. Later the zygote is transformed into an asexual vegetative individual. The course of the sexual process in *Macrospironympha*
has a general resemblance to the process of maturation and fertilization
in Metazoa.

However, the two-division meiosis is not observed in all the diploid
flagellates from the alimentary tract of termites. Cleveland (1950c, 1951)
describes one-division meiosis in *Notila* and *Urinympha*.

MACROSPIRONYMPHA

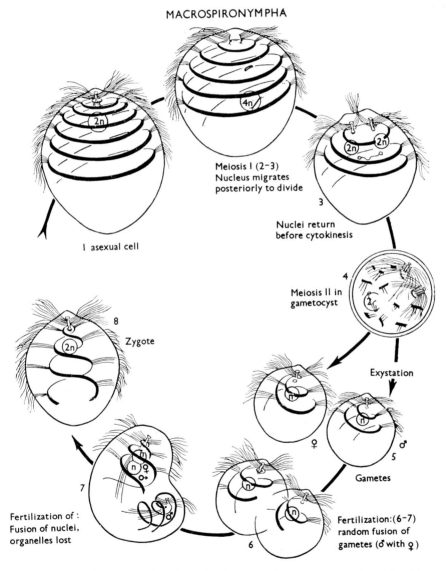

FIG. 178. Sexual process and cycle of development of *Macrospironympha*. (After Cleveland, 1956a.)

The forms of sexual processes are most varied in different species of flagellates from *Cryptocercus*. As we have seen above, in *Trichonympha* and *Macrospironympha*, gametes are formed and their copulation occurs. But in some species of flagellates the typical form of paired merogamy undergoes considerable secondary modifications. *Notila* (Cleveland, 1950b) among the Oxymonadina Polymastigina may serve as an example (Fig. 179). In this original form the copulating 'gametes' are diploid ($2n=28$). The cell formed as a result of their fusion retains two diploid nuclei, but there is a fusion of axostyles. Cleveland calls this stage the 'prezygote'. Later, as shown in the scheme (Fig. 179), each of the diploid nuclei goes through one-division meiosis, in the course of which the female nucleus remains at the anterior end while at the expense of its centrosomic apparatus new axostyles and flagella are formed (the old being absorbed), whereas the male nucleus moves towards the posterior end and its centrosomic apparatus does not take part in the formation of the locomotor organoids. The female pronuclei are formed at the anterior end, and male ones in the middle of the body. Then karyogamy occurs (Fig. 179) and as a result of it a stage with two synkaryons is produced, called by Cleveland the double zygote. During the division of this, which is not accompanied by nuclear division, uninucleate diploid individuals are produced, which later proceed to asexual reproduction.

The sexual process in *Notila*, described above, is most peculiar, in that the nuclear and cytoplasmic processes are as it were displaced in relation to each other: changes in the cytoplasm 'outstrip' the nuclear processes, the 'gametes' being formed and copulating while the nucleus remains diploid; hence the nuclear processes are shifted to later stages.

One of the most remarkable phenomena in the sexual processes of flagellates from *Cryptocercus* is their regular correlation with the moulting of the host. Evidently this correlation is determined by the effect of the hormones of the host on the parasite. Various species of flagellates react differently to these stimuli (Fig. 180). In some the sexual processes begin long before ecdysis starts (e.g., *Leptospironympha wachula*), in others they are very close to the moment of ecdysis (e.g., *Trichonympha*), &c. The duration of the sexual process may vary considerably: in some species it extends over a considerable period of time; in others it is completed comparatively quickly. Cleveland carried out experiments on the transfer of different species of flagellates into the alimentary tract of *Cryptocercus* at different periods in the preparation for ecdysis, and during the actual moulting period (Cleveland, 1957). In these experiments it was shown that vegetative individuals of flagellates from a non-moulting cockroach usually perish when transferred into one in a state of ecdysis, at a moment when the given species of flagellates is undergoing the sexual processes within the host. This indicates that the environment of the alimentary tract changes considerably, becoming unfavourable for the vegetative, neutral individuals and stimulating the occurrence of sexual processes. Moreover, the reaction of different species of parasites to the changes of the environment (effect of hormones) varies (Fig. 180).

Cleveland's investigations on the reproduction of flagellates from *Crypto-cercus*, carried out in the course of the last 10–12 years, have revealed a number of extremely interesting and somewhat unexpected phenomena.

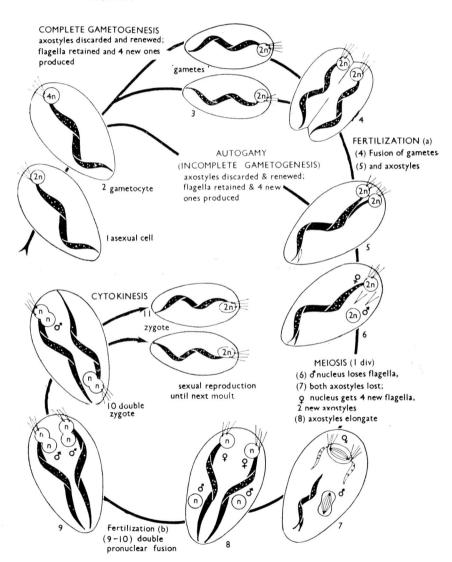

FIG. 179. Sexual process and cycle of development of *Notila*. (After Cleveland, 1956a.)

In the majority of Protozoa the haploid or diploid state of the nucleus, the occurrence of zygotic, gametic, or intermediate reduction constitute a feature characteristic of large taxa of a high systematic category. In contrast to this, according to Cleveland, in flagellates from *Cryptocercus*, closely related genera may differ from each other in the character of their chromosome complex: while some are haplonts (for example, *Oxymonas*), other,

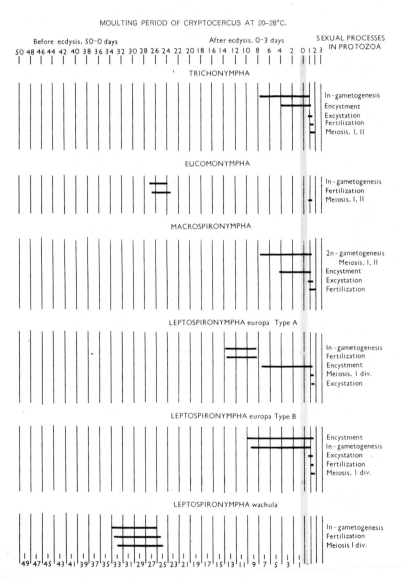

FIG. 180. Correlation between period of ecdysis of *Cryptocercus* and sexual

closely related species, are diplonts (for example, *Notila*). The same applies to the mechanism of meiosis. In closely related genera sometimes a one-division, sometimes a two-division meiosis is observed. Finally, even within the same species the course of a sexual process may vary considerably. For instance, in the case of *Notila* discussed above (Fig. 179), side by side with

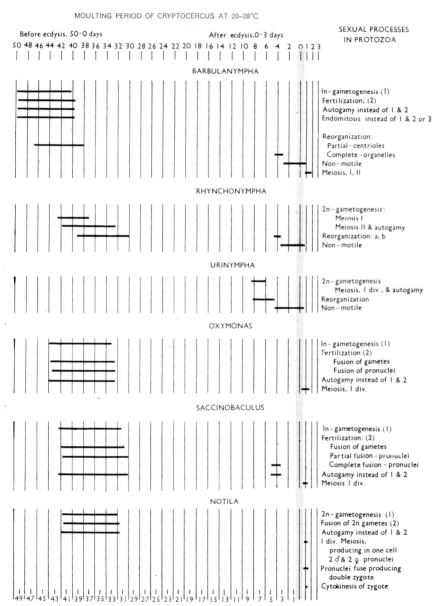

processes of its flagellates. (After Cleveland, 1957.)

the formation of diploid 'gametes' cellular division may be omitted and the process acquires the character of autogamy.

Cleveland has observed an exceptionally wide variability in the course of the sexual process in *Barbulanympha* (1953, 1954*a*, *b*, *c*). In this flagellate (Fig. 181), which is a haplont with zygotic reduction belonging to the two-

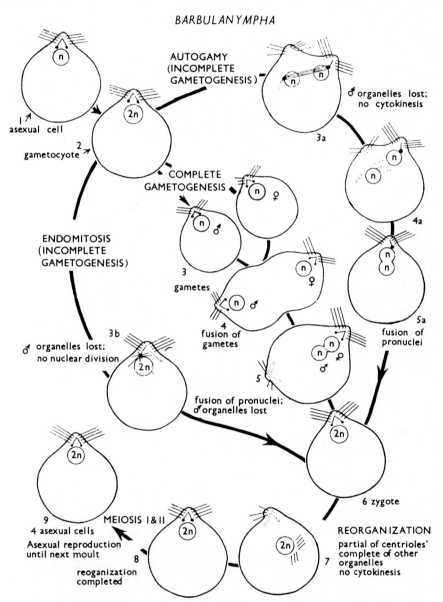

FIG. 181. Sexual process and cycle of development of *Barbulonympha*. (After Cleveland, 1956*a*.)

division meiosis type, the sexual process is accomplished in three different ways. The first way is the formation of gametes followed by their copulation, the second is autogamy, and the third an increase in the number of chromosomes, not by karyogamy, but by endomitosis.

At the present it is still difficult to draw any definite conclusions regarding the causes of the peculiarities of the sexual process in flagellates from the alimentary tract of *Cryptocercus*. As a tentative hypothesis, it may be suggested that the flagellates from *Cryptocercus* have possibly originated

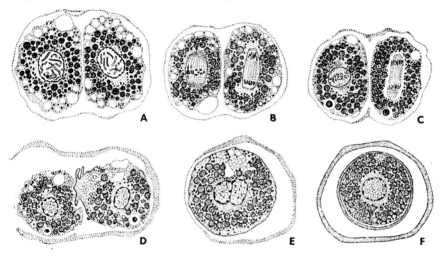

FIG. 182. Paedogomy in the heliozoan *Actinophrys sol*.

(*A*) two gametocytes inside a cyst formed by one vegetative individual; (*B*), (*C*) gametocytes go through maturation division and become gametes; (*D*) one of the gametes (male) has produced pseudopodia directed towards the other gamete; (*E*) copulation of gametes; (*F*) encysted zygote. (After Bělǎr, 1922.)

secondarily from species inhabiting the alimentary tract of termites, devoid of sexual process and reproducing only agamously. The sexual process of flagellates from *Cryptocercus* might have arisen secondarily and is philogenetically a recent acquisition. This may be the reason for its variable, unstable character.

The next example of paired merogamy has been known for a long time; it is the copulation of the heliozoan *Actinophrys sol* (Fig. 182). Under certain conditions it retracts its pseudopodia, surrounds itself by a gelatinous envelope, and undergoes binary fission inside it, as in ordinary vegetative division. In this way two gametes are produced, looking like small heliozoa. The nucleus of each gamete undergoes two maturation divisions (see above, p. 301). After this one of the gametes, previously indistinguishable from the other, projects a bundle of short pseudopodia in the direction of the other and fuses with it.

This more active reaction of one of the gametes evidently corresponds to the male element. The nuclei of the fused gametes also fuse, producing a spherical zygote, which becomes enclosed inside the jelly-like mass by a second, compact, membrane. In due course the cyst ruptures and one vegetative heliozoon emerges from it.

The comparative rarity of cases of paired merogamy, a few reliable examples of which were given above, is perhaps partly due to its being unsuitable for rapid reproduction. In fact in both cases the processes of gametogenesis and copulation take a very long time (in *Actinophrys* more than 24 hours, in flagellates even several days), in spite of which the process initiated by a single individual yields only one individual—the zygote.

The following steps may be noted when comparing the cases described. Gametogenesis frequently occurs inside a special membrane (the gameto-cyst); in the case of *Actinophrys* the whole process of copulation takes place inside it, after which the zygote encysts within another dense membrane. Hence here we can distinguish the consecutive formation of two cysts—one the progamous (gametocyst), the other the metagamous (the resting cyst). Further, it is of special importance that in certain cases sister individuals, originating from a single nucleus of one and the same mother cell, act as gametes. Phenomena of this type are known as paedogamy, and their sig-nificance will be discussed below.

2. *Multiple merogamy.* In multiple merogamy, which forms a predominant majority of cases, the gametes are produced from a vegetative individual (by means of its previous multiplication) in considerable numbers. Multiple merogamy might be further subdivided into categories according to various criteria, but perhaps the most convenient way is to arrange them in the order of the transition from isogamy, for example a complete morphological identity of both copulating gametes, in the direction of increasing sexual differentiation, that is to anisogamy. A gradual transition to anisogamy is observed simultaneously in diverse groups of Protozoa, on account of which the sexual processes cannot be considered simply in the systematic order.

(*a*) *Isogamous copulation.* First of all isogamous copulation is widespread among the flagellates in a number of Phytomonadida, especially in solitary species. The best example is provided by certain species of *Chlamydomonas*. Thus *C. steinii* divide palintomically into many identical isogametes, which coalesce by their posterior ends, cast off their flagella, and fusing together become enclosed by a strong membrane. However, in spite of such evident isogamy, the copulating gametes are physiologically not identical, but belong to opposite sexes. The physiological side of the process of ferti-lization and sexuality will be considered below (p. 408).

Among the colonial Phytomonadida the gametes are morphologically identical in the colonies of *Gonium* and *Stephanosphaera*: each cell of the colony divides into a group of identical gametes.

In isogamous as well as in hologamous Phytomonadida, the gametes retain a close similarity to ordinary vegetative individuals, representing a repetition of the neutral state of the species, without displaying any special adaptations for the peculiarities of the sexual period.

Among other flagellates some fragmentary isogamous cycles were either described or indicated in different Dinoflagellata.

As early as 1920 Chatton (1920b and later) had detected the occurrence of reproduction by means of a multitude of small zoospores in a number of parasitic Dinoflagellata, living either on or in plankton animals. Adult parasitic Blastodinidae frequently lose all their similarity with flagellates, case off their flagella, lose the grooves on their body, change the structure of their nucleus, and acquire the appearance of plasmodia, &c. However, their zoospores are not only supplied with two flagella, but all the remaining structures of their body resemble Dinoflagellata so closely that they have been named dinospores. The idea that dinospores in a number of cases represent gametes and are intended for copulation has been expressed a long time ago, but convincing proof has been lacking.

In the majority of free-living Dinoflagellata the sexual process is unknown and possibly non-existent. Previous descriptions of copulation in *Ceratium hirudinella* (Zederbauer, 1904) have not been confirmed by later investigators and seem to be doubtful. Among the more recent works only the investigation of Diwald (1938), describing the sexual process in *Glenodinium lubiniensiforme*, may be noted. According to Diwald, *Glenodinium* produces, by two palintomic divisions, four isogametes, which retain all the characteristic morphological features of Dinoflagellata, viz. two flagella, sulcus, &c. The copulation is of the isogamic type in which the copulating gametes always originate from different individuals. Since Diwald's is the only description of a sexual process in free-living Dinoflagellata, it is most desirable to check it and make it more precise.

Chatton and Biecheler (1934, 1936) have observed in some parasitic Dinoflagellata a sexual process, proceeding according to the type of isogamous copulation. It is interesting that the gametes themselves (Figs. 183, 184) possess a structure characteristic of Dinoflagellata—two flagella, sulcus, &c., that is, they do not differ morphologically in any way from dinospores. As an example one may mention *Coccidinium duboscqui* (Fig. 184), parasitic on the free-living planktonic Dinoflagellata, studied by Chatton and Biecheler. In addition, a sexual process is probably present in *Duboscquella* and *Duboscquodinium*, parasitic on the plankton ciliates Tintinnoidea (Chatton, 1952).

Finally, in *Noctiluca miliaris* the so-called multiple budding off of numerous small dinospores has been known for a long time, but their further development has not been followed. In 1934 Gross succeeded in observing the isogamous copulation of these zoospores. However, the further fate of the zygotes of *Noctiluca* is not known.

The fats observed in different flagellates are of a great phylogenetic significance. They indicate that the gametes of flagellates retain the structure of ancestral forms. Thus, in Phytomonadida the gametes have the appearance of chlamydomonads with two anterior flagella; in Dinoflagellata they are dinospores. Finally, in the copepod crustacean *Acartia*, Chatton (1927) found a parasitic protozoal plasmodium which he called *Paradinium*, the isogametes of which very closely resembled *Cryptomonas*. On the basis of this it can be assumed with a high degree of probability

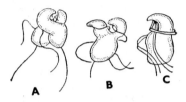

FIG. 183. Copulation of gametes in *Coccidinium mesnili* (Dinoflagellata) from *Cryptoperidinium foliaceum*.

(*A*), (*B*) two stages of the fusion of dinospores; (*C*) zygote with 4 flagella. (After Chatton and Biecheler, 1936.)

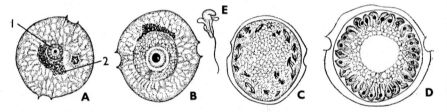

FIG. 184. Cycle of development of dinoflagellate *Coccidinium* parasitic in planktonic Dinoflagellata.

(*A*) young parasite (1) near nucleus, (2) of host-cell; (*B*) parasite dislodging nucleus of host; (*C*), (*D*) sporogony giving rise to dinospores, which apparently copulate; (*E*) developed dinospore. (After Chatton and Biecheler, 1934.)

that *Paradinium* originated from a member of the order Cryptomonadida, which became a parasite.

We can now consider isogamic copulation within the class Sarcodina. There are a series of separate indications in the literature of the existence of a sexual process in Amoebina and Testacea, but most of them belong to the first decade of the twentieth century and need verification. Therefore we prefer to ignore a number of papers of that period on the copulation in *Amoeba proteus*, *Pelomyza*, *Arcella*, which have since been either refuted or not confirmed. The only reliable data on this question concern the amoeba *Sappinia* (see above, on hologamy, p. 308) and the testaceous rhizopod *Cromia oviformis*. Le Calvez (1938) gives a short description of the latter, and depicts the formation of gametes with one long flagellum, and a globular accumulation of fat.

Sexual processes in Foraminifera have been studied in some detail in recent years, mostly by Le Calvez and Grell, as well as by Myers (1935, 1936, 1940). The life-cycles of these Protozoa will be discussed below in a special chapter (Chapter VIII); in this place we shall consider only the structure of their gametes.

Isogamy occurs in all Foraminifera whose sexual process has so far been studied. However, the structure and number of gametes formed at the expense of the gamont may vary considerably. In Foraminifera flagellated gametes, which are sometimes formed in enormous numbers, are most frequently observed. Thus, for example, Le Calvez believes that in *Iridia Lucida* one gamont, measuring 1 mm. in diameter, produces approximately 70 million gametes, 1·5–2 μ in diameter. Each gamete possesses two flagella, a nucleus, and a fairly large fat drop (Fig. 185). The gametes are very motile, swimming up to 150 μ per second. The gametes are negatively phototactic and are able to live in a hanging drop for not less than 24 hours. It is noteworthy that during gametogenesis of *Iridia*, and probably of some other Foraminifera as well, the process proceeds first by repeated nuclear division inside the common cytoplasm, but these divisions are not carried through to the end, as was formerly thought. The future gametes are separated from the common mass and are equipped with flagella (Fig. 185) at the stage preceding the last nuclear division, which takes place in the free-swimming state. Copulation takes place in sea water, apparently between gametes originating from different gamonts.

In some Foraminifera the formation of gametes is preceded by the union of two, and sometimes a greater number of gamonts (for example, in *Patellina corrugata*, according to Grell, from two to fourteen individuals unite) into a syzygy, during which a fine envelope is sometimes secreted around the united gamonts. Gametes are formed in each of the gamonts united into a syzygy, the structure of the former varying in different species. In *Discorbis patelliformis*, according to Myers (1940), gametes with three flagella are formed (Fig. 185). Their dimensions are much greater than in species with free-swimming gametes, attaining approximately 10 μ, though the number of gametes is comparatively small. Each gamont gives rise to 250–300 gametes, and copulation takes place between gametes derived from different gamonts. Part of the gametes remains unused ('Restgameten'), being phagocytosed by the resulting zygotes. In distinction from the gametes of *Discorbis*, those of *Patellina corrugata* (Grell, 1959) are devoid of flagella; they are amoeboid, and endowed with movement. The number of gametes formed is small, and is measured in dozens. As was shown by Grell in special experiments, the gamonts are sexually differentiated. Gametes that copulate are formed in gamonts with different sexual tendencies. Moreover, a certain number of 'Restgameten' are left over; and are later phagocytosed by the zygotes. In some species of Foraminifera the amoeboid gametes are formed within one individual (gamont), where their paired copulation takes place, i.e. the sexual process proceeds according to the autogamy type. This type of copulation occurs among species of the genus *Rotaliella* (Grell, 1954, 1958c).

The sexual processes in Radiolaria have so far been very little studied, and data on the structure of their gametes and their copulation are only fragmentary.

The data on the presence in radiolarians of two types of gametes (iso-

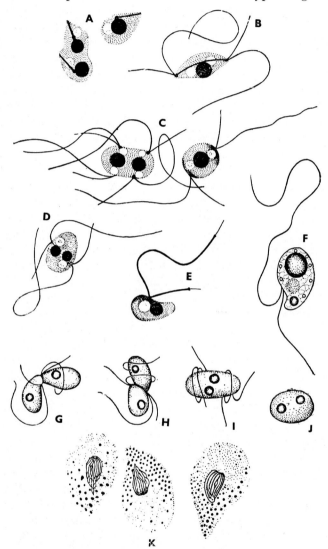

FIG. 185. Gametes of various Foraminifera.

(A)–(E) *Iridia lucida*, transformation of gametocytes into gametes;
(F) *Webbinella crassa*: gamete *in vivo;* (G)–(*J*) copulation of gametes of
Iridia lucida in vivo (after Le Calvez, 1938); (K) *Patellina corrugata*,
gametes (after Grell, 1959).

spores and anispores) lost its significance after Chatton (1920*a*, 1934) and Hovasse (1924) demonstrated that radiolarians frequently harbour parasitic Dinoflagellata, whose stages of reproduction were mistaken for those in the life-cycle of the radiolarian. For the same reason the detailed studies of Brandt (1895) and Huth (1913) on the earlier stages of gameto-genesis in Collidae and *Thalassicolla* are no more reliable. On account of this, the only available data are those on the structure of the gametes of Acantharia in the monograph by Ševjakov (1926) and the fragmentary data of Le Calvez (1935, 1938) on the structure of the gametes of two species of Acantharia (Figs. 186, 187). Ševjakov, who observed not only the copulation of the gametes, but also the development of the young stages of Acantharia themselves from the zygote, in most cases depicted small, round-oval or flagellate gametes. However, he has described in a few species (*Phracto-pelta, Diploconus, Acanthochiasma*) uniflagellate gametes. It is difficult to decide whether this is an error of observation or whether the number of flagella actually varies in the gametes of different species. According to Ševjakov, the gametes invariably contain several globular fat-inclusions. Le Calvez noted a great similarity between these gametes and those of Foraminifera: they are minute gametes with two flagella of different length and several (not a single one as in Foraminifera) fat-inclusions. It also appears that the 'dance' of sexual individuals in radiolarians begins (as also in Foraminifera) not at the stage of formed gametes, but at the stage of gametocytes of the second order, before they divide into gametes, but when they are equipped with two sets of flagella and two nuclei. The zygote of the radiolarians casts off its flagella, and is transformed directly without encystation into a young radiolarian. Copulation in Acantharia takes place not on the surface layers of water, where the adult individuals usually live, but at a depth of 50–100 metres to which radiolarians descend for repro-duction.

A large variety of methods of copulation is observed in Sporozoa; more-over, cases of isogamous copulation are by no means rare among them.

The life-cycle in the majority of Sporozoa consists of an alternation of two generations, the asexual or schizonts, and sexual or gamonts. Only in the majority of Gregarinida the asexual generation falls out and mogony only remains. An alternation of two generations is retained only by the first, more primitive, suborder of gregarines, the Schizogregarinae. As regards the development of the external characters of heterosexuality, some Schizogregarines retain the primitive features, in that they possess complete isogamy. The isogamy, however, reveals a series of secondary modifications, which are partly due, as in many other Sporozoa, to the acquisition of a parasitic mode of life. In the majority of gregarines the sexual process is initiated by the mating of two gamonts, which may take place long before the onset of copulation. In this process the gamonts usually only adhere to each other, forming an active freely motile pair—a syzygy. Sometimes,

namely in gregarines of the group Polycystidae, the syzygites are distinguished from each other by a series of cytological features, for example by
a somewhat different arrangement of the Golgi apparatus, by a different
degree of stainability of the mitochondria, &c. In some gregarines the
difference between syzygites is clearly demonstrated by intravital staining

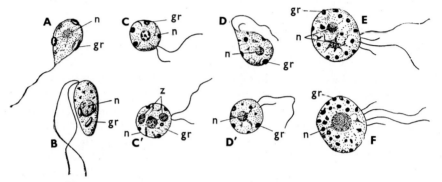

FIG. 186. Gametes and their copulation in Acantharia (*in vivo*).

(*A*) gamete of *Phyllostaurus cuspidatus*; (*B*) gametes of *Pleuropsis costata*; (*C*) gamete of *Acanthometra pellucida*; (*C'*) same with two spores of Zooxanthella (*Z*); (*D*), (*E*), (*F*) *Acanthostaurus purpurscens*; (*D*) and (*D'*) gametes; (*E*) copulation; (*F*) synkaryon in zygote; *n*, nucleus; *gr*, fat drops. (After Ševjakov, 1926.)

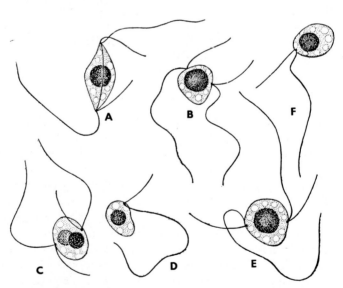

FIG. 187. Gametocytes and gametes of certain Acantharia.

(*A*)–(*D*) *Acanthometra pellucida*: (*A*) gametocyte with two kinetids united
by kinetodesmose; (*B*) same without kinetodesmose; (*C*) binucleate
gametocyte; (*D*) gamete; (*E*), (*F*) *Xiphacantha alata*; (*E*) gametocyte;
(*F*) gamete. (After Le Calvez, 1935.)

of the animal with neutral red. Although these differences are already noticeable during the vegetative period of the life of the gamonts, long before the beginning of the sexual process, they nevertheless bear a sexual character, since one of the syzygites always forms female gametes and the other the male ones. Hence it should be concluded that these distinctions between the two kinds of gamonts represent a peculiar secondary sexual character of the Protozoa in question.

In Schizogregarinae both gamonts unite just before copulation and are surrounded by a common membrane, under the protection of which the sexual process takes place. Moreover, in different representatives a number of stages of a progressively increasing productivity of the sexual generation may be detected. In *Ophryocystis* (Léger, 1907) (Fig. 188) from the Malpighian tubes of beetles, each gamont first undergoes one nuclear division in the cyst, giving rise to one somatic and one generative nucleus. The former does not divide any more, while the latter undergoes another division. One of these nuclei represents the nucleus of the future gamete. The gamont is surrounded by approximately one-third of the cytoplasm in the form of a round body, 5 μ in diameter, which is very similar to a coccidian cell. The gametes are identical; on fusing within the middle part of the cyst they produce a zygote, while the latter gives rise to a single oocyst, inside which eight sporozoites are formed by repeated division. A similar course of development also takes place in *Mattesia dispora* from the larva of a moth (Naville, 1930), except that each gamont gives rise to four nuclei, two of which (resulting from two consecutive divisions) perish, while the two others give rise to rounded isogametes. In this way the cyst of *Mattesia* produces two oocysts. In other Schizogregarines, eight, sixteen, and even a very large number of gametes, and then of spores, may be formed in the cyst. In some of them (*Selenidium*) isogamy was described, in others (Schizocystis) anisogamy.

Among the Eugregarinae, those with a more simple structure, possessing non-segmented body (the group Monocystidea), are on the way to the development of anisogamy. In addition two species with complete isogamy, with round motionless gametes (*Monocystis rostrata*, according to Mulsow, 1911), there is a series of transitions to a more and more pronounced anisogamy. In gregarines of the Polycystidea group, whose body is segmented into a protomerite and a deutomerite, anisogamy becomes the rule and becomes more pronounced, as is shown in Fig. 189.

Among the Cnidosporidia, isogamy is apparently also observed in a number of cases. However, there is still so much disputable and obscure in the interpretation of the cycle of their development, that we shall not dwell here on their gametes, while their life-cycle will be dealt with below.

(*b*) *Anisogamous copulation.* Copulation by means of anisogametes is represented in different groups of Protozoa by a whole series of gradations in the development of the most pronounced stages of anisogamy and the transition from copulation to the pattern of the sexual process in Metazoa. This series is particularly complete in solitary and colonial members of the order Phytomonadida. This group can serve as a most suitable example, since the Chlamydomonad genera belonging to it (*Chlamydomonas, Dunaliella*, and others) have been subjected to exceptionally detailed and profound cytological and experimental analysis during the last twenty years.

From the entirely isogamic *Chlamydomonas eugametos*, one may proceed to such species as *C. braunii* and a whole series of other anisogamous species (Fig. 190). A similar initial isogamic member of a series among the colonial

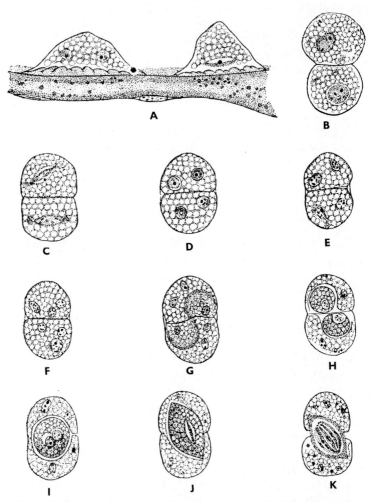

FIG. 188. Sexual reproduction in *Ophryocystis mesnili* (Schizogregarina). (*A*) two individuals attached to the cells of Malpighian tubes; (*B*) union of two gamonts; (*C*)–(*E*) maturation division of the nuclei in both gamonts; (*F*)–(*I*) formation of two spherical gametes and their copulation; (*J*)–(*K*) metagamous division giving rise to 8 sporozoites in one oocyst. (After Léger, 1907.)

Volvocineae is represented by the 8-cellular colony of *Stephanosphaera*. In both these forms each vegetative individual undergoes 3–4 palintomic divisions, without periods of intermediate growth, giving rise to a corresponding number of considerably smaller individuals. These divisions represent the progamous period, and the last of them gives rise to gamete

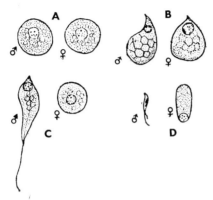

FIG. 189. Gametes of different gregarines.

(*A*) *Monocystis*; (*B*) *Urospora lagidis*; (*C*) *Stylorhynchus*; (*D*) *Echinomera hispida*. (From Dogiel, 1951, after various authors.)

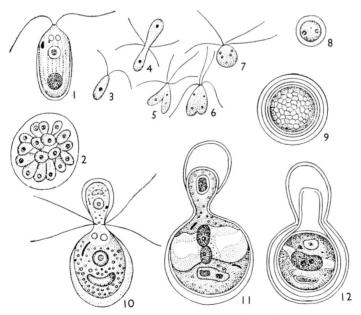

FIG. 190. Isogamy and anisogamy in *Chlamydomonas*.

1–9, isogamy in *Chlamydomonas steini*; 10–12, heterogamy in *Chlamydomonas brauni*. (After Gorozankin, 1890, 1891.)

generation. Both in *Chlamydomonas* and in *Stephanosphaera* during copulation both gametes are enclosed in membranes fused into one, and after formation of the zygote the latter secretes one more inner membrane. Furthermore, the development of anisogamy progresses in both series, i.e. in solitary and colonial Phytomonadida. This development is manifested mainly in an increasing divergence of the rate of development of male and female gametocytes. In *Chlamydomonas euchlora* the number of progamous divisions is not yet stabilized, so that, in accordance with the number of such divisions, the number of gametes produced from one gametocyte varies from 4 to 8, 16, 32, and 64 with a corresponding diminution of their size. A great variety of combinations are observed during copulation of these gametes. Anisogamy is most pronounced in *C. coccifera*, in which the macrogametocyte not only does not divide before copulation but even grows considerably in size and loses its flagella, while the microgametocyte, on the contrary, undergoes repeated palintomy resulting in a large number of minute motile microgametes.

Among the colonial Volvocineae, the 16-celled colony *Pandorina* can be placed next to the isogamous *Stephanosphaera* as the second member of the series. All the cells of the vegetative colony divide into 8–16 gametes, anisogamous pairs are formed, and an encysted zygote is produced. The sizes of the gametes may vary. However, there is no pronounced anisogamy in *Pandorina*: thus larger gametes may copulate with smaller ones, but copulation is also possible between two small ones or two large ones. During the development of the zygote a large flagellate emerges from it, eventually giving rise to a new vegetative colony by palintomy. In the 32-celled colonies of *Eudorina* this phenomenon goes even as far as oogamy, i.e. there is a complete loss of locomotion of the macrogametes, which are transformed into ova. *Eudorina* colonies belong to two sexes, so that the individual male colonies produce a large number of fine minute microgametes, while those of female colonies becomes rounded, lose their flagella, and are all transformed into macrogametes (Fig. 191). Finally, this process goes furthest of all in *Volvox* and related forms. In *Volvox* the colonies of some species are dioecious (*V. aureus*) as in *Eudorina*, while the colonies of other (*V. globator*) are hermaphrodite. In both cases only a few of the members of the colony of many thousands of zooids are capable of forming gametocytes, while all the rest are somatic individuals of the colony which eventually perish. Microgametocytes divide 7–8 times successively, producing 256–512 extremely minute microgametes. Macrogametocytes are devoid of flagella; they grow considerably in size and each of them is wholly transformed into a very large macrogamete. Microgametes mature earlier than macrogametes, and therefore they fertilize the macrogametes of other colonies. It is noteworthy that with the increase of anisogamy the gametes of both sexes differ more and more in structure from their ancestral form of a phytomonad flagellate, the female individual losing its flagella and becoming like large, round eggs of Metazoa; while the male individual becomes thinner and longer, acquiring the appearance of a spermatozoon. The zygote of *Volvox*

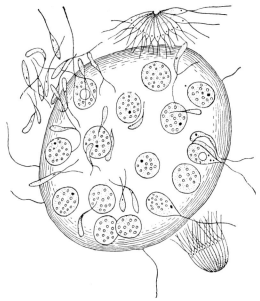

FIG. 191. Sexual reproduction in heterogamous *Eudorina elegans*. (After Göbel, 1882.)

is enclosed in a compact membrane, and goes through a period of rest, after which it experiences repeated palintomy and, by a process of multiplication of cells, resembling egg cleavage in the lower Metazoa, it produces a new young colony.

In flagellates of the order Opalina, which are parasitic in the alimentary tract of amphibians, anisogamous copulation of gametes is observed (Fig. 192). The sexual process in these organisms has a strictly seasonal character, taking place in the spring, when the tadpoles are infected by the opalines. Both the macro- and microgametes of *Opalina* are motile, equipped with numerous flagella, and differ from each other chiefly in size.

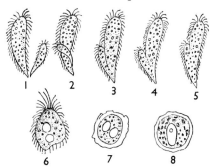

FIG. 192. Gametes and copulation in *Opalina*. 1, gametes; 2–6, copulation; 7–8, encysted zygote. (After Konsuloff, 1922.)

In Sarcodina, as we have seen, the anisogamous method of copulation is not developed; however, in Sporozoa it is frequently encountered and displays many modifications. A very clear series of patterns of the development of progressive anisogamy is observed in Eugregarines.

At the very beginning of the series are gregarines of the group Mono-cystidea, in which, as has been shown by many investigators, the paired gamonts, enclosed in a membrane, undergo repeated nuclear division, after which a large number of minute gametes are detached from the plasmatic body of both partners; these gametes being either completely isogamous or slightly anisogamous. Such slight anisogamy is found, for example, in the coelomic gregarines of polychaetes, *Urospora lagidis*, both gametes being more or less pyriform with a pointed anterior end. The microgametes may be distinguished from the macrogametes by being slightly smaller than the female and by having a more pointed anterior end; the gametes have no flagella.

According to data obtained by many authors, a more pronounced aniso-gamy is observed in the gregarines Polycystidea (Fig. 193) from land arthropods. Studies of representatives of the majority of families have demonstrated everywhere a pronounced differentiation into flagellated 'spermatozoa' and spherical macrogametes.

In the families *Stylocephalidae*, *Clepsidrinidae*, and *Actinocephalidae* copulation has an identical character. The microgametes formed from the body of a male syzygite become pyriform, while at a distended anterior end there is a sharp tip, the rostrum, containing at its end a siderophilic granule, the centriole, while the posterior end of the body is narrowed and prolonged into a thin flagellum. A fine, straight siderophilic filament extends from the centriole to the end of the flagellum through the whole body of the gamete. Female gametes have a regular spherical form. The ratio of the sizes of gametes of both sexes differ as follows in various genera of gregarines: in *Hoplorhynchus* the length of the body of the microgamete is $6·4 \mu$, its width $3·7 \mu$, the length of the tail $12–15 \mu$, the diameter of the macrogamete attains $3·2–3·5 \mu$. In *Actinocephalus* the microgamete is only $3·2 \mu$ long, the length of the tail is 8μ, the diameter of macro-gametes 3μ. In *Gregarina munieri* the flagellated tail of the microgamete is fine and devoid of a rhizoplast, and it disappears almost completely soon after the formation of the gamete, leaving only a short appendix; the length of the microgamete is $5–6 \mu$, the diameter of the macrogamete is $3·5 \mu$.

The representatives of the family Dactylophoridae, namely *Nina gracilis* and *Echinomera*, have exceptionally small microgametes. The minute 'spermatozoa' of these species (7μ long together with the tail) are very narrow, and contain a small amount of cytoplasm; a delicate undulating membrane runs from the base of the tail along one of the sides of the spermatozoon. The eggs are elongated and slightly pointed at their nuclear end; they are $9–10 \mu$ long and 4μ wide; the cytoplasm of the macrogametes contains large granules of reserve food substances.

The destiny of all the copulated zygotes of Eugregarinae is the same. They become enclosed in a double membrane and then pass into the stage of oocyst.[1] The contents of the oocyst undergo a threefold division of the synkaryon, as the result of which the cytoplasm of the former zygote divides into eight vermiform sporozoites, which give rise to new vegetative individuals when they find their way into the organism of a suitable host.

For all Eugregarinae the most characteristic feature of their life-cycle

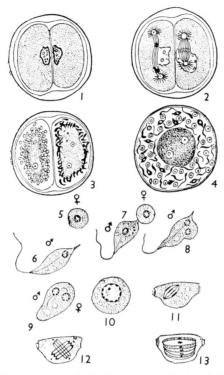

FIG. 193. Anisogamous copulation in gregarine *Stylocephalus longicollis*.

1, two encysted gamonts; 2, first division spindle of nucleus; 3, 4, formation of macro- and microgametes; 5–6, macrogamete and microgamete; 7–10, copulation of gametes and formation of zygote; 11–13, formation of oocyst and of 8 sporozoites inside it. (After Léger, 1904.)

is the loss of the asexual part of it, viz. of schizogony, so that all the descendants of the zygote, i.e. the sporozoites, after going through a series of stages of growth and vegetative life, again proceed directly to the sexual process.

In other Sporozoa, i.e. Coccidia and Haemosporidia, the sporozoites first give rise to schizonts, which multiply vegetatively either once or many

---

[1] The oocysts of the gregarines are often called spores. However, this terminology is not correct. 'The spores' of gregarines are identical to the oocystis of Coccidia, since both represent a membrane produced by the zygote. In Coccidia the spores are formed inside the oocyst, whereas in gregarines there are no structures homologous to the spores of Coccidia and the formation of sporozoites takes place in the oocyst itself.

times, and produce merozoites, which in their turn grow into schizonts. Only the last generation of merozoites develops differently, giving rise to sexual individuals.

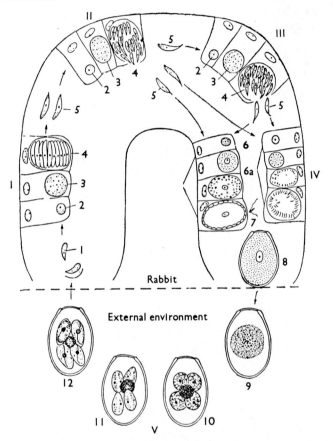

Fig. 194. Cycle of development of coccidium *Eimeria magna* (Coccidia).

I, first generation schizogony; II, second generation schizogony; III, third generation schizogony; IV, gematogony; V, sporogony. 1, sporozoites; 2, young schizont; 3, growing schizont with numerous nuclei; 4, schizont segmented into merozoites; 5, merozoites; 6, development of macrogamete; 6a, development of microgamete; 7, microgamete; 8, oocyst; 9, oocyst proceeding to sporogony; 10, oocyst with four sporoblasts and residual body; 11, development of sporocysts; 12, mature oocysts with four spores, with two sporozoites in each. (Original drawing by Chejsin, 1947.)

The sexual process in Coccidia proceeds according to two main types, corresponding to their subdivision into two suborders: Eimeriidea and Adeleidea.

The most abundant genus—*Eimeria* (Fig. 194)—from the intestinal walls or from the liver of diverse vertebrates, from fish to mammals, may serve as an example of the first order. The life-cycle of *Eimeria* has been studied in special detail in fowls in a series of works by Tyzzer (1927–32) and in rabbits by Chejsin (1947). There are several species of *Eimeria* in the alimentary tract of rabbits. Infection occurs when they ingest the oocysts with spores and sporozoites. Sporozoites emerge from the spores and penetrate into the epithelial cells of the intestine. There the vermiform sporozoite develops into a much larger spherical schizont. The merozoites or some schizonts are transformed into micro- and the others into macro-gametocytes. At first both retain the appearance of typical merozoites, distinguishable only by slight cytological features. After the penetration of gametocytes into the cells of the alimentary tract they begin to differen-tiate in two directions. The female gametocyte becomes rounded, retaining the vesicular karyosomic nucleus typical of *Eimeria*. The microgametocyte also grows and becomes rounded inside the intestinal cell; then its nucleus undergoes repeated division, in the course of which the nuclei are arranged in one layer on the periphery of the microgametocyte. The nuclei then stretch out and break away from the enormous residual body together with minute quantities of the cytoplasm in the form of flagellated microgametes. The microgametes appear as long, extended flagellates, stained completely with nuclear stains, and possessing two flagella, longer than the body of the gamete itself, which are given off from the anterior end of the cell. *Cyclospora caryolytica* and *Isospora felis* have similar microgametes, except

that in the latter the number of mi-crogametes produced by one micro-gametocyte is very large, exceeding 2,000. A fertilized macrogamete of Coccidia is enclosed in a compact membrane, the resulting zygote in Coccidia bearing a special name—oocyst. The nucleus and cytoplasm within the oocyst divide into several separate bodies each of which be-comes invested in a membrane and is transformed into a spore. The contents of a spore divide into a de-finite number (differing in various genera of Coccidia) of sporozoites.

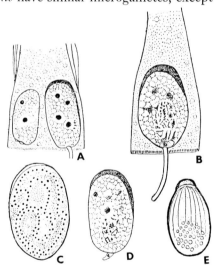

Among the other Eimeriidea, *Pfeif-ferinella impudica* (Fig. 195) is distin-guished by the originality of the struc-ture of its macrogamete, the posterior end of which projects from the epi-thelium of the gut into its lumen (Léger and Hollande, 1912). From this end of the mature macrogamete

FIG. 195. Sexual process in *Pfeifferinella impudica* (Coccidia).

(*A*) macrogamete with 'vaginal tube' being formed; (*B*) 'vaginal tube' completely formed; (*C*) microgametocyte; (*D*) fertilization of macro-gamete; (*E*) oocyst with sporozoites. (After Léger and Hollande, 1912.)

there protrudes into the lumen of the gut a plasmatic spur, known as the

'reception tubule' or 'vaginal tube', which serves as a peculiar 'micropyle' for the admittance of the microgamete into the macrogamete.

A somewhat peculiar type of microgamete is present among the Eimeriidea, in the genus *Aggregata* (Fig. 196), whose life-cycle involves an alter-

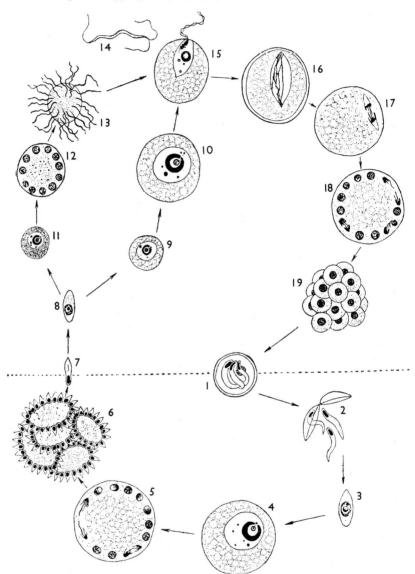

FIG. 196. Cycle of development of *Aggregata eberthi* in crab *Portunus* (below) and in
cephalopod *Sepia* (above).

1, spore; 2, emergence of three sporozoites in intestine of crab; 3–6, growth of schizont and
formation of merozoites; 7 and 8, merozoite; 9–10, growth of macrogamont; 11–13, microgametogenesis; 14, microgamete; 15, copulation; 16, reduction division; 17 and 18, formation
of sporoblasts inside oocyst; 19, sporoblasts. (After Dobell, 1925.)

nation of hosts: marine decapod crustaceans and cephalopod molluscs. The schizogony of *Aggregata* takes place entirely in the intestinal submucosa of crabs, while sporogony proceeds in the intestinal wall of cephalopods, where the merozoites which had penetrated into it are transformed directly into micro- and macrogametocytes. The microgametes have a filamentar body with two anterior flagella and an undulating membrane running along the body. Before fertilization the macrogamete discharges

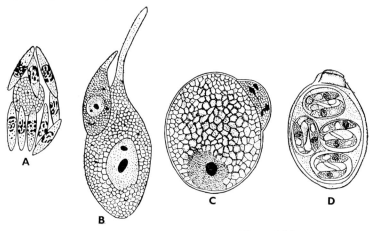

FIG. 197. Stages of the life-cycle of coccidium *Adelina*.

(*A*) group of merozoites; (*B*) pairing of micro- and macrogamonts; (*C*) macrogamete with adherent microgamont dividing into 4 microgametes; (*D*) oocyst with four spores. (After Schellack, 1913.)

from its nucleus into the cytoplasm two small 'secondary nuclei', which probably represent nucleoli. As regards the chromosomes, the whole nuclear cycle of *Aggregata* is haploid as in other Coccidia. Only the nucleus of the zygote is diploid after fusion of the male and female pronuclei. The zygote is enclosed in a compact membrane and it divides into a considerable number of spores with sporozoites.

In the suborder Adeleidea the sexual part of the cycle differs mainly in the fact that microgametogenesis leads to the formation of only four or even two gametes while the microgametocytes themselves have the appearance of merozoites, and the gametes frequently lose their flagella. Moreover in the majority of Adeleidea a paired arrangement of micro- and macrogametocytes is observed (as, for example, in *Adelina*, Fig. 197), both gametocytes being enclosed in a thin common membrane, under which the gametes develop. This combination corresponds to the formation of cysts with syzygies in gregarines. In some forms (*Karyolysus*) mating of gametocytes is accompanied by an active association of vermiform merozoites of the last progamous generation; in others (*Klossia*), merozoites of the last generation are evidently of hermaphrodite nature. Having penetrated into the cell of the kidney epithelium of its host (a snail), such a gametocyte divides twice giving rise to four cells enclosed by a thin, common membrane. One of these cells grows intensely and becomes a macrogametocyte. The remaining three are microgametocytes; the latter either all yield 4 gametes each, or one or two of the gametocytes cease to develop altogether. Many phases of gametogenesis in *Klossia* are labile; thus, for example, a male gametocyte frequently produces not 4 but 8 and even 16 minute gametes. In the forms described the microgametes still retain their character of biflagellate forms, but they are much swollen and shortened. Finally, in such forms as *Karyolysus*, the microgametocyte mated with the macrogametocytes, does not develop flagella, but divides into two round-oval bodies, microgametes, one of which fuses with the macrogamete.

In Haemosporidia (genera *Haemoproteus*, *Plasmodium*) the life-cycle is accompanied by an alternation of hosts (vertebrates and insects). Asexual reproduction (schizogony) takes place in the cells of the inner organs (liver, vascular endothelium, and others) and in the erythrocytes. Part of the resulting merozoites invade the erythrocytes, to form gametocytes. In order to develop further, these must get into the organisms of an arthropod. Later, in the arthropods the female gametocyte becomes rounded and is transformed into a macrogamete. The male gametocyte also becomes rounded and undergoes nuclear division into 4–8 daughter nuclei; the nuclei move to the periphery of the gametocyte, extend in length, and are transformed into long, thin filamentous gametes. These filaments bend actively and gradually detach themselves from the residual body. This period of the breaking away of the gametes from the spherical cytoplasmic body of the gametocyte when they beat intensely in all directions like whips is known as 'exflagellation' of microgametes. The detached gametes are devoid of flagella, and their locomotion is accomplished by simple bending of the body. All the preceding stages, beginning with the development of the gametes, do not take place in the blood of a vertebrate any more, but exclusively in the alimentary tract of a blood-sucking insect. The gametes formed in the alimentary tract of an insect copulate, the fertilized macrogamete acquires a vermiform shape and passes into the stage of the so-called ookinete. The ookinete finds its way through the wall of the intestine and is encysted on its outer surface. The oocyst grows intensively and its contents divide by syntomy into a very large number (thousands) of sporozoites. Later the sporozoites emerge from the ruptured cyst into the body cavity of the insect, whence they gradually penetrate into the salivary glands of their insect host.

General features of sexual processes of the copulation type

After this cursory inspection of a very large number of examples of copulation, which was necessary because of its exceptional variety in Protozoa, we shall try to draw some general conclusions based on this review, classifying these conclusions according to different phases of the sexual process.

1. *Progamous period.* The progamous period consists in the formation of gametocytes, i.e. of stages directly preceding the formation of sexual cells, or gametes. When speaking of the gametocytes, it should be pointed out first of all that it would not be correct to compare them to the corresponding stages of the sexual cycle of Metazoa, i.e. to spermatocytes or oocytes. The spermatocytes in Metazoa constitute in all groups a firmly established homologous stage, composed of the stage of spermatocytes of the first order, each of which divides into two spermatocytes of the second order, and these, in their turn, divide into two spermatids which are transformed into spermatozoa. As we have seen, in Protozoa this part of the sexual process is by no means so stabilized nor so sharply demarcated from the preceding period, which may be likened to the period of the formation of spermatogonia from the germ epithelium.

In fact, in cases of hologamous copulation the progamous period, as a period of a preliminary multiplication of the number of sexual cells, is in general omitted, so that it can be said that during the entire cycle of *Chlamydomonas eugametos*, *Polytoma*, and *Sappinia* there are as many gametes as the number of individuals formed during asexual reproduction.

In the case of merogamous copulation the progamous period is more pronounced and lasts for various periods of time. It is shortest in some cases of paired merogamy, namely in *Trichonympha*, where the usual vegetative individual, when passing into the gametocyte stage, undergoes only one progamous division. If we leave out of consideration the fact that one of the gametes produced is male and the other female, it may be said that the gametocyte of *Trichonympha* corresponds to a certain extent to the spermatocyte of the second order in Metazoa, which gives rise to two spermatids, which are then transformed into gametes. We do not find here any other signs of preparation for copulation. In the other case of paired merogamy studied, such as *Actinophrys*, the pattern is on the whole the same. However, here the problem is complicated by the fact that the nucleus of each of the gametes produced undergoes two meiotic divisions. If the divisions observed by Bělǎr, when he failed to trace the fate of the chromosomes, really correspond to maturation divisions, then in this case the initial vegetative individual may be regarded as corresponding to a gametocyte of the first order, which develops not according to the type of the spermatocyte but to that of an oocyte. Such a gametocyte behaves like a maturing egg, producing only one gamete and three polar bodies. In the final count of paired merogamy each vegetative individual potentially gives rise to two gametes.

Multiple merogamy is accompanied by a considerable increase in the number of gametes during transition from the vegetative to the sexual part of the life-cycle, at least as regards its male gametes, but frequently also as regards the females.

During isogamy the progamous period consists of the formation, by repeated or multiple division, of different numbers of completely identical gametes. The number of them in flagellates is often equal to four or eight, while in Foraminifera and radiolarians there are sometimes many millions. Frequently this long series of nuclear divisions proceeds according to one pattern; in other cases the divisions preceding the differentiation of gametes are distinguished by certain peculiarities which mark them out as divisions of the progamic type. Thus we have seen that in Foraminifera and Radiolaria, towards the end of a long series of syntomic nuclear divisions, at the beginning of the last division the gametocyte develops a double (as compared to the gamete) set of flagella, breaks away from the residual body of the vegetative individual, and only then divides into two gametes, when already in a free-swimming state. Thus in these animals the 'dance' of the gametes in preparation for copulation begins one stage earlier than usual, namely at the gametocyte stage.

Among the Protozoa with anisogamous copulation, it has been shown that in Coccidiomorpha, with alternating generations, the transition to the progamous state is determined by the transition to the last generation of merozoites, consisting not of ordinary merozoites, which continue to reproduce vegetatively, but of gametocytes of two sexes. The female gametocytes are directly transformed into gametes, so that here the progamous period is always shortened. In male gametocytes the process proceeds in various ways. In some cases, as in Eimeridea, the nucleus of the male gametocyte divides many times before the gametes begin to form, i.e. the progamous period is prolonged; in others (Adeleidea) the nucleus of the gametocyte divides only twice or even once before the formation of the gametes.

In anisogamous flagellates the number of divisions, preceding the formation of gametes from vegetative individuals (*Chlamydomonas euchlora*), is at first not stabilized; then, especially in colonial Volvocinea, the number of progamous divisions increase to 7–8, while the size of the microgametes diminishes.

The behaviour of gregarines (Eugregarinae) during the sexual process is noteworthy. Although anisogamy is pronounced in the gregarines Polycistidea their gametogenesis follows the same pattern as that of the isogamous Monocystidea. Namely, both encysted syzygites, or gamonts, undergo nuclear division proceeding at approximately the same rate, and resulting in the formation of hundreds of minute nuclei, with male and female gametes formed around these nuclei usually not differing from each other in size, except for certain Dactylophoridae, where the male forms are considerably smaller than the female ones. Thus the gregarines are characterized by the absence of hypertrophic growth of macrogametes, a phenomenon observed in Coccidia, Haemosporidia, and the higher representatives of colonial Volvocinea.

A comparison between the progamous period in Protozoa and Metazoa shows the absence in Protozoa of any precise differentiation of the separate stages of development of the gametes, both as regards space and time, into periods corresponding to the primordial zone, zone of growth (e.g. spermatogonia), and maturation zone (e.g. spermatocytes of the first and second orders) in Metazoa. Moreover, as has been shown above, meiosis and reduction may occupy various places in the cycle of Protozoa, thereby bringing about a change in the relationship between the haploid and the diploid phases.

As has been mentioned before, progamous divisions leading to the formation of gametes may be accomplished in as many different ways as the division of individual Protozoa during vegetative reproduction. Thus progamous reproduction very often proceeds by repeated palintomic division (Phytomonadida, Dinoflagellata, amoeboid gametes of certain Foraminifera); in other cases there is syntomy or multiple division (many Sporozoa); in Foraminifera and Radiolaria all the initial stages of gametogenesis proceed according to the syntomy type, while the formation of gametes themselves from the gametocytes takes place by longitudinal division; finally, in *Noctiluca* the process of formation of gametes from a vegetative individual resembles the exogenous budding of Suctoria, while in certain Schizogregarines the single gamete is produced by endogenous budding.

The question arises whether the gametes of Protozoa (Fig. 198) are of any significance in determining the phylogenetic relations between different groups of Protozoa. On consideration of this question one should concentrate his attention on the fact that gametes of most Protozoa are flagelloid. Thus among Mastigophora the formation of flagelloid gametes is the rule. First, all Phytomastigina possess them, moreover in solitary Phytomastigina (Chlamydomonads, *Polytoma*, Dinoflagellata and others), especially in isogamous forms, the gametes do not differ in any respect from the vegetative individuals, which also indicates the primitive character of this type of gametes. The gametes retain the same number and arrangement of flagella—2 identical anterior ones in Phytomonadida, 1 anterior and 1 transverse one in Dinoflagellata, and 2 dissimilar ones at the anterior end of Cryptomonadida. If there is a stigma in the vegetative state, it is retained in the gametes. Transverse and longitudinal grooves in the body of Dinoflagellata, the dentiform process of the body of adult *Noctiluca*, the short, transverse groove at the anterior end of Cryptomonadida, all these structures are also retained in their gametes. These facts indicate that the structure of gametes in Mastigophora might be regarded as an essential phylogenetic character of this class. It may be of special significance in the determination of the systematic position of forms in which parasitism has produced considerable alterations (Blastodinidae, *Haploozon*, and others). However, even among the flagellates there appear cases of deviation of the sexual individuals, i.e. gametes, from their original form. One type of such modification is evident in the gametes of flagellates with pronounced anisogamy. This concerns chiefly male gametes, since female gametes in all anisogamous Protozoa have the same tendency to lose their flagella, to increase the volume of the body, and to acquire a spherical form. The male cells of anisogamous Phytomonadida differ from vegetative individuals not only in a considerable reduction in size, but also in attenuation of their body, which assumes the appearance of a thin rod (*Chlorogonium*) or of a cigar (*Volvox*), while the vegetative individual of *Volvox* is short, broad, and pyriform. However, the other characteristics of the group Volvocidae are fully retained. We regard the rod-like elongation of the gametes as an indication of progressive adaptation for the development of greater mobility; furthermore the rod-like gametes in colonial Volvocidae can be conveniently packed in large numbers within the limited space of a single multicellular layer; while the shape of such a multicellular layer is determined by the longitudinal direction of the division, which is peculiar to all flagellates. Similar features of progressive evolution of gametes are encountered in other Protozoa.

The modification of gametes noted by us in *Trichonympha* and other flagellates from the alimentary tract of *Cryptocercus* is of an entirely different character. We consider that in such cases the gametes exhibit the characters acquired by this group of flagellates during their long evolution in the alimentary tract of their hosts, i.e. termites. Consequently the present form of the gametes of trichonymphids represents a newly acquired character; we therefore propose to refer to analogous cases as examples of the development of coenogenetic gametes in which these acquire the structures attained by the vegetative stages during their progressive evolution. In Trichonymphidae and others this coenogenetic adaptation makes the structure of the gametes more complex than in the more ancient, free-living flagellates, but this is not an improvement achieved by the gametes themselves, but a feature developed by the vegetative stages and merely transferred to the gametes. Thus it may be said of these flagellates that they have lost their former type of gamete formation and have developed a new method of formation of special coenogenetic gametes.

The main mass of Sarcodina, namely Foraminifera and Radiolaria, have flagelloid isogametes of a simple structure, without any special adaptations for copulation apart from their extremely small size of $1 \cdot 5$–$2 \, \mu$ in diameter. Therefore it may be assumed that they reflect to some extent the pattern of their hypothetical ancestor. In that case their ancestor must have had a round-oval body with a round fat-inclusion and two dissimilar flagella, of which the shorter was directed backwards.

However, among the Sarcodina there are not a few representatives which, having acquired the amoeboid form, have retained it in their gametes. In other words in such Sarcodina the gametes have acquired coenogenetically an amoeboid type of structure.

Such are the gametes of certain Foraminifera (of *Patellina* type), *Sappinia*, and some of the Heliozoa. The existence of biflagellate swarmers is known for some Heliozoa, but their connexion with the sexual process has not been established.

If we interpret the relationship of Rhizopoda and Mastigophora in a different way and regard the amoeboid form, and not the flagelloid one, as the primitive structure (which we think more probable), then the amoeboid gametes should be accepted as the primary form. In that case the flagelloid gametes would represent a further stage of complication. However, this will not affect the general character of the foregoing arguments.

Gametes of the members of the Sporozoa group show a considerable variety of forms. First of all the gametes of a large number of Sporozoa, at least those of the male sex, have a flagelloid character. Among the monocystid gregarines only one species of *Monocystis* is known in which the posterior end of the body of microgametes extends into a long tail. Typical flagelloid gametes are widely distributed among the Polycystidea. In this case the occurrence of adaptations whereby the male gamete is transformed into the likeness of a real spermatozoon is of great interest—namely the anterior end of the pyriform gamete of Polycystidea extends in the form of a pointed rostrum with a centriole in its anterior extremity. A comparison of the rostrum with the perforator in the sperms of certain Metazoa naturally comes to one's mind. Furthermore, there is a siderophilic filament running from the anterior centriole, which bends around the nucleus, and continues posteriorly up to the very end of the backward-directed flagellum. This arrangement of the supporting filament again resembles the structure of the caudal part of the spermatozoon of Metazoa. Finally, in such Polycystidea as *Nina gracilis*, the gamete undergoes further marked modifications, becoming smaller and thinner and acquiring a longitudinal undulating membrane. Such a gamete is comparable to the spermatozoa of certain Metazoa, possessing a caudal marginal membrane. We believe that the acquirement of such specific gametes of the Polycystid gregarines have probably progressed beyond the limits of the structure possessed by the gametes of the free-living ancestors of gregarines. In other words, it would appear that in gregarines, the male gametes have evolved beyond the level of organization reached by the ancestral flagellates and have undergone a secondary complication of their organization, similar to that which had already taken place even to a greater extent in the spermatozoa of Metazoa. In this respect the gametes of gregarines are also coenogenetically modified, but in a different direction from that of the amoeboid gametes of Foraminifera and of the gametes of *Trichonympha*. Here the structural features of adult gregarines have not been transferred to the gametes, but they retain and improve the flagelloid organization of the ancestral gametes, leading to its convergence with the form of the specialized spermatozoa of Metazoa. Gametes of this type may be called progressive coenogenetic, in contrast to stabilized coenogenetic, to which belong those gametes which retain the structure of the vegetative stage of the groups which had originated from Mastigophora. As will be shown below, this last type of coenogenetic gametes is very common among Sporozoa.

Another example of progressive coenogenetic gametes is encountered among certain Coccidia, namely *Aggregata*. In this coccidium the microgametes have a filamentar, elongated body, two anterior flagella, and a well-developed undulating membrane running along the whole body. We cannot regard this powerful membrane as an ancestral character of *Aggregata*, since free-living flagellates with a membrane are practically unknown, and this feature is also absent in the gametes of all the other Coccidia. In our opinion, the membrane was acquired by the genus in the course of progressive adaptation to the parasitic mode of life, and represents a progressive coenogenetic feature.

In all other Eimeriidea the gametes have the form of biflagellar flagellates, devoid of a membrane. In another suborder of Coccidia, namely Adeleidea, a gradual decrease is observed in the number of microgametes produced by a gametocyte, as well as a simplification of the structure of the flagelloid gametes. This simplification becomes possible owing to the pairing of the micro- and macrogametocytes (pseudoconjugation), thereby facilitating contact between the male gametes and the macrogamete and ensuring successful copulation.

The gametes in Gregarinida, Monocystidea, and in Schizogregarinae are simplified in the same manner. In Monocystidea the microgametes, without being reduced in numbers, acquire a pyriform shape with a pointed end devoid of flagella, but possessing a siderophilic inclusion at the end, apparently representing a centriole, pointing to the presence of flagella in the past.

In Schizogregarinae, as we have seen, the gametes are isogamous and their number decreases to two (in *Mattesia*) and even to one (in *Ophryocystis*). At the same time the gametes of both types are devoid of locomotor organoids and have the appearance of regular spheres or ovoids resembling more than anything the vegetative stages of coccidia. All the non-flagellate gametes of Sporozoa might, in spite of their apparent variety, be united under the name either of simplified gametes, or of gametes of the coccidioid type, since one group of them is more like schizonts, and the other like merozoites of coccidia. This similarity is evident not only in the external shape of their body but also in the structure of their nucleus, which is of vesicular structure.

Thus, summing up all that has been said about the structure of the gametes of Protozoa, we obtain the following patterns (Fig. 198):

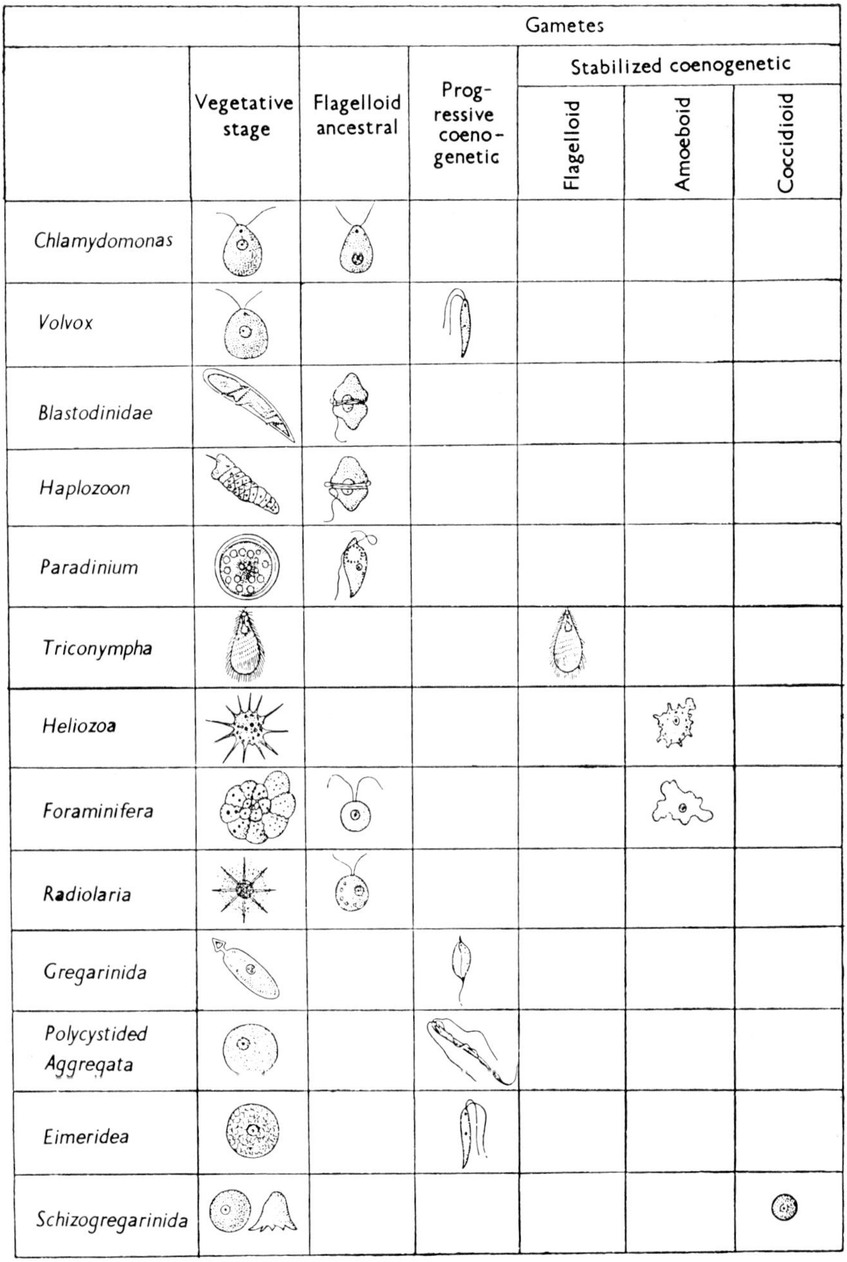

| | | Gametes | | | | |
| | | | | Stabilized coenogenetic | | |
	Vegetative stage	Flagelloid ancestral	Prog-ressive coeno-genetic	Flagelloid	Amoeboid	Coccidioid
Chlamydomonas						
Volvox						
Blastodinidae						
Haplozoon						
Paradinium						
Triconympha						
Heliozoa						
Foraminifera						
Radiolaria						
Gregarinida						
Polycystided Aggreqata						
Eimeridea						
Schizogregarinida						

FIG. 198. Diagram showing different types of gametes in Protozoa and their phylogenetic significance. (Original.)

Flagelloid gametes, retaining the structure of the original group of Mastigophora, represent the main type of gametes in Protozoa; in some parasitic groups (part of the Sporozoa) a secondary simplification of the flagelloid gametes takes place, accompanied by simplification or even complete reduction of the flagellar apparatus—these are the coenogenetic gametes of the simplified type. The third category is composed of gametes of the stabilized coenogenetic type. In these gametes the structure of the initial flagelloid type disappears altogether and is replaced by a new form of gamete, which does not recapitulate the type of the ancestral flagellate, but that of the vegetative stage of the given group of Protozoa, i.e. of an amoeba in the case of Amoebina and certain Foraminifera, of a heliozoan in the case of Heliozoa, and of a trichonymph in Trichonymphidae.

Finally, the last category of gametes, which we call the progressive coenogenetic type, continues the line of the development of the flagelloid type, improving it by the addition of new progressive characters such as rostrum, supporting filament, and undulating membranes. Among the different types of gametes only the flagelloid type of gametes is, strictly speaking, of phylogenetic significance, i.e. this significance is retained only within the limits of the class Mastigophora where the shape of the gametes may serve often as a criterion for the determination of the origin of certain flagellates, especially ones strongly modified by a parasitic mode of life.

2. *Eugamous period.* This period comprising the copulation of the gametes itself may take place under two different conditions: either a freely motile state, or within a special cyst. Apparently, the first one is more primitive, but the second has also acquired a wide distribution.

Copulation in the motile state is particularly characteristic of flagellates, including not only the free-living Mastigophora, but also those representatives that have been deeply affected by parasitism, such as Blastodinidae, *Haplozoon*, and Trichonymphidae. Moreover, we encounter it also among Radiolaria, in almost all the Foraminifera, in Haplosporidia, in some of the Coccidiida (Eimeriidea), and finally in Opalinina.

Copulation in an encysted state is observed in Heliozoa, certain Foraminifera (*Patellina* and others), in gregarines, and in some Coccidia (Adeleidea).

However, the temporary transition to the encysted state is observed in various periods of the sexual process and may have a different biological significance (see p. 474).

Method of union of the gametes and their position at the moment of copulation may vary considerably in different Protozoa. In the majority of the isogamous or slightly anisogamous Phytomonadida the pointed ends of the gametes come in contact with each other and the gametes copulate in this position, frequently with their flagella interlacing. In the case of elongated gametes, after establishing contact with their anterior poles, they bend towards each other at an angle, and the lateral parts of the bodies fuse

(*Stephanosphaera* and others). In Dinoflagellata, according to some data, fusion takes place at the ventral sides, which bear the flagella. In Foraminifera, according to Le Calvez, fusion of the anterior ends of the gametes takes place, although, according to Schaudinn's figures the flagellar ends of the gametes are directed backwards, i.e. copulation proceeds by the posterior ends.

In gregarines in some cases (*Nina*) a minute microgamete enters the anterior, nuclear end of the macrogamete, whereas in other cases (Actinocephalidae) fusion apparently proceeds somewhat obliquely. In Coccidia (*Eimeria, Adelea*) the microgamete frequently enters the spherical macrogamete at the point where the female nucleus touches its surface, although the male gamete would have to go round the whole periphery of the macrogamete to reach it.

Interesting adaptations for the admission of the male gamete are observed in the macrogamete of the coccidium *Pfeifferinella* and in *Trichonympha* (see p. 337). The copulation act is particularly original in *Trichonympha*, where the male gamete penetrates into the female one through a special fertilization cone at the posterior end of the latter. It is possible that the point of penetration of the gamete in this case is determined by the fact that the posterior pole in *Trichonympha* serves for the swallowing of food particles, and in this case the male gametes behave as such.

3. *Metagamous period*. The metagamous period is frequently, even in most cases, characterized by encystment of the zygote, and also by phenomena of its reproduction differing from the usual vegetative reproduction.

Cysts. During the course of the sexual process, encystation, apart from the metagamous period, sometimes occurs considerably earlier; moreover cysts formed at different periods vary in character and significance, according to which they can be divided into several categories (Fig. 199).

1. *Gamontocysts* are a type of cysts which appear in the sexual cycle earlier than all the others and serve for a closer union of two individuals of the progamous generation, i.e. of two gamonts or two gametocytes; in most cases, but not always, these cysts have delicate walls and serve to facilitate the ensuing act of copulation between gametes of two sexes.

Gamontocysts are most frequent and typical in many coccidia Adeleidea. Thus in *Adelina* a male and female gamont are invested in a thin membrane, under which the female gamont is transformed into a female gamete, while the male gives rise to 4 gametes; one of these copulates with the macrogamete, while the others perish within the gamontocyst.

The cysts of the syzygies in gregarine, in which the gametes are formed later, should also be regarded as gamontocysts.

2. *Zygocysts* or *cystozygotes* serve for the protection of the zygote resulting from fertilization and possess more compact walls. They usually serve for a prolonged protection of either the zygote or the products of its multiplication.

It can be seen in the same object, that is *Adelina*, that after fertilization

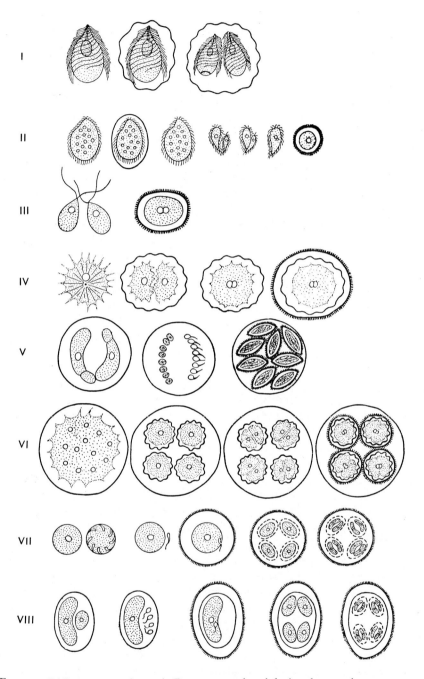

FIG. 199. Different types of cysts in Protozoa, produced during the sexual process.

I, *Trichonympha*; II, *Opalina*; III, *Chlamydomonas*; IV, *Actinophrys*; V, Gregarine; VI, *Actinosphaerium*; VII, *Eimeria*; VIII, Adeleidae. Wavy outline indicates gametocysts; even outline, gamontocysts; unilaterally hatched outline, zygocysts; interrupted outline, sporocysts. (After Dogiel, 1951.)

the macrogamete, which has now become a zygote, is enclosed in a compact envelope, apparently covering the gamontocyst. In coccidia and gregarines the stage of the oocyst presumably corresponds to the zygocyst.

3. *Sporocysts* are supplementary cysts of protective significance, formed inside the zygocyst in those cases when the zygote breaks up into separate units enclosed in an envelope. Such a stage exists in *Adelina*, which was taken as an example. Hence in *Adelina* three different categories of cysts either succeed or supplement each other during the sexual process.

4. *Gametocysts* are very rarely formed, and represent cysts encountered in some Protozoa during the progamous period. The cyst is secreted by a vegetative individual. Its uninucleate body divides directly into two gametes of different sexes.

Actinophrys provides the most typical example. The vegetative individual is surrounded by a gametocyst, within which the body divides into two amoeboid isogametes, which then fuse with each other again, i.e. copulate. The secretion around the newly formed zygote of *Actinophrys* of a new, denser envelope representing the true zygocyst is proof that the gametocyst is a structure distinct from the zygocyst.

In the multinucleate *Actinosphaerium* this process is similar, with this difference, however, that a common gamontocyst is first formed around the multinucleate heliozoan. Hence in this case also three cysts are secreted during the cycle.

The formation of the gametocyst in the cycle of *Trichonympha* belongs to the same category, with this essential difference, however, that the two gametes formed inside the cyst by division of the vegetative individual do not copulate with each other, but escape from the gametocyst and mate with other gametes formed at the same time in the alimentary tract of the host.

In the light of the subdivision into the categories established above some of the terms accepted up to the present must be revised. The membranes surrounding the gamonts and gametocytes have hitherto usually had no special name, therefore we have introduced a new term for it. It is justified since it refers to precisely determined stages of the cycle and in the majority of cases has a definite significance. In the majority of cases gamontocysts serve to ensure the meeting of gametes of both sexes, therefore they are encountered most frequently when the female gamete is motionless, while the microgametocyte produces a small number of not very motile gametes (Adeleidea, Schizogregarinae, and *Patellina* among the Foraminifera and *Actinosphaerium*).

Gamontocysts with a large number of gametes are found only among Eugregarinae. Gamontocysts of different significance (propagative cysts) are found only among the Opalinina.

The significance of zygocysts and their right to an independent name are beyond doubt. It should only be noted that up to the present an inaccurate terminology has been employed for the sporocysts of Eugregarinae.

The sporocysts of gregarines do not correspond to those of coccidia. The sporocysts of coccidia enclose the products of reproduction of the zygote, whereas the sporocysts of gregarines cover the zygote itself; hence they belong to the category of zygocysts.

We are leaving the name of the true sporocysts unchanged.

Finally, the term 'gametocyst', recently applied by Cleveland to the original cysts of *Trichonympha*, has been extended by us for the paedogamic cysts in Heliozoa. Our revision of the terminology introduces a definite uniformity and eliminates the meaningless names of cysts that were employed for the three categories of cysts in *Actinosphaerium*: maternal cyst (i.e. gamontocyst), primary cyst (i.e. gametocyst), and secondary cyst (i.e. zygocyst). For a correct understanding of our terminology we adduce below schemes of the sexual cycle of various Protozoa with the corresponding names of stages (Fig. 199).

DISTRIBUTION OF DIFFERENT TYPES OF CYSTS AMONG PROTOZOA

Name of organism	Gamontocyst	Gametocyst	Zygocyst	Sporocyst
Chlamydomonadidae			+	
Trichonympha		+		
Sappinia			+	
Patellina	+			
Actinophrys		+	+	
Actinosphaerium	+	+	+	
Schizogregarinae	+		+	
Eugregarinae	+		+	
Eimeriidea			+	+
Adeleidea	+		+	+
Haemogregarinae	+		+	
Aggregata			+	+
Haemosporidia			+	
Opalinina	+		+	

We do not refer the formation of gametes in the old pellicle of the vegetative individual (for example in certain Chlamydomonads) to the processes of cyst formation, which are always new structures. In the accompanying table we have noted chiefly those cycles whose authenticity is beyond doubt. Certain groups of Sporozoa, which have not been sufficiently investigated in this respect, are not included in the table. Moreover in the case of Myxosporidia it should be borne in mind that their spores of zygocysts have a completely different cellular origin from that of the other Protozoa, and therefore represent structures *sui generis*.

The destiny of the zygote before the formation of the first vegetative individuals

The metagamous period of development of the zygote may proceed in various ways in different Protozoa.

1. *The zygote is transformed directly into an individual of the first vegetative generation.* This, the simplest and shortest way of transition from the sexual generation to the asexual, is excellently illustrated by the destiny of the zygote in Foraminifera, Radiolaria, Heliozoa, and *Sappinia*. The developmental of the zygotes in Opalinata belongs to the same type.

2. *Reversion to the vegetative state is preceded by division of the zygote within the zygocyst.* The first generation of vegetative individuals is formed directly from the zygote inside the zygocyst. Single Phytomonadida provide the best illustration of this type of metagamous changes. Here the contents of the zygocyst usually divide twice in succession, giving rise to four individuals, which then escape from the cyst and become the first vegetative individuals.

In this case the occurrence of two divisions in the zygote is evidently due to the fact that they represent reduction divisions, whereby the descendants of the zygote revert to the haploid state and to the structure of vegetative individuals.

All the Schizogregarinae and Eugregarinae belong to this category. And indeed, the cyst formed at the beginning of the sexual process envelops the gametocytes or gamonts, but not the gametes; therefore it is a gamontocyst, and not a zygocyst. It is the membranes enclosing the product of the copulation of gametes that should be regarded as real zygocysts, i.e. the oocysts of the gregarines. Inside the zygocyst of this type a certain number of sporozoites, i.e. young stages of development of the vegetative individual, are produced by repeated divisions. Hence this terminates the sexual part of the cycle. In this case reduction is also zygotic.

3. *The first generation of vegetative individuals is not formed directly in the zygocyst, but within a special supplementary cyst—the sporocyst.* The sporocyst represents a secondary, intercalated system of membranes, which reinforce the protective properties of the zygocyst. This type of the development of the zygote is common among the Coccidiida, the zygocyst of which is called the oocyst. Sporocysts contain sporozoites. The difference between the sporozoites of Coccidia and the sporozoites of gregarines is particularly clearly seen in such Coccidia as *Caryospora simplex*, where the purely protective function of the sporocyst is striking. The oocyst of *Caryospora* forms only one sporocyst, which thus represents merely a second, inner membrane for the eight sporozoites contained in it (the same number of sporozoites as in the zygotes of gregarines). The similarity between the oocyst of *Caryospora* and the zygocysts of gregarines is emphasized still more by the fact that the spore membrane is sometimes absent in *Caryospora*, and always absent in another representative of Eimeriidea, namely *Pfeifferinella*, i.e. the oocysts in this case fully correspond to the multiple zygocyst of gregarines. The further phase of the evolutionary development of the sporocyst in Coccidia may be illustrated by such forms as *Isospora*. In *Isospora* the zygote in the oocyst divides into two, but instead of continuing

to divide into 8 sporozoites (as in the case of gregarines), each daughter element (sporoblast) is invested in a membrane and two sporocysts are produced, 4 sporozoites being formed in each. In other Coccidia the number of sporocysts may increase up to 160 (*Klossia*), the number of sporozoites in the sporocyst up to 20 and more (*Hepatozoon* in *Glossina palpalis*). An example of the other extreme as regards the number of sporozoites in the sporocyst is provided by *Barrouxia* (Eimeriidea), which forms a large number of sporocysts but with only one sporozoite in each.

Apart from the similarity to gregarines exemplified by *Caryospora*, the secondary character of the sporocysts is also indicated by extreme variation in the time of their formation during the development of the zygocyst, by the diversity of the number of sporozoites, and in their behaviour. On the basis of these facts we arrive at the conclusion that the sporozoites of Coccidia are in general homologous to those of the gregarines, since both may be regarded as the first generation of vegetative individuals, although in gregarines these individuals do not reproduce vegetatively, but represent only the vegetative phase of the development of the gamont; while on the other hand, in Coccidia they initiate the schizogonic generations. The difference between Coccidia and gregarines consists also in the fact that in Coccidia the development of sporozoites from the zygote is prolonged, they are provided with supplementary membranes, and sometimes the process is even complicated by the introduction of an additional stage of sporokinetes, observed in *Karyolysus* (of Adeleidea).

In *Karyolysus lacertae* (Fig. 200) the life-cycle is accompanied by an alternation of hosts: schizogony takes place in the endothelial cells of the vessels of lizards; merozoites of the last generation invade the erythrocytes of the blood and are differentiated into micro- and macrogametocytes, i.e. they already belong to the sexual part of the cycle. Their further development takes place in the blood-sucking mite *Liponyssus*, into the alimentary tract of which the gametocytes are taken in together with the blood of the lizard. Here the erythrocytes are digested, and the gametocytes of different sexes form syzygies, adhering closely to each other. The microgametocyte produces two non-flagellated gametes, one of which copulates with the macrogametocyte, leading to the formation of a zygote invested in a zygocyst. The next stage of the cycle is of special interest. The zygote divides repeatedly into 12–15 bodies known as sporokinetes, which are similar in shape to large merozoites ($40–50\,\mu$) and rich in the nutritive material. The sporokinetes instead of forming spores, leave the zygocyst, penetrate through the walls of the intestine into the egg cells of the mite, and only there become invested in a membrane, within which about 30 minute sporozoites are produced. When a lizard devours the infected mites, the sporozoites penetrate into the submucosa of the alimentary tract and enter the blood-vessels and their endothelium. Hence in *Karyolysus* the process of secretion of the spore membrane around the bodies which are eventually transformed into spores is greatly prolonged, and at the same time the process of division of the bodies themselves into sporozoites is also protracted. In the case of *Karyolysus* one might have expected the formation within the zygocyst of 450 (15 × 30) sporozoites, encased in 15 sporocysts. Instead of which 15 large sporokinetes are produced, while their transformation into sporocysts with sporozoites is greatly protracted and is transferred to a different site, i.e. the eggs of the mite. Hence the impression of

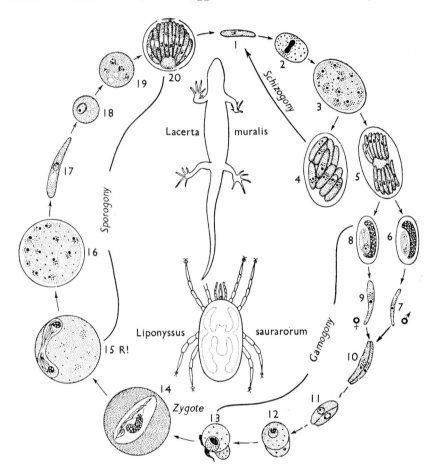

FIG. 200. Life-cycle of *Karyolysus lacertarum*. Schizogony in *Lacerta muralis*, gamogony and sporogony in mite *Liponyssus saurarum*.

1, sporozoite penetrates through gut epithelium into blood-vessels and thence into endothelial cells; 2–4, schizogony and formation of macromerozoites; 5, micromerozoites invade erythrocytes and form gamonts, further development proceeds in epithelial cells of gut in mite; 6–7, microgamonts; 8–9, macrogamonts; 10, pairing of gamonts; 11–13, growth of macrogamont and formation from microgamont of 2 microgametes; 14, zygote; 15, reduction division; 16, multinuclear zygote and formation of sporocyst (17); sporocyst penetrates into egg of a mite, where it grows, becomes rounded, and is invested in a membrane (18–20). Resulting spore has up to 20–30 sporozoites. (After Reichenow, 1921, from Grell, 1956a.)

the interpolation into the cycle of a special sexual generation, the sporo-kinetes, although in principle this cycle does not differ from the pattern characteristic of other Coccidia.

In *Aggregata* the cycle also takes place in two hosts, but the entire sexual part of the cycle proceeds in one place (in the submucosa of the intestine of cephalopod molluscs), therefore the sporocysts are also formed there within the zygocyst, so that at this stage the cycle follows the normal pattern for Coccidia.

As we have seen above, in certain genera of Coccidia the formation of sporocysts around the sporozoites may be left out, either regularly or occasionally, so that only one membrane is left, viz. the zygocyst. Most investigators regard this phenomenon occurring in Coccidia as secondary.

The extension of the same process of omission of the sporocysts to the order Haemosporidia leads us to transfer this group, which is essentially related to the Coccidia, to the preceding category in respect of the type of zygote development. And indeed, in Haemosporidia, the zygocyst, formed in the walls of the alimentary tract of mosquitoes, gives rise to thousands of minute sporozoites, each of which develops in the body of vertebrate host into a tissue schizont, i.e. into a vegetative individual.

A consideration of the sexual cycles in different Protozoa leads to the conclusion that in spite of their apparent diversity they may be reduced to a comparatively small number of basic types.

Conjugation

It is considered that the main difference between conjugation and copu-lation is that in the former the sexual process consists not in complete fusion but only in a temporary union of two individuals, during which they ex-change parts of their nuclear apparatus. The second essential difference follows from this. The process of conjugation is not directly connected with the processes of reproduction: the two conjugants usually separate from each other and return to an independent existence, so that after the completion of conjugation there is no visible direct result of it—progeny is absent. The main biological significance of conjugation is the modification of the hereditary properties of both conjugants as a result of the sexual process. Conjugation demonstrates most clearly that the sexual process and that of reproduction represent two distinct phenomena in Protozoa. Conjugation is limited to one class of Protozoa only, namely the ciliates.

I. Typical Conjugation

In the great majority of ciliates conjugation takes place between indivi-duals identical in shape and size, i.e. according to all its morphological characteristics, conjugation is isogamous. As in copulation, there are three periods in conjugation, the first being a preparatory period.

(1) *Preconjugation period.* This period has been least investigated and often passes almost unnoticed. In free-living ciliates the only sign of approaching conjugation consists in the ectoplasm of the preconjugants becoming sticky. This stickiness enables the ciliates to adhere to each other at the moment of conjugation. Frequently no other obvious peculiarities are observed in free-living ciliates; however, it has now been shown, especially after Dogiel's work, that among parasitic forms a whole series of species belonging to different groups of ciliates undergo a special pre-conjugation division, differing from the usual ones. This division transforms the vegetative, or, in Dogiel's terminology, 'neutral individuals' into the state of 'preconjugants'. This division is first of all characterized by a swelling of the micronucleus, reminiscent of the behaviour of micronuclei at the beginning of conjugation. Preconjugants can be easily distinguished from neutral individuals by this feature. The second characteristic of division consists in the fact that the preconjugants do not grow from after the preconjugation period right up to the end of the sexual process. On account of this, each preconjugant can also usually be distinguished (in Entodiniomorpha) from neutral individuals by the shape of its body. This is especially clear in such genera as *Cycloposthium*, in which not only do both preconjugants, produced as a result of division, differ from neutral individuals in having a shorter and relatively broader body, but also in the fact that the anterior and posterior conjugants are distinguishable from each other: the body of the anterior one has a somewhat deformed posterior end, as the result of incomplete restoration of the posterior pole of the body due to an arrest in the growth of the preconjugants. There is a still greater difference between the preconjugants in *Opisthotrichum* (Fig. 201). This special preconjugation division is characteristic of the whole suborder Entodiniomorpha. Furthermore, it has been noted by Dogiel in the parasitic Bütschliidae, Isotrichidae, Paraisotrichidae, and by Chatton and Pérard (1921) in Pycnotrichidae and others. The pronounced difference in the structure of the micronucleus during the preconjugation division in *Cyclosthium* and other Entodiniomorpha depends on the fact that in these ciliates this division is actually representative of the first conjugation mitosis (meiotic division) of the micronucleus, transferred, however, into the preconjugation period. In many free-living and parasitic ciliates conjugation is preceded by one special division not accompanied by subsequent growth, but without the first conjugation mitosis being transferred into the progamic period.

In *Cryptochilidium echini* from the alimentary tract of sea-urchins (Dain, 1930) there is a pronounced progamous division, during which the dividing micronucleus, in distinction from the usual agamous division, does not form a long connecting strand and acquires the shape of a comma without becoming rounded during telophase. Because of this the preconjugants of *Cryptochilidium* differ from neutral individuals not only in their smaller size but also in the shape of their micronucleus. Bogdanowicz (1930) points out that in free-living *Loxodes striatus* and *L. rostrum* (*L. magnus*) there are a number of marked morphological differences between the preconjugants and the neutral individuals. The preconjugants of *Loxodes* are considerably smaller than neutral individuals, differing from the latter also in the number and structure of their nuclei. Wichterman describes (1937) in the parasite

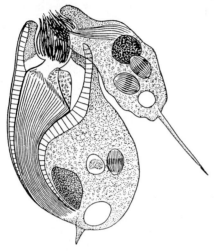

of amphibia *Nyctotherus cordiformis* the presence of a special preconjugation division, as a result of which minute individuals are formed, which proceed to conjugation. J. Rajkov (1958a, d) has also found in the marine ciliate *Trachelocerca phaenicopterus* preconjugants characterized by a relatively small size and certain peculiarities in the structure of the nuclear apparatus, viz. in the absence of the formation of a 'complex nucleus'.

The small size of the conjugants points to the occurrence of a preconjugation division preceding their formation, while anisogamy, observed in some cases, indicates that during each vegetative division, not

FIG. 201. Anisogamous conjugation in ciliate *Opisthotrichum janus* (Ophryoscolecidae). (After Dogiel, 1925a.)

followed by a period of growth, the anterior and posterior individuals differ somewhat from one another in size and even in the shape of the body.

The duration of the preconjugation period is apparently not great, as shown by the fact that the preconjugants unite without a previous period of growth.

(2) *Conjugation period.* This period begins from the moment the two preconjugants unite and lasts till the time of their separation and their return to independent life. In the majority of ciliates the conjugants adhere to each other in a longitudinal direction and also symmetrically. In most cases the initial simple contact is transformed into a complete union of the cytoplasm of the partners along the so-called 'plasmatic connecting bridge'. The length of this bridge varies from a narrow cross-piece (often in the area of the cytostome) to union of both partners throughout half the length of the body and even more. Fusion occurs most often by the ventral or later-ventral sides of their bodies. However, in this respect, too, there are many exceptions. Thus *Didinium* unite with each other by their anterior ends. The stability of the plasmatic connexion between the conjugants also varies, depending first of all on a different density of the exterior layer of the body. Thus in *Euplotes*, which has a very compact pellicle, no real plasmatic bridge is formed: the migrating pronucleus of each partner breaks to the

exterior through the anterio-ventral wall of the body, moves somewhat backwards, and penetrates into the other conjugant through its cytostome. Many Entodiniomorpha conjugate by their anterior ends, but the presence in them of a firm cuticle hinders the formation of a plasmatic bridge. They interlace each other by the cirri of their adoral spirals.

From the very moment of the pairing of the partners a series of changes begin in the cytoplasm and nuclear apparatus of both of them. These changes proceed to a certain extent parallel, but for convenience of understanding they may be considered separately for the cytoplasm, the macronucleus, and finally the micronucleus.

Changes in the plasmatic body. The peristome and the adoral cilia of the conjugants are in most cases absorbed, while the peristomial cavity itself may be smoothed away. Only in Entodiniomorpha does the adoral ciliary apparatus remain completely intact, since it ensures contact between the two conjugants. The structure of the endoplasm and the arrangement of the mitochondria may also change. Poljanskij (1934) has shown that in *Bursaria* the loose cytoplasm filled with comparatively large vacuoles becomes homogeneous and the vacuoles diminish in size; while the mitochondria, formerly uniformly distributed through the endoplasm, accumulate at the surface of the body at the border between the ecto- and endoplasm. Cinger (1929) has also observed in *Paramecium* a change in the form of mitochondria, which become rounded. The amount of reserve nutritive material in the cytoplasm also changes in the course of conjugation. According to Zweibaum (1922), in *Paramecium* the amount of glycogen in the cytoplasm is reduced to a minimum before conjugation, but after reconstruction of the macronucleus and the restoration of its oxidizing function the amount of glycogen increases considerably. Zweibaum believed that conjugation always takes place between individuals differing from each other considerably in the amount of glycogen. However, this opinion of the Polish investigator is not supported either by his own drawings, or by the revised data of Rammelmejer (1925). During conjugation the amount of fats in *Paramecium* is reduced; furthermore, the chemical composition of their fatty substances is changed: thus, neutral fats disappear and, apparently, fatty acids appear in the cytoplasm as a result of hydrolytic decomposition; the same type of fat appears under conditions of asphyxia, and Zweibaum calls it 'degenerative'. After conjugation the drops of this fat disappear, but an increased production of neutral fats begins.

Although feeding ceases completely during the period of conjugation, Poljanskij (1934) found in *Bursaria* an increased amount of fat during the first period of conjugation, but during subsequent reorganization of the nuclei and plasmatic structures fat is to a considerable extent absorbed.

It has been observed that during conjugation change in the amount of RNA in the cytoplasm takes place. Šubnikova (1947) and Gromova (1948) have noted an accumulation of DNA in *Paramecium caudatum* in the course of conjugation. This is probably connected with the process of the absorption of the old macronucleus, which is rich in both RNA and DNA. Finley and Williams (1955) have discovered in the process of conjugation in *Vorticella microstomata* a change in the composition of the amino acids. The amount of amino acids detected by the chromatographic method increases during this process from 10 to 15 bands.

Changes in the macronucleus during conjugation. The disintegration and absorption of the macronucleus in the bodies of both conjugants represent one of the constant and clear features of conjugation.

The character of morphological alterations in the macronucleus during conjugation, and the time when they set in, vary in different species. In certain ciliates, for instance in *Cryptochilidium echini* (Dain, 1930), *Tetrahymena pyriformis* (Ray, 1956), *Paramecium bursaria* (Egelhaaf, 1955), and others, the macronucleus does not undergo fragmentation during conjugation, but, at the end of it, when primordia of the new macronucleus are formed from the derivatives of the synkaryon, it undergoes complete pycnosis and is absorbed in the cytoplasm. More frequently, however, the macronucleus already breaks up into numerous fragments during the process of conjugation, which are gradually absorbed in the cytoplasm, sometimes being retained for a fairly long time—even until the merogamous divisions of the exconjugants. In some species (for example, *Bursaria truncatella*, Poljanskij, 1934) fragmentation of the macronucleus takes place at the very beginning of conjugation, during the first meiotic division of the micronucleus. In others, for example *Paramecium aurelia*, this process begins somewhat later, approximately at the moment of the third division of the micronucleus and the formation of the synkaryon. In *P. aurelia, P. caudatum*, and certain other species, the macronucleus produces before its fragmentation numerous evaginations and knots, being transformed as it were into a loosely wound skein of thick filaments (Fig. 202). It remains in that state for a considerable time, and undergoes further decomposition only in the exconjugant. In rare cases, for example in *Collinia branchiarum* (Collin, 1909), during conjugation the spherical macronuclei of both partners are extended into long strands, one half of each entering into the cytoplasm of its partner. In this way an exchange of portions of the macronucleus takes place, after which it degenerates.

In some cases a new macronucleus may be regenerated after conjugation from the fragments of the disintegrating macronucleus; in such cases the macronucleus originates from the old nucleus, not from derivatives of the synkaryon. Thus the fragments of the macronucleus, at least in the early stages of disintegrations, are not degenerated structures, since they are physiologically capable of regeneration. This phenomenon was discovered and studied by Sonneborn (1947) in *Paramecium aurelia*.

Sonneborn succeeded in obtaining experimentally the regeneration of the macronucleus from fragments, by exposing conjugating *P. aurelia* to a temperature of 38° C. This causes a delay in the development of Ma-Anlagen from the synkaryon, with the result that a new macronucleus is regenerated from fragments of the old one. This process may be regarded

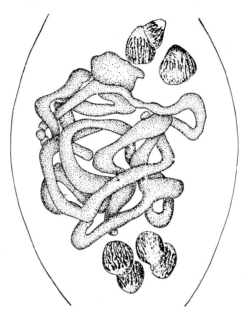

FIG. 202. Disintegration of macronucleus during conjugation of *Paramecium caudatum*. Exconjugant. Eight undifferentiated micronuclei. (After Calkins and Cull, 1907.)

as one of the proofs of the polyploid nature of the macronucleus. It may be assumed that its fragments contain complete genoms, which enables them to restore—probably by means of endomitosis—a fully valid new macronucleus.

Changes in the micronucleus during conjugation. In their main features they proceed in all ciliates according to the same pattern, as has already been shown by Maupas (1889). They may be divided into a very definite series of stages. The process consists of two main periods, each of which in its turn may be subdivided into several phases. The first period consists of the maturation and copulation of the sexual nuclei with the formation of a synkaryon (Fig. 203); the second period consists of the reconstruction of the normal nuclear apparatus (Fig. 204). The first period consists of three phases, which will be considered consecutively.

a. Meiotic divisions of micronucleus. The nuclear processes of conjugation begin with meiosis of the micronucleus proceeding according to the type of the two-division meiosis (two maturation divisions). This process leading to the reduction of the number of chromosomes has already been described above in the section on meiosis (p. 297). As the result of two meiotic

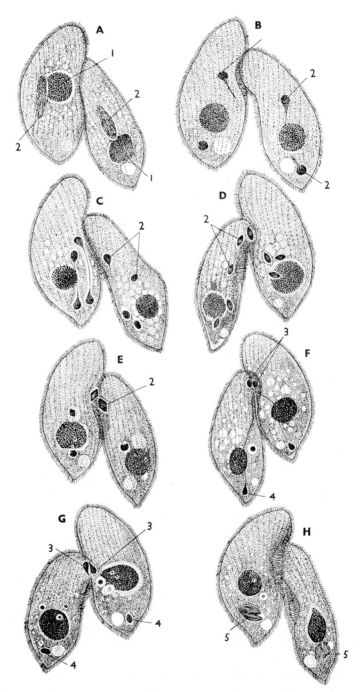

FIG. 203. Conjugation of *Cryptochilidium echini*.

(*A*) first division spindle of micronucleus; (*B*) first division of micronucleus completed; (*C*), (*D*) second division of micronucleus and formation of spindles of third division; (*E*), (*F*) degeneration of three micronuclei and fourth progamous division of micronucleus; (*G*) exchange of male pronuclei; (*H*) formation of synkaryon. 1, macronucleus; 2, micronucleus; 3, male pronuclei; 4, female pronuclei; 5, synkaryon. (After Dain, 1930.)

divisions 4 nuclei are produced. Many ciliates have not one but two or a larger number of micronuclei. In all these cases all or almost all the micronuclei undergo the two first divisions. For example, *Paramecium aurelia* (Fig. 204) normally has 2 micronuclei, producing as a result of meiosis 8

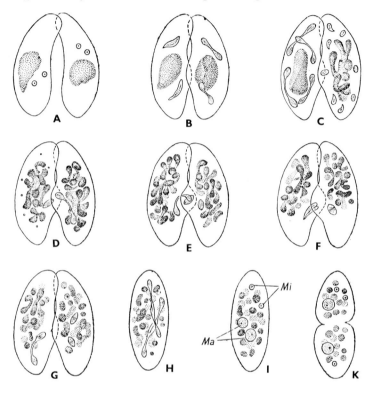

Fig. 204. Diagram of conjugation in *Paramecium aurelia*. The development in the right partner is somewhat more rapid than in the left one.

(A)–(K) successive stages of conjugation: *Mi*, micronucleus; *Ma*, macronucleus; *Sy*, synkaryon. (After Grell, 1956a.)

nuclei. In *Bursaria truncatella* (Infusoria, Heterotrıcha) the number of micronuclei in a neutral individual is 15–24 (Poljanskij, 1934). Almost all of them undergo two synchronous maturation divisions (Fig. 205), as a result of which a very large number of minute nuclei is produced. Of all these numerous nuclei only one eventually undergoes a third maturation division, leading to the formation of pronuclei. So far the only known exception from this rule is *Trachelocerca*, in which a multiple formation of pronuclei takes place (Rajkov, 1958b). This case, which is of special interest, will be discussed in greater detail below. Sometimes several nuclei, which had completed meiosis, begin a third maturation division, for example *Bursaria truncatella*. However, only one nucleus goes through to the end, that is to the formation of pronuclei (except *Trachelocerca*), while all the others are later absorbed in the cytoplasm.

b. Formation of pronuclei, their migration and karyogamy. This process differs in various ciliates, chiefly according to the method of union of the conjugants. The third maturation division represents a true haploid mitosis.

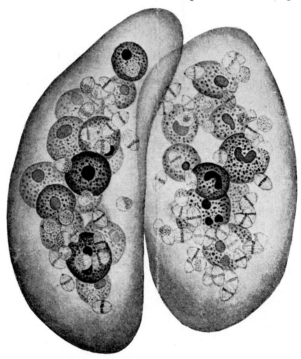

Fig. 205. Metaphase of second maturation division of micronuclei in *Bursaria truncatella*. (After Poljanskij, 1934.)

In *Paramecium aurelia* and *P. caudatum* a special protuberance ('paroral cone') directed towards the partner is formed by this time in both con-jugants at the point of contact between them, in the region of the peri-stome. This is the point where the third maturation division takes place. Of the two resulting spindle-shaped pronuclei, one (the migratory or male) actively penetrates through the pellicle into its partner, and moves towards the stationary (female) pronucleus, with which it fuses (karyogamy), to form a synkaryon. As a result of this, the diploid complex of chromosomes is restored. During this process a temporary cytoplasmic bridge is estab-lished between the two conjugants. It has been proved for *P. aurelia* (Sonneborn, 1947) that sometimes an exchange of cytoplasm takes place across this bridge, in the course of which 'particles' of 'kappa' are trans-mitted by individuals possessing the 'killer' trait.

In some cases the achromatic spindle apparently plays an active role in the transfer of the pronuclei, by, as it were, 'pushing' the migrating nucleus into the cytoplasm of the partner. Such is the case in *Cryptochilidium echini* (Fig. 203), in which the stationary nucleus is situated in the posterior end of the ciliate, while the transfer of the migrating pronuclei takes place at the anterior end. Sometimes, for example in *Didinium nasutum* (Prandtl, 1906), *Stentor* (Mulsow, 1913), *Dogielella* (Poljanskij, 1926), the migrating

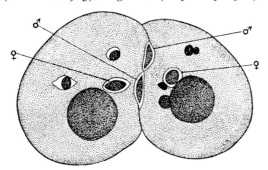

FIG. 206. Interchange of pronuclei during conjugation in *Dogielella sphaerii*, showing stationary (♀) and migratory (♂) nuclei in each individual. (After Poljanskij, 1926.)

nucleus attaches itself to the pellicle at the border between the conjugants (Fig. 206), and then, probably, a local rupture or dissolution of the pellicle occurs and the nuclei are interchanged.

In a few ciliates, at the moment of karyogamy, a special intermediate homogeneous zone of cytoplasm is formed between the two partners, which, strictly speaking, does not belong to either of the conjugants. Within this zone fusion of the pronuclei takes place. The synkaryons thus formed, together with the cytoplasm surrounding them, then separate into both individuals. This process is well defined in *Bursaria truncatella* (Fig. 207) (Poljanskij, 1934).

In the examples described above there are no marked morphological differences between the migrating and stationary pronuclei. This is usually the case when fairly close contact is established between the two conjugants. Morphological differences between both sexual nuclei were first described by Prandtl (1906) in *Didinium nasutum*, in which the male pronucleus is somewhat more elongated than the regularly rounded female. As has been mentioned above, in certain ciliates possessing a firm cuticle a cytoplasmatic bridge is not formed (*Euplotes*, Turner, 1930; Entodiniomorpha, Dogiel, 1925). In these cases the male pronucleus penetrates into the cytoplasm of the partner through its pharynx. In Entodiniomorpha (Fig. 208) a considerable area of the exterior medium has to be traversed on the way, since the two conjugants are united to each other only by the interlaced cirri of the adoral zone. As the result of these peculiarities, the migrating

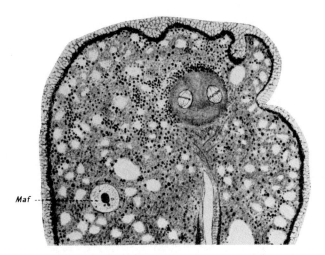

Maf

FIG. 207. Formation of synkaryon in *Bursaria truncatella*. Two synkaryons lying in homogeneous zone of cytoplasm. *Maf*, fragment of macronucleus. (After Poljanskij, 1934.)

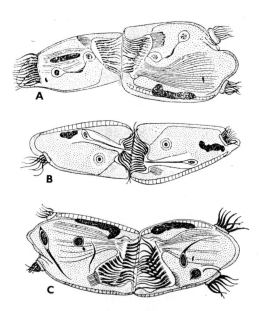

A

B

C

FIG. 208. *Cycloposthium bipalmatum*: stages of conjugation; the partners are united by peristomes.

(*A*) third division of micronucleus; (*B*), (*C*) interchange of migratory micronuclei which have appearance of spermatozoa (head and tail). (After Dogiel, 1925*a*.)

pronucleus acquires the shape of a true spermatozoon, as was first shown by Dogiel (1925) for *Cyclopostium bipalmatum*, and subsequently also in other Entodiniomorpha (Poljanskij and Strelkov, 1938*a*). In this case the last maturation division, leading to the formation of pronuclei, has a heteropolar character (Fig. 208). At the end of the spindle a regular spherical nucleus, surrounded by a faint cytoplasmic halo, is formed. This is the stationary pronucleus. At the same time the other sexual nucleus undergoes profound changes. A siderophilic arrow-shaped point—analogous to the perfuratorium in the spermatozoa of Metazoa—is formed at its pole. At the opposite pole the male pronucleus is drawn out into a long tail-like appendage, apparently formed at the expense of the achromatic spindle, part of which is cast off into the cytoplasm. In this way a motile male pronucleus is formed, which is completely analogous to the spermatozoon of Metazoa (Fig. 208, *C*). In *Cycloposthium*, as well as in other Entodiniomorpha, the spermatozoon leaves the cytoplasm and penetrates into its partner through its pharynx, thus passing quite a considerable distance outside the body of the ciliate. Then the spermatozoon bends forward, enters the cytoplasm, moves towards the female pronucleus, and fuses with it.

The process of karyogamy itself may also vary in ciliates. Usually the fusing pronuclei are spindle-shaped, and the synkaryons that are formed proceed to the first metagamous division at once (*Paramecium, Cryptochilidium, Euplotes, Bursaria*). In other cases the fusing pronuclei appear like nuclei at rest, and mitosis takes place only later (*Dogielella, Loxodes*).

Various deviations from the normal course, leading sometimes to anomalies, are observed in the processes of meiosis in the formation of pronuclei and in karyogamy of ciliates. Wichterman (1940) and Diller (1940) described in *Paramecium caudatum* the phenomenon of so-called cytogamy which represents a peculiar modification of typical conjugation. In cytogamy, which at first proceeds like ordinary conjugation, the migrating pronucleus does not cross over into the neighbouring individual but fuses with the stationary nucleus of the same individual. Thus outwardly cytogamy proceeds like conjugation (the union of two individuals), while by the character of its nuclear processes it should be referred to autogamy. Chen (1940) describes in *Paramecium bursaria* numerous races, the micronuclei of which have polyploid chromosomes. He traces their origin to various disturbances in the normal course of conjugation, such as the fusion of more than two pronuclei into a polyploid synkaryon. This may take place in different ways: at the expense of the formation of extra pronuclei (not one but two nuclei going through the third division); or as a result of a delay in the crossing of one pronucleus into the other conjugant, &c.

In cases of anisogamous conjugation observed in sessile ciliates, Peritricha, and in certain Suctoria, the processes of meiosis and karyogamy acquire a somewhat special character.

Anisogamous conjugation in Peritricha should be regarded as an adaptation to a sessile mode of life. In these ciliates larger macroconjugants and much smaller microconjugants can be distinguished. In some solitary species (*Vorticella, Opercularia*) these two categories of individuals are the product of an irregular division into a larger and smaller individual (Fig. 209). The

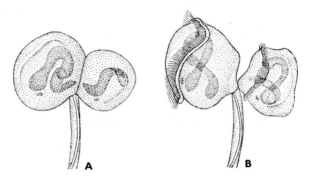

FIG. 209. Formation of macroconjugant and microconjugant in *Vorticella campanula*.

(*A*) irregular division; (*B*) circlet of cilia developed in micro-conjugant. (After Grell, 1956*a*.)

larger individual remains attached to the substratum by means of a stalk, and represents the macroconjugant, whereas the smaller one, the micro-conjugant, develops a ciliary circlet and swims away. In colonial Peritricha microconjugants are formed as a result of two or three palintomic divisions of the separate individuals of the colony. In the polymorphic colonies of *Zoothamnium arbuscula* with their complex structure, macro- and micro-conjugants are formed in strictly defined areas of the colony (Furssenko, 1929)—the macroconjugants at the bases of the main branches in young colonies and the microconjugants at the ends of the branches of the larger colonies. As has already been established by Maupas (1889) and Popoff (1908), the microconjugants swim and crawl actively over the colonies, until they meet the macroconjugants and unite with them. The two con-jugants differ in their further development (Fig. 210). In a macroconjugant the micronucleus undergoes two divisions; three nuclei out of four perish, and one becomes a pronucleus. In a microconjugant the micronucleus usually undergoes three divisions. Seven out of eight resulting nuclei perish, and one becomes a pronucleus. Later the pronucleus of the micro-conjugant migrates into the cytoplasm of the macroconjugant where it fuses with the pronucleus of the latter, forming a synkaryon. After this the microconjugant shrivels and perishes. Thus in this case fertilization is uni-lateral, and not mutual as in other ciliates. However, this is undoubtedly a secondary phenomenon connected with the sessile mode of life. In some Peritricha, for example in *Vorticella monilata* (according to Maupas), one more division of the micronucleus is retained, so that two pronuclei are formed in each conjugant, and a mutual exchange of migrating nuclei takes place. However, the synkaryon is formed only in the macroconjugant, while in the microconjugant all the nuclei and the microconjugant itself perish and are absorbed.

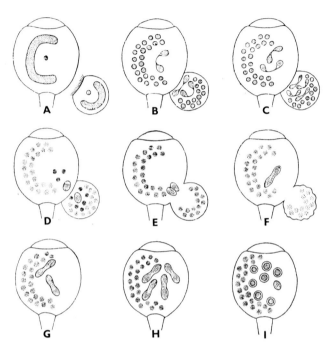

FIG. 210. Diagram of anisogamous conjugation in Peritricha.

(*A*)–(*I*) successive stages of conjugation. (After Grell, 1956*a*.)

Apart from Peritricha, anisogamous conjugation is observed also in certain Suctoria, Chonotricha, and a few Holotricha.

Among the Suctoria, which are also sessile forms, in some species conjugation is represented by the ordinary isogamy. Two neighbouring individuals approach each other until they are in contact, their micronuclei undergo three maturation divisions, and a typical exchange of pronuclei takes place with the formation of a synkaryon in each conjugant.

The process proceeds in this manner in *Stylocometes digitatus* (Škreb-Guilcher, 1955) and in a number of other species. In other Suctoria, e.g. *Tokophrya cyclopum* (Collin, 1912) and *Ephelota gemmipara* (Grell, 1953*a*), there is a peculiar form of anisogamy, arising in the course of conjugation. Thus when conjugation is disturbed, in *E. gemmipara*, the two individuals attached to stalks first unite with each other (Fig. 211), then one of them breaks away from its stalk and is transformed into a microconjugant. Maturation division of the micronucleus proceeds in both individuals, but the formation of a synkaryon and the development of a new macronucleus takes place only in the one (usually the larger one) which retains its stalk. This individual later engulfs the second partner entirely.

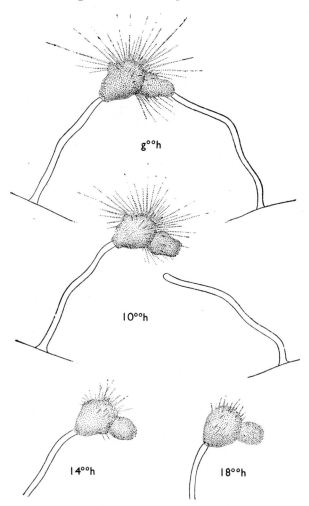

Fig. 211. *Ephelota gemmipara.* Different stages of conjugation, drawn from living organisms. (After Grell, 1953*a*.)

A pattern of conjugation similar in general lines to that of *Ephelota* is observed in *Spirochona gemmipara* belonging to Infusoria Chonotricha (Tuffrau, 1953). These curious solitary ciliates, which are attached to the gill plates of crustaceans, first approach each other by their anterior ends, then one of them breaks away from the substratum and moves to the top of the one that is still attached to the substratum. According to Tuffrau, two synkaryons are formed, both within the individual attached to the substratum. The upper individual—the microconjugant—consisting only of cytoplasm eventually drops off. It is still unknown whether both synkaryons take part in the formation of the nuclear apparatus of the single exconjugant.

Among the free-swimming ciliates anisogamic conjugation is a rare exception. In *Metopus sigmoides* (Noland, 1927) the differences between

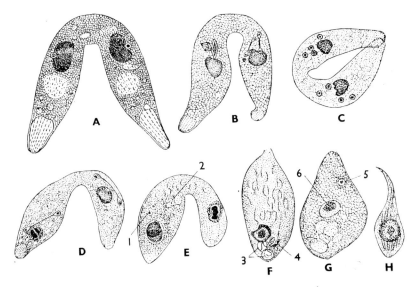

FIG. 212. Conjugation of *Metopus sigmoides*.

(*A*) beginning of process; (*B*) second division of micronuclei; (*C*) termination of second division; (*D*) formation of pronuclei; (*E*) all four pronuclei (1 and 2) have moved into larger conjugant; (*F*) female pronucleus of large conjugant and male pronucleus of smaller one are swollen (3), the remaining nuclei degenerate (4); (*G*) the large individual has lost its old pronucleus, while new macro- and micronuclei (5 and 6) are formed from the synkaryon; (*H*) smaller individual, deprived of micronucleus, perishes. (After Noland, 1927.)

the members of the pair are slight at the beginning of conjugation (Fig. 212), the microconjugant being only slightly smaller than its partner. However, the later development of the conjugants is quite different. Both pronuclei of the microconjugant pass over into the partner, where the male pronucleus of the microconjugant fuses with the female one of the macroconjugant, forming a synkaryon. After this the two conjugants separate from each other and the macroconjugant reconstructs its nuclear apparatus, while the superfluous nuclei perish. The microconjugant, left with only the old macronucleus, perishes.

Before dealing with the different types of the exconjugation period, the duration of conjugation itself in different ciliates may be noted. The duration of conjugation is reckoned from the moment of pairing of the two conjugants to the moment of their separation:

	Hours
Prorodon griseus	3–4
Dileptus gigas	10
Paramecium caudatum and *Paramecium aurelia*	12
Didinium nasutum	12–18

(at 25° C.: 6–9 hours)

	Hours
Euplotes patella	12–15

	Days
Bursaria truncatella	2½
Metopus sigmoides	7

It is evident that the duration of conjugation may vary considerably in different species. Further data on the subject are needed, but from the available ones it is seen that in Holotricha and Hypotricha conjugation lasts 10–15 hours, whereas in Heterotricha it extends to several days. The cause of this difference is so far unknown, and in any case it does not depend on the size of the animals, since *Metopus*, which conjugates for a whole week, is of almost the same size as *Paramecium*, namely 160–200 μ.

3. *Restoration of the nuclear apparatus and the exconjugation period.* This last period of conjugation consists of a number of metagamous divisions of the synkaryon, from the products of which the nuclear apparatus of the neutral individual, viz. the macronucleus and micronuclei, is restored. All the divisions of the synkaryon are mitotic, in the course of which the diploid complex of chromosomes is retained.

This period is characterized by great diversity, determined by the number of synkaryon divisions, their later destiny, and the number of metagamous divisions of the exconjugant itself prior to the restoration of the normal nuclear apparatus.

We shall not enumerate all the types of restoration of the nuclear apparatus in ciliates described in the literature. This would take too much space, and is not of great theoretical interest. We shall limit the discussion to those types which differ most markedly from each other. Some of them are represented diagramatically in Fig. 213.

In the simplest case the synkaryon divides only once, one of the resulting nuclei giving rise to a micronucleus, while the second undergoes complex transformations (the nature of which will be considered below) and becomes a macronucleus. In this manner the exconjugant is transformed directly into a neutral individual without undergoing any metagamous divisions. This type of reconstruction is observed, for example, in *Chilodonella* (Enriques, 1907) and in the majority of Entodiniomorpha (Dogiel, 1925*a*; Poljanskij and Strelkov, 1938*a*).

In very many ciliates synkaryons undergo two divisions, as a result of which four nuclei are produced, the destiny of which may differ considerably. In *Euplotes patella* (Fig. 213) (Turner, 1930) two of them degenerate, and of the remaining two one is transformed into a micronucleus, the second into a macronucleus. Hence there is no metagamous division of the exconjugant in this case either. In *Stylonchia* (Peškovskaja, 1948) and *Pleurotricha* (Manwell, 1928) and in a number of other ciliates the process

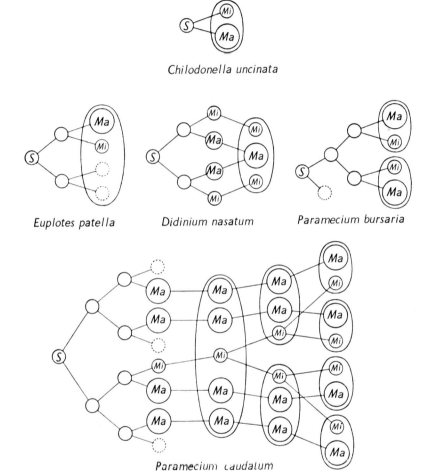

Chilodonella uncinata

Euplotes patella   *Didinium nasatum*   *Paramecium bursaria*

Paramecium caudatum

FIG. 213. Diagram of exconjugation period in different ciliates.

Mi, micronucleus; *Ma*, anlage of macronucleus; *S*, synkaryon. (After Grell, 1956a.)

proceeds in an analogous manner. However, two divisions of the synkaryon are more frequently accompanied by a special metagamous division of the exconjugant itself. *Paramecium aurelia*, in which the morphological side of the process of conjugation had been studied already by R. Hertwig (1889) and Maupas (1889), may serve as an example. Of the four nuclei arising from two divisions of the synkaryon, two are transformed into macronucleus-Anlagen and two into micronuclei. This is followed by a metagamous division of the exconjugant during which the Ma-Anlagen are distributed between the two daughter individuals. The two micronuclei also divide. Thus every individual formed as a result of metagamous division of the exconjugant receives a nuclear apparatus typical of *P. aurelia*, i.e. one macronucleus and two micronuclei. In *Tetrahymena pyriformis*, in which there are also two divisions of the synkaryon (Elliott and Hayes, 1953; Ray, 1956), two nuclei give rise to Ma-Anlagen, one becomes a micronucleus and one degenerates. During metagamous division of the exconjugant the Ma-Anlagen are distributed, while the single Mi divides. *Leucophrys* (Maupas, 1889), *Dogielella* (Poljanskij, 1926), and a number of other ciliates have a similar type of restoration of their nuclear apparatus. In rarer cases the differentiating Ma-Anlagen fuse. For example, in *Didinium nasutum* (Prandtl, 1906), after two divisions of the synkaryon two Ma-Anlagen are produced, which then fuse, and form one macronucleus (Fig. 213). A fusion of Ma-Anlagen during the development of the macronucleus was described in *Stentor* (Mulsow, 1913), *Nicollelidae* (Chatton and Perard, 1921), *Paraisotricha* (Dogiel, 1930), and others. In *Cryptochilidium echini*, of the four derivatives of the synkaryon three are transformed into Ma-Anlagen and one into a micronucleus. The distribution of Ma-Anlagen takes place as a result of two metagamous divisions of the exconjugant, during which the single micronucleus is divided each time (Dain, 1930).

There is an even greater diversity in the form of reconstruction of the nuclear apparatus in species of ciliates whose synkaryon divides three times. A typical example is provided by *Paramecium caudatum* (Hertwig, 1889; Maupas, 1889) in which eight nuclei are produced as a result of three divisions of the synkaryon. Four of these are transformed into Ma-Anlagen, three perish, and one becomes a micronucleus. In the course of the following two metagamous divisions of the exconjugant the Ma-Anlagen are distributed without division among four individuals. During each of these divisions the single micronucleus undergoes mitotic division. In *Paramecium bursaria* (Fig. 213) there are also three divisions of the synkaryon; however, immediately after the first of these one of the nuclei degenerates. The remaining one undergoes two divisions, and from the products of these two Ma-Anlagen and two Mi are developed, which are distributed, as a result of one metagamous division, among the daughter individuals (Wichterman, 1943; Egelhaaf, 1955). In *Bursaria truncatella* (Poljanskij, 1934) the derivatives of the synkaryon do not perish. After three divisions eight nuclei are formed, of which four are arranged in the middle of the body of the ciliate, and four at its posterior end (Fig. 214). The former are eventually transformed into Ma-Anlagen, the latter into micronuclei. The micronuclei continue to divide, so that their number increases. The exconjugants undergo two metagamous divisions, during which the distribution of Ma-Anlagen takes place.

The reconstruction of the nuclear apparatus in the majority of Peritricha proceeds in a peculiar way. After three divisions of the synkaryon, of the resulting eight nuclei seven are transformed into Ma-Anlagen and only one into a micronucleus. As a result of three metagamous divisions of the exconjugant, accompanied by division of the micronucleus, the distribution of the Ma-Anlagen among the ciliates takes place.

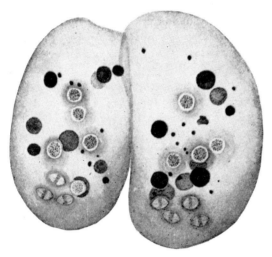

FIG. 214. Exconjugants of *Bursaria truncatella*. Metaphase of fourth division of synkaryon and beginning of differentiation of primordia of macronucleus. (After Poljanskij, 1934.)

There are many other variations in the reconstruction of the nuclear apparatus in ciliates, but we shall not dwell on them any longer here.

It is noteworthy that, in the reconstruction of the nuclear apparatus in ciliates, apart from differences in the course of this process among diverse species, there is considerable individual variation, which is also observed in the types of nuclear reconstruction described above.

The behaviour of the separate derivatives of the synkaryon is not strictly determined and is subject to individual variations, the extent of which differs with the species. We shall limit ourselves only to a few examples. In *Didinium nasutum*, in addition to the type of reconstruction described above, Prandtl (1906) observed in individual cases not a union of Ma-Anlagen but their distribution. He also described the transformation of all the four derivatives of the synkaryon into Ma-Anlagen, probably giving rise to an amicronucleate race. Sometimes three, instead of two, divisions of the synkaryon take place in *Didinium*. A variation in the number of divisions of the synkaryon was observed in certain Hypotricha (Manwell, 1928), *Pleurotricha* (Turner, 1930), and *Euplotes*. Dogiel has described a very considerable variation in the course of reconstruction of the nuclear apparatus in *Bütschlia parva* (1928) and *Paraisototricha colpoidea* (1930); there is also a very wide variation in *Bursaria truncatella* (Poljanskij, 1934). Instead of the 'normal' four Ma-Anlagen and four micronuclei, encountered in the majority of individuals, the development of the derivatives of the synkaryon varies considerably. Thus there has been observed, on the one hand, a transformation of part of the nuclei, which usually give rise to Ma-Anlagen, into micronuclei, so that instead of four only two Ma-Anlagen developed. In some cases the opposite process took place, viz. the majority of micronuclei were transformed into Ma-Anlagen. In one extreme case of redistribution of the derivatives of the synkaryon in the exconjugant *Bursaria*, thirty-two Ma-Anlagen were found and not a single micronucleus. All these facts indicate an extreme instability in the behaviour of the derivatives of the synkaryon. One cannot exclude the possibility of the transformation of the derivatives by the conditions of their development in the cytoplasm, and, in particular, by their position in the body of the ciliate.

The development of the macronucleus from the derivatives of the synkaryon has not been sufficiently investigated from the cytological point of view. This process was to some extent considered above in connexion with the hypothesis regarding the polyploid nature of the macronucleus. The ontogeny of the macronucleus passes through the following main stages (Fig. 40, p. 68, Fig. 215). The volume of the nucleus increases rapidly, then filamentar structures—the chromosomes—become visible in it, after which a shortening (coiling) of the chromosomes takes place. After this they split longitudinally (Figs. 40, 215), a process which should apparently be regarded as endomitosis leading to polyploidization. Then the chromosomes become somewhat more diffuse (in *Bursaria* they somewhat resemble the 'Lampbrush' during the oogenesis of amphibia), and finally they cease to stain with nuclear stains and to produce Feulgen's nuclear reaction. It is possible, though this cannot be considered as proved, that the loss of microscopic visibility is associated with uncoiling of the chromosomes. Simultaneously with the nuclear changes mentioned above, a karyosome-like structure appears giving a clear Feulgen reaction, i.e. containing a large amount of DNA. Later in the karyoplasm of the developing Ma-Anlagen there is a gradual accumulation of DNA, the intensity of Feulgen reaction increasing progressively. At the same time, numerous small nucleoli appear, giving the characteristic RNA reaction. With the accumulation of DNA in the nucleus the size of the karyosome-like chromatin structure diminishes and eventually it disappears. This completes the formation of the fully developed macronucleus rich in DNA. As mentioned above, the pattern of the formation of chromosomes and their splitting observed during the development of the macronucleus have served as the morphological basis for the theory regarding the polyploid nature of the macronucleus. These patterns have been observed with greater or less clarity, apart from *Bursaria* and *Ephelota*, also in *Stentor* (Mulsow, 1913), *Climacostomum* (Peškovskaja, 1936), *Stylonychia* (Peškovskaja, 1948), and *Fabrea*

(Ellis, 1937). However, in a number of ciliates, *Paramecium caudatum* (Klitske, 1915), and *P. bursaria* (Egelhaaf, 1955), the pattern of endomitosis during the development of Ma-Anlagen has so far not been discovered, and this process has not yet been studied cytologically in the majority of ciliates. In any case the question of the connexion between the chromatin (DNA) of the definitive macronucleus and the chromosomes of the Ma-Anlagen

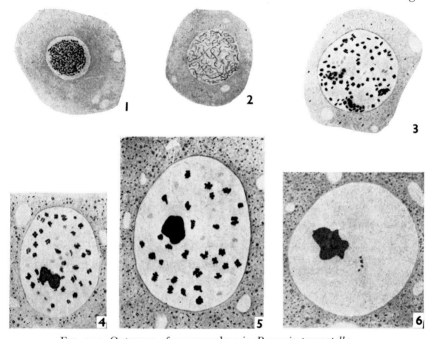

FIG. 215. Ontogeny of macronucleus in *Bursaria truncatella*.

1, primordium of macronucleus after 3rd division of synkaryon; 2, beginning of growth of primordium of macronucleus, stage of thin filaments; 3, shortening of chromosomes and beginning of their endomitotic splitting; 4 and 5, further stages of growth of macronuclear primordium, continuation of splitting of chromosomes, formation of karyosphere rich in DNA; 6, stage of 'primordial vesicle'; chromosomes do not stain; large karyosphere visible. (After Poljanskij, 1934.)

remains unsettled, for they cannot be detected morphologically during the development of this nucleus. Likewise, the state of the chromosome apparatus in the definitive macronucleus is not clear.

II. FORMS OF CONJUGATION DEVIATING FROM THE USUAL TYPE

We can now consider some cases of conjugation differing essentially from the typical scheme. A most peculiar and, one might say, paradoxical picture is described by Minkiewitz (1912) and Chatton and Lwoff (1935*b*) for ciliates of the order *Apostomata, Polyspira,* and *Gymnodinioides,* which in an encysted state live on the gills and in active state in the moults of hermit crabs (Fig. 216).

Large individuals of *Polyspira* adhere to each other in pairs by their sides and form a so-called syzygy. These individuals represent neutral forms,

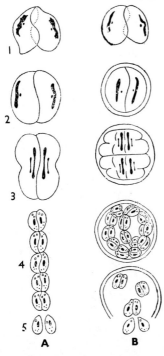

which unite prematurely, and, when paired, undergo a series of divisions which are not brought to an end, so that a chain of individuals, very like that in the Apostomata (Fig. 216), but a double instead of a single one, is formed. Such chains sometimes contain up to twelve pairs. When this type of palintomic division, not accompanied by intervals of growth of the multiplying members, finally comes to an end, then the processes of maturation of the micronuclei and all the subsequent phenomena of conjugation start simultaneously in all the pairs. They proceed at the same rate in all the pairs and are identical with typical conjugation: there occurs a reduction division of the micronucleus, the destruction of three nuclei, and the formation of pronuclei at the expense of the fourth nucleus; and then the migration of the male nuclei, their fusion with the female ones, and the formation of the synkaryon in each individual. At this stage the members of the whole chain separate, becoming exconjugants, and only from this moment do the old macronuclei begin to disintegrate and a new nuclear apparatus be formed at the expense of the synkaryon. Minkiewitz called this aberrant case of conjugation 'syndesmogamy', but Chatton and Lwoff (1935) have replaced this term by 'zygopalintomy'.

FIG. 216. Diagram of process of conjugation in Apostomata: (*A*) *Polyspira delagei*; (*B*) *Gymnodinioides inkystans*.

1, two preconjugants at moment of union; 2, next stage (in *Gymnodinioides* it encysts); 3, parallel incomplete division of conjugants; 4, formation of temporary chain colony of conjugants in the course of the sexual process; 5, separation of conjugants after interchange of their pronuclei. (After Chatton and Lwoff, 1935.)

The conjugation of *Trachelocerca phaenicopterus*, studied by Rajkov (1958*a*, *b*), is of special interest in the understanding of the origin of conjugation as a very distinctive form of sexual process. This ciliate, whose peculiar structure of nuclear apparatus has been mentioned above, possesses six micronuclei. All, or nearly all, the nuclei undergo the first two maturation divisions, accompanied by the formation of well-pronounced tetrads. Of the 24 nuclei produced, a varying number (5–13) undergo the third maturation division, which leads to the formation of a large number of spherical pronuclei (Fig. 217, *A*). After some time part of these nuclei are transformed into migratory pronuclei, and the rest become stationary. The migratory nuclei become pyriform (Fig. 217, *B*), and pass over simultaneously from one conjugant into the cytoplasm of the other. This is the only case among the many forms of conjugation observed in ciliates of a multiple interchange of pronuclei. After the exchange of nuclei many synkaryons are formed in each conjugant as a result of karyogamy (Fig. 217, *C*). However, only one synkaryon is retained and develops

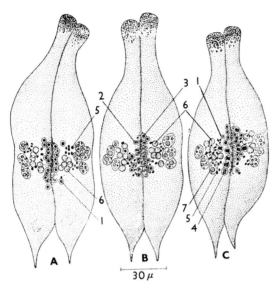

FIG. 217. Conjugation of *Trachelocerca phaenicopterus*.

(*A*) stage of pronuclei; (*B*) interchange of migratory pronuclei; (*C*) gonomeric synkaryons (reconstruction from sections). 1, pronucleus; 2, migratory pronucleus; 3, stationary pronucleus; 4, 5, 6, placenta; 7, fragments of complex macronucleus. (After Rajkov, 1958*b*.)

in each individual, while the others are absorbed. The single synkaryon in each conjugant divides four times. Of the 16 resulting nuclei, 4 usually perish, 6 are transformed into Ma-Anlagen, and 6 into micronuclei. In the course of nuclear processes in *Trachelocerca* the multiple formation and migration of pronuclei is of special interest. Rajkov's interpretation (1958*a, b*) of this phenomenon is probably correct. He thinks that the formation of numerous pronuclei in *Trachelocerca* represents a recapitulation of gametogenesis. If we assume that conjugation originated on the basis of the sexual process of the type of copulation, then the pronuclei correspond to the gamete nuclei. In ordinary conjugation each conjugant produces two gametes (male and female pronuclei). The occurrence of this small number of gametes is undoubtedly a secondary phenomenon. Therefore it can be assumed that the formation of multiple pronuclei (gametes) and fertilization in *Trachelocerca* is a primitive feature, retained from the ancestral forms of ciliates.

Autogamy, endomixis, and other forms of reconstruction of the nuclear apparatus in ciliates

Fermor (1913) was the first to describe in the cysts of *Stylonychia pustulata* the reconstruction of the nuclear apparatus, accompanied by the formation of a new macronucleus from the products of division of the micronucleus. In 1914 Woodruff and Erdmann studied the process of reorganization of the nuclear apparatus without conjugation in *Paramecium aurelia* and *P. caudatum*, and called it 'endomixis'. The same process was studied almost simultaneously in the same subject by R. Hertwig (1914), who called it 'parthegenesis'. Since then endomixis has been frequently described for different species of ciliates belonging to various orders. According to Woodruff and Erdmann, during endomixis the destruction and resorption of the macronucleus takes place. The micronucleus usually undergoes two divisions, probably corresponding to maturation divisions, in the course of which part of the nuclei perish, while the reconstruction of the new macronucleus and micronucleus occurs at the expense of one or two of the remaining nuclei, which sometimes experience additional divisions (the authors describe several variations in the course of endomixis). Endomixis is characterized by the absence of karyogamy, on account of which Hertwig compared this process to parthenogenesis.

Numerous further studies of the reconstruction of the nuclear apparatus in *Paramecium*, which became the favourite subject for genetic research by Sonneborn's school, have shown that Woodruff and Erdmann were right only as regards the fact that in *P. aurelia* there is a periodical reorganization of the nuclear apparatus without conjugation. However, the interpretation of the nuclear changes taking place during it given both by Woodruff and Erdmann and by Hertwig was not quite correct.

The process of the reorganization of the nuclear apparatus without conjugation was studied in detail by Diller (1936). His thorough investigation leaves no doubt that this process represents not endomixis, but autogamy (Fig. 218). The behaviour of the micronucleus is exactly the same as in conjugation. After the third maturation division of Mi two pronuclei are formed. By this special evaginations (paroral cones), resembling those in conjugation, are formed. Both pronuclei move into this paroral cone, where their fusion (karyogamy) occurs and a synkaryon is formed. The further behaviour of the latter and the whole process of restoration of the nuclear apparatus is identical to that of conjugation (Fig. 218). Thus autogamy differs from conjugation only in the occurrence of self-fertilization, i.e. autogamy, instead of cross-fertilization. We have already referred to a special form of conjugation called cytogamy, in the course of which self-fertilization processes take place; they differ only in the fact that in cytogamy a temporary union of the individuals occurs, whereas in autogamy it does not occur.

In addition to *P. aurelia*, autogamy follows the same pattern in *P. poly-*

caryum (Diller, 1954), while in *Tetrahymena rostrata* the same process takes place in cysts (Corliss, 1952, 1956*a*, *b*).

Apart from cytological observations, the occurrence of autogamy in *Paramecium aurelia* is convincingly demonstrated by genetic data (Sonneborn, 1947), since after autogamy *P. aurelia* always becomes homozygous. This is due to the fact that after the first two divisions of the micronucleus, which are always meiotic, the nuclei have a haploid set of chromosomes, i.e. only one set of genes. They are doubled in the third division and

FIG. 218. Changes in nuclear apparatus during autogamy in *Paramecium aurelia*. (After Diller, 1936.)

then, during karyogamy, when the diploid set appears again, each allele is represented by two genes. The heterozygous state in *P. aurelia* may arise only as a result of the interchange of pronuclei during conjugation. Either conjugation or autogamy is an indispensable process in the life-cycle of *Paramecium aurelia* (Sonneborn, 1954). In the absence of the one or the other depression occurs and the culture perishes. The problem of the physiological significance of the separate elements of the life-cycle of ciliates will be considered in more detail below.

It is interesting to note that whereas in *Paramecium aurelia* autogamy (or conjugation) is indispensable for the preservation of the viability of the ciliates, in *P. caudatum* autogamy is, apparently, normally absent (Gilman, 1959). Autogamy has been obtained experimentally in some ciliates, in which it does not normally occur, by means of early artificial separation of conjugating pairs. Apparently in this case the process once begun must proceed to the end. The pronuclei formed, being unable to pass over into the partner, fuse with each other. Such experimentally induced autogamy was observed in *Bursaria* (Poljanskij, 1938), *Paramecium bursaria* (Chen, 1940), and also in *P. caudatum* (Wichterman, 1940). Hence in *Parameciur caudatum*, *P. aurelia*, *P. bursaria*, and *P. polycaryum* there is no endomixis in the sense described by Woodruff and Erdmann. The question arises, does it exist in other ciliates? There are numerous accounts in the literature of reorganization of the nuclear apparatus without conjugation, but most of them do not give a complete picture of nuclear reorganization and in many cases they should probably be referred to the category 'hemixis' described above, which has nothing in common with the sexual process. However, in certain ciliates the occurrence of endomixis, i.e. of the development of a new micronucleus without karyogamy, can be considered as proved. Diller (1928) demonstrated the occurrence of this process in *Trichodina*. This ectoparasitic ciliate, belonging to the Peritricha, has one horseshoe-shaped macronu-

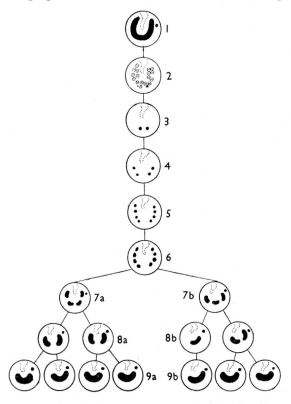

FIG. 219. Endomixis in *Trichodina*. (After Diller, 1928.)

cleus and one micronucleus. During endomixis (Fig. 219) its micronucleus is destroyed, while its micronucleus divides three times. Of the resulting eight nuclei one gives rise to a micronucleus and seven are transformed into Ma-Anlagen, which are later distributed one in each during division of the ciliate. It is interesting to note that the number of Ma-Anlagen formed during endomixis is the same as during conjugation (all Peritricha are characterized by the presence of seven Ma-Anlagen during conjugation).

Kidder (1938) has described endomixis during encystation in *Paraclevelandia simplex* (Ciliata Heterotricha), where it proceeds in a most peculiar manner. This ciliate possesses one Ma and one Mi. On encystment its macronucleus divides into two parts. The posterior one soon degenerates, but the anterior one survives. At the same time its micronucleus divides mitotically. One of the products of its division swells up and fuses with the anterior section of the macronucleus, thereby producing a new macronucleus. The second product of division remains a micronucleus. Thus in *Paraclevelandia* a new macronucleus is formed during endomixis as a result of the fusion of part of the old Ma with one of the products of division of Mi.

In its simplest form endomixis is accomplished in *Epistylus articulata* (Seshachar and Dass, 1953). During division of this ciliate an anomaly is frequently observed which consists of one complete macronucleus passing over into one of the daughter individuals, while the second one is left with only a micronucleus. In such cases this single micronucleus divides, and one of the products of this division is transformed into a macronucleus, while the second remains a micronucleus, thereby restoring the nuclear correlations to normal. Attention should be drawn to the interesting fact that in some lower Holotrichous ciliates each division is accompanied by the formation of macronuclei from micronuclei, while the macronuclei themselves are incapable of division: they are merely distributed among the daughter individuals. The same relations exist among species of the genera *Loxodes*, *Trachelocerca*, *Geleia*, and some others (Joseph, 1907; Kazancev, 1910; Rossolimo, 1916; Fauré-Fremiet, 1954; Rajkov, 1958a, d; and others). As has been rightly pointed out by Fauré-Fremiet (1954), this process is comparable in every respect to endomixis in other ciliates. These peculiar relations are probably associated with the inability of the diploid macronuclei of these species to divide. In the course of phylogenesis the macronuclei acquired the capacity to divide only as a result of further polyploidization. This problem has already been considered above.

Apart from endomixis various other forms of reorganization of the nuclear apparatus are observed in ciliates; they are probably associated with the physiology of the vegetative nucleus, the macronucleus, and are known under the common term 'hemixis'. These processes have been discussed above in the description of macronuclei.

In concluding our survey of the morphology of sexual processes in ciliates we must again draw attention to their great variability. As has been noted above, the same species frequently exhibits different types of the sexual process and of the reorganization of the nuclear apparatus. For example, *Paramecium aurelia* may undergo conjugation, cytogamy, autogamy, and hemixis. A particularly great variety of forms of the sexual process is displayed by *Paramecium trichium* (Diller, 1948, 1949; Jankovskij, 1960, 1962). This species undergoes, apart from normal conjugation, cytogamy and autogamy, as well as various forms of development of the macronucleus from a micronucleus not preceded by syngamy. Jankovskij has shown that the diverse forms of reorganization of the nuclear apparatus in *P. trichium* represent hereditary features of separate races, which he calls 'myxotypes'.

PHYSIOLOGY OF SEXUAL PROCESSES IN CILIATES

Life-cycle of ciliates

The study of conjugation, autogamy, and other forms of reorganization of the nuclear apparatus in ciliates is not limited to cytological and morphological research: a large number of works are devoted to the study of the physiological aspects of these processes.

In the eighties of the last century, Weismann (1884, 1902) formulated his theory of the 'potential immortality' of Protozoa. According to him, death, as a natural biological phenomenon, first appeared in multicellular organisms during the process of evolution, in connexion with the differentiation of the cells into 'potentially immortal sexual' cells and somatic cells, which were subject to natural death. According to Weismann's concept, since unicellular organisms reproduce by division, they do not experience natural death.

Contrary to Weismann, Bütschli (1889) expressed the opinion that in ciliates agamous reproduction cannot continue for an indefinitely long time. In a series of successive agamous generations the rate of division is retarded and, unless conjugation takes place, the ciliates perish. However, Bütschli based his conclusions on very limited experimental data.

The classical investigations of Maupas (1888, 1889), based on abundant material, played an important part in elucidating the problem of the physiological significance of conjugation. Maupas's main conclusions do not agree with the opinions of Weismann.

According to Maupas, prolonged agamous reproduction of ciliates is impossible. After a certain number of asexual generations, more or less defined for every species, senile degeneration and death set in. Conjugation, which can occur only at a definite period of 'maturity', leads to karyogamic rejuvenation, with the restoration of vital activity and of the normal rate of division. Thus, according to Maupas, the life-cycle of ciliates is composed of regularly alternating periods, comparable to the life-cycle of multicellular organisms. An exconjugant first enters the period of 'youth' when conjugation has not yet taken place. Then, after a certain number of asexual generations, the ciliates become 'mature' and capable of conjugation. If for some reason the sexual process does not take place, the ciliates enter the period of 'senility' (at this stage they lose their capacity for conjugation), terminating in senile degeneration and death. These views of Maupas, although expressed more than seventy years ago, have not yet entirely lost their significance, and they agree in many points with the results of contemporary investigations by Sonneborn (1954), which will be dealt with below. R. Hertwig (1889, 1903, 1914) and Popoff (1908) have put forward a cytophysiological explanation of the necessity for a periodical occurrence of the sexual process, based on Hertwig's well-known theory on the preservation of the karyoplasmic relation ('Kernplasmarelation') as an indispensable condition for the normal functioning of the cell.

According to Hertwig's views, during the process of the vital activity of the cell a disturbance in the ratio between the mass of the nucleus and that of the cytoplasm takes place, the nuclear substance increasing relatively more slowly than the cytoplasm. The normal karyoplasmic ratio is restored when the cell divides. However, when ciliates go through a long period of asexual reproduction, the divisions do not lead to complete restoration of the karyoplasmic ratio. There is a gradual hypertrophy of the macronucleus as the result of which the ciliate goes into a state of depression. During conjugation, as well as autogamy, which Hertwig regarded as parthenogenesis, accompanied by the destruction of the old macronucleus and the formation of a new one, restoration of the normal karyoplasmic ratio takes place. Of course, in the light of modern cytoplasmic data, Hertwig's views are now antiquated in many respects, for he did not take into consideration either the presence of two distinct components in the macronucleus—RNA and DNA—or the forms of interaction between the nucleus and cytoplasm discovered later. However, Hertwig's main concept that depression is the result of a disturbance in the functions of the macronucleus has not lost its significance even at the present time.

The classical researches of Maupas and Hertwig laid the foundation of a long series of experimental work on the life-cycle of free-living ciliates. We shall briefly consider only the main ones, which throw light on the present state of our knowledge of the problem in question. A characteristic feature of most investigations of the life-cycle of ciliates is the employment of individual cultures of ciliates, with an accurate estimate of the rate of division under optimum and uniform conditions of the environment throughout the experiment (nutrition, chemical composition of the medium, temperature, &c.). As has been shown by numerous investigations of various authors (Calkins, 1906, 1915a, b, 1916, 1919a, b, c, 1920, 1933; Enriques, 1916; Woodruff, 1911, 1915, 1917, 1921, 1925a, b; Woodruff and Erdmann, 1914; Woodruff and Spenser, 1924; Baitsell, 1914; Mast, 1917; Beers, 1926; Jennings, 1913, 1929, 1944a, b, c, d, 1945; Metalnikov, 1919, 1924; and others) the duration of the period of agamous reproduction (studied in ciliates of the genera *Paramecium, Oxytricha, Uroleptus, Didinium, Spathidium*, and others) can be considerably increased by optimum conditions of existence and by the removal of the products of metabolism from the culture fluid. The onset of the sexual process is determined not only by internal factors but also by environmental factors.

At the beginning of the present century the problem of the physiological significance of conjugation was considered from two closely related points of view: (1) Could the ciliates under definite favourable conditions reproduce infinitely by the asexual method, i.e. is the sexual process an inherently essential phase in their life-cycle? (2) Do conjugation and other forms of the sexual process (autogamy) represent factors which rejuvenate the ciliates, restoring their vital activity.

There are numerous investigations dealing with the first question, but their results are most contradictory. We shall consider only the most important of these.

In 1907 Woodruff began his well-known experiments which lasted for over twenty-five years. Having isolated *Paramecium aurelia* in an individual culture, he maintained several parallel lines and keeping precise record of the number of agamous generations and of the rate of division, he obtained more than 15,000 agamous generations without depression or conjugation. These investigations seemed to have solved the question regarding the possibility of infinitely prolonged agamous reproduction of ciliates. However, Woodruff himself pointed out that this problem is much more complicated. During many years of observations of individual cultures of *Paramecium aurelia* Woodruff observed characteristic periodical fluctuations in the rate of division (known as 'rhythms'). It was shown by morphological studies (Woodruff and Erdmann, 1914) that during this period a complete reorganization of the nuclear apparatus takes place, which they called endomixis. Later investigations (Diller, 1936) proved that this reorganization is in fact autogamy. It was thus shown that in Woodruff's cultures the sexual process takes place periodically, and that his investigations provided no proof of the possibility of prolonged agamous reproduction in *P. aurelia*.

In the numerous works by Calkins and his school on various ciliates (*Paramecium aurelia*, *Didinium nasutum*, and especially *Uroleptus mobilis*) this distinguished American protistologist arrived at conclusions that were essentially similar to the point of view of Maupas set out above. His views on the life-cycle of the Ciliata are set out with particular clarity and consistency in his excellent book *The Biology of Protozoa* (1933). The views of Calkins are essentially as follows: he distinguishes in animals two aspects of their organization, the 'fundamental' and the 'derived' organizations. In Metazoa the fundamental organization is characteristic of the sexual cells, while in the process of ontogenesis a very complex 'derived' organization is formed. The components of this latter die, after their individual life is completed. Calkins distinguishes these two categories in the structure of Protozoa as well. In ciliates the basic structures of the cytoplasm and of the nuclei, the chondriosomes, belong to the 'fundamental' organization, while the ciliary apparatus, the peristome, and also the macronucleus belong to the 'derived' organization. In contrast to Metazoa, the elements of the 'derived' organization in Protozoa do not die (except for various alloplasmatic structures, like shells, &c.) but are periodically reorganized and restored at the expense of the 'fundamental' organization. This reorganization takes place first of all during division, but in most ciliates this is not sufficient for the restoration of their vital activity. Conjugation takes place periodically and is accompanied by the restoration of the macronucleus, or processes which replace conjugation (autogamy, endomixis), leading to the restoration of the macronucleus of the ciliates. These views of Calkins are based on abundant experimental data, mainly obtained in researches carried out on *Uroleptus mobilis* (Calkins, 1919a, c, 1920, 1933).

However, in addition to data demonstrating the existence in ciliates of a definite life-cycle which includes various forms of the sexual process and of reorganization of the nuclear apparatus, there are also contradictory data, indicating the possibility of indefinitely prolonged agamous multiplication in the absence of conjugation, autogamy, or endomixis. Enriques (1916) obtained in Glaucoma, grown under optimum conditions of culture, many hundreds of agamous generations without conjugation or endomixis, while Weyer (1930) did not observe any signs of depression in *Gastrostyla steinii* during prolonged agamous reproduction. Indefinitely prolonged agamous reproduction is also possible in *Tetrahymena* (Corliss, 1953; Nanney, 1957) and *Tillina* (Beers, 1946) and certain other ciliates.

Apparently there is no general answer to the question whether infinitely prolonged agamous reproduction of ciliates is possible which would apply to all the species of this class. In some species indefinitely prolonged, gamous reproduction without depression is possible, while in others a periodical intervention of the sexual process is essential, since without it depression occurs and the ciliates perish. While *Paramecium aurelia* possesses a typical life-cycle, in another species of the same genus, *P. caudatum*, autogamy does not occur, and apparently agamous reproduction may continue for an unlimited time (Gilman, 1959). It should be noted that, in some other groups of Protozoa possessing the sexual process, the possibility of indefinitely prolonged agamous reproduction under optimum conditions of cultivation has also been proved. Bělǎr (1924) demonstrated this in *Actinophrys sol*, in which he obtained 1,244 agamous generations without any lowering of the rate of division and without depression. Hartmann (1921, 1924) cultivated *Eudorina elegans* for five years under conditions of artificial illumination in a mineral medium and obtained more than 1,500 asexual generations. Thus in such organisms the occurrence of the sexual process depends to a considerable degree on the environmental conditions and can be eliminated under optimum conditions of development. Finally, it should be remembered that in some free-living and parasitic Protozoa the sexual process is absent altogether (many naked amoebae, Euglenacea, and others) and in them agamous reproduction is the only form of multiplication.

Fauré-Fremiet (1953) connects the phenomenon of senescence, observed in the majority of ciliates, with the dualism of their nuclear apparatus and with the polyploidy of their macronucleus. During agamous reproduction of ciliates, when the macronucleus undergoes amitotic division ('segregation of genomes', according to Grell: see p. 64), as a result of endomitoses the intactness of the genomes (aneiploidy) is gradually disturbed and hyper-ploidy occurs. These changes lead to the disturbance of the normal function-ing of the macronucleus and to senescence, while conjugation and autogamy, accompanied by a complete replacement of the macronucleus and the development of the new one, bring about a restoration of the physiological functions. In some ciliates there are processes partially retarding hyper-ploidization, representing the phenomenon of extrusion of some of the chromatin of the macronucleus during division and hemixis (see p. 75). In this connexion it should be noted that extrusion of chromatin from the macronucleus during division occurred in the very species of ciliates in which indefinitely prolonged, agamous reproduction was observed. Ex-trusion occurs in many Hypotricha, in *Colpodidae* (Burt, Kidder, and Claff, 1941), in *Tetrahymena* (Dysart, 1960), and in many other Holotricha. One may agree with Fauré-Fremiet that the capacity of some ciliates for agamous reproduction during an unlimited period of time is associated with the fact that during each division there is a partial regulation of the growing hyper-ploidy by means of extrusion of some nuclear substance into the cytoplasm.

When examining the first of the above questions, regarding the possibility of unlimited agamous reproduction of ciliates, the second problem, that of the physiological significance of conjugation and autogamy, was partially touched upon. A number of investigators, viz. Calkins (1915*a*, 1919*a, b, c,* 1920, 1933) in the case of *Didinium* and *Uroleptus*, Woodruff and Spencer (1924) in *Spathidium spatula*, Jennings (1944–5) in *Paramecium bursaria*, Sonneborn (1954*a, b*) in *P. aurelia*, and others, have demonstrated that vitality is restored by conjugation and autogamy. Direct measurements of the energy of the oxidation processes in the large ciliate *Bursaria truncatella* (Barbarin and Solovieva, 1947) have shown that respiratory energy is increased in the exconjugants. However, the problem of the influence of conjugation and autogamy on vitality and their 'rejuvenating' significance proved to be very complex. As will be discussed in greater detail below (Jennings, Sonneborn), sexual processes may exert different influences on ciliates at various periods of their life-cycle. Furthermore, the fate of the descendants of individual exconjugants may vary considerably (Jennings, 1913, 1929; Raffel, 1930; and others). Whereas the descendants of some pairs manifest after conjugation an increased vitality and a high rate of division, the progeny of other exconjugants, on the contrary, are characterized by a retardation of their rate of division. Finally, a con-siderable mortality (varying in different cultures) is observed among the exconjugants. Thus among the exconjugants there is a pronounced in-crease of variability in both their physiological and morphological features. As a result of conjugation, which represents one form of amphimixis, a recombination of genes takes place, and new genotypes are formed (segregation), including both sublethal and lethal genotypic combinations.

The physiological effect of conjugation and autogamy on ciliates have been studied thoroughly and in great detail by Jennings (1944–5) and Egelhaaf (1955) in *Paramecium bursaria* and Sonneborn (1954) in *P. aurelia*. We can now consider briefly the results of their research. Jennings studied for several years the rate of division, the conjugation, and the fate of exconjugants in numerous pure lines of *Paramecium bursaria*, totalling more than 20,000 exconjugants. His main conclusions are as follows.

The progeny of ciliates derived from exconjugants by agamous reproduction (division) is incapable for some time of conjugating anew. This period of immaturity varies within very wide limits, lasting in various clones from twelve days to one year and more. Its duration and the onset of the period of maturity are greatly affected by the environmental conditions. In some strains derived from the division of the same exconjugant some lines were cultivated with frequent subculturing, avoiding overpopulation and under optimum conditions of nutrition, while other lines were grown under conditions of rare subculturing, with overpopulation and deficient nutrition. These experiments showed that favourable conditions of life promote more rapid maturation, while unfavourable ones delay it. When the next stage in the development of the culture—maturity—is reached, the ciliates acquire the capability of conjugating (on condition that individuals belonging to different mating types unite). The fate of the exconjugants has been carefully studied in relation to the age of the clone.[1] The term 'age' indicates the time during which asexual reproduction continues after conjugation. The duration (measured in months) and the rate of division of the lines (under favourable conditions) remains high, and the exconjugants, obtained when different strains are crossed, produce new lines, the majority of which are viable. Later (in a year or more) the process of senescence of the culture begins, accompanied by slowing down of the rate of division, and leading eventually to death. At the same time the percentage of mortality among the exconjugants gradually increases and eventually reaches 100 per cent.

This is illustrated by the following figures taken from the work of Jennings (1944*a*).

Number of clones	Age (average of ages of both partners) (months)	Average percentage of mortality in exconjugants
6	Less than 12	6·3
11	From 11 to 13	18·5
15	From 30 to 40	39·5
8	More than 40	3·0

In certain clones there is considerable variability in the survival of exconjugants, evidently depending on their genetic constitution. However, the tendency for the mortality of exconjugants to increase in ageing clones is a general rule.

[1] For definition of clone see p. 394.

In addition to the ageing of the clones, another factor lowering the viability of exconjugants is inbreeding. Jennings has carried out on many lines parallel experiments of two methods of cross-breeding. In one of these the lines reproduced asexually and periodically mated with each other (Fig. 220, I), after which the viability of the exconjugants was studied. The percentage of mortality remained on about the same level for

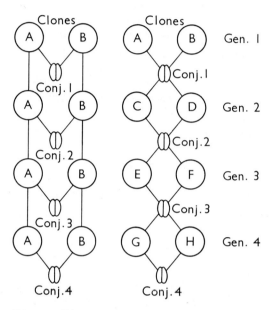

Fig. 220. Diagram of interbreeding in *Paramecium bursaria*. (After Jennings, 1944c.)

$1\frac{1}{2}$–2 years; then with the ageing of the clone mortality began to increase gradually. In the second method of cross-breeding the lines were maintained not by asexual reproduction, but by preservation of the exconjugants' progeny. In this way the inbred ciliates represented the progeny of two exconjugants of one pair, and thus the mating was really a very close inbreeding. In this method of mating the mortality among exconjugants increased sharply, and after 3–4 consecutive conjugations almost all the exconjugants died. In one of the experiments carried out according to this scheme, the following result was obtained: in the first interbreeding between two unrelated lines of *Paramecium bursaria*, carried out on 12 December 1941, mortality among the exconjugants was 13·3 per cent.; the second interbreeding, carried out between the descendants of the exconjugants of one pair on 5 May 1942, gave a mortality of 72·4 per cent. among the exconjugants; as a result of a third interbreeding (according to the same scheme) on 6 December 1942 mortality among the exconjugants rose to 97·9 per cent. Thus the mortality among the exconjugants increases much more rapidly as a result of inbreeding than during the 'ageing' of clones reproducing themselves asexually. The destructive role of inbreeding might be connected with genetic causes—homozygosity, when the lethal and sub-lethal recessive genes pass into a homozygous state and in this state they are manifested phenotypically. Sonneborn (1954*b*, 1957) studied in detail the relation of autogamy to senescence and rejuvenation in *Paramecium aurelia*. In the absence of conjugation and autogamy, attained as a result of abundant feeding (see Sonneborn, 1938), the rate of division in daily isolated lines is lowered and eventually they perish. The duration of life in lines without conjugation and autogamy differed in various stocks of *P. aurelia*. For instance, in variety 1 stock R it was about 130 days, in the course of which the ciliates underwent 350 successive divisions; in variety 2 stock W, 165 days and about 300 generations, &c. The rate of division is not lowered at once after autogamy or conjugation: it is more or less constant till about the middle of the potential period of agamous repro-duction; this is followed by a period of a slow decrease and finally by a rapid drop in the rate of division, terminating in death.

The effect of autogamy (or conjugation) may differ according to the state of the culture. If autogamy takes place comparatively often (for instance after 50–60 agamous generations), before the onset of the retardation of the rate of division, then the majority of the lines retain their viability and the original rate of division till the next autogamy. However, in part of them (usually small) the rate of division is lowered and they die. Consequently there is, strictly speaking, no rejuvenation here, but a maintenance of viability and of the rate of division. The results of a later autogamy, taking place later during the slow decrease of the rate of division, are more varied. In this case some of the lines restore their high rate of division, and resume their life-cycle anew, i.e. rejuvenation takes place. Some of the clones do not increase their rate of division, which remains at about the same level as in the ageing parental lines. This low rate of division remains for some time unchanged (in contrast to the parental lines where it continues to fall). Hence in this case there is only a temporary stabilization of the lowered rate of division. In the third group of lines the low rate of division continues to fall without being stabilized. Finally, part of the lines after autogamy become non-viable and die. The frequency of the appearance after auto-gamy of non-viable lines and of lines with a lowered rate of division increases with the age of the parental lines. When the ageing of these has gone too far, no viable clones at all are produced as a result of autogamy.

During the last stages of the life-cycle, when the rate of the division of ciliates is very low, autogamy is produced with difficulty and only among a small percentage of individuals.

In his general characterization of the life-cycle of *Paramecium aurelia*, Sonneborn (1954*b*) divides it into the following successive periods: (1) de-velopment of a new 'somatic' nucleus from a germinal nucleus, accompanied by the disappearance of the remnants of the previous (somatic) macro-nucleus; (2) capacity to mate (except after conjugation in stocks possessing an immature period), but not to undergo autogamy; (3) loss of ability to mate accompanied by gain of capacity to undergo autogamy, the latter capacity increasing until up to 100 per cent. of the animals can be induced to do so; (4) decreasing capacity to undergo autogamy and its eventual loss; (5) death.

These five stages are not strictly fixed as regards their duration, and they may shift somewhat in respect of each other. For instance, death may occur at the (3) or (4) stage, conjugation at the (1) stage (reconjugation), &c.

Sonneborn's investigations show also that conjugation may be completely replaced by autogamy in the life-cycle. But either one or the other form of sexual process is essential for *Paramecium aurelia*. Sonneborn (1954*b*, p. 38) sums up this position in the following words:

> Yet in spite of all the risks involved the animals must undergo autogamy (or conjugation) or perish. The end result of our study is thus to place on a firm experimental basis the conclusions to which Woodruff and Erdmann (1914) were forced forty years ago by the logic of the situation even in the absence of experimental analysis: conjugation is not essential for *P. aurelia*, autogamy (endomixis) alone can maintain the organisms in life and vigor.

A comparison of the results of the investigations of Jennings on the life-cycle of *P. bursaria* and of Sonneborn on *P. aurelia* reveals the difference in the significance of inbreeding in these species. In *P. bursaria* inbreeding leads to a sharp increase of mortality among the exconjugants, whereas in *P. aurelia* autogamy (which is in fact a most typical form of inbreeding since it represents self-fertilization) not only does not lead to an increase of mortality, but in many cases it leads to rejuvenation. It may be assumed that, since autogamy in *P. aurelia* represents a usual, normal link in the life-cycle, during the process of natural selection in this species all the lethal genotypical combinations, which arose as a result of homozygosis during inbreeding, had already been eliminated. In the case of *P. bursaria* cross-breeding (conjugation) of non-related individuals is more common; therefore a certain degree of heterozygosity is maintained. Hence inbreeding and its consequence, homozygosity, leads to a large number of lethal and sublethal genetic combinations.

Many problems of the physiology of the life-cycle of free-living ciliates were solved by the comprehensive investigations of Jennings and Sonneborn. These investigations have demonstrated that the same form of sexual process—conjugation or autogamy—taking place at various periods of the life-cycle may have an entirely different effect on the rate of division and on vitality. Further investigations in this direction will probably determine more definitely the role of the macronucleus in the phenomena of senescence and rejuvenation, as well as elucidate the physiological significance of different forms of nuclear reorganization (hemixis, chromatin extrusion, &c.) for the preservation of vitality in ciliates.

If we turn from the question of the life-cycle of ciliates to the wider problem, as to whether indefinitely prolonged agamous reproduction is possible in Protozoa, the answer must be in the positive. The experiments of Bělăr on *Actinophrys* and of M. Hartmann on *Eudorina* have proved beyond doubt that complete omission of the sexual process from the life-cycle does not lead to death.

It must be remembered that in many Protozoa the sexual process has not been described at all, and is apparently absent (Euglenacea, free-living amoebae, and others), so that in them agamous reproduction is the only form of multiplication. The ciliates, as has been rightly pointed out by Fauré-Fremiet, whose concept we have set out above (p. 387), occupy a special position. The dualism of the nuclear apparatus, the development of a complex polyploid macronucleus, and the general complexity of the organization have produced in many of them the need for periodical reorganization, commonly expressed in conjugation or autogamy.

Apart from the important investigations of the life-cycle of ciliates, Jennings and then Sonneborn and his collaborators have discovered and studied in detail other important phenomena related to the physiology of conjugation. They relate to 'mating types' and the processes connected with them, which will be dealt with in the next section.

Mating types

A very important phenomenon in the physiology and biology of the process of conjugation in ciliates is the occurrence of specific mating types among them. This phenomenon was first discovered in *Paramecium aurelia* by Sonneborn (1937) and in *P. bursaria* by Jennings (1939). It has now been found in a number of other species of ciliates (*Paramecium trichium*, *P. caudatum*, *P. calcinsi*, *P. multimicronucleatum*, *Tetrahymena pyriformis*, *Euplotes patella*, *Oxytricha bifaria*, *Stylonychia putrina*, and some others). We shall consider this phenomenon in the case of *Paramecium aurelia*, which has been most thoroughly studied in this respect (see Sonneborn, 1947; Beale, 1954; Sonneborn, 1957).

Before we turn to mating types, it is necessary to define certain terms which came into use in the course of experimental genetic and physiological investigations of ciliates, with which we shall constantly have to deal in the following pages. These terms are as follows: stocks, clones, and caryonides.

A stock is a culture derived by the multiplication of a single individual collected at a particular place.[1]

Ciliates attributed to one stock always belong to one variety (= syngen). However, as a result of various types of nuclear reorganization (autogamy,

---

[1] These definitions are taken from the book by Beale (1954); *The Genetics of Paramecium aurelia.*

hemixis), they may produce different mating types and may possess to a certain extent a genotypical heterogeneity. The word clone will be used for all animals derived by asexual reproduction (binary fission) from a single animal.

Thus within a clone the individuals have a high degree of genotypic homogeneity. However, if the clone is derived from a conjugant or an individual which had undergone autogamy, such an individual possesses not one macronuclear primordium (Ma-Anlagen) but two or more (although they all originate from a single synkaryon). These Ma-Anlagen are later distributed during fission among the succeeding generations. Thus, within a clone the macronuclei may be derived from different Ma-Anlagen. This circumstance, as will be seen later, is of special significance for the determination of mating types.

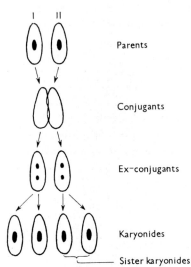

FIG. 221. Diagram illustrating conjugation in *Paramecium aurelia*.

I and II, individuals belonging to the complementary mating types. (After Sonneborn, 1937.)

The term karyonid was coined by Sonneborn (1938) to denote a group of paramecia all containing macronuclei derived from a single macronucleus. Thus a karyonid is characterized by the continuity of the macronucleus. Within one clone there may be several karyonids (according to the number of Ma-Anlagen) (Fig. 221).

The phenomenon of mating types is manifested in the fact that individuals belonging to the same karyonid do not, as a rule, conjugate with each other. Conjugation is possible between ciliates belonging to different karyonids; moreover (complementary), karyonids, which conjugate with each other, belong to different mating types. Sonneborn (1957), who has studied this problem in detail in *Paramecium aurelia*, has shown that there is a fairly considerable number of varieties within this species (in his latest works Sonneborn prefers to use the term *syngen* instead of variety) and within each variety there are two opposite (complementary) mating types. Thus, the differentiation into mating types within a variety has a dual character, each syngen being represented by two mating types. Syngens are denoted by arabic figures, mating types by roman. Thus, within variety 1 mating types I and II are distinguished; within variety 2 mating types III and IV; within variety 3 mating types V and VI, and so forth.

At present sixteen varieties of *P. aurelia* have been described with different degrees of completeness by Sonneborn and his associates.

Within each syngen, therefore, there is a bipolar system of two mating types (variety 16 has not yet been sufficiently studied in this respect). As regards the relationship between different syngens, in the majority of cases (the few exceptions will be considered below) there is no interbreeding (conjugation) between them. Thus within the limits of the species *P. aurelia* (analogous relations exist also in other ciliates) there is a considerable number of isolated groups or syngens, which do not interbreed with each other, and which constitute as it were elementary or 'biological species'. The significance of this differentiation of species into separate closed groups in the problem of speciation of Protozoa will be discussed below in Chapter IX; however, we shall now limit ourselves to the explanation of the significance of this fact in the formulation of breeding-systems in *P. aurelia*. How are mating types determined after conjugation or autogamy? In the case of *P. aurelia* there are two groups which behave differently. Sonneborn has called one group A and the other group B. Group A comprises the syngens 1, 3, 5, 9, 11, and apparently 7 and 15, while group B includes the syngens 2, 4, 6, 8, and probably 10, 12, and 14. Variety 16 has not yet been studied in this respect, while variety 13 apparently occupies an intermediate position between groups A and B. Let us first consider how the mating types are determined in group A. Among the progeny of exconjugants of a given variety different mating types may arise in various karyonids. All possible combinations are observed in this respect. Of the four karyonids formed as a result of conjugation (Fig. 221) all may belong to the mating type I, or to mating type II, or give rise to mating types I and II in various combinations. Moreover, both sister karyonids may belong to the same or to different mating types. But during further reproduction within each karyonid the mating type remains unchanged as a rule until the following conjugation.

The arrangement of mating types after conjugation may be illustrated by the following two tables compiled from Sonneborn's data (1937).

INHERITANCE OF MATING TYPES I AND II, AFTER
CONJUGATION, IN VARIETY 1. (SONNEBORN, 1937)

Analysis of four karyonids from individual pairs of conjugants

No. of pairs	No. of karyonids	
	I	II
1	4	0
18	3	1
21	2	2
13	1	3
3	0	4

Analysis of two sister karyonids from each exconjugant

No. of ex-conjugants	No. of karyonids	
	I	II
35	2	0
70	1	1
34	0	2

From these tables it is seen that the distribution of the mating types between the karyonids is haphazard. The same pattern is observed also as a result of autogamy. After autogamy, 2 karyonids are formed, since in a ciliate, which had undergone an autogamy, 2 Ma-Anlagen are formed. Both these karyonids may belong either to the same or to different mating types.

From observations on the distribution of mating types among the exconjugants and the karyonids within the varieties of *P. aurelia* belonging to group A, Sonneborn (1937, 1938*b*, 1939, 1957, and others) was led to the conclusion that the difference between the mating types is determined by the macronucleus. Each exconjugant has normally 2 Ma-Anlagen; while in both exconjugants produced by one pair 4 Ma-Anlagen in all are formed. They are distributed among 4 karyonids and determine the mating types of these. A convincing proof of the accuracy of this point of view is provided by the change observed by Sonneborn (1939) in the nature of the determination of the mating type in cases when the normal number and distribution of Ma-Anlagen has been disturbed. Thus in stock R (variety 1) Sonneborn observed more than 2 macronuclei (from 3 to 10) in 20 per cent. of the conjugants. The determination of the mating types was accordingly somewhat delayed and coincided with the moment of the distribution of the macronuclei during the metagamous divisions of the exconjugants. Convincing evidence of the importance of the macronucleus in the determination of the mating type is provided by observations on exconjugants in which the macronuclei regenerate instead of developing from Ma-Anlagen (Sonneborn, 1957*a*). In all these cases the mating type remains unchanged, and corresponds to the old macronucleus.

The problem of the nature and mechanism of the effect of the macronucleus upon the determination of the mating type remains unsolved. It must be borne in mind that all the nuclei formed as a result of fertilization within one conjugating pair have the same genotype. They develop from two synkaryons formed as a result of the fusion of identical pronuclei.

Thus all the nuclei of all the karyonids derived from one pair have an identical genotypic composition. Thus the separation into different mating types cannot be regarded as Mendelian segregation. It has been suggested (Nanney, 1953) that the determination of one or other mating type may depend on the different degree of polyploidy of the macronucleus. However, so far there is no serious factual evidence to support this hypothesis.

The determination of the mating type is also to a great extent influenced by environmental conditions, especially temperature (Sonneborn, 1939). A comparatively high temperature facilitates the appearance of mating type II in variety 1, mating type VI in variety 3, and mating type X in variety 5.

At high temperatures even numbers of mating types are predominant, at low temperatures odd ones. For instance, in variety 1 the number of karyonids of mating type II at 10° C., in one of the experiments, was 38 per cent., while at 35° C. in the same material it was 88 per cent. Similar results were obtained in other varieties.

The determination of mating types after conjugation and autogamy in the varieties of *P. aurelia* belonging to group B is of a different character from that in group A. The mating type of the exconjugant clone is here almost always the same as that of the parents: i.e. of the individual which proceeded to conjugation. For instance, if conjugation takes place among ciliates of variety 4, between mating types VII and VIII, then almost all the individuals of the clone derived from the exconjugant of mating type VII will belong to mating type VII, while the progeny of the other exconjugants belong to mating type VIII. Thus, contrary to group A, in group B a strong parent-progeny correlation is observed in respect to its mating types. Nevertheless, a small number of individuals belonging to group B undergo a modification of the mating type after conjugation and autogamy. For instance, Sonneborn (1948) observed among ciliates of mating types VIII after autogamy the appearance of mating type VII, in a ratio of about 1 : 50. Still more rare is the appearance of mating type VIII among the karyonids of mating type VII: viz., once in several hundred cases of autogamy. Modification of the mating type during conjugation, though still very rare, occurs a little more frequently; for instance, in variety 4 in about 10 per cent. of cases. However, an overwhelming majority of clones show a parent-progeny correlation. What are the causes of the differences in the character of the determination of mating types between the varieties of *P. aurelia* belonging to groups A and B? Evidently these differences must be determined first of all by the cytoplasm. The constancy of the mating types in group B gives reason to assume that this group possesses some cytoplasmic determinants absent in group A. Only on this assumption can the continuity and the persistence of the mating types in exconjugants and in their progeny produced asexually be explained. When then do changes in the mating types occur after conjugation in a small percentage of cases in group B? This process should probably be explained by the fact that in certain conjugating pairs there takes place an exchange not only of pronuclei but also of parts of the cytoplasm (Beale, 1954; Sonneborn, 1957). During this exchange the determinants of the mating types pass over together with the cytoplasm. Various necessary modifications of the mating types associated with this are shown in Fig. 222.

Are the cytoplasmic determinants of the mating types independent of the macronucleus or are they determined by the macronucleus and merely pass the information from the old macronucleus to the one newly formed after conjugation or autogamy? Some experimental data support the second of these suppositions. Thus, in one of Sonneborn's experiments (1954a, 1957) ciliates of mating types VII and VIII conjugated; during conjugation an exchange of considerable amounts of the cytoplasm took place (Fig. 223); the ciliates were subjected to the effect of high temperature, which impeded the development of Ma-Anlagen in one of the exconjugants. Instead of this in this exconjugant (of mating type VII) regeneration of the old macro-nucleus took place; although it had received a considerable amount of cyto-plasm from its partner, which belonged to mating type VIII, it continued to belong to mating type VII. This points to the determining role of the

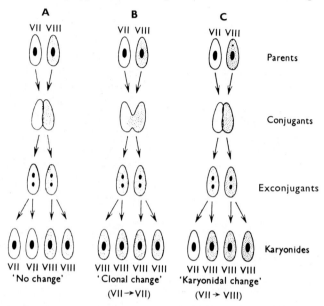

FIG. 222. Inheritance of mating types during conjugation between types VII and VIII in group B, variety 4, of *Paramecium aurelia*.

macronucleus, not of the cytoplasm. In discussing the problem of nucleo-cytoplasmic interactions in the B system of *P. aurelia*, Nanney (1954, p. 279) arrives, in agreement with Sonneborn's data, at the following conclusions:

Since the mating type of the parent is clearly controlled by the macronucleus, and since the cytoplasmic condition necessary for the inheritance of the mating type through nuclear reorganization is strongly correlated with the parental mating type, it follows that the cytoplasmic condition is ultimately controlled by the old macronucleus. Thus, though the cytoplasm determines the nature of the new macronucleus, the cytoplasm is in turn controlled by the old macronucleus. This results in a cyclical interdetermination of the nucleus by the cytoplasm and of the cytoplasm by the nucleus.

If in group B the mating type is controlled primarily by the macro-nucleus, as it is in group A, then the differences between these two forms of determination of the mating type is not so pronounced, being more of a qualitative nature.

As has been shown above, conjugation occurs as a rule between two mating types within the limits of one variety. However, in some exceptional

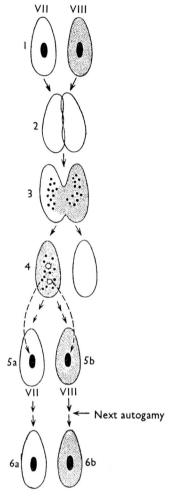

FIG. 223. Inheritance of mating type in variety 4 (group B) of *Paramecium aurelia*, after conjugation involving both cytoplasmic exchange and macro-nuclear regeneration. (Note. In the diagram the micronuclei are not shown). (After Sonneborn, 1954a).

1. Two parental animals, one of mating type VII, the other of mating type VIII.
2. The two animals conjugate.
3. Cytoplasm of type VIII conjugant passes into mate; macronuclear fragments shown in black.
4. Left-hand exconjugant contains macronuclear fragments, two anlagen (unshaded circles) derived from fusion nucleus, and cytoplasmic elements derived from type VIII parent.
5a. Exconjugant containing macronucleus developed in the normal way from an anlagen; mating type VIII.
5b. Exconjugant containing macronucleus derived from fragments of old macro-nucleus: mating type VII. The cytoplasmic materials from the type VII parent (shown stippled) are presumed to exert an influence on the developing macro-nuclei of 5a, but not 5b.
6. The two types reproduce true to type after the next autogamy.

cases it may occur between mating types belonging to different varieties. Intervarietal sexual reactions are altogether unknown for seven out of the 16 varieties of *P. aurelia*. All the other cases of intervarietal reactions described for *P. aurelia* up to 1957 are given in the following Table I.

Intervarietal mating reactions usually differ from intravarietal reactions by the lesser intensity of the former. In the majority of cases conjugation between two individuals belonging to different varieties, even if it is completed (i.e. terminates in the formation of the synkaryon and the development of a new nuclear apparatus from it), produces either unviable individuals or individuals of low viability; the rate of division of most of them is low and they die out. Thus, although in some rare cases interbreeding does take place between ciliates of different varieties, it does not produce a viable progeny. This leads Sonneborn (1957, p. 168) to the following conclusion: 'In short the genes of every variety are virtually isolated from the genes of every other variety.' If mating reaction does take place in the case of intervarietal mating between individuals belonging to odd- and even-numbered mating types, an odd-numbered mating type of each variety mates with an even-numbered mating type of the other. This is an indication that the odd- and even-numbered mating types (or the $+$ and $-$ types) of different varieties possess certain common properties in respect of the mating reaction.

Within the same karyonid the mating type is, as a rule, retained during asexual reproduction. However, there are a few exceptions to this rule. These exceptions are represented by the special, so-called 'selfing' karyonids, their peculiarity consisting in the appearance of a small number of individuals of the opposite (complementary) mating type during agamous reproduction of these karyonids. An account of this phenomenon was given by Kimball (1939) for variety 1 of *Paramecium aurelia*. As a result of conjugation or autogamy 3 per cent. of unstable or 'selfing' karyonids were produced among the ordinary stable karyonids. During asexual reproduction about 1 per cent. of individuals of the opposite (complementary) mating type appeared among these 'selfings'. Nanney (1954) succeeded in obtaining the fusion of both Ma-Anlagen (by means of starvation) in the exconjugants of *P. aurelia*. Selfing karyonids are produced more often than is usual by ciliates with such macronuclei. The appearance of selfing karyonids is observed not only in *Paramecium*: it has been discovered and studied in detail in *Tetrahymena pyriformis* by Allen and Nanney (1958). The authors have put forward the hypothesis that the macronucleus of ciliates is composed of a certain number of morphologically indistinguishable 'subnuclei' which control one or other of the mating types. In the case of homogeneous subnuclei only one type of mating is observed, but when the subnuclei are heterogeneous, various mating types are produced during their distribution among the daughter individuals during the process of division. The quantitative aspect of this process depends on the

TABLE I

The system of sexual reactions among mating types of those varieties of P. aurelia in which intervarietal reactions occur.[1] (After Sonneborn, 1957)

Variety		1		3		4		5		7		8		10		14	
	Mating type	I	II	V	VI	VII	VIII	IX	X	XIII	XIV	XV	XVI	XIX	XX	XXVII	XXVIII
1	I	–	++	–	–	–	–	–	+	–	+	±	±	–	–	–	–
	II	C	–	+	–	–	–	+	+	+	+	+	+	–	–	–	–
3	V	o	o	–	++	–	–	–	–	±	–	+	+	–	–	–	+
	VI	o	o	C	–	–	–	–	–	–	–	–	–	–	–	–	–
4	VII	o	o	o	o	–	+++	–	–	–	–	++	++	–	–	–	–
	VIII	o	o	o	o	C	–	–	–	–	–	++	++	–	–	–	+
5	IX	o	o	o	o	o	o	–	++	–	–	±	–	–	–	–	–
	X	o	o	o	o	o	o	C	–	–	–	–	–	–	–	–	–
7	XIII	o	o	o	o	o	o	o	o	–	++	–	–	–	–	–	–
	XIV	o	o	o	o	o	o	o	o	C	–	–	–	–	–	–	–
8	XV	o	o	o	o	o	o	o	o	o	o	–	+++	–	–	C	+
	XVI	o	o	o	o	o	o	o	o	o	o	C	–	–	–	–	+
10	XIX	o	o	o	o	o	o	o	o	o	o	o	o	–	+++	C	+
	XX	o	o	o	o	o	o	o	o	o	o	o	o	C	–	–	+
14	XXVII	o	o	o	o	o	o	o	o	o	o	o	o	o	o	–	+++
	XXVIII	o	o	o	o	o	o	o	o	o	o	o	o	o	o	C	–

[1] Symbols over the diagonal refer only to occurrence of mating reactions (adhesion, agglutination); symbols below the diagonal refer to the occurrence of complete conjugation. Varieties 10 and 14 are newly discovered and still incompletely studied; their reactions may be more extensive than now known. +++ maximal reaction. ++ reduced mating reaction. + weak mating reaction. ± barely detectable reaction. – no mating reaction. C conjugants formed. o no conjugants formed.

correlation between different subnuclei in the macronucleus. Nanney's concept of 'subnuclei' agrees well with the theory of macronuclear polyploidy mentioned above. Perhaps each subnucleus should be regarded as one of the genomes of a highly polyploid macronucleus. This hypothesis cannot yet be regarded as well established, chiefly because the nature of the factors controlling the mating types is not clear.

We have considered in sufficiently full detail the problem of mating types in a ciliate best studied in this respect: *Paramecium aurelia*. Therefore we can deal much more briefly with the mating types in other ciliates, since in this respect there are many common features between *P. aurelia* and in other ciliates. Breeding systems similar to that of *P. aurelia* and composed of several varieties, each with two mating types, have been described for *Paramecium caudatum* (Gilman, 1939, 1949, 1956; Hiwatashi, 1949; Chen, 1944; Vivier, 1960; and others) and for *P. calkinsi* (Wichtermann, 1951). So far sixteen varieties have been investigated in *P. caudatum* (Sonneborn, 1957), each with two mating types.

In addition to breeding systems, which may be called bipolar (i.e. containing two mating types), 'multipolar' mating type systems are widespread among ciliates. This phenomenon has been most fully investigated in *Paramecium bursaria*, where it was first discovered by Jennings (1939), and has since been studied by many authors (Jennings and Opitz, 1944; Chen, 1946). Six varieties which do not interbreed (or practically do not cross) with each other have been described for *P. bursaria*. However, in distinction from *P. aurelia*, within each variety there are not two but a larger number of mating types, and the individuals of one mating type can conjugate with all the remaining mating types of a given variety. These relations are well illustrated by the following Table II.

It is seen from the table that out of the six varieties of *P. bursaria*, variety I has four mating types, variety II eight, variety III four, variety IV only two (as in *P. aurelia*). Variety V has so far been little investigated and its mating types have not been described; and, finally, variety VI again has four mating types. This table also shows all possible combinations of mating reactions. In *P. bursaria* conjugation between varieties occasionally takes place (as already noted in the case of *P. aurelia*). Mating type R of variety IV is particularly interesting in this respect. However, here too interbreeding between different varieties usually has a lethal result.

In recent years eight varieties have been described for *Tetrahymena pyriformis*, which has been studied in detail (Elliott and Hayes, 1953; Nanney and Caughey, 1953; Cruchy, 1955; Sonneborn, 1957, and others). Among them three varieties, 5, 7, and 8, have two mating types each, while a multipolar scheme, like that in *Paramecium bursaria*, is observed in the others; thus varieties 4 and 6 have three mating types each, variety 9 five, variety 1 seven, variety 3 eight, variety 2 no fewer than eleven mating types. All this indicates that there is no difference in principle between the bipolar and multipolar systems and that both systems may be encountered in different varieties of the same species. Sonneborn (1938) discovered a multipolar system consisting of three mating types in *Paramecium trichium*. However, in the case of this species further investigations are needed, since its forms of sexual process and of reconstruction of the nuclear apparatus vary considerably (Diller, 1948; Jankovsky, 1960). A multipolar scheme composed of four mating types was described for *P. multimicronucleata* (Giese, 1939, 1941). A complex multipolar system among the Ciliata Hypotricha was investigated by Downs (1959), who found among them two varieties, one of them comprising 15 mating types, the other 11.

TABLE II

The system of breeding relations in P. bursaria; + *indicates the occurrence of conjugation,* — *indicates that no conjugation occurs in mixtures of the two mating types represented in the corresponding row and file.* (*After Sonneborn, 1947*)

Variety	Mating type	I				II								III				IV		V	VI			
		A	B	C	D	E	F	G	H	J	K	L	M	N	O	P	Q	R	S	T	U	V	W	X
I	A	−	+	+	+	−	−	−	−	−	−	−	−	−	−	−	−	−	−	−	−	−	−	−
	B	+	−	+	+	−	−	−	−	−	−	−	−	−	−	−	−	−	−	−	−	−	−	−
	C	+	+	−	+	−	−	−	−	−	−	−	−	−	−	−	−	−	−	−	−	−	−	−
	D	+	+	+	−	−	−	−	−	−	−	−	−	−	−	−	−	−	−	−	−	−	−	−
II	E					−	+	+	+	+	+	+	+	−	−	−	−	+	−	−	−	−	−	−
	F					+	−	+	+	+	+	+	+	−	−	−	−	−	−	−	−	−	−	−
	G					+	+	−	+	+	+	+	+	−	−	−	−	−	−	−	−	−	−	−
	H					+	+	+	−	+	+	+	+	−	−	−	−	−	−	−	−	−	−	−
	J					+	+	+	+	−	+	+	+	−	−	−	−	−	−	−	−	−	−	−
	K					+	+	+	+	+	−	+	+	−	−	−	−	+	−	−	−	−	−	−
	L					+	+	+	+	+	+	−	+	−	−	−	−	+	−	−	−	−	−	−
	M					+	+	+	+	+	+	+	−	−	−	−	−	+	−	−	−	−	−	−
III	N													−	+	+	+	−	−	−	−	−	−	−
	O													+	−	+	+	−	−	−	−	−	−	−
	P													+	+	−	+	−	−	−	−	−	−	−
	Q													+	+	+	−	−	−	−	−	−	−	−
IV	R																	−	+	−	−	−	−	−
	S																	+	−	−	−	−	−	−
V	T																			−	−	−	−	−
VI	U																				−	+	+	+
	V																				+	−	+	+
	W																				+	+	−	+
	X																				+	+	+	−

Euplotes patella, of the order Hypotricha, possess a special form of mating types, distinct from those of the holotrichous ciliates examined above. However, before turning to the discussion of these phenomena, we shall consider the characteristics of the mating reaction in *Paramecium*.

The first thing observed during the union of ciliates belonging to opposite (complementary) mating types, when the ciliates are in a mature state, is the reaction of agglutination, when the ciliates unite and adhere to each other, forming whole clumps sometimes composed of dozens of ciliates. From the clumps formed as a result of agglutination conjugating pairs are separated later. For the reaction of agglutination direct contact between the ciliates is essential (Metz, 1954). Filtrates of cultural medium from one mating type have no effect on its complementary one (in contrast to *Euplotes*: see below). The reaction of agglutination is evidently associated with the presence of special substances discharged by the surface structures of ciliates. This reaction stimulates in the ciliates a whole series of subsequent processes characterizing the course of conjugation. Apparently the substances causing the reaction of agglutination (mating reaction) are connected with the cilia. A convincing argument in favour of agglutination being caused by special substances located in surface structures is the capacity for mating reaction between live *Paramecium* and individuals belonging to the opposite (complementary) mating type killed by various substances. These facts point to the presence of special highly specific mating-type substances controlling the mating reactions. This reaction can be compared with the antigen–antibody reactions and fertilizing–antifertilizing reaction during fertilization. As has been shown by a careful biochemical analysis, carried out with the aid of various enzymes and other substances (Metz and Butterfield, 1951), mating substances represent proteins or substances closely associated with protein. The mating reaction activates the ciliates for the sexual process, which follows it. The mating reaction which affects only the ciliary apparatus is followed by a holdfast union of the ciliates by the anterior ends; after which the paroral cone is formed through which exchange of pronuclei takes place. The holdfast union initiates the process of meiosis in the micronucleus, involving the entire chain of complex nuclear changes, described in detail above. The mating reaction and the subsequent changes (holdfast union paroral cone formation) are associated with different physiological mechanisms. This is convincingly proved by the observations of Metz and Foley (1949) on the CM-mutant (cannot mate) of *Paramecium aurelia*. This mutant produces a well-defined mating reaction but is incapable of going through all the subsequent series of changes characterizing the process of conjugation. In the CM-mutant all the processes following the mating reaction are blocked. In contrast to conjugation, autogamy is not associated with the changes characteristic of the mating reaction, and begins directly from the stage of the process which corresponds to the formation of the paroral cone and to the beginning of meiosis of the micronucleus. The correlation between the above-mentioned stages is represented diagrammatically in Fig. 224.

We can now consider the special form of mating types which occurs in *Euplotes patella* (Kimball, 1939*b*, 1942, 1943; Katashima, 1952). This species possesses two or three varieties which do not interbreed with each other, but the mating types have been studied only in one of them. There are six mating types, forming a multipolar group, but the nature of the mating reaction here differs essentially from that in *Paramecium bursaria*, for example. During the union of different (complementary) mating types, the sex reaction does not take place at once, as in *Paramecium*, but after 1·5–2 hours. There is moreover no immediate agglutination of a large number of ciliates, but separate pairs are formed. However, the most essential peculiarity is that substances discharged by the ciliates into the surrounding

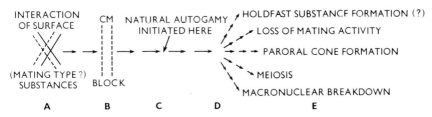

FIG. 224. Scheme of activation during the sexual processes in paramecia. (After Nanney, 1954.)

medium cause conjugation according to the selfing type within the limits of a different (complementary) mating type. Thus conjugation within the limits of one or other mating type may be stimulated by the addition of cultural fluid (without ciliates) inhabited by individuals of another (complementary) mating type. As we have seen above, in *Paramecium* the mating reaction occurs only when there is immediate, direct contact between individuals of different mating types. When *Euplotes patella* of different mating types are mixed, pairs of two categories are formed: some are formed by individuals of one and the same mating type (under the influence of substances discharged by individuals of a different mating type); others represent the union of ciliates belonging to different mating types. The correlation of the mating reaction among the six mating types is very complex. A diagrammatic representation of it is given in the following Table III:

TABLE III

Conjugation—Inducing action of animal-free culture in Euplotes
patella. (*After Kimball, 1942; Sonneborn, 1947*)

Animal-free Fluids. Fluid Agent	Mating type	Animals					
		IV	VI	III	I	II	IV
1	IV	—	+	+	—	—	+
2	VI	+	—	+	—	+	—
3	III	+	+	—	+	—	—
1·2	I	+	+	+	—	+	+
1·3	II	+	+	+	+	—	+
2·3	V	+	+	+	+	+	—

Conjugation ('selfing') is indicated by +; failure to observe conjugation —.

Kimball (1942) suggested the following explanation of the facts observed, which has been accepted by many authors (Sonneborn, 1947; Metz, 1954, and others). The ciliates of different mating types of *Euplotes patella* discharge three different substances (1, 2, and 3—see Table III), inducing conjugation. Moreover, three of the mating types (IV, VI, III) discharge these substances in a pure state, and the three others (I, II, V) discharge two substances each, in different combinations. In those discharging only one substance sex reactions occur when the substance acting on the ciliates differs from that discharged by themselves. A particular fluid agent induces conjugation only in those animals which do not produce the same agent. As regards the mating types forming two substances, they induce the sex reaction in all other mating types (apart from themselves). This complex scheme of correlations among the six mating types depends on and is controlled by differences in their genetic structure. According to Kimball, three genes belonging to one multiple allele take part in the control of the mating types of *Euplotes patella*. Mating types discharging one substance are homozygous; those discharging two substances are heterozygous. Thus the six mating types of *Euplotes patella* expressed in genetic symbols will be represented in the following manner:

Mating type	Genotype	Substance produced
I	$mt^1\ mt^2$	1 and 2
II	$mt^1\ mt^3$	1 and 3
III	$mt^3\ mt^3$	3 only
IV	$mt^1\ mt^1$	1 only
V	$mt^2\ mt^3$	2 and 3
VI	$mt^2\ mt^2$	2 only

The foregoing genetic scheme is confirmed by interbreeding and by the resulting pattern of segregation into different mating types (Kimball, 1942).

Although these cytophysiological and genetic explanations of the peculiarities of the mating types in *Euplotes patella* suggested by American authors are most plausible, we must regard them as hypotheses in need of further experimental proof. However, irrespective of their true interpretation, there remains the indisputable fact of the existence of pronounced differences in the phenomenon of 'mating types' among the Holotricha (*Paramecium, Tetrahymena*) and *Euplotes patella* examined in this respect. In *Paramecium* and *Tetrahymena* the mating reaction takes place only on direct contact, and conjugation occurs between individuals belonging to different mating types. In *Euplotes*, the substances inducing the formation of pairs are discharged into the surrounding medium and conjugation occurs mainly within the clone (selfing). The fact that differentiation and determination of the mating types of *Paramecium* occurs within the same genotype also represents an essential difference. If Kimball's system is correct, the mating types of *Euplotes* are due to genotypical differences (diverse gene composition along the multiple allele *mt*.)

Heckmann (1963) studied the mating types of the marine ciliate *Euplotes vannus*. Five mating types were found, belonging to a single syngen and forming, as in other species of the same genus, a multipolar mating system. In *E. vannus*, mating types are determined genotypically (as well as in other *Euplotes* species). By means of genetic analysis Heckmann established that the mating type determination in *E. vannus* is based on a multiple allele including five genes. Unlike *E. patella*, in *E. vannus* there is a complete dominance within this allele, which results in the fact that homozygous and heterozygous individuals having the same dominant gene belong to the same mating type. Heckmann proposes the following scheme of gene dominance:

$$mt^5 > mt^4 > mt^3 > mt^2 > mt^1.$$

Owing to the complete dominance, the genotypical composition may be different within a single mating type, which is clearly illustrated in the following table:

Mating type	Genotypes
I	$mt^1\ mt^1$
II	$mt^2\ mt^2$, $mt^2\ mt^1$
III	$mt^3\ mt^3$, $mt^3\ mt^2$, $mt^3\ mt^1$
IV	$mt^4\ mt^4$, $mt^4\ mt^3$, $mt^4\ mt^2$, $mt^4\ mt^1$
V	$mt^5\ mt^5$, $mt^5\ mt^4$, $mt^5\ mt^3$, $mt^5\ mt^2$, $mt^5\ mt^1$

All these combinations (except $mt^5\ mt^5$) were obtained by the author experimentally by means of crosses.

A substantial difference distinguishes *E. vannus* from *E. patella*. This is the absence of any secretion of soluble substances, which induce the mating reaction, into the surrounding medium. In this respect *E. vannus* resembles *Paramecium*, for the mating reaction is accomplished here only at direct contact of animals of complementary mating types.

In concluding this short survey of mating types in ciliates, we may discuss the problem of the nature and biological significance of this phenomenon. The first question to arise is whether the differences between the mating types are the manifestations of sexual differentiation in ciliates. In our opinion this question should be answered in the negative. The ciliates represent bisexual, hermaphrodite organisms. Sexual differences should be sought in the pronuclei (stationary and migratory) within each individual, and these differences are entirely comparable with the sexual differences between gametes. We can speak of sexual differentiation in ciliates only in cases of anisogamous conjugation. For example, in the Peritricha, on the basis of the original hermaphroditism, the female sexual tendency is usually suppressed in the microconjugant and the female pronucleus does not usually undergo karyogamy. The microconjugant is comparable to a male derived from a hermaphrodite individual.

As regards mating types, this phenomenon is *sui generis*, having no direct connexion with the two opposite sexual tendencies. The existence of multipolar breeding systems (*Paramecium bursaria*, *Tetrahymena*) is a weighty argument against equating the mating types with sexual differences. According to M. Hartmann's well-substantiated theory, there are only two opposite sexual tendencies, this bipolarity and bisexuality representing one of the most characteristic features of the phenomenon of sex as a biological phenomenon in Protozoa, Metazoa, and Metaphyta. On the other hand, there are no multipolar systems of sexual differences.

Thus the mating types of the ciliates is a distinct phenomenon, a peculiar 'superstructure' over sexuality. It would appear that this phenomenon plays an exceptionally important role in the ecology and evolution of ciliates. The existence of mating types assures the union of individuals during conjugation, and facilitates their interbreeding. At the same time the existence of the mating types within the limits of each variety is associated with a complex differentiation of the species in ciliates into numerous breeding systems, a problem brilliantly worked out by Sonneborn and his school on *Paramecium aurelia* and some other ciliates. It must be emphasized that so far comparatively few species of ciliates have been studied in respect to their mating types and their breeding systems. However, the great diversity of forms assumed by this phenomenon (*Paramecium* and *Euplotes*) is evident even from the data already at our disposal. There is, however, a pressing need of further investigation in this field. Further comparative cytophysiological and genetic investigations, covering a large number of species belonging to different systematic groups of ciliates, are required for the creation of a general theory concerning mating types and for the elucidation of their biological significance.

Sexuality, sex-determination, and the physiology of copulation in Protozoa

In earlier chapters we have dealt with a variety of most dissimilar forms of the sexual process in Protozoa. The morphological basis of the sexual process is the fusion of two gametes (or two nuclei), leading to the formation of a zygote. As a rule, the nuclei participating in karyogamy are haploid, whereas the zygotes formed as a result of the sexual process always have a diploid nucleus. Copulating gametes (or nuclei) show various phases of differentiation—from a complete morphological identity of the gametes (isogamous copulation) to more or less clearly marked morphological differences between male and female sexual cells (anisogamous copulation).

Naturally the question arises as to the physiological side of the sexual process—the nature of sexuality and the differences between the copulating gametes. Are there any physiological differences between the gametes in isogamous copulation or does fusion occur indiscriminately between any gametes? At present there is abundant factual material indicating that in all cases of both isogamous and anisogamous copulation there is sexual differentiation of the gametes, i.e. sexual bipolarity. The theory of sexuality, which we are about to consider, has been studied and developed mostly as a result of the work of M. Hartmann and his associates.[1]

The differences between the sexual cells may be determined by the diverse gene composition of gametes with opposite sexual tendencies. In such cases, which are most widespread among both Protozoa and multi cellular animals and plants, there is a genotypic determination of sex. In certain organisms (among both Protozoa and multicellular organisms) there are no genotypic differences either between the gametes or between the organisms which produce them. In such cases a phenotypic manifestation of one or another sexual tendency in a bisexual organism is determined by factors that are extraneous to the developing gametes; in other words, a phenotypic (or modificatory) sex-determination takes place (Hartmann's 'modifikatorische Geschlechtsbestimmung').

Both genotypic and modifying (phenotypic) sex-determination may take place in either the haploid or diploid phase. We shall deal later in greater detail with the genetic aspect of these phenomena, but will first turn to the physiological aspect of the process.

As an example, let us consider genotypic sex-determination in the haplophase of certain isogamous Phytomonadina—*Gonium pectorale, Chlamydomonas eugametos, Dunaliella salina*, and some others. In these Protozoa copulation of gametes never takes place within the limits of one clone (i.e. the asexual progeny of a single cell). A study of the sexual reaction of a certain number of clones isolated from natural habitats reveals the occurrence of clones with opposite sexual tendencies that copulate with each other. Furthermore, no copulation takes place between the gametes belonging to clones of the same sex. The results of a test on the sexual reaction in seven clones of *Gonium pectorale*, carried out by Schreiber (1925), are given in Fig. 225. Clones 1, 3, 4, 5, and 6 belong to one sex, clones 2 and 7 to the other. The genotypic character of sex-determination is particularly convincingly proved by the so-called tetrad analysis. Each zygote by two successive divisions gives rise to four vegetative cells (tetrad), of which two always belong to one sex and two to the other. The result of such a tetrad analysis of the zygote of *Gonium pectorale* is given in Fig. 226. It may be recalled that in Phytomonadina reduction is zygotic. Thus the sex ratio of 1 : 1, as a result of meiosis, is evidently connected with the divergence, in the course of reduction division during the transition from diplophase to haplophase, of the genes which determine the opposite sexual tendencies.

Convincing evidence that copulation occurs between gametes belonging to different clones was given by Lerche (1937) in his study of sexual

---

[1] For a detailed survey and analysis of this problem see M. Hartmann, *Die Sexualität* (G. Fisher Verlag, Stuttgart, 2. Auflage, 1956).

processes in the flagellate *Dunaliella salina*. In this species typical isogamous copulation takes place, but by changing the conditions of cultivation visible differences between various clones may be obtained. If *Dunaliella salina* is grown in a medium deficient in phosphorus and nitrogen, then, owing to deposition of carotin, the cells acquire a reddish coloration. When such a

	+ 1	+ 2	+ 3	+ 4	+ 5	− 6	− 7
+1	o	o	o	o	o	Z	Z
+2	o	o	o	o	o	Z	Z
+3	o	o	o	o	o	Z	Z
+4	o	o	o	o	o	Z	Z
+5	o	o	o	o	o	Z	Z
−6	Z	Z	Z	Z	Z	o	o
−7	Z	Z	Z	Z	Z	o	o

FIG. 225. Sexual reaction of 7 clones of *Gonium pectorale*.

Z, copulation and formation of zygotes; o, absence of copulation. (After Schreiber, 1925.)

	a	b	c	d
a	o	o	Z	Z
b	o	o	Z	Z
c	Z	Z	o	o
d	Z	Z	o	o

FIG. 226. Tetrad analysis of *Gonium pectorale*. (After Schreiber, 1925.)

clone is united with another of the opposite sex and coloured green, it can be observed that each pair of the copulating gametes always consists of two cells, one reddish and the second green. This marking of the gametes leaves no doubt that copulation takes place only between gametes of opposite sexual tendencies.

In typical cases the sexual reaction of the gametes proceeds in a very characteristic way and consists of two phases. When two clones, containing gametes of the opposite sexes, are mixed, at first agglutination takes place, i.e. gametes of opposite sexual tendencies adhere to each other, forming large clumps, sometimes composed of several dozens and even hundreds of cells. After some time these aggregations begin to break up into separate pairs of mating gametes—this represents the second phase of the sexual reaction.

The agglutination reaction of the gametes begins with the adhesion of the flagella, which intertwine with each other. Later a fine cytoplasmic bridge is formed between the anterior ends of the gametes (Lewin, 1954), followed by closer union (Fig. 227) and fusion of the gametes.

The union of the gametes is accompanied by the secretion of some specific substances, called gamones, which cause much adhesion of the cells. These substances are discharged into the surrounding medium and retain their effect in filtrates. If the filtrate of the gametes of one sex (conventionally called female) is allowed to act on gametes of the other (male) sex, the latter display a characteristic reaction of agglutination (clumping), which is, however, not followed by copulation (Fig. 228).

The action of the gamones is strictly specific in the sense that clumping of male gametes occurs only under the influence of the filtrate of female

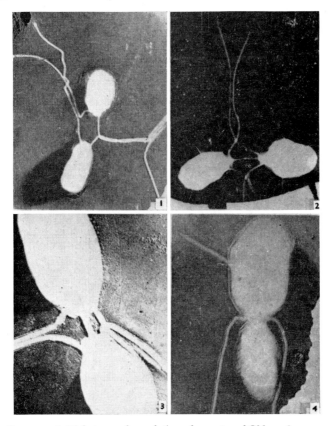

FIG. 227. Initial stages of copulation of gametes of *Chlamydomonas* (electron-micrograph).

1, agglutination of flagella; 2, beginning of formation of cytoplasmic bridge; 3, cytoplasmic bridge; 4, beginning of fusion of gametes. (After Lewin, 1954.)

gametes, and vice versa. In most cases the specificity of the gamones extends to species, i.e. gamones of one species do not induce the clumping reaction in the gametes of another species.

Certain differences are observed between the male and female gamones as regards their response to various physical and chemical factors (Förster and Wiese, 1954). The gamones are inactivated by high temperature; however, the thermostability of female gamones proved to be much greater than that of the male. In the case of *Chlamydomonas eugametos* this difference is clearly demonstrated in the experiments of Förster and Wiese (1954), which are set out in the following Table IV:

TABLE IV

The effect of high temperatures on the inactivation of male and female gamones of Chlamydomonas eugametos (*Förster and Wiese, 1954*)

Temperature	Time (in minutes) till loss of activity	
	♂ filtrate	♀ filtrate
30°	300	..
35°	180	..
40°	60	..
50°	< 10	..
60°	..	90
80°	..	20
90°	..	8
100°	..	< 3

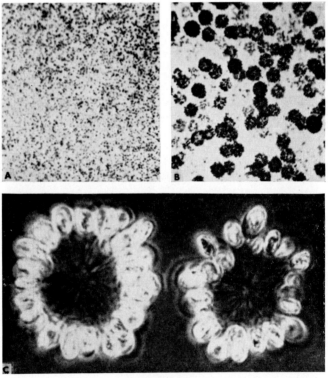

FIG. 228. Agglutination of ♂ gametes in *Chlamydomonas eugametos* on addition of filtrate of ♀ gametes to the medium.

(*A*), (*B*) general view: (*A*) without filtrate, (*B*) with filtrate; (*C*) two groups of gametes with flagella directed to centre, highly magnified. Living objects. Phase contrast. (After Hartmann, 1956.)

Female gamones are also more resistant than male ones to the action of different acids. They also differ in their response to light. Thus female gamones are active both in the dark and in the light, whereas a male gamone apparently requires light for its activation (Förster and Wiese, 1954).

In a series of works, Moewus (1938, 1940, and others) asserted that the gamones of *Chlamydomonas* are derivatives of crocein, namely esters of crocetin dimethyl. The male or female tendency of the gametes is determined by the ratio of the cis- and trans- forms of this ester. In its turn, this ratio changes with the duration and strength of the illumination, blue and violet rays being especially active.

However, these concepts of Moewus, developed by him in the course of a number of years in a long series of works, have not been confirmed by later authors, and many of his experiments supporting his concept could not be reproduced by other investigators. Therefore there are at present good reasons for rejecting the biochemical concepts of Moewus (Hartmann, 1956) regarding the nature and interrelationship of male and female gamones.

There is reason to believe (see Hartmann, 1956) that the gamones are substances of a glycoproteid nature.

The genotypic sex-determination in haplophase (during the transition from diplo- to haplophase) was proved for many Phytomonadina, both solitary and colonial. It probably also occurs in other Protozoa, though in many groups this question remains insufficiently investigated. According to the investigations of Cleveland (1951) genotypic sex-determination occurs in some Hypermastigina from the alimentary tract of *Cryptocercus*. For instance, in *Urinympha* two nuclei, differing morphologically from each other, are formed as a result of one-division meiosis. In one of them the centrosome is retained while in the second it is resorbed. Eventually autogamy takes place and the two nuclei fuse. In this case differentiation of the sexual nuclei—not of the gametes—takes place and it is connected with reduction division, and so we can speak of the genetic determination of sexual differences.

The problem regarding the mechanism of sex-determination in gregarines and Coccidia has not yet been solved. As we have seen, within these large groups zygotic reduction is observed. Whether this is accompanied by a segregation of genes determining the sexual differences remains obscure. Experimental evidence on this question would require the production of a progeny from a single sporozoite. In the case of genotypic sex-determination, gametocytes and gametes of only one sex should develop in such a progeny. Such an experiment, however, is most difficult to carry out. Infection with one oocyst (which has been produced on many occasions) cannot provide an answer to the mechanism of the sex-determination, since each oocyst is the result of the development of a zygote and, consequently, in the case of genotypic sex-determination it should contain a 1:1 ratio of sporozoites with opposite sexual tendencies.

However, Reyer (1937) carried out an investigation on the Coccidium *Barrouxia schneideri*, which supports the genotypic sex-determination in Coccidia. In this species, parasitic in the alimentary tract of the myriapod *Lithobius*, the spores contain only one sporozoite. Reyer infected *Lithobius* with a single spore, and found that in all such cases no oocysts were formed, which indicated the absence of fertilization. However, when the myriapod was infected by two or three spores, they sometimes developed into oocysts, which was probably due to the presence of sporozoites possessing opposite sexual tendencies.

Some authors, who studied the morphology of the life-cycle of Coccidia, described two categories of schizonts, which were regarded as a manifestation of sexual differentiation. Schizonts differing morphologically eventually give rise to sexual cells of opposite sexes. For instance, Hosoda (1928) described this kind of differentiation in *Isospora lacazei* from the alimentary tract of passerine birds, and Ray (1930) in *Dorisiella scolelepis* from the polychaete worm *Scolelepis fuliginosa*. The latter author describes a particularly clearly marked differentiation of schizonts. Some of them, which are large, producing 40–50 merozoites, represent female individuals, and eventually develop into macrogametes; the others, which are much smaller and produce only eight merozoites, develop into microgametes. However, the majority of authors who studied the life-cycles of Coccidia do not associate the observed morphological differences among schizonts and merozoites with their sexual differentiation. It is conceivable that the difference in the structure of schizonts and merozoites corresponds to various asexual generations of the endogenous part of the cycle, as was shown, for instance, by Chejsin (1947) for various species of *Eimeria* parasitic in rabbits. However, the existence of genotypic sex-determination in Coccidia is contradicted by some facts, such as the differences in the number of macrogametes and microgametocytes. The number of macrogametes usually considerably exceeds that of the microgametocytes. In cases of genotypic sex-determination one would expect the ratio between them to be 1:1. Finally, Grell (1953) proved experimentally the existence of phenotypic sex-determination in *Eucoccidium dinophili* (for details see below).

It is clear from the foregoing that the question of the mechanism of sex-determination in Sporozoa is still obscure, and requires further investigation. We believe that it is conceivable, on analogy with what is observed in Mastigophora, that some species of Sporozoa possess a genotypic (during haplophase) and others a phenotypic (modificatory) mechanism of sex-determination.

We can now consider the phenotypic (modificatory) sex-determination in the haplophase. In the process of haplo-modificatory sex-determination sex is not determined directly by definite genes, but depends on the external conditions under which the gametes develop. These conditions may either be created directly by the abiotic factors of the environment or be determined by some internal conditions within the organism itself, which are nevertheless external in relation to the gametes. Therefore haplo-modificatory sex-determination is characterized by the absence of genotypic differences between the gametes, whereas the presence of such differences is characteristic of haplogenotypic sex-determination. In gametes, according to Hartmann, bisexual by nature (for theory of bisexuality see below) the inhibition of one of the sexual tendencies in genotypic sex-determination is brought about by special genes, while in the modificatory type (phenotypic) it depends on the conditions under which the gametes develop. However, in both cases, mature gametes capable of copulation manifest phenotypically only one sexual tendency, and are sexually differentiated. Among Phytomonadina genotypic or modificatory sex-determination is sometimes encountered among allied species of the same genus. In some cases even within the limits of one species there are different strains, some of which possess genotypic and other modificatory sex-determination, as, for example, among *Polytoma uvella* and among some species of *Chlamydomonas* (Moewus, 1935; Hartmann, 1956).

In contrast to the haplogenotypic, in haplo-modificatory sex-determination copulation of the gametes may take place within the limits of one clone. Examples of this are provided by a number of species of Phytomonadina— *Stephanosphaera pluvialis, Chlamydomonas monoica, Haematococcus pluvialis,*and others.

The formation of the so-called residual gametes ('Restgameten') in the case of haplo-modificatory sex-determination provides evidence that copulating gametes have opposite sexual tendencies. This phenomenon can be summarized as follows: after copulation and the formation of zygotes a certain number of 'unused' gametes are usually left over within the clone. These 'residual gametes' are incapable of copulating with each other because they possess an identical sexual tendency, i.e. they belong to the same sex. This can be easily proved by the addition of gametes of the opposite sex to the 'residual gametes', after which the clumping reaction and copulation takes place immediately. The mechanism of the haplo-modificatory sex-determination is apparently much less 'precise', and does not ensure the ratio of 1 : 1 between the gametes of opposite sexual tendencies, as in the case of haplogenotypic determination. The influence of the environmental factors which determine the realization of one or another sexual tendency is more or less fortuitous, so that gametes of opposite sexes are formed in different numerical ratios. As a result, some of them are found lacking partners ('residual'). Residual gametes are also observed in the case of genotypic sex-determination, when for some reason the numbers of gametes of opposite sexes coming into contact with each other are not equal.

Haplo-modificatory sex-determination occurs in different groups of Protozoa, but this question has by no means been sufficiently studied in all groups. As already stated, this form of sex-determination occurs in some Phytomonadina. Moreover, according to Cleveland's investigations (1956a) among the Mastigophora, it is observed in a number of species of haploid Hypermastigida from *Cryptocercus*. Thus, in *Trichonympha*, whose cycle of development has been described in detail above, meiosis and reduction take place during the first division of the zygote, whereas the differentiation of the male and female gametes occurs during division of the haploid gametocyte (Fig. 176), which is not accompanied by a reduction of chromosomes, and therefore cannot lead to genotypic differences between the nuclei of the gametes. However, any differences between the gametes that do arise are due only to the modificatory determination of sex.

Modificatory (phenotypic) sex-determination is widespread among Foraminifera, as shown by the numerous investigations of Le Calvez and Grell (see below). For example, in *Patellina corrugata* the gamonts uniting in syzygy (Fig. 241) have different sexual tendencies and give rise to iso-gametes of different sexes. Since different numbers of gamonts, often uneven, may unite in syzygy, gametes of opposite sexual tendencies are formed in unequal numbers, as a result of which a considerable number of 'residual gametes' are usually left over after copulation. These 'unused' residual gametes are later phagocytosed by zygotes which give rise to agamonts. As regards sex-determination in Foraminifera, it is interesting to note that opposite sexual tendencies make their appearance long before the formation of gametes, namely in the gamonts, which unite into syzygy. Hence, it is evident that the phenotypic manifestation of sexual differences may occur at different phases of the life-cycle, and not only immediately during the formation of gametes.

Grell (1953) has conclusively demonstrated that among Sporozoa haplo-modificatory sex-determination occurs in *Eucoccidium dinophili*, a peculiar Coccidium, devoid of schizogony, whose cycle of development will be discussed below (Fig. 245). In *Eucoccidium*, as in all Coccidia, reduction is zygotic. If sex-determination in this case were haplogenotypic half of the developing spores would give rise to macrogametes, when introduced into a new individual host, and half to microgametes.

Grell has carried out numerous experiments on the infection of *Dinophilus* by one spore (sporocyst). In such cases only macrogametes were always produced in the host (from one to six, depending on the number of sporozoites that underwent further development). Macrogametes produced from a single spore later developed parthenogenetically without fertilization (Fig. 229), giving rise, as in ordinary sporogony, to numerous spores, and secreting an oocyst membrane. A peculiarity of the parthenogenetic development of oocysts is the absence of reduction division, which usually takes place when the oocysts are formed from a zygote. Thus the sporogony of an unfertilized macrogamete can be regarded as haploid parthenogenesis. If such parthenogenetically produced oocysts are used to reinfect *Dinophilus* (the infection this time being massive, since more than a hundred spores with six sporozoites in each develop in each oocyst), then both macro- and microgametes will develop from them. Since only one spore was used in the original inoculation, the development of the macro- and microgametes

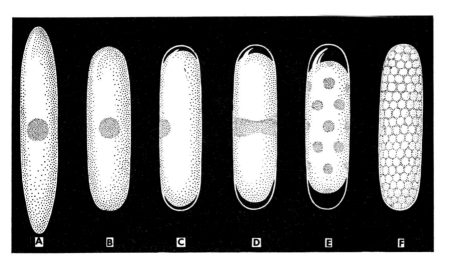

FIG. 229. Parthenogenesis of *Eucoccidium dinophili* (Sporozoa). Observation of living macrogamonts in reflected light. (*A–F*), successive stages of sporogony. (After Grell, 1953*b*.)

provides conclusive evidence of haplo-modificatory sex-determination. The question arises as to why microgametes do not develop during the original infection of *Dinophilus* with one spore. As has been shown by Grell, this is due to the fact that microgametes develop only in the case of massive infection of the host, whereas in the case of scanty infection (as that produced by one spore) it is always only macrogametes that develop.

It is possible that haplo-modificatory sex-determination also occurs in certain gregarines. Thus Weschenfelder (1938), who studied the cycle of development of *Actinocephalus parvus*, observed the formation of syzygy from three gamonts. Since in this case the presence of a large number of residual gametes was not observed, he suggested that it represented an instance of modificatory sex-determination.

In contrast to what was said above regarding sex-determination in Foraminifera, where it occurs at the gametocycle stage, it has to be assumed that in *Actinocephalus* sex-determination occurs later—during the process of gametogenesis itself. In any case, so far no experimental data has appeared in the literature providing a solution of the question concerning the form of sex-determination in gregarines.

Haplo-modificatory sex-determination occurs in ciliates, in which in the process of conjugation or autogamy meiosis (see Chapter VII) takes place during the first two divisions of the micronucleus. The haploid nucleus undergoes the third division, leading to the separation of the male and female pronuclei, and this division represents the usual equation mitosis. Thus both pronuclei derived as a result of the third division are geno-typically identical; nevertheless, one of them becomes a migratory male nucleus, the other a stationary female one. Evidently this represents the phenotypic (modificatory) sex-determination. It is possible that the direction in which the pronuclei develop depends on their position in the body of the conjugating ciliates. In some of them, in spite of the modificatory character of sex-determination, important morphological differences are observed between the male and female pronuclei (for example in Ento-diniomorpha).

In ciliates another peculiar type of differentiation of the conjugants is observed—namely the 'mating types'. However, in our opinion, this phenomenon is not directly associated with sex-determination and should be regarded as a special type of intraspecific relationships which occur in bisexual hermaphrodite organisms as a kind of 'superstructure' over sexuality. This phenomenon was considered in a separate chapter.

In a relatively small number of Protozoa modificatory (phenotypic) sex-determination occurs in the diplophase. In these cases the opposite sexual tendencies arise under the influence of environmental factors at the diploid stage of development, before meiosis. *Actinophrys sol*, whose cycle of development has been extensively studied by Bělǎr (1922), provides an example of this type of sex-determination. In this Heliozoon the sexual process proceeds, as shown above, in the form of a paedogamy. An encysting individual of *Actinophrys* produces by mitotic equation division two cells that are evidently genetically identical, but one of them is differentiated into a male and the other into a female gametocyte. The former produces pseudo-podia directed towards the female individual. After meiosis, which takes place in both gametocytes, these are transformed into gametes, which afterwards copulate. The unequal division (resembling budding), which takes place in ciliates of the order Peritricha during the formation of macro- and microconjugants, should probably be regarded as phenotypic determination of sexual differences. Sex-determination in some diploid Hypermastigida from the alimentary tract of *Cryptocercus* (for instance in *Notila proteus*, according to Cleveland, 1950c) probably conforms to this type.

If we turn for comparison to the mechanism of sex-determination in multicellular animals and plants, it will be recalled that in an overwhelming majority of cases among them genotypic sex-determination takes place during the diplophase. Sex is determined at the moment of fertilization and depends on the differences in the combination of sexual chromosomes (heterochromosomes) and their relation to the autosome complex.

This scheme is well known from textbooks of general biology and genetics, therefore it need not be dealt with in this book except to emphasize the difference between the genotypic sex-determination in multicellular organisms as compared with Protozoa. In multicellular organisms the sex of the embryo is determined at the moment of fertilization, whereas in Protozoa, in haplogenetic determination of sex, the appearance of sexual differences is associated with the moment of reduction, during transition from diplophase to haplophase. As regards genotypic determination in diplophase, such cases are so far unknown among Protozoa.

The phenomenon of relative sexuality discovered by Hartmann (1925) throws important light on the nature of sexual differences. This phenomenon was first discovered and studied in brown algae (*Ectocarpus siliculosis*) and then detected in other groups of lower plants (in various groups of algae and fungi) and in Phytomonadina. Among the latter relative sexuality was studied in detail by Moewus (1939). Variations of the activity of the sexual reaction have been observed in diverse species and races of algae and Protozoa. In some cases it is manifested almost immediately after the union of the gametes of different sexes, and is represented by a vigorous formation of large groups of gametes, composed of hundreds of cells which later break up into separate pairs. In other cases the reaction proceeds less vigorously, and agglutination leads to the formation of comparatively small groups of cells. In the case of weak sexual reaction, the formation of groups of cells does not take place at all and the reaction is manifested only in copulation of gametes in pairs. Hartmann used the term 'comparative sexuality' to denote the presence of sexual differences within one sex, representing differences in the vigour of the sex in question. This difference in the vigour of gametes is sometimes called their valency and can be indicated by conventional units. In extreme cases, when the difference in vigour (valency) of gametes of the same sex is very great, copulation between them becomes possible. In this case the copulation takes place between weak and the strong gametes of the same sex.

Hartmann sees in the phenomenon of relative sexuality one of the chief proofs of his theory of sexuality. According to this theory, all organisms, as well as the gametes, possess a bisexual potentiality, represented by factors determining the development of the characteristics of the male or female sex. However, one of these potentialities is not manifested phenotypically, but is present in a cryptic (recessive) state. In the case of genotypic determination it is suppressed by definite genes; in phenotypic (modificatory) determination by the conditions of the development of the gametes. In this case the genotype of all the gametes remains the same, carrying the genes of both sexes.

The degree of the phenotypic manifestation (vigour or valency) of the sexual characters may vary. The accomplishment of copulation between gametes with opposite sexual characters requires a definite quantitative

difference between these properties. If it is great, the reaction proceeds
vigorously; when it is smaller, but still sufficient, the reaction is weak.
When a very 'strong' and very 'weak' gamete of the same sex unite, the
difference in sexual tendencies is found to be sufficient for copulation. This
demonstrates the existence of opposite sexual tendencies (bisexuality) in
gametes of the same sex. Hartmann's scheme explaining the nature of the
phenomenon of relative sexuality and of the varying valency of the gametes

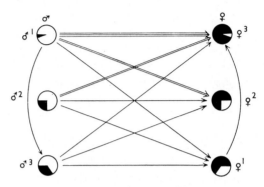

Fig. 230. Diagram illustrating the bisexuality and relative sexuality
of gametes.

White-coloured male, black-coloured female, substance in gametes: on
the left different types of male, on the right, female gametes. Lines with
arrows indicate a positive reaction, which is strong in the case of triple
lines, average in the case of double ones, and weak in the case of single
ones. Gametes, towards which the sharp end of the arrows point, behave
as females in relation to those from which the arrows point away. (After
Hartmann, 1925.)

is given in Fig. 230. Female sexual substances (gamones) are represented
in the scheme in black, and male ones in white, and their interrelationship
in various types of gametes. The arrows of different thicknesses represent
the vigour of the sexual reaction.

According to Hartmann, there are three main bases, or as he calls them
laws, of his theory of sexuality: (1) the law of general bipolar bisexuality;
(2) the law of general bisexual potentiality; and (3) the law of comparative
vigour of sexual determination.

The first rule recognizes the existence in all organisms, possessing sexual
reproduction, of only two sexes—male and female. The second rule postulates the presence in every organism and gamete of bisexual potentiality.
According to the third rule, the strength of the degree of sexual potentiality
may vary quantitatively. The main evidence supporting Hartmann's theory
of sexuality has already been mentioned above.

It should be noted, however, that some criticism has been raised against
the basic concepts of Hartmann's hypothesis. Some authors (Czurda, 1933a,
b; Mainx, 1933; Pringsheim and Ondratschek, 1939) denied the existence

of sexual differentiation of isogametes and associated their capacity to copulate merely with a definite degree of maturity. However, in our opinion these objections are not sufficiently substantiated from the purely factual point of view. Since the publication of these works considerable new factual material has accumulated confirming the main positions of Hartmann's theory. It should also be emphasized that Hartmann's theory of sexuality is in agreement with recent data on the genetics of sex in higher animals and plants, where, since the well-known works of Correns, Goldschmidt, Bridges, and others, the concept of potential bisexuality, and of the presence of hereditary factors of the opposite sex in the genotype system of every dioecius organism, has been well established.

In his large work on problems of sexuality Hartmann considers in detail the probable genetic schemes of various types of sex-determination. However, we do not propose to deal with the genetic aspects of his theory here.

VIII

LIFE-CYCLES OF PROTOZOA

THE life-cycles of Protozoa have been studied by many zoologists, but have so far not been sufficiently investigated. First of all, it is necessary to define what is meant by a life-cycle. In most cases this term denotes the combination of consecutive stages of development of the individual taking place during a period between two definite moments. One of these is arbitrarily taken as the initial, the other as the final moment, after which the life-cycle is resumed. In multicellular organisms it is considered that the cycle begins with the laying of the egg by the maternal individual and lasts till the formation of an egg by the daughter individual, after the organisms have passed through a series of intermediate morphologically and ecologically distinct phases. This life-cycle may be further complicated by periodical interpolation of asexual reproduction; moreover, any cycle proceeds in a definite medium and therefore its occurrence and duration are closely associated with changes in diverse environmental factors, including the seasonal factor, which frequently influences the life-cycle.

In Protozoa the processes of reproduction are invariably cyclical and, in distinction from the Metazoa, the vegetative individual reproduction itself by the agamous method should be regarded as the initial stage of the cycle. This is because all Protozoa possess this type of reproduction, whereas the sexual process has so far not been found in all forms, and in some cases it only rarely interrupts the asexual reproduction. In Protozoa asexual reproduction, unlike that in Metazoa, is not as it were complementary to the sexual process, but constitutes a leading phase in the life-cycle, in that it determines the numerical strength of the species. Some Protozoa reproduce only asexually and this apparently represents their primary method of multiplication.

The question arises whether continuous asexual reproduction, uninterrupted by a sexual process, can be regarded as cyclical, and whether one may speak of a life-cycle in the case of those Protozoa which reproduce themselves only by the agamous method? This would seem to be fully justified, since a series of agamous reproductions taking place one after another corresponds to a series of successive generations of a given Protozoon. This is particularly clear in the case of multiple division among Sporozoa and Foraminifera, where the separate agamous generations of the same species differ essentially in their morphology. Moreover, in the interval between two divisions Protozoa undergo a whole series of physiological changes, while in ciliates and flagellates each division is accompanied by a reconstruction of the whole locomotor apparatus and of some other organoids.

Thus in species of Protozoa reproducing by the agamous method cyclical modifications do take place. They are even more pronounced in those Protozoa in which sexual and asexual reproduction alternate.

However, the life-cycle of Protozoa undoubtedly represents a more complex phenomenon than the mere combination of successive stages of development occurring between two definite moments. This process could, properly speaking, be called the *cycle of development* of the Protozoon. The simplest cycle of development is represented by a continuous change of generations reproducing themselves by the asexual method. More complicated cycles of development are characterized by an alternation of generations reproducing themselves by different methods. This alternation may be either optional or obligatory in different groups of Protozoa. However, in reality every cycle of a free-living or parasitic Protozoon has developed historically under the closest influence of its environment and at the present time it takes place under definite conditions. Hence the life-cycle of Protozoa should be regarded as the cycle of development of the species affected under the actual environmental conditions. In order to understand it, the Protozoa must be studied under the natural conditions of its habitat in the course of the whole year in order to observe the influence of seasonal changes upon the cycle.

Such investigations of life-cycles under natural conditions, especially when seasonal changes are taken into account, are comparatively rare. In this respect parasitic organisms have been studied better than free-living ones. In the case of parasitic organisms the effect of the organism of the host, representing their primary environment upon life-cycles, has been established, and the significance of the secondary environment, i.e. of that which the host itself inhabits, has been elucidated.

In some cases, when the cycle of development of the Protozoon is strictly fixed in time, as in some Sporozoa, the concepts of the life-cycle and of the cycle of development practically coincide. We shall therefore consider these processes together. In other cases we shall first deal with the separate types of the cycles of development and then examine life-cycles as they occur under natural conditions.

I. *Cycle of development with asexual reproduction*

In Protozoa the most primitive cycle of development is the one in which there is asexual reproduction only and no alternation of generations reproducing by different methods is observed. The continuously repeated division of free-living, naked, or shelled amoebae or of some representatives of the order Euglenida can be regarded as examples of such a primitive cycle. Moreover, it should be noted that the individuality of the unicellular organism is preserved throughout each fission, and, as long as the external conditions remain stable, there are no morphological differences in the series of continuously dividing individuals.

It is quite possible that in some parasitic flagellates, for example in Polymastigida and Hypermastigida from termites and in Trypanosomidae, the repeated asexual reproduction by longitudinal division (monotomy) represents a primary phenomenon. Among Trypanosomidae, *Trypanosoma equiperdum*, the causative agent of dourine in horses, reproduces itself by continuous division, in the course of which it retains the same structural type. It should be noted, however, that the simplicity of this cycle is the result of a simplification of the more complex cycle characteristic of other Trypanosomidae, in which sexual reproduction is absent. *T. equiperdum* is transmitted from host to host by contact, and, as will be shown below, there is every reason to regard this development as a shortened cycle of the development of digenetic trypanosomes. The cycle of development of *T. evansi* is also simple, except that in this species horse-flies serve as vectors in the transmission of the trypanosomes among their vertebrate hosts: the trypanosomes are transmitted from one host to another mechanically by the bite of the vector. Moreover, the trypanosomes undergo no changes, and their multiplication by longitudinal division is not complicated by any other processes.

In many Trypanosomidae the continuous asexual reproduction may be complicated by the fact that during the process of division the type of structure of the flagellate undergoes periodical modifications. Thus, during one method of reproduction there is an alternation of morphological types, which usually succeed each other in a definite order. Sometimes this alternation of morphological types is associated also with an alternation of different forms of asexual reproduction, for instance of monotomic and multiple division.

In monogenetic Trypanosomidae of the genera *Leptomonas*, *Crithidia*, and *Herpetomonas*, which are chiefly parasitic in the alimentary tract of insects, the following alternation of morphological forms takes place. Genus *Leptomonas* has the simplest method of development: in *L. culicis* (Fig. 231) the preflagellate leishmanial form from the mosquito larva apparently first reproduces by multiple fission; but when the larva is transformed into the pupa, the parasites pass into the leptomonad stage with a free flagellum, whose starting-point is in the anterior end of the body. This form reproduces itself by fission in the alimentary tract of an adult mosquito. In its hind gut they are again transformed into the leishmanial form, which becomes encysted and is voided into the water with the faeces of the host, where the cysts are again swallowed by the larvae of the mosquito and the cycle is repeated.

In *Crithidia*, from the intestine of water bugs, fleas, and other insects, the preflagellate leishmanial forms reproduce themselves by monotomic or multiple division, after which they are transformed into crithidial forms, whose flagellum starts from a blepharoplast situated near the nucleus. They reproduce themselves by the monotomic method. The crithidial forms are localized either in the stomach or the hind gut of the insect. Leptomonad forms are sometimes also encountered among them (Fig. 232).

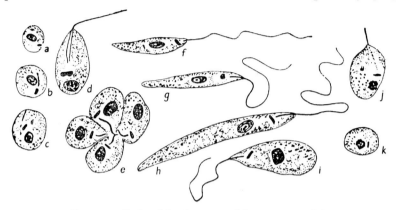

FIG. 231. Cycle of development of *Leptomonas culicis*.

(a) pre-flagellate stage; (b), (c), same; growth and formation of flagella; (d) early flagellate stage, beginning of division; (e) same, showing multiple division; (f)–(h) typical leptomonad forms; (i), (j) transition to post-flagellate stage, reduction of flagella; (k) post-flagellate stage (cyst). (After Patton, from Hoare, 1925.)

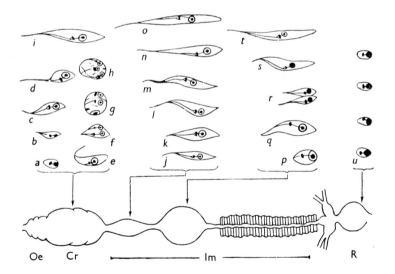

FIG. 232. Cycle of development in *Crithidia euryophthalmi* in the gut of the bug *Euryophthalmus convivus*.

(a)–(i) forms from crop: (a) infective cyst; (g)–(h) somatelles; (j)–(t) various forms from gut; (u) cysts from rectum. Oe, oesophagus; Cr, crop; R, rectum. (After Grassé, 1952.)

In the hind-gut the flagellate forms are transformed into leishmanial ones which give rise to cysts.

Finally, in *Herpetomonas* the cycle also includes the trypanosome stage, in which the flagellum starts from a blepharoplast situated in the posterior end of the body. In *H. muscarum*, from the alimentary tract of various flies, the pre-flagellate stage in the anterior part of the alimentary tract is first transformed into the leptomonad stage, and then into the crithidial and trypanosome stages. In the hind-gut the latter stage is transformed into the leishmanial one, which encysts.

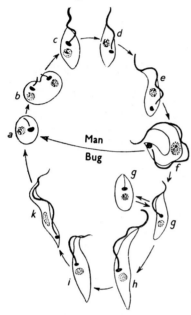

FIG. 233. Cycle of development of *Trypanosoma cruzi*.

(*a*)–(*f*) development in man: (*a*)–(*b*) leishmanial forms; (*c*)–(*d*) crithidial forms; (*e*)–(*f*) trypanosome forms from peripheral blood; (*g*)–(*k*) development in Reduvüd bug; (*g*)–(*i*) crithidial forms; (*k*) metacyclic trypanosome from rectum. (From Hoare, 1949.)

A similar change of morphological forms with an alternation of diverse modes of asexual reproduction is also observed in digenetic trypanosomes.

Such cyclical changes are observed not only in different periods of life within the same host, but also occur regularly when the hosts are changed. For example, *T. cruzi*, which causes Chagas' disease in man in South America, lives in the blood in the non-reproducing trypanosome stage. The trypanosomes periodically disappear from the blood and penetrate into different cells of the reticulo-endothelial system or into the muscle cells, where they lose their flagellum and assume the leishmanial form. In that stage they multiply by binary fission. Then the leishmanial forms become elongated and are transformed into crithidial forms; the latter divide, giving rise to trypanosome forms, which again find their way into the blood (Fig. 233). In the alimentary tract of the vector (various triatomine bugs) the trypanosomes again acquire the crithidial form, and then in the hind-gut they are transformed into metacyclic trypanosomes, which are transmitted to the vertebrate host by faecal contamination, when the cycle is resumed with the formation of leishmanial forms.

In *T. lewisi*, parasitic in the blood of rats, multiple fission is often included in the monotomic cycle during different periods of life, both in the blood of rats and the alimentary tract of the flea vector (Fig. 234). In the rat it takes place during the first 8–9 days after contamination. Multiplication proceeds in crithidial forms which divide repeatedly without fission of the cytoplasm, with the result that a complex (somatella) with many nuclei, kinetoplasts, and flagella is formed. This complex eventually divides into a corresponding number of trypanosomes, which persist in the blood for a long time without undergoing division. When ingested by a flea with the rat's blood, the trypanosomes penetrate into the epithelial cells of

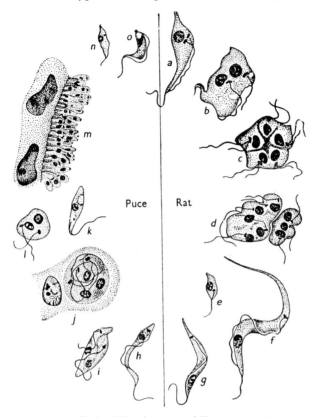

FIG. 234. Cycle of development of *Trypanosoma lewisi*.

(a)–(d) multiplication in rat's blood; (e) crithidial form, originating from somatella;(f)–(g) typical blood form; (h) trypanosome from gut of flea; (i) division in insect gut; (j) multiple division in epithelial cell; (k) crithidial stage; (l) its division; (m) crithidial stages in rectum of flea; (n), (o) transformation of crithidial stage into metacyclic trypanosome in rectum of flea. (After Grassé, 1952.)

the stomach, where they reproduce themselves by multiple fission; the daughter individuals emerge into the lumen of the intestine, and in the rectum they are transformed into crithidial forms, and finally into metacyclic trypanosomes.

An alternation of monotomic and multiple fission was observed in *Trichomonas augusta* (Kofoid, 1941) from the alimentary tract of frogs. Binary fission is predominant in the cycle of this flagellate, but it is sometimes interrupted by the formation of eight or sixteen cellular somatells

with a common cytoplasm, where each individual possesses a complete set
of organoids. These somatells give rise, by consecutive plasmotomy, to free
flagellates, which continue to multiply by monotomic fission. Here, as in
trypanosomes, there is no fixed alternation of forms of multiplication, and
the transition from one method of reproduction to another is probably
controlled by factors in the environment. In any case, in trypanosomes the

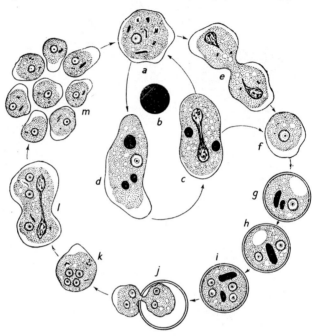

FIG. 235. Cycle of development in *Entamoeba histolytica* in man.

(a) 'minuta' form from lumen of gut; (b), (c) tissue forms of amoebae which have
ingested erythrocytes; (d) erythrocyte; (e) division of amoeba; (f) precystic amoeba;
(g)–(i) cysts; (j) excystment; (k) excysted 4-nucleate amoeba; (l) 8 uninucleate
amoebae; (m) 8 amoebulae resulting from (k), (l) which found their way into the large
intestine. (After Hoare, 1949.)

alternation of hosts or of changes in their habitat within the same host
are accompanied by modification of morphological types and of forms of
agamous reproduction.

The alternation of monotomic and multiple fission is sometimes associated with the process of encystment. In various parasitic amoebae, for instance in *Entamoeba coli* and *E. histolytica*, the tropozoites in the alimentary
tract of the host may multiply by monotomic fission for a long time; but
periodically, as a result of a similar division, small precystic individuals
are formed, which become rounded, accumulate reserve nutrient substances, and then encyst (Fig. 235). The nucleus in such cysts divides
successively into four or eight nuclei. Such mature cysts are discharged

with the faeces into the external medium, where they do not undergo any further changes, apart from the utilization of the reserve nutrient substances. When a cyst is ingested by the appropriate host the multinucleate amoeba excysts and divides into small amoebae corresponding to the number of nuclei. The cycle of development is then repeated (Fig. 235).

Among the flagellates a similar alternation of different forms of agamous reproduction with the formation of cysts is observed in Chrysomonadina, Cryptomonadina, and many Euglenida and some Diplomonadina, &c.

II. *Cycles of development with alternating sexual process and asexual reproduction*

Such cycles are frequently encountered in all classes of Protozoa. Hartmann (1929) distinguishes a primary alternation of generations, i.e. the alternation of a sexual generation with one that reproduces itself by separate asexual cells or agametes, and a secondary one, when sexual reproduction alternates with vegetative reproduction, i.e. reproduction by means of multicellular structures, or by parthenogenesis. The first type is encountered in unicellular organisms, the second in Metazoa. The most essential moment in the alternation of generations is the change of nuclear phases at different stages of the cycle, i.e. alternation of diploid and haploid phases of the nuclei, regardless of whether it occurs in the zygote, or at the maturation of the gamete, or, lastly, during agamous cytogony.

As has been stated above, the changes in nuclear phases are associated with reduction division. The alternation of generations may be homophasic with zygotic or gametic reduction, or heterophasic, with an intermediate reduction during the formation of agametes. In zygotic reduction all the stages of the cycle, except the zygote, are haploid, whereas in gametic reduction all stages, except gametes, are diploid. In the third case, the gamonts are haploid and the agamonts diploid.

A. *Homophasic alternation of generations with zygotic reduction*

The cycle with zygotic reduction may be regarded as the most typical and widespread among the Protozoa. Many flagellates and the majority of Sporozoa develop according to this type.

In flagellates of the order Phytomonadina the alternation of the generations has an optional character. In fact, agamous reproduction of Chlamidomonads may continue for a long time without a transition to sexual reproduction. The formation of gametes, their copulation and the formation of the zygote occurs, as has been noted by Klebs (1896), only under unfavourable conditions of life. Those vegetative individuals, which under favourable conditions of nutrition, light, and temperature divide longitudinally, diminish considerably in size when conditions deteriorate, and become gametes. If they are transferred into a nutritive solution, they may develop parthenogenetically without copulation; otherwise, when there is a deficiency of nutritive substances, zygotes are formed after copulation, which encyst and produce four or eight vegetative individuals by division. These in their turn proceed to agamous cytogony.

A similar alternation of generations is observed in higher colonial phyto-monods of the family Volvocidae, in whose life-cycle a protracted agamous reproduction is predominant. In experiments with *Eudorina* this colonial flagellate was successfully cultivated for months without the onset of sexual reproduction (Hartmann, 1921).

In parasitic Protozoa a tendency to stabilize the cycle of development, by timing the alternation of generations, is observed. This is particularly evident in Coccidia, among which in many representatives of the suborder Eimeriidea the alternation of generations may be regarded as being firmly fixed (Tyzzer, 1929; Chejsin, 1939, 1940, 1947). The majority of Sporozoa, developing either in the same host or with an alternation of hosts, are characterized by agamous reproduction by schizogony followed by a sexual process (gamogony), which terminates in fertilization of the macrogamete and the formation of an encysted zygote. The subsequent metagamous division of the zygote, known as sporogony, leads to the formation of various numbers of sporozoites (from eight to many hundreds) which serve for the propagation of the parasite. When they infect new hosts, the cycle of development is resumed (Figs. 196, 199). This cycle of development occurs in members of the order Adeleida and the order Coccidiida, of the subclass Coccidiomorpha, as well as in the order Schizogregarinida of the subclass Gregarina (Fig. 236).

While in free-living flagellates asexual reproduction may be repeated many times without the intervention of a sexual process, in Sporozoa, in particular in members of the suborder Eimeriidea, the number of agamous generations is in most cases strictly limited. This was established experi-mentally by a single inoculation of the host with sporulated oocysts and by protecting it against spontaneous reinfection. As a result it was demon-strated for the Coccidia of fowls, rats, rabbits, dogs, cattle, and some other animals that the number of agamous generations reproducing by schizo-gony does not exceed five. More frequently three generations are produced (for instance in *E. tenella*, *E. brunetti*, *E. necatrix* from fowls, *E. meleagrimitis* from turkeys, *E. seperata* and *E. miyairii* from rats, *E. media* and *E. intesti-nalis* from rabbits, &c.), more rarely two (for instance in *E. praecox* from fowls, *Isospora delos* from cats, and others), or four (*E. nieschulzi* from rats, *E. irresidua* and *E. piriformis* from rabbits). In *E. magna* from the rabbit, five generations are produced (Chejsin, 1947); on the other hand, *E. bovis* produces only one generation of very large schizonts (up to 425 μ in diameter), which give rise to thousands of merozoites (up to 170,000) (Hammond, Bowman, Davis, Simens, 1946).

In cases when there are more than two agamous generations, part of the merozoites of the second generation (or the third, when there are five generations) and all the merozoites of the last generation (three to five), which are often referred to as telomerozoites, are transformed into gamonts after penetrating into the epithelial cells of the alimentary tract, and the process of gamogony starts. For instance, in *E. magna*, which produces

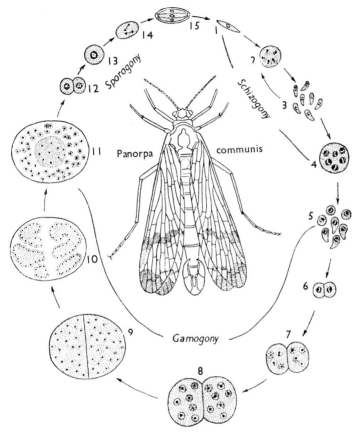

FIG. 236. Life-cycle of *Lipocystis polyspora* (Schizogregarinida) in fat-body of *Panorpa communis*. (From Grell, 1956a.)

The oocyst gains entrance to the gut of the host. 1, sporozoite in intestinal epithelium; 2, schizont; 3, merozoites; 4, schizont in tissues of fat-body; 5, merozoites with large nuclei, which are transformed into gamonts; 6, union of gamonts; 7–9, growth of gamonts and nuclear division; 10, formation of gametes; 11, copulation of isogametes and formation of residual body within gamontocyst; 12, copulation of gametes; 13, zygote; 14, metagamous division; 15, oocyst with 8 sporozoites.

five agamous generations in the alimentary tract of rabbits, a small number of merozoites of the third generation undergo gamogony, while others become schizonts of the next agamous generation; the majority of mero-zoites of the fourth generation become gamonts and the whole of the fifth generation is transformed into gamonts. When two generations are present only the last one is transformed into gamonts.

Thus in Eimeriidea agamous reproduction is self-limited. The same probably occurs in Adeleida, thus *Adelina deronis* from the coelome of oligochaetes produces only two generations of schizonts, the second being entirely transformed into gamonts.

The duration of each generation of schizonts usually varies from 12–18 to 48 hours. Only in a few species does it last longer: for instance, in *E. bovis* it probably lasts 12–17 days.

Gamogony lasting 24–28 hours ends in the formation of oocysts which are discharged from the organism of the host into the external medium. As a rule, in the presence of free oxygen sporogony takes place in the oocysts, leading to the production of spores (the number of which varies with the species), within each of which sporozoites are formed. Sporozoites are rarely formed directly in the oocyst itself (sub-family Cryptosporidiinae). A few species, e.g. *E. subepithelialis* and *E. carpelli* from the alimentary tract of cyprinoid fish, *Isospora bigeminun* from cats and others, sporulate before leaving the organism of the host, probably at the expense of the oxygen present in the tissues surrounding the oocyst.

The time of the appearance of oocysts after a single infection of the host is strictly fixed for each species of Coccidia. It is known as the prepatent period. The length of this period is determined by the duration of each agamous generation, by the number of generations, by the time of the transition of the merozoites to gametogony, and by the duration of the latter. Therefore, the length of the prepatent period varies with the species of Coccidia (from 3 to 22 days), being constant for each of them.

In a host infected once, oocysts are discharged only for a limited length of time, not indefinitely; the length of this period depending on the time of the penetration of sporozoites into the cells of the host, the duration of the agamous generations and their numbers, on the number of oocysts formed and on the localization of the endogenous stages of the development of the Coccidia, as well as on factors promoting the mechanical evacuation of the oocysts out of the host. It has been established for the majority of Coccidia examined that the duration of the discharge of oocysts (parent period) is limited to a relatively short period, viz. from 3–5 to 18–20 days, after which—unless reinfection takes place—the host is completely free of the Coccidia. Therefore, the development of Coccidia in the organism of the host is self-limited in time, and this depends on the strictly fixed number of agamous generations in each species.

There arises the question regarding the cause of the cessation of agamous reproduction and the transition to gamogony. Is it the result of the development in the host of protective mechanisms, i.e. determined by external conditions, or is this process hereditarily fixed and controlled by the parasite itself? Experiments carried out by Roudabush (1935, 1937) with *E. nieschulzi* on rats and by Levine (1940) on fowl Coccidia provide an answer to this question. Both authors used a similar scheme of experiments. The animals were infected with oocysts and some of them were dissected two days before the end of the prepatent period, while schizogony was still going on in the alimentary tract. Merozoites from the infected animals were introduced directly into the intestine of animals free of Coccidia, and then the time of the appearance of oocysts in them was determined. If restriction of the duration of the developmental cycle is due to the host, then, as a result of the inoculation of the animal with merozoites, the oocysts should appear in as many days as are required for the completion of the patent period in the given species. In *E. nieschulzi* the patent period was found to be equal to 7 days, in *E. maxima* and *E. hagani* to 6 days, and in *E. tenella* to 7 days. However, after the infection of rats and chicks with merozoites, oocysts appeared in them two days after the introduction of merozoites; hence the entire duration of the development of Coccidia remained unaltered. Therefore the transition to gamogony is not determined by the development of immunity in the host, but depends on hereditary characteristics of the parasite itself. In Roudabush's words, the cycle of these Coccidia 'is limited not by the host, but by the parasite itself'.

The conclusion regarding the hereditarily fixed cycle of development of Coccidia cannot yet be extended to all the representatives of the suborder Eimeriidea, since experiments have been carried out only on a few species. However, the occurrence of numerous cases of complete elimination of Coccidia from their hosts, provided there is no secondary infection, provides evidence that the majority if not all the members of the suborder Eimeriidea have a fixed cycle of development. Up to the present, uninterrupted agamous reproduction, like that in flagellates, has not been observed among them. Boughton's (1938) data on the prolonged discharge of oocysts of *Isospora lacazei* in sparrows are not fully convincing. According to this author, the infection runs a chronic course and the development of the parasite in the host is not self-limited. It is quite possible that in this case we are dealing with reinfections; especially because in another representative of this genus, *I. felis*, the cycle of development is self-limited. Schellack and Reichenow (1913) pointed out that the number of agamous generations is not fixed in *Barrouxia schneideri* from the centipede *Lithobius forficatus*, but Reyer (1937) disputed this statement. This problem is in need of further investigation.

A characteristic feature of the cycle of development common to all the Eimeriidea and Schizogregarinida is the strong development of agamous reproduction, which facilitates auto-infection of the host's organism and the formation of a large number of gamonts, thereby promoting an abundant output of the parasite. Thus one generation of schizonts in *E. bovis* produces about 170,000 merozoites. A rabbit inoculated with one oocyst of *E. magna* discharged throughout the patent period about 600–800 thousand oocysts (Chejsin, 1939). This is due to the fact that each schizont of the first generation forms up to 24 merozoites, of the second up to 40, of the third up to 80, of the fourth up to 120, and of the fifth up to 60 merozoites (Chejsin, 1940). *E. intestinalis* from the alimentary tract of the rabbit is just as prolific: thus schizonts of the first generation produce up to 60 merozoites, of the second up to 120, and of the third up to 80 (Chejsin, 1947). *E. tenella* from the caeca of fowls produce in the first generation up to 90 merozoites, in the second up to 200–350, and in the third about 25 (Tyzzer, 1929). *E. nieschulzi* from rats produces four generations: each respectively producing 26, 12, 16, and 50 merozoites. About 62,000 oocysts are discharged after inoculation of one oocyst of this species (Roudabush, 1937). The productivity of Schizogregarinida is slightly less but still considerable. In *Ophryocystis* each schizont gives rise to 40 merozoites and schizogony is repeated several times. The same is observed in *Lipotropha* from the larvae of *Systemus* (Diptera) and in *Caulleryella pipientis* from the larvae of *Culex pipiens*, &c.

The cycle of the development of Haemosporidia (Fig. 237) and Haemogregarinidae does not differ essentially from those described above for Eimeriidea. Schizogony is replaced by gamogony; this is followed by fertilization and the formation of the zygote. Sporogony is initiated by metagamous division of the zygote and leads to the formation of a large number of sporozoites. This cycle is further complicated by schizogony occurring in one host (vertebrate), while gametogony only commences in the same host (always in the formed elements of the blood) but ends in an invertebrate host, where sporogony takes place. Among Eimeriidea an alternation of two invertebrate hosts is observed only in the family Aggregatidae; in all the others the entire cycle proceeds in the same host.

Schizogony in Haemosporidia varies considerably, as regards both the structure of the schizonts themselves and their localization. In *Haemoproteus* the schizonts produce a large number of small merozoites situated in the endothelial cells of the vessels of various internal organs of birds. The same is characteristic also of *Leucocytozoon*. On the other hand, in certain representatives of Haemoproteidae, such as *Hepatocystis kochi* from monkeys, the schizonts develop in the liver parenchyma, where they attain 2 mm. in diameter, and produce many thousands of merozoites. Moreover, they frequently break up into separate segments or cytomeres, on account of which they are called merocysts (Bray, 1957).

Members of the genus *Plasmodium* differ from *Haemoproteus*, *Nycteria*, and other Haemoproteidae in that they have two kinds of schizonts: erythrocytic and excerythrocytic, the latter developing outside the erythrocytes or reticulocytes.

After their introduction into the organism of the vertebrate host with the saliva of a mosquito, the sporozoites penetrate into the cells of the internal organs, within which they undergo the so-called pre-erythrocytic schizogony (Huff, 1948, 1951; Garnham, 1948, 1954, 1959; and others).

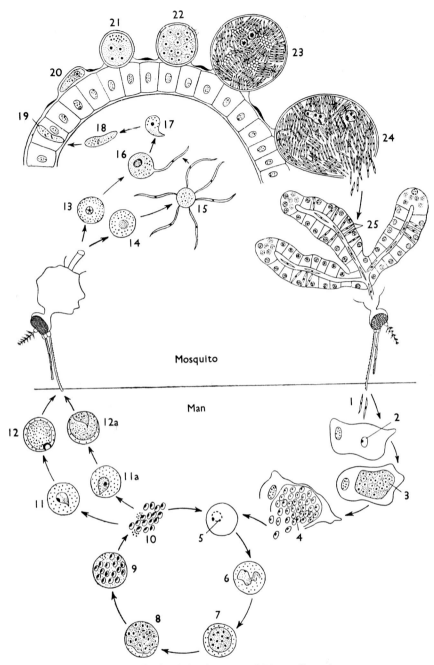

FIG. 237. Cycle of development of *Plasmodium vivax.*

1, sporozoite; 2–4, pre-erythrocytic schizogony in liver; 2, sporozoite in a liver cell transforming itself into schizont; 3, growing schizont with numerous nuclei; 4, schizont undergoing segmentation into merozoites; 5–10, erythrocytic schizogony: 5, young schizont, in shape of a ring; 6, growing schizont with pseudopodia; 7–8, growing schizont; 9, segmentation of schizont into merozoites within erythrocyte, which contains also pigment granules; 10, merozoites escaping from erythrocyte; 11, young macrogamont; 11a, young microgamont; 12, mature macrogamont; 12a, mature microgamont; 13, macrogamete; 14, microgamont; 15, formation of microgametes (ex-flagellation); 16, penetration of microgamete into macrogamete (copulation); 17, zygote; 18, motile zygoto-okinete; 19, ookinete penetrating through gut wall of mosquito; 20, ookinete attached to outer wall of mosquito gut and being transformed into an oocyst; 21–22, growing oocyst with dividing nuclei; 23, mature oocyst with sporozoites and residual body; 24, sporozoites escaping out of oocyst membrane; 25, sporozoites in salivary gland of mosquito. (Original diagram of Chejsin.)

Pre-erythrocyte schizogony of *P. gallinaceum* and *P. cathemerium* proceeds in endothelial cells, and two generations of pre-erythrocytic schizonts develop before the appearance of the erythrocytic stage. They are usually called crypto- and meto-cryptozoites respectively. *P. elongatum* schizonts of birds develop in cells of the haemopoietic system, while the schizonts of *P. cynomolgi* of monkeys, and *P. vivax* and *B. ovale* of man, develop in the parenchymatous cells of the liver, probably producing one pre-erythrocyte generation with large schizonts, which undergo segmentation into 800–1,000 merozoites, and a multitude of generations of phanerozoites, i.e. exoerythrocytic schizonts developing parallel with the erythrocytic schizogony. The schizogony of *P. falciparum* (from man) proceeds in the liver, where only one pre-erythrocytic generation of schizogony develops (Shortt, Fairley, Covell, Shute, and Garnham, 1951). In this species of *Plasmodium* generations of phanerozoites have not been discovered.

In contrast to Eimeriidea, in Haemosporidiidea agamous reproduction in the vertebrate host, produced by a single infection, may continue for a long time, with gamont formation proceeding without interruption, probably at the expense of merozoites of each generation, beginning from the first pre-erythrocytic one. This feature of the cycle, when there is no limitation to the repetition of agamous reproduction, may possibly have arisen as an adaptation to blood parasitism and to the transmission of the parasite through a blood-sucking vector. The constant and prolonged formation of gamonts, appearing in the blood for only a short period, provides the best means of ensuring infection of the vector and consequently of completing the cycle.

In the intestinal Coccidia, which develop without a vector, the cycle of development can be easily completed even when there is a limited number of agamous generations, since the host may always contact sporulated oocysts from the external medium.

In a vertebrate host the agamous cycle of *Plasmodium* is likewise not unlimited, and may be completed independently after a definite period. According to Nikolaev (1939) the development of *P. vivax* in the human organism ceases and the parasites disappear in approximately 800–870 days, while infection with *P. falciparum* is terminated even in 10–12 months. Probably the cessation of the asexual reproduction of *Plasmodium* is determined by a change in the condition of the host.

Gamonts are formed during the whole period of agamous reproduction of *Plasmodium*, though Knowles and Dasgupta (1932) found a strain of *P. knowlesi*, which reproduced for many years by the agamous method only, without forming gamonts. Huff and Gambrell (1934) observed the same phenomenon in *P. cathermerium*. However, this loss of the capacity to form may be regarded as an abnormal phenomenon.

The completion of the sexual process, the copulation of gametes, and the formation of a motile zygote (ockinete) occur in the alimentary tract of the vector. In all Haemosporidia the development in the vector proceeds in the same manner. The ookinete penetrates through the wall of the stomach, is encysted on its outer surface and is transformed into an oocyst. During the metagamous period several thousand of sporozoites are formed by multiple fission. They find their way into the salivary glands of the insect-vector and return into the organism of the vertebrate when introduced with the saliva during the act of biting (Fig. 236). The metagamous part of the cycle (sporogony) in Haemosporidia is more productive than in Eimeriidea. In the oocysts of the latter 8–16 or 32 sporozoites are usually produced, and only in a few does this number reach 100 (Hoare, 1933, 1956).

It should be noted that the alternation of nuclear phases in the cycle of development of the Haemosporidia has not been fully traced. There are some data on the chromosome composition of the erothrocytic stages of the malaria parasites (see Chapter I), but no precise data are available regarding meiosis. The observations of Schaudinn (1903) on *P. vivax* and of Thomson (1917) on *P. falciparum* on the formation of reduction bodies during the development of macro- and microgametes have not been confirmed by analysis of the chromosome apparatus and therefore cannot be regarded as authentic. Therefore there is no convincing evidence of gametic reduction.

The later investigations of Lüdicke and Piekarski (1952) have shown that during microgametogenesis in *P. falciparum* the nucleus divides by a process similar to endomitosis, producing as many as twelve nuclei of microgametes, but no process resembling reduction division was observed. During the formation of macrogametes the chromatin masses were concentrated in three to four pairs; a polar body was also detected, but whether its formation is associated with the reduction of the number of chromosomes remains obscure. These authors pointed out that after fertilization the nucleus undergoes mitotic division. More precise data are required for the solution of the question regarding meiosis in Haemosporidia.

However, since the cycles of development of Haemosporidia and Eimeriidea are basically very similar, one may assume on analogy that—as in Eimeriidea—there is zygotic reduction in Haemosporidia.

Homophasic alternation of generations with the occurrence of gametic reduction is encountered in Heliozoa (*Actinophrys*), in certain Polymastigida, and in all Ciliata.

Heliozoa can reproduce by the agamous method for a long time, while a sexual process of the type of paired merogamy (see above) occurs only under certain conditions of the environment. It is accompanied also by a process of encystment.

An alternation of generations in diplonts of Polymastigida, such as *Notila*, *Urinympha*, and *Macrospironympha*, was described in Chapter VII. Their transition to gamogony is controlled by external factors. Prolonged asexual reproduction occurs in *Cryptocercus* cockroaches only in the interval between the processes of ecdysis, whereas the sexual process always coincides with ecdysis of the host. The introduction of the ecdysis hormone (ecdyson) into the nymphs of the cockroaches may stimulate the sexual process in the flagellates (Cleveland, Burke, and Karlon, 1960). For instance, if 60 units of ecdyson are given to the nymphs 40–45 days before ecdysis, then *Urinympha*, in which under ordinary conditions gametic meiosis begins 6–8 days before ecdysis, passes over to the sexual cycle 6–7 days after the introduction of ecdyson, i.e. 30 days earlier than the normal process.

It is most probable that gametic reduction occurs also in Opalinina, although it has not yet been verified cytologically (Metcalf, 1923). According to Chen (1948), the trophozoites of *Zelleriella* always have paired chromosomes, so that they can be regarded as diplonts. Occasionally Chen encountered haploid trophozoites, but they had not two but four nuclei.

The cycle of development of Opalinina follows the same pattern in different representatives. Thus, in *Opalina ranarum* (Fig. 238) the multinucleate trophozoites reproduce for a long time by longitudinal division, after which division is accelerated and the opalinas become smaller, being transformed into precystic forms with two to eight nuclei. They become infective cysts, which are discharged from the alimentary tract of the frogs into the water, where they are ingested by tadpoles. In their alimentary tract gamonts emerge from the cysts, and undergo rapid division, as a result of which macro- and microgametes are formed. These copulate and the resulting zygote may encyst. The cysts are discharged into the water and serve to infect tadpoles. From the cysts swallowed by the tadpoles emerge young uninucleate opalinas, which rapidly grow into multinucleate trophozoites, after which a new period of asexual reproduction is initiated. Sometimes the zygotes may begin to grow without encystment and are transformed into trophozoites.

It is interesting to note that the process of copulation may sometimes be omitted from the cycle of development. Some infective cysts ingested by a tadpole do not form gametes in the alimentary tract, but excyst, and small opalinas which had emerged from them begin to grow and are rapidly transformed into adult trophozoites. However, this method of development of opalinas is probably not obligatory (Konsuloff, 1922; Sukhanova, 1953).

The question as to whether the cycle of development of opalinas is fixed has not yet been finally settled, but the transition to sexual reproduction is probably connected with changes in certain environmental factors. As will be shown below, the cycle of development of the opalinas is strictly correlated with the cyclic changes in the host.

As regards the cycles of development of ciliates their transition to a sexual process is determined mainly by environmental factors.

B. *Heterophasic alternation of generations*

It was formerly considered that this type of digenesis is characteristic only of certain lower plants, but the researches of Le Calvez (1950, 1953) and Grell (1954, 1956a, b, 1957, 1958a, b, c, 1959, 1960) leave no doubt that heterophasic alternation of generations is observed also in many unilocular and multilocular Foraminifera.

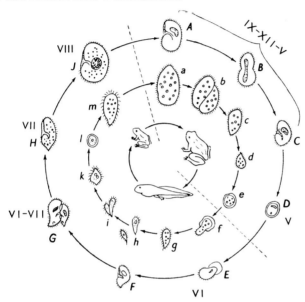

FIG. 238. Diagram of annual life-cycle of *Opalina ranarum* and *Nyctotherus* from gut of frogs in ponds at Peterhoff. Months are marked in margins in Roman figures; the cycle is divided by radial dotted lines into parts: passed in the frog (on right) and in tadpole and young frog before its emergence on to land (on left).

A–C, vegetative stages of *Nyctotherus*; *D, E*, encystment and hatching from cyst in gut of tadpole; *F–G*, formation of preconjugants and conjugation; *H* and *J*, exconjugants; *a–c*, vegetative stages of *Opalina*; *d–f*, formation of cysts and hatching from cysts in gut of tadpole; *g–h*, formation of gametes; *i*, copulation of gametes; *k*, zygote; *l–m*, encystment of zygote and hatching from cyst of young vegetative individuals in gut of young frogs. (After Boeva-Petruševskaja, 1933.)

The cycle of development of these organisms has the following general pattern: the sexual generation, gamonts, form gametes; the latter unite in pairs (copulate) and form a zygote. Then an asexual generation of agamonts develops, giving rise to agametes by multiple division; the latter grow and are transformed into gamonts. Meiosis takes place during the formation of agametes. In all foraminifers there is a definite morphological difference between the gamonts and agamonts. In unilocular and small multilocular *Rotaliella* it is usually manifested by the difference in the size of the shells, the gamonts being somewhat smaller than the agamonts (Fig.

240). In the majority of multilocular Foraminifera the difference between both generations is evident from the size of their embryonic chamber (proloculum): the gamonts possess a large one (macrosphaera) and this generation is called macrospheric or megalospheric. The agamonts have a small proloculum (microsphaera) and that generation is called microspheric.

The gamonts and agamonts also differ in the fact that the former are always uninucleate during their phase of growth, whereas the latter are usually multinucleate. The only exception is *Iridia* with its uninucleate agamonts.

The process of gamogony in foraminifers follows one common pattern, but differs in methods. Le Calvez distinguishes two types of gamogony, the monogamous and plastogamous.

In the first case the formation of gametes occurs in isolated gamonts, which the formation of both flagellated gametes, which copulate in the external environment after leaving the membrane of the gamont (*Myxotheca*, *Peneroplis*) and of amoeboid gametes, which copulate with each other within the membrane of the gamont, i.e. autogamy takes place (*Rotaliella*). To the monogamous rhizopods Le Calvez refers *Myxotheca* and *Iridia* among the unilocular foraminifers and *Peneroplis perfusum*, *Elphidium crispum*, *Planorbylina mediterranensis* among the multilocular ones, as well as *Rotaliella heterocaryotica* and *R. roscoffensis* (Grell, 1954). In plastogamic gamogony, two or more gamonts are united before the formation of gametes into one syzygy under a common membrane. The united gamonts may form amoeboid (*Patellina*, *Rubratella*) or flagellated gametes (*Glabratella*), and copulation usually takes place under the common membrane of the gamontocyst. The following represent plastogamous species: *Patellina corrugata*, *Discorbis patelliformis*, *Glabratella*, *Spirillina vivipara*, and *Rubratella*.

In all the foraminifers studied agamogony proceeds in a similar manner and comprises two phases. The first phase lasts from the moment of the formation of the agamont to the beginning of its growth and is characterized by successive divisions of the nuclei. In multilocular rhizopods the first phase takes place before the emergence of the young agamonts from the membrane of the gamontocyst, so that by that time the agamonts become multinucleate.

The second phase, which is associated with meiosis, begins when the agamont attains a definite size after a period of growth. This phase terminates with the formation of agametes.

We can now consider in further detail certain developmental cycles in Foraminifera.

The cycle of development of *Myxotheca arenilega* (Fig. 239) can serve as an example of alternation of generations in unilocular foraminifers with monogamous gamogony. According to Grell (1958c), the process of gamogony proceeds as follows. The spherical gamonts possess one large nucleus, which begins to divide rapidly, and eventually each nucleus

becomes surrounded by a portion of cytoplasm, and the gamont breaks up
into many biflagellate gametes, which escape from the shell of the gamont
and swim about in the water, where their copulation takes place. The
nucleus of the zygote undergoes several mitotic divisions, in the course of

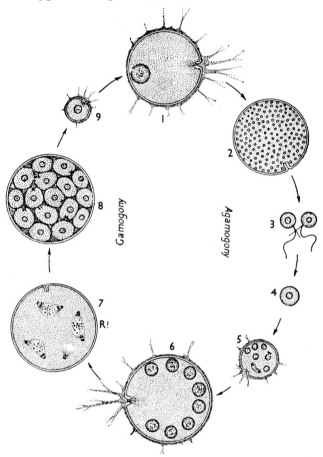

FIG. 239. Cycle of development of *Myxotheca arenilega*.

1, uninucleate gamont; 2, gamont after formation of nuclei of gametes; 3, copulation of gametes;
4, zygotes; 5, young agamont (first phase of agamogony); 6, growing agamont; 7, meiosis (reduction
moment); 8, formation of agametes; 9, young agamete (=gamont). (After Grell, 1956a.)

which it is invested in a shell and becomes an agamont. This brings to an
end the first phase of agamogony. The second phase begins with intensive
growth of the multinucleate agamont. When the agamont attains its maximum size, its nuclei undergo meiotic division, then each nucleus becomes
surrounded by an area of cytoplasm giving rise to rounded agametes, which
remain for a certain time within the membrane of the agamont. The agametes possessing one haploid nucleus are covered by a fine shell and are

transformed into gamonts. Eventually the gamont grows to the size of an adult agamont and the cycle is resumed. A similar development is observed in *Iridia lucida* and in other unilocular rhizopods (Le Calvez, 1953). The agametes are sometimes called merozoites, since they are produced by multiple fission or schizogony (Le Calvez, 1953).

The developmental cycle in multilocular foraminifers is somewhat more complicated. An example (Fig. 240) of such development is provided by *Rotaliella heterocaryotica* and *R. roscoffensis* (Grell, 1954, 1957). It should be noted that Grell observed the development of these species, as well as of some others (*Patellina, Rubratella*) in artificial cultures of the rhizopods and he succeeded in following the consecutive stages of their life-cycles by time-lapse cinematography (Grell, 1960).

The chambers of the gamonts of *R. roscoffensis* are smaller than these of the agamonts (Fig. 270). Their nucleus is usually situated in the embryonic chamber (proloculum). At the beginning of gamogony, when the nuclei proceed to division, the inner septa of the chambers are dissolved. As the result of gamogony amoeboid gametes are produced, which remain within the membrane of the gamont. Copulation is autogamous in character. Under the gamont membrane the nuclei of the resulting zygotes undergo two metagamous divisions by mitosis, as a result of which four nucleate agamonts are formed. One of the nuclei is somatic while the other three, in which condensation of the chromatin takes place, are generative nuclei. After this the agamonts emerge from the membrane of the gamont, and the first phase of agamogony is completed. A young agamont contains a variable number of generative nuclei, since frequently one or two of them may degenerate. Agamonts with three nuclei are the most frequently encountered. After this the agamont grows intensively. During this process the generative nuclei are situated in the embryonic chamber while the somatic one lies in one of the first chambers of the agamont. When the agamont attains its maximum size, the generative nuclei undergo a meiosis consisting of two consecutive divisions, in the course of which they move into the penultimate chamber and the somatic nucleus into the last. While the generative nuclei are going through the first meiotic divisions, the somatic nucleus increases in size and its chromosomes become thicker. Although the somatic nucleus goes through the initial processes of meiosis, the homologous chromosomes do not unite and remain univalent, and after dissolution of the nuclear membrane, they are distributed unevenly in the cytoplasm of the last chamber and degenerate (*R. roscoffensis*). In another species, *R. heterocaryotica*, the somatic nucleus becomes pycnotic and degenerates, without any 'attempt at meiosis'.

The number of agametes produced corresponds to the number of generative nuclei. They later grow into gamonts and the cycle is resumed again. Grell (1957) notes that when an agamont does not contain any generative nuclei, but only one somatic nucleus, it is able to grow but perishes after the elimination of the nucleus. It is conceivable that the somatic nucleus is the nucleus which controls the process of metabolism, and that therefore in its absence growth of the agamont does not take place. Generative nuclei take part only in reproduction. Grell did not observe any adult agamonts without a somatic nucleus.

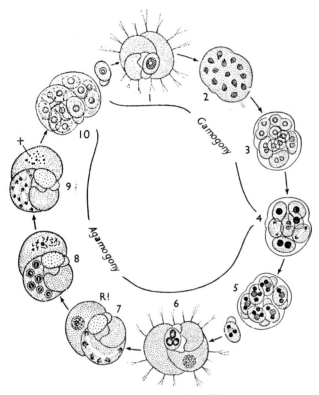

FIG. 240. Cycle of development of *Rotaliella heterocaryotica,*

1, gamont; 2, formation of nuclei of gametes; 3, autogamous copulation of gametes; 4, zygotes and first metagamous division; 5, young 3- and 4-nuclear agamonts; 6, adult agamont with generative and vegetative nucleus; 7, anaphase of first meiotic division (R, moment of reduction); 8, metaphase of second meiotic division; 9, anaphase of first meiotic division and disintegration of generative nucleus; 10, formation of agametes. (After Grell, 1957.)

The developmental cycle of plastogamous multilocular rhizopods can be followed in several examples illustrating different variants of this cycle.

The gamonts of *Patellina corrugata* (Fig. 241) are considerably smaller than its agamonts. Sexual reproduction begins by the union of several gamonts into one syzygy. In most cases there are three gamonts, which are enclosed in a thin membrane which separates them from the external environment. Although the gamonts are indistinguishable from each other, they are sexually differentiated. When three gamonts are present two usually form '+' gametes and one a '−' gamete.

After a series of nuclear divisions, the plasmatic body of the gamont emerges from its shell and becomes rounded. All further processes take place in the space between the shell of the gamonts and the outer membrane surrounding them. The nucleus of each gamont divides many times

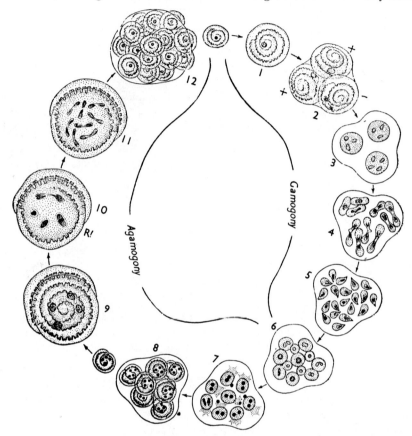

FIG. 241. Cycle of development of *Patellina corrugata*.

1, gamont; 2, aggregate of 3 gamonts [two of one (+) and one of another (−) sexual tendency]; 3, gamont with several nuclei; 4, subsequent mitoses of gamonts and formation of gametes; 5, gametes: 12 and 8-; 6–8, zygotes and 4 remaining gametes (Restgameten); 7, binucleate agamont after first metagamous mitosis; 8, young 4-nucleate agamonts; 9, growing 4-nucleate agamont; 10, meiosis I; 11, meiosis II; 12, formation of agametes. (After Grell, 1958c.)

and then it breaks up into pyriform gametes. When three or more gamonts are present in the syzygy, an unequal number of ' − ' and ' + ' gametes is produced, with the result that a certain number of so-called residual gametes of one sex are left over after copulation. The zygote undergoes two nuclear divisions and four-nucleate agamonts are produced. In contrast to *Rotaliella*, nuclear dualism does not take place in *Patellina*.

Each four-nucleate agamont becomes surrounded by a shell and leaves the membrane of the gamontocyst. The agamont then grows, its nuclei undergo meiotic fission and, as a result of this, an agamont gives rise to sixteen agametes, which are transformed into gamonts.

In other plastogamous species studied by Le Calvez (1950) and Grell (1958) the developmental cycle is in general similar to that of *Patellina*, differing only in certain details. Thus, in *Rubratella intermedia* and

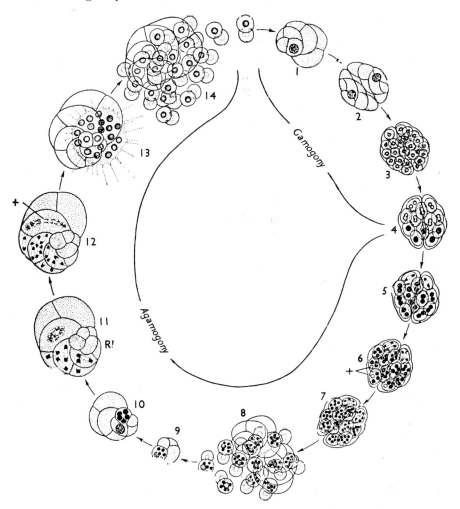

FIG. 242. Cycle of development of *Rubratella intermedia*.

1, gamont; 2, mating of two gamonts; 3, formation of gametes; 4, zygote (karyogamy partly visible); 5, binucleate agamonts (second metagamous division still visible in some); 6, three-nucleate agamonts (second metagamous division still visible in some, and degeneration of one nucleus (+) made up of four sister-nuclei is partly visible); 7, six-nucleate agamonts (third metagamous division visible in some); 8, emergence of young agamonts, showing somatic nucleus and 5 generative nuclei in each; 9–10, stages of growth of agamont; 11, first meiotic division; 12, second meiotic division (somatic nucleus (+) much elongated); 13–14, formation of agametes. (After Grell, 1958a.)

Glabratella sulcata (Fig. 242), the gamonts unite into a paired syzygy, but are not enclosed in a common membrane. The gamonts are usually of the same size, but the gamonts of *Rubratella* sometimes differ markedly in size. In *Discorbis patelliformis* both gamonts unite into a common syzygy and the shells of the partners become firmly joined. The gamonts produce the same number of gametes, therefore after copulation no unused gametes are left over. The nucleus of the zygote in *Rubratella* undergoes three metagamous divisions, but since one pair of nuclei degenerates after the second division the agamont emerging from the membrane of the gamonts has six nuclei. In *Glabratella* the number of metagamous divisions varies; therefore the young agamonts have different numbers of nuclei.

A characteristic peculiarity of agamogony in these species is the formation of one or several somatic nuclei during the first phase. Therefore *Rubratella* and *Glabratella*, as well as *Rotaliella*, are heterokaryotic organisms.

In fully grown agamonts the generative nuclei undergo meiotic divisions during the second phase of development, and the agamont breaks up into a large number of agametes.

Thus in Foraminifera there is a regular alternation of microspheric and macrospheric gamonts, i.e. dimorphism of the different generations is clearly manifested. As has been shown by Myers (1934, 1935, 1943), Hofker (1930), and Le Calvez (1938), in some foraminifers (*Elphidium crispum*, *Streblus beccarii* var. *flavensis*) the agamonts may not be of one type but of two (Fig. 243). At first a microspheric generation of agamonts is produced, and then —instead of gamonts—a new generation of agamonts already possessing a macrospheric shell develops from the agametes; they differ from the gamont in being multinucleate. Later such agamonts break up into a multitude of agametes, which escape from the shell and are transformed into gamonts. Hence in this case the developmental cycle of Foraminifera is associated with trimorphism.

III. *Cycles of development with alternation of gamogony and sporogony*

Developmental cycles without schizogony are observed in all Eugregarinida and in *Eucoccidium* (Grell, 1953*b*), a very peculiar member of the subtype Coccidiomorpha. The developmental cycle of gregarines (Fig. 244) is characterized by the fact that the sporozoite, having found its way into the organism of the host, penetrates into the cells of its alimentary tract and becomes a gamont, which proceeds to grow without multiplying by division. The gamonts in gregarines represent the most prolonged stage in the development cycle with a greatly protracted process of growth, whereas the development of gamonts in Coccidiomorpha is very restricted in time and they are as short-lived as the stages of agamous multiplication (the schizonts).

Having attained their maximum growth the gamonts unite in pairs to form a syzygy and become enclosed by a membrane forming a gamontocyst.

The process of gamogony properly begins from this point. Each gamont forms a multitude of gametes (Fig. 193) after copulation of which a zygote is formed. The latter encysts and is transformed into an oocyte. Metagamous division is associated with meiosis, and leads to the formation of eight sporozoites. Zygotic meiosis has been described for a whole series of

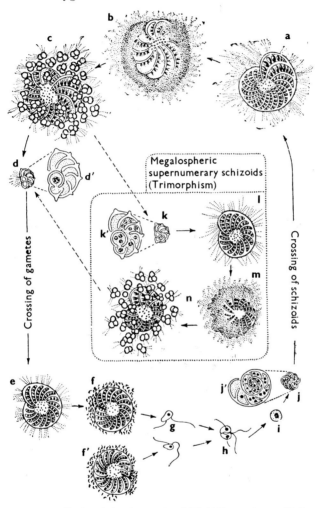

FIG. 243. Cycle of development of *Elphidium crispum* (*Poly-stomella crispa*).

(*a–b*) schizogony; (*a*) schizont (microspherical shell); (*c*) formation of embryos; (*d*)–(*i*) gamogony; (*d*) growth of embryos (young gamont with one haploid nucleus, megalospherical shell); (*e*) mature gamont; (*f*) completion of gamogony, liberation of gametes; (*g*) gametes; (*h*) copulation; (*i*) zygote; (*j*) young schizonts; (*k*)–(*n*) schizogony of megalospherical generation; (*k*) young schizont; (*l*) adult schizont with megalospherical chamber; (*m*), (*n*) schizogony with formation of megalospherical embryos. (After various authors, from Grassé, 1953.)

gregarines, for example *Stylocephalus longicollis* (Grell, 1940), *Actinocephalus parvus* (Weschenfelder, 1938), and for various Monocystidae from oligochaetes (Loubatières, 1955). The correctness of these investigations is beyond doubt.

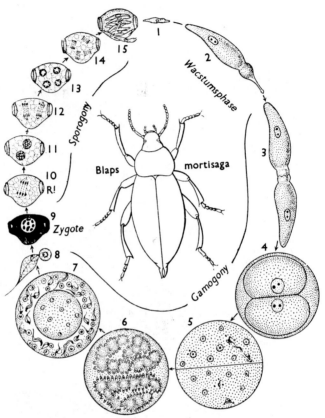

FIG. 244.   Cycle of development of *Stylocephalus longicollis*
(*Eugregarina*).

1–4, in gut of *Blaps mortisaga*, and 5–14, in outer environment. 1, sporozoite; 2, gamont; 3, formation of syzygy; 4, gamontocyst with two rounded gamonts; 5–6, division of nuclei of gamonts and formation of gametes; 7, gametes formed; 8, copulation; 9, zygote (oocyst); 10, sporogony: first reduction division; 11–15, formation of 8 sporozoites. (From Grell, 1956a.)

In contrast to Coccidia, in gregarines gametogenesis proceeds identically during the formation of male and female gametes: both female and male gametes are formed by multiple division. In Coccidia only the male gametes are formed in this manner, whereas in the development of the females there are no progamous divisions and only a single macrogamete is formed from one gamont. The productivity of gregarines is determined by the number of gametes formed by a gamont. Usually very many of them are produced and a large number of oocysts are present in the gamontocyst; however, if one oocyst finds its way into the host, at best only four syzygies are formed, whereas in Coccidia infected by one oocyst, owing to the existence of schizogony, a considerable number of macrogametes and correspondingly many oocysts are produced. The higher productivity of Coccidia may explain the much higher incidence of these parasites among their hosts as compared with gregarines, which as a rule are rarely encountered among their hosts, and are always present in small numbers in an individual host.

The developmental cycle of *Eucoccidium dinophili* from the body cavity of the marine oligomerous polychaete, *Dinophilus gyrociliatus*, has been traced by Grell (1953*b*). When oocysts containing a large number of spores (up to 250), each of which contains six or sometimes twelve sporozoites, are ingested by a worm, infection takes place (Fig. 245). The sporozoites which have emerged in the intestine of the worm penetrate through its wall into the body cavity, where they develop extracellularly and undergo a period of growth. The macrogamont increases greatly in size and becomes vermiform. The microgamont also increases considerably in size and divides into 12–32 saucer-shaped microgamonts, possessing two flagella. Before fertilization the macrogamont becomes rounded and then a microgamete penetrates into it. A large synkaryon is formed in the fertilized macrogamete, and soon afterwards the first mitotic spindle appears. The fertilized macrogamete is then invested in a membrane and becomes a zygote. The first metagamous division of the nucleus of the zygote is meiotic; from this moment sporogony is initiated. It is quite possible that a similar development also takes place in some Coccidia of invertebrates, such as *Angeiocystis*, *Myriospora*, and others, in which schizogony has hitherto not been described. Possibly in these Coccidia schizogony proceeds in a different host, as in the case of *Aggregata*. This question can only be solved by further investigations.

It is conceivable that the absence of schizogony in *Eucoccidium* is the result of omission of agamous reproduction, which is characteristic of intestinal Coccidia, rather than a primitive condition. This supposition is based on the assumption that the ancestors of Coccidia were most probably free-living flagellates, in the cycle of development of which asexual reproduction by schizogony was predominant. The loss of schizogony in *Eucoccidium* was probably associated with their transition to coelozoic parasitism. The absence of schizogony in *Eucoccidium* is compensated for by a high productivity of sporogony. In fact, even one oocyst ingested by the worm liberates in it at least 1,500 sporozoites.

IV. *Life-cycles with alternation of asexual reproduction, formation of spores, and sexual process*

The life-cycles of representatives of the order Myxosporidia (class Cnidosporidia), most of which are fish parasites, are very peculiar. Up to now, data on the life-cycle of these Protozoa remain still controversial enough, the controversies concerning mainly the mode of pansporoblast formation, the character and the very presence of sexual process, and the place of the reductional division.

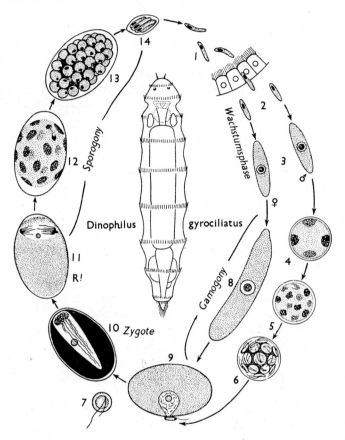

Fig. 245. Cycle of development of *Eucoccidium dinophili.*

1, sporozoite penetrating wall of gut into body cavity (2); 3, formation of micro- and macrogamonts; 4–6, microgametogenesis; 7, microgamete; 8, cigar-shaped macrogamete; 9, fertilization; 10, spindle of fertilization in zygote (oocyst); 11, meiosis; 12–13, division of nuclei and formation of spores inside oocyst; 14, mature spore with 6 sporozoites. (After Grell, 1953*b*.)

In most Myxosporidia, the vegetative stage of the parasite is represented by a multinuclear plasmodium (of the symplast type), reproducing either by plasmotomy or by formation of buds on its surface. Sometimes a multiple division, resembling schizogony, is observed within the plasmodium. According to Noble (1944), the asexual reproduction of the plasmodium is likely to be realized rather by nucleogony, than by schizogony.

The nucleus divides here many times, a cytoplasmic region being separated around each nucleus consequently, but not simultaneously, as in the case of schizogony. Thus a multinuclear plasmodium is formed. In the plasmodium, for example in that of *Myxobolus gigas* (Auerbach, 1910), two categories of nuclei are differentiated: vegetative ones, dividing apparently by amitosis, and generative or propagative ones, dividing mitotically and serving for reproduction.

The process of spore formation within the plasmodium begins with isolation of an uninuclear cell, which becomes a pansporoblast. These pansporoblasts are formed permanently as the plasmodium grows. Further on, each pansporoblast forms 1 or 2 multicellular spores including polar capsules and an amoeboid germ (sporoplasm). This process has been rather well studied, and is known to proceed more or less alike in different species, as will be shown below.

The very process of pansporoblast formation, on the contrary, has been studied less well, and in this respect different viewpoints exist.

According to some authors, the uninuclear cell formed within the plasmodium is a sporont, which later on becomes a pansporoblast (in *Leptotheca ohlmacheri*, Kudo, 1922). If one spore is formed from a sporont, the latter is called monosporoblast; if two spores are produced, it is named disporoblast or pansporoblast.

Other authors (Keysselitz, 1908, on *Myxobolus pfeifferi*; Schröder, 1910, on *Sphaeromyxa sabrazesi*) believe that propagative cells, being isolated within a plasmodium, are gametoblasts or gametes, and that a pansporoblast originates from a coalescence of two such cells into one, a zygote. Keysselitz maintains that the nucleus of the gametoblast divides unequally into both a large and a small nuclei, which further become two cells. Then they unite, develop a common envelope, and become a pansporoblast. The nuclei divide, and two small and two large cells appear. Further, such a four-cellular pansporoblast gives rise to two spores. According to S. W. Awerinzew (1909), in *Ceratomyxa drepanopsettae* the process of pansporoblast formation is even more complicated. Primary cells, giving rise to the pansporoblasts, are binuclear, which is, in Awerinzew's opinion, a result of division of one nucleus (although it might be a result of fusion of two mononuclear cells). Then the two nuclei undergo a division, which results in the formation of two small vegetative nuclei and two large generative ones. The latter become surrounded with a cytoplasmic region and form two cells: a larger female gametocyte and a smaller male gametocyte. Both give rise to two gametes (female or male respectively), which fuse with each other forming two zygotes. Thus, the pansporoblast becomes four-cellular with two zygotes and two cells having vegetative nuclei. Further, spores are formed from each zygote.

Later studies of Naville (1928, 1930) on *Myxobolus guyenoti* and *Myxidium incurvatum* led him to the following concept of the process of pansporoblast formation. In *M. incurvatum*, for instance, a cytoplasmic region separates around the generative nucleus, and such a cell divides twice, leading to the formation of two macro- and two microgametes. These unite pairwise, but their nuclei do not coalesce, and binuclear pansporoblast primordia (or prozygotes) are formed. Both nuclei divide further, leading to a four-nucleated pansporoblast. In *M. guyenoti*, a true zygote is formed, the gametic nuclei fusing with each other.

Contrary to these data, Noble (1943, 1944) failed to observe in *Myxidium gasterostei* any gamete formation before the development of spores from a pansporoblast. Mononuclear cells formed within the plasmodium are transformed directly into pansporoblasts by two nuclear divisions. Thus, pansporoblast formation appears to be unconnected with any sexual process.

Whatever the mode of pansporoblast formation might be, the further development of the spores fits generally into one scheme. In the quadrinuclear pansporoblast two nuclei are vegetative and two generative ones. The former occupy a peripheral position beneath the envelope and soon degenerate. Generative nuclei divide repeatedly and form twelve nuclei, which are grouped six-by-six in two separate sporoblasts. Of the twelve nuclei, four (two in each sporoblast), occupying central positions, become nuclei of the two future amoeboid sporoplasms. These are gametic nuclei, (Keysselitz, 1908). Eight peripheric nuclei (four in each sporoblast), with surrounding cytoplasm, take part in the formation of the envelopes of the two spores (four nuclei) and of the four polar capsules (four nuclei, two in each spore). In the mature spore, the sporoplasm is binuclear. Further, these nuclei fuse, and the sporoplasm becomes a zygote, which gives rise to the multinuclear plasmodium after getting into a new specimen of the host.

For understanding the life-cycle of the Myxosporidia, it is essential to elucidate the question of the character of their sexual process and, correspondingly, of the place of the reductional division.

Awerinzew, Auerbach, Naville, and others assumed an existence of two sexual processes, with twice repeated formation of zygotes, in the life-cycle of Myxosporidia (*Myxidium, Myxobolus, Chloromyxum, Sphaeromyxa*). During the first sexual process, occurring at pansporoblast formation, the reductional division is thought to precede the appearance of macro- and microgametes; consequently, gametes are considered to be haploid. This is the first haploid phase (haplophase). The gametes unite pairwise forming the first zygote, which becomes a pansporoblast. Further on, at the first or second division of the zygote nucleus, a new chromosome reduction is assumed, and therefore all sporoblast and sporoplasm nuclei appear to be haploid again. This is the second haploid phase or 'dihaplophase' (Naville's term). Thus, the second sexual process is thought to be accomplished during the end of the sporogenesis, by fusion of the two haploid sporoplasm nuclei into one diploid nucleus of the sporoplasm, the latter being the second zygote. This cycle implies the presence of two haplophases and of two diplophases, the former predominating slightly over the latter.

In our opinion, a developmental cycle of this kind seems hardly probable, the repeated gametogeneses and double reduction being especially subject to doubts.

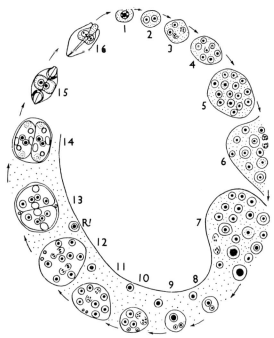

FIG. 246. Cycle of development of *Myxidium gasterostei*.

1, amoeboid embryo (sporoplasm) with one diploid nucleus; 1–7, nucleogony; 2–6, formation of multinucleate plasmodium; 7, formation of sporoblasts; 8–14, sporogony; 8, formation of one generative and vegetative nucleus; 9–12, division of nuclei: generative nucleus undergoes reduction division (12); 13–14, formation of sporoblasts; 15, mature spore; 16, emergence of sporoplasm (of amoeboid embryo) with two haploid nuclei. (After Noble, 1943.)

A number of authors believe things to be different. For example, Georgévitch (1919, 1935) could not find two reductional divisions and, consequently, two haploid phases in *Myxidium*, *Myxobolus*, and *Sphaeromyxa*. He assumes that all the life-cycle is diploid with the exception of the sporoplasm nuclei, during the formation of which the unique reductional division takes place.

Noble (1941, 1943, 1944) studied in detail the life-cycles of *Myxidium gasterostei* (Fig. 276) and of *Ceratomyxa blennius*, and he also failed to reveal the two different sexual processes with two reductional divisions at different times. Noble maintains that only the sporoplasm nuclei are haploid, and that the sporoplasm with a synkaryon represents a diploid zygote. Thus, the pansporoblast formation is not connected with any sexual process and takes place during a purely agamic reproduction. In *Myxidium gasterostei*, after Noble, the nucleus of the pansporoblast divides to form both a generative and a vegetative nuclei; then the latter divides once and degenerates. The generative nucleus divides mitotically three times, thus forming eight nuclei (Fig. 276). Each group of four nuclei becomes isolated into a separate sporoblast. Two of the four nuclei of the latter do not divide more, taking part in the formation of the spore wall. One of the resting nuclei divides into two and forms two polar capsules. The last nucleus undergoes a meiotic division, which results in formation of two haploid nuclei of the sporoplasm (with two chromosomes in each). Thus, Noble recognizes only one reductional division, assuming the sexual process to be strongly reduced and restricted to autogamy only. All stages of the life-cycle appear to be diploid, except the nuclei of the sporoplasm. We consider these data as more logical and probable ones, than, for example, Naville's ideas.

Hence, in the myxosporidian life-cycle autogamy is always followed by formation from the diploid sporoplasm (zygote) of a plasmodium, which reproduces further asexually by nucleogony (and probably also schizogony). This leads to a multicellular condition, and spores are continuously formed during this process.[1]

Of course, further and more precise studies are necessary to make final conclusions about the character of the myxosporidian life-cycle.

The cycle of development of Microsporidia bears some resemblance to that of Myxosporidia, although the question of the change of nuclear phases remains open. The spores of various Microsporidia (*Nosema, Thelohania*) contain an amoeboid embryo with two nuclei (Fig. 247). On the emergence of this amoeboid embryo from the spore these nuclei fuse. It is quite probable that this corresponds to the process of fertilization. The uninucleate amoeboid embryo (planont) penetrates into the cells of the host, after the latter ingests the spore. Within the cells monotomic of multiple division begins and small plasmodia are formed. Sporogony begins from the unicellular stage—the sporoblast. As a result of nuclear division, five, rarely six, nuclei are produced, two of which form the membrane of the spore, one nucleus takes part in the formation of the wall of the capsule, while two nuclei remain in the amoeboid embryo. Thus two periods can be recognized in the cycle of development: one, the agamous reproduction of the planont; and the second, the spore formation. A typical sexual process has not been detected in their cycle, unless the fusion of nuclei of the sporoplasm is regarded as a typical caryogamy. Here, as in the case of Myxosporidia, the progamous period is considerably reduced.

[1] We abstain from applying to the Myxosporidia the term 'sporogony', which indicates in the Sporozoa the development of sporozoites from a zygote within an oocyst. In the Myxosporidia, no sporozoites are formed during spore formation, and the very concept of the 'spore' does not correspond to that in the Sporozoa (Cheissin, 1956).

V. *The cycle of development of Protozoa of uncertain systematic position*

In some parasitic Protozoa the cycles of development are still insufficiently studied, especially from the point of view of the alternation of nuclear phases, on account of which it is impossible to refer them to any definite type of cycles. The Piroplasmoidea, Theileriidea, Sarcosporidia,

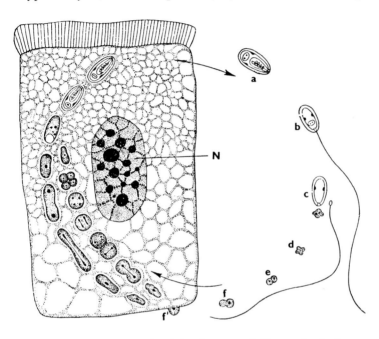

FIG. 247. Diagram of cycle of development of *Nosema bombycis*.

(*a*) mature spore with embryo; (*b*)–(*f*) emergence of amoeboid embryo from spore; (*f*) penetration into epithelial cell of gut of *Bombyx mori*; (*f'*) multiplication of microsporidia and formation of spores in cell; *N*, nucleus of host cell. (After Stempell, from Grassé, 1953.)

and Haplosporidia, whose systematic position has not yet been elucidated, owing to scanty knowledge of their cycles of development, may serve as an example.

Diametrically opposite points of view have been expressed regarding the cycle of development of piroplasmids. Dennis (1932) thinks that in *Babesia bigemina* there is an alternation of asexual and sexual reproduction, the latter proceeding according to the type of isogamous copulation. On the other hand, Regendanz and Reichenow (1933) deny the presence of asexual process in *B. canis*. The investigations of Poljanskij and Chejsin (1959) on *Babesiella bovis* and especially of Chejsin and Muratov (1959) on *Piroplasma bigeminum* have not confirmed Dennis's data and have shown that the piroplasms reproduce only by the agamous method. According to Chejsin and Muratov the cycle of development of *P. bigeminum* proceeds in the following manner. In the blood of the vertebrate host the trophozoites multiply continuously by the asexual method, during which there is a facultative alternation of monotomous and multiple division. In the tick vector, *Boophilus calcaratus*, the pyriform trophozoites, ingested with the blood of the vertebrate host, continue to multiply by the agamous method

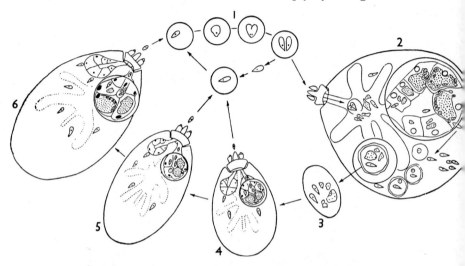

FIG. 248. Cycle of development of *Piroplasma bigeminum*.

1, in blood of cattle; 2, in female of tick *Boophilus calcaratus* gorged with blood; 3, in egg laid by infected female; 4, in larva; 5, in nymph, and 6 in female which has begun to feed on blood of cattle. (Original.)

in the lumen of the alimentary tract or intracellularly. This process is characterized by the formation of multinucleate plasmodia, from which agamonts, which become club-shaped, are budded off. These stages of development are distributed throughout all the inner organs where they again form multinucleate plasmodium-like stages of agamous reproduction. This reproduction alternates with monotomic division of the club-shaped forms. The latter penetrate into the egg cells of the tick, where they continue to multiply asexually. When the larvae emerge from these infected eggs the club-shaped stages of the piroplasm penetrate into all their organs, concentrating mainly in the salivary glands. Here, as well as in the organs of the female, multinucleate plasmodia are formed, which break up into a multitude of fine pyriform agamonts as soon as the larva starts sucking the blood of the host; the further development of the agamonts takes place in the vertebrate host. The same process as that in the larvae is repeated in the nymph and the adult tick (Fig. 248). Further investigations are of course required to elucidate the complete cycle of their development.

The cycle of the development of the Theileriida is not quite clear. Its development has been studied in greatest detail in *Theileria dispar* (Sergent *et al.*, 1936, 1945). In the cells of the reticulo-endothelial system of cattle, mainly in the lymph nodes, multiple division of the so-called 'grenade-like bodies' ('corps en grenade') takes place. They break up into agametes,

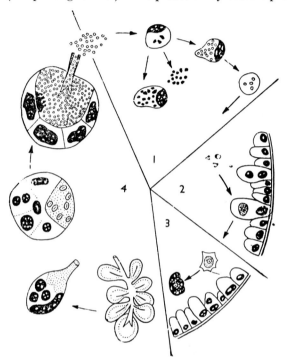

FIG. 249. Cycle of development of *Theileria dispar*.

1, schizogony in cells of cattle; 2, sexual process and formation of zygotes in the gut of larva of tick *Hyalomma mauritanicum*; 3, sporogony in gut of nymph; 4, sporogony in salivary glands of adult tick. In sporocytes are formed sporoblasts, which find their way into the blood of the vertebrate host together with saliva of tick. (From Grassé, 1953, after Sergent *et al.*, 1945.)

which again penetrate into similar cells and again divide by multiple fission. Other 'grenade-like bodies' form minute rod-shaped gamonts which penetrate into erythrocytes and circulate in the peripheral blood. The gamonts undergo further development in the alimentary tract of the larva or nymph of the tick *Hyalomma mauritanicum* (Fig. 249). Here they become gametes, which copulate and form a zygote. This penetrates into the epithelial cells of the alimentary tract of the tick and encysts. As the tick develops the cysts grow in size, and during ecdysis of the nymphs the cysts find their way into the lumen of the gut; then in the adult tick the zygote excysts and penetrates into the salivary glands, where the nucleus divides repeatedly and sporoblasts are formed, which in their turn give rise to sporozoites. These represent the infective forms which are transmitted to the vertebrate host (cattle). In this cycle the question regarding the existence of isogamous copulation remains obscure. Owing to the extremely small size of the parasite an error of observation might easily have been made.

The cycle of development of Sarcosporidia, parasites in the muscles of many vertebrates, is probably achieved without a sexual process; in any case no traces of it have been detected. The significance of the cysts (sarcocysts or Miescher's tubes) in the muscles, filled with the so-called 'spores' or sporozoites, is not yet clear.

The cycle of development of the Haplosporidia, parasites on annelids, is quite obscure; neither is it certain whether they belong together with Sarcosporidia to Protozoa or represent some lower fungi (see Caullery, 1953; Corliss, 1959).

VI. *Alternation of various forms of asexual reproduction with conjugation*

We have already considered the characteristic features of the life-cycles of ciliates in Chapter VII. It remains to describe only one special type of complex cycle of development observed in the ciliates Apostomata. The unusual cycle of development in these ciliates has been worked out in detail by Chatton and Lwoff (1935b). This almost exclusively marine group of ciliates depends for its existence on various trophic associations with other marine animals. These associations often bear the character of true parasitism while in other cases they are symbiotic.

The cycle of these ciliates consists in its vegetative part of a complex chain of modifications; into this chain is from time to time and without any regular intervals interpolated conjugation, which in some Apostomata displays an unusual course.

We shall first of all give an outline of the vegetative part of the cycle, retaining the terminology for the stages proposed by Chatton and Lwoff.

In *Spirophrya subparasitica* (Figs. 250–2) the cycle begins at the stage of the phoretic cyst attached to the shell of the copepod Idya; each cyst contains a small ciliate, the so-called phoront. Cysts on living copepods and on those that have died a natural death do not develop further, but eventually degenerate. However, if the copepod is crushed to death or swallowed by a predator, most frequently by a hydroid polyp *Cladonema*, a small ciliate emerges from the phoretic cyst, penetrates into the ruptured body of the copepod, and ingests its contents, with the result that in one hour it inflates to 3–4 times its own size. This is *Spirophrya* in the stage of trophont. When the contents of the copepod is partly eaten by the ciliate and partly digested by the digestive fluid of the hydroid, the trophont is ejected from the mouth of the polyp with the indigestible remains. The trophont then attaches itself to the stalk of the polyp and encysts, forming the tomont stage. This is a reduction phase, since the tomont divides repeatedly (palintomy), giving rise to a cluster of minute ciliates, the tomites.

The tomites are equivalent in their significance to the swarmers of sessile ciliates, e.g. the Peritricha. The tomites leave the trophont cyst and settle on the shell of the copepod Idya, where each is transformed into a phoretic cyst. This completes the agamous cycle.

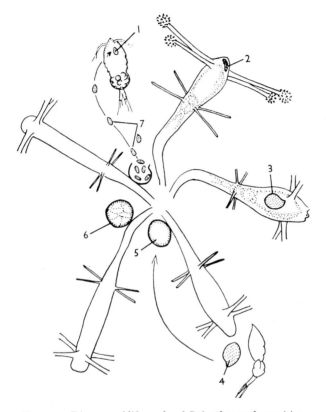

FIG. 250. Diagram of life-cycle of *Spirophrya subparasitica*.

1, encysted phoront on a crustacean; 2, young trophont swallowed by a polyp; 3, trophont growing inside a polyp; 4 and 5, emergence of the trophont (with the remains of the crustacean) out of the polyp and its encystment on the polyp; 6, formation of tomites in the cyst (tomitogenesis); 7, emergence of the tomites from the cyst and their attachment on the crustacean. (After Chatton and Lwoff, 1935*b*.)

Thus *Spirophrya* represents a ciliate in which the parasitic cycle is associated with two carrier hosts and consists of a long series of stages of different physiological significance. If compared with other ciliates these stages can be interpreted as follows.

Phoretic cysts with phoronts represent resting cysts which excyst only under the action of the peptones from a crushed copepod. The trophont is a stage of intensive nutrition and hypertrophic growth. The tomont corresponds to the multiplicative cyst of other ciliates; finally the tomites represent the stage of swarmers or the stage of dispersion.

Two lines of development lead from the species of Apostomata of the *Spirophrya* type: one runs in the direction of an intensification of the

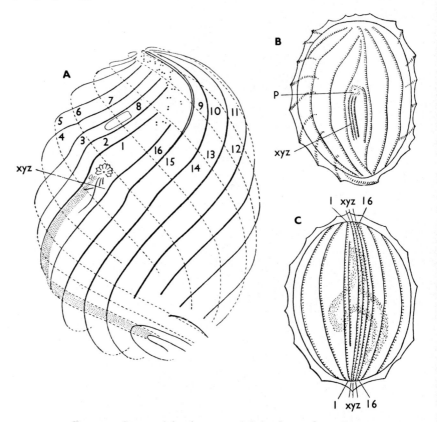

FIG. 251. Stages of development of *Spirophrya subparasitica*.

(*A*) adult trophont; (*B*) encysting trophont; (*C*) formed tomont; 1–16, ciliary rows; *xyz*, post-oral rows; *p*, mouth and pharynx. (After Chatton and Lwoff, 1935*b*.)

parasitic phase, the other in the direction of the so-called histiophagy, i.e. nutrition on decomposing tissues of animals. The widespread genus *Foettingeria* belongs to the first line. The phoretic cysts of *Foettingeria* are not very specific in their choice of hosts and they could be obtained experimentally on the carapaces of different copepods, Ostracoda, Amphipoda, and Decapoda. These cysts rupture and release the phoront only when the crustacean is swallowed by various genera of actinozoa (*Actinia*, *Sagartia*, *Bunodes*, and others) and digested in their stomach. Here the phoront feeds intensely and is transformed into a trophont; this stage of the cycle is the longest. Therefore *Foettingeria* is a parasite of actinozoa, living at the

expense of its food, throughout all the trophont part of its cycle. The motile
trophonts never multiply. Reproduction begins only when the trophont is
ejected through the mouth of its host into the exterior with the undigested
remains of food. Then the ciliate is covered by a mucous cyst and passes

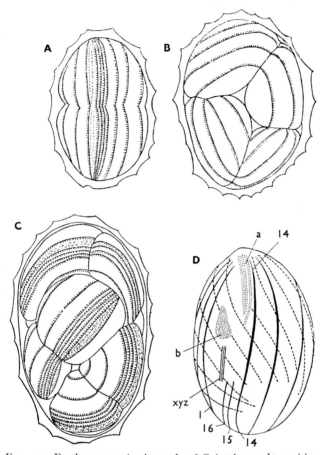

FIG. 252. Further stages in the cycle of *Spirophrya subparasitica.*

(*A*)–(*C*) palintomy into 2, 4, and 8 individuals inside a cyst; (*D*) ciliary apparatus
of the formed tomite. *a*, falciform ciliary field; *b*, 'pointed' ciliary field (other
explanations as in Fig. 251.) (After Chatton and Lwoff, 1935*b*.)

into the tomite stage. At this stage the ciliate undergoes a complex metamorphosis which is particularly clearly expressed in the uncoiling of the
spiral ciliary rows, which wind round the body, and their conversion into
straight meridional rows. The structure of the ciliary bands also changes,
the body is shortened, &c. Then the sausage-shaped tomont begins to divide
transversely. This division is palintomic, leading to the formation of sixty-
four small tomites. However, the process of palintomy does not end here
for the resulting tomites undergo further metamorphosis. The ciliary rows

coil again, but differently from the trophont, the abdominal side of the body becomes flattened, near its anterior end a flat area is formed, covered with long cilia that serve for attachment to the substratum, while at the posterior end a long sensory seta develops. Such fully formed tomites (Fig. 253) have a distinctive appearance, differing markedly from all other stages of the cycle. The tomites leave the reproductive cyst, attach themselves to the shell of crustaceans, and form phoretic cysts. Within these cysts the tomites again reorganize their ciliary apparatus and other features characteristic of the tomite stage into the structure of the spirally ciliated trophont.

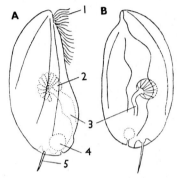

FIG. 253. Tomite of *Foettingeria.*

(*A*) from right and (*B*) from ventral surface; 1, bunch of thigmotactic cilia; 2, circlet-shaped pharynx; 3, mouth; 4, contractile vacuole; 5, caudal seta. (After Chatton and Lwoff, 1935*b*.)

The second line of modifications leads from the *Spirophrya* cycle to the genus *Gymnodinioides* containing a series of forms whose phoretic cysts are attached to crustaceans, and their development proceeds inside the cast-off shells in the exuvial fluid of the host. Development in this case takes place in the same host. Thus, in *G. inkystans* the phoronts encysted on hermit crabs hatch only during moulting of the host under the influence of its appropriate secretions, and the young trophonts penetrate into the cast-off carapace of the crustacean. There they absorb large quantities of exuvial fluid with substances dissolved in it, which accumulate in a large central vacuole, forming a food reserve. The trophont possessing nine ciliary rows, coiled in a complicated manner, grows considerably. Such a trophont leaves the cast-off shell, reorganizes its ciliary system into a meridional one, and encysts, forming a tomont. The tomont divides repeatedly in the transverse direction, giving rise to sixty-four tomites. The tomites escape from the cyst and swim actively; they are carried away by a current of water into the branchial chamber of crustaceans, where they form phoretic cysts on the gills, after undergoing a metamorphosis. In the genus *Polyspira*, belonging to the same category, the palintomy of its tomonts is modified, for the resulting tomites remain connected with each other right up to their last division, and only then does the whole chain of tomites break up at once into separate individuals.

As already stated above, conjugation is only rarely interpolated in this cycle and even then it assumes the peculiar features of syndesmogamy (Minkewitch, 1912) or zygopalintomy (Chatton and Lwoff, 1935*b*). It takes place among the trophonts and is continued to the stage of tomonts and tomites (Fig. 253).

The agamous part of the cycle is invariably connected with one or even two species of invertebrates, with which Apostomata, at different stages of its cycle, enters into phoretic (phoretic cysts on crustaceans), commensal (trophonts of *Spirophrya* in hydroids), or parasitic (trophonts of *Foettingeria*) associations. Furthermore, the agamous cycle is accompanied by recurrent metamorphoses during the cycle. In this metamorphosis the most interesting feature is the modification of the tomites, derived from the tomont in the cyst, into a form of 'swarmers' ready to emerge from the cyst. These swarmers have a form most closely resembling that of certain free-living ciliates (of the order Thigmotricha), and undoubtedly reflect the ancestral form of the Apostomata, so that they are comparable to the palingenetic larvae in the development of Metazoa. Their macronuclei are also of the typical elongated-oval shape, whereas the macronuclei of trophonts have often a reticular, diffuse structure.

The second phase of metamorphosis is initiated when the tomites within the phoretic cysts are gradually transformed into phoronts and then into trophonts, characterized by the heteropolar spiral structure of their ciliary apparatus. Finally, the third phase of metamorphosis covers the period when the ciliary spirals of the encysted trophont unwind; there is a considerable change and growth of separate ciliary rows, and the trophont is transformed into a homopolar tomont. Since the swarmers are separated from the tomont, the trophont from the swarmers, and the tomont from the trophont by pronounced changes in their mode of life (the stages of encystment, the inclusion of parasitism), and tomites from the tomont also by the successive course of the agamous generations (a new generation), one might be inclined to regard these phases not as three fragments of one metamorphosis, but as three different metamorphoses, which were possibly interpolated into the cycle of Apostomata consecutively, in connexion with the gradual complication of the cycle in the course of adaptation of these ciliates to their peculiar mode of life. Chatton and Lwoff designate these three periods of metamorphosis by different terms: the first is the metapalintomic or tomitogenesis; the second the phoretic metamorphosis; and the third the propalintomic metamorphosis.

The sequence of the introduction of these stages is difficult to define, but one might interpret them as follows. First of all, we believe that the primary method of division in ciliates must have been monotomic, a form of division that is not associated with a hypertrophy of the dividing individual. Hence the primitive form was monotomic and moreover a free-living or epibiotic ciliate. The strongly pronounced hypertrophy of the trophic stage, i.e. the trophont, must have appeared as an adaptation to an endoparasitic life with a possibility of unlimited feeding. This change in the mode of life led to phoretic metamorphosis and to the formation of trophonts. Before their transition to pronounced hypertrophy, the trophonts reproduced themselves by the method of their ancestors, i.e. by monotomy. However, the increase of hypertrophy made possible the transition to palintomic division.

This latter at first took place in the free-swimming stage, as in *Chromidina*, which also belong to the Apostomata, but subsequently it was transferred to the stage of reproductive cysts. In connexion with the transition to palintomy and a tendency to a more regular distribution of the plasmatic material among the tomites, there arose a regular, radial shape of the tomont (round the longitudinal axis of its body). This necessitated the development of a second propalintomic metamorphosis, whereby the spirally coiled trophont could be transformed into a regular, sausage-shaped tomont.

Finally, the process of palintomy. The animal, by temporarily reverting to the ancestral free-living mode of life, at the same time modifies its structure to that of an ancestral ciliate from the group Thigmotricha, i.e. thereby initiating the metapalintomic metamorphosis. As regards the peculiarities of conjugation, the double chains of conjugants could not have arisen earlier than at the period of establishment of regular linear palintomy in the Apostomata.

Thus, apart from an extremely curious ecology, the Apostomata are characterized by a strongly pronounced age polymorphism and a complex metamorphosis, which distinguish this group from most of the other ciliates. And lastly, during the agamous cycle the two types of cysts, reproductive and resting, invariably alternate.

VII. *Life-cycles of Protozoa under natural conditions*

In free-living Protozoa, especially for the ciliates, certain cyclical changes associated with the seasonal changes have been demonstrated. Thus, according to Rylov (1924), the colonial *Epistylis rotans* (Peritricha), in the ponds near Leningrad, multiply during the summer by the agamous method, while from the end of September until May they disappear from the ponds, and probably encyst.

The ciliates *Loxodes rostrum*, characteristic inhabitants of various ponds, are encountered in maximum numbers in August/September. Bogdanovich (1930) has shown that in ponds in the vicinity of Leningrad, *Loxodes* conjugates only in August, i.e. shortly before the autumn maximum of the reproduction of the ciliates.

Fursenko (1929) has shown that the colonial ciliate *Zoothamnium arbuscula* spends the winter in stalked resting cysts. From the end of April large swarmers hatch from the cysts, giving rise to the first generation of palm-shaped colonies. Then up to the end of June vegetative macrozoid-swarmers are produced by the agamous method, giving rise to a corresponding series of vegetative colonies. At the end of June and the beginning of July an epidemic of conjugations is observed in such colonies, lasting for a month and gradually subsiding. From the end of June exconjugant macrozoids arising on the colonies produce cysts, whose formation continues until the beginning of November. These cysts are destined to last out the winter. The colonies disappear during November, and only cysts remain in the ponds until the end of April. Conjugating colonies differ from the vegetative ones in certain essential morphological features.

Poljanskij (1934) studied the life-cycle of *Bursaria truncatella* in the same ponds that were inhabited by *Loxodes*. In the course of five-year-long observations he proved that this ciliate normally spends the greater part of the year in the encysted stage. In its active stage it was abundant in the ponds only from August to November. In some years *Bursaria* was encountered also in May but in incomparably smaller numbers. Under natural conditions conjugation of *Bursaria* takes place in September–October. The animals keep mainly near the bottom and apparently belong to α- and β-mesosaprobes. The absence of *Bursaria* in December, due to encystment, was probably caused by the appearance of H_2S and the complete disappearance of oxygen. *Bursaria* has two types of cysts: the vegetative ones with a ribbon-like nucleus and the exconjugant ones with four Ma-Anlagen.

According to Visscher (1927) the conjugation of *Dileptus gigas* in nature takes place in the spring, while Diller (1928) found that in *Trichodina* endomixis occurs chiefly in June.

In colonial green flagellates asexual reproduction takes place during the summer, while the onset of the period of sexual reproduction occurs by the end of it. This is probably due to the fall in the temperature of the water. Hofker (1930) has shown for a number of Foraminifera that their life-cycle, in which several agamous generations alternate with a sexual one, is annual. In *Streblus beccarii* var. *flevensis* representatives of the agamous microspherical generation are encountered usually in winter and in spring. In the winter they are young and the shell is formed by 2–3 whorls; while in the spring adult individuals are already encountered; they encyst in June. The second agamous generation develops in July, while the gamonts appear in August and gamogony takes place until September/October. Young agamonts appear already in November.

The life-cycle of some parasitic Protozoa is closely correlated with the biological cycle of its host and depends upon it.

Various Polymastigide and Hypermastigide flagellates from the alimentary tract of the cockroaches *Cryptocercus* (Cleveland, 1957) may serve as a good example of this. Their transitions to sexual reproduction is influenced by the hormones of the host and coincides with the cyclical repetitions of the periods of ecdysis. Under natural conditions a cockroach moults twice a year in its nymphal stage and the flagellates inhabiting them undergo two sexual cycles (for details see p. 317).

The life-cycles of some parasitic Protozoa in the alimentary tract of the frogs are also clearly correlated with seasonal changes in their host (Fig. 238). Thus, *Opalina ranarum* and *Nyctotherus cordiformis* reproduce themselves in the summer, in the autumn, and throughout the winter up to early spring by fission exclusively. In the spring, when the temperature of the environment rises, the opalinas become smaller as a result of intensified divisions, and encyst. When the frogs move into water for spawning the cysts of *Opalina* are discharged from the alimentary tract and are swallowed by tadpoles, in the intestine of which excystment and formation of gametes takes place. In *Nyctotherus* the cysts are discharged into the water and find their way into tadpoles. The cysts give rise to preconjugants which conjugate in the intestine of the tadpole. By the autumn adult, vegetative, multinucleate forms of *Opalina* develop in the young frogs. The exconjugants of *Nyctotherus* also grow up into adult trophozoites by the end of summer.

In the case of *Opalina* it has been established that their sexual processes, and in the first place their encystment, are always correlated with the preparation for reproduction in its host. Moreover, some investigators (Bieniarz, 1950; Čehović, 1956; McConnachie, 1960) have shown that the seasonal character of cyst-formation in *Opalina* is controlled by hormonal influences on the part of the host. The gonadotrophic hormone which stimulates the maturation of oocytes and sperms acts directly or indirectly on the opalinids, inducing an acceleration of their fission and encystment. The injection of pregnancy urine or frog pituitaries into frogs in January/ February promotes the encystment of opalinids. McConnachie has also shown that in *Rana temporaria* the encystment of the opalinids was not stimulated by the administration of chorionic gonadotropin (pregnyl), whereas the hormone hypophysin, introduced into the frogs as early as September/December, stimulated encystment of the opalinids in 43 per cent. of the frogs. Sperms matured in the seven males injected with the hormone and encystment of the opalinids occurred in five of them.

On the other hand, the experiments of Sukhanova (1953) on the transplantation of the pituitary gland into frogs in January/March did not produce positive results at a temperature of 10–12° C. The frogs themselves became sexually mature and spawned but the opalinids did not encyst. This author had carried out experiments on the effect of a temperature of 15–22° C. on frogs in winter with the object of inducing encystment of the opalinids, but the results of these experiments were likewise negative, although the frogs were kept under observation for about a month. At the same time, if frogs were kept for two months at this temperature they began to spawn as early as March, and the opalinids encysted, although in nature this process occurs only at the end of April. In winter, *Opalina* began to encyst when exposed to temperatures of 28–30° C. for a fortnight. Apparently a prolonged effect of temperatures higher than that prevailing in winter in their natural habitat is one of the main factors which facilitate encystment in *Opalina*.

More light is thrown on the regularities of the cyclical changes in *Opalina* in experiments on their cultivation (Sukhanova, 1953). In cultures kept in the winter at temperatures of about 1° C., the opalinids were similar in appearance to the ones in the alimentary tract of a frog during the same season. In the spring, when the surrounding temperature became higher, that of the medium in which the opalinids were cultivated also rose. Beginning from the end of April opalinids of smaller size, like the precystic forms, appeared in these cultures and later cysts were formed. This period corresponded in time with the period of cyst-formation in the natural environment. Thus encystment may occur without any participation or influence on the part of the host. Additional experimental data are undoubtedly required for the solution of the problem regarding the factors controlling encystation in *Opalina*.

The gregarine *Geneiorhynchus aeschnae* from the dragon-fly *Aeschna* are encountered in their larvae, in the stages of growing trophozoites and gamonts, from autumn until spring. In June/July, during the period of the preparation for metamorphosis of the larvae, the gamonts form syzygies and encyst. Gamontcysts are voided into the water with the faeces and adult dragon-flies are usually devoid of gregarines. In July/August sexual processes take place in the water, and in the autumn the larvae of dragon-flies become infected (Stein, 1960).

VIII. *Physiological changes in Protozoa at various phases of their life-cycle*

As has already been noted, during the period between divisions in the course of agamous reproduction, Protozoa experience a series of morphological and physiological changes. In fact, during the period between fissions in ciliates or in flagellates not only is there a complete reorganization of most of their organoids but also a change in metabolic activities. This is manifested both in a change of the rate of fission and in changes in the processes of respiration and synthesis of proteins, carbohydrates, fats, and nucleic acids.

Thus, Barbarin and Solovjeva (1948) have noted that in *Bursaria truncatella* the intensity of respiration decreases after their fission, and then begins to increase, reaching a maximum 18–20 hours after division. Then shortly before the onset of division it falls sharply. Markova noted that the sensitivity of *Paramecium* to KC1 decreases 10 hours after their division, the greatest sensitivity being observed 2 hours after fission. The same was observed in respect of $CaCl_2$. The sensitivity decreased, beginning from 4 hours until 10 hours after fission. The sensitivity of paramecia to the effect of KCN and $CaSO_4$ decreases in the same direction. There is thus a certain regularity in the action of salts on ciliates of different ages. With age the sensitivity of ciliates decreases, beginning from 2 hours for KCl and 4 hours for other salts.

During division an increase of sensitivity in respect of KCl is observed. As regards the action of other salts, the period of increased sensitivity covers not only the moment of fission itself but also the following few hours.

Investigations revealing changes in the amounts of RNA and DNA during different periods of division and in the intervals between them are also noteworthy. These data were obtained for ciliates. Thus Gromova (1948) observed in *Bursaria truncatella* an increase of basophilia depending on the presence of RNA directly after division, and a gradual decrease by the end of the interphase, i.e. before the fission. It has been shown by ultra-violet photometry that in the macronucleus of *Paramecium aurelia* the synthesis of DNA increases during the second half of the interphase, and at the same time there is also an increase in intranuclear RNA during this period (Kimball and Barka, 1959). In *P. caudatum* the DNA synthesis in the macronucleus begins only in the second half of the interphase, which is 18–19 hours long, the doubling of DNA quantity being reached only just before division of the macronucleus and of the cytoplasm (Cheissin, Ovchinnikova, and Selivaniva, 1963). On the other hand, in *Stentor coeruleus* this process takes place during the greater part of the interphase (Guttes and Guttes, 1960). By applying the autoradiographic method on *Tetrahymena pyriformis*, Prescott (1960) demonstrated that the synthesis of protein proceeds from one division to another at a constant rate, but RNA increases most rapidly during the second half of the interphase, whereas DNA is synthesized more intensively during the first half of the period between two divisions.

Protozoa undergo essential physiological changes during different periods of their cycle of development when there is a change in their mode of reproduction.

In ciliates, as shown by Zweibaum as early as 1922, during the period preceding conjugations, there is a decrease in the energy of their oxidizing processes, while during conjugation the consumption of oxygen increases 4–5 times. Before conjugation the cytoplasm of *Paramecium* contains much fat, which disappears after conjugation; the author associates this with a change in the intensity of oxidation processes. Solovjeva (1946) and Barbarin and Solovjeva (1948) found that in *Bursaria truncatella* respiration decreases during the first period of conjugation, and then becomes more intensive again, attaining a maximum in exconjugants. Nastjukova (1939) has shown that the ciliates are most sensitive to quinacrine during the first phase of conjugation. In exconjugants, on the contrary, the greatest resistance to quinacrine was manifested during the period of restoration of the macronucleus.

Recently there have appeared works on the cytochemical analysis of different stages in the life-cycle of Protozoa. They have revealed a series of regular changes in the distribution and amounts of certain chemical components of the nucleus and cytoplasm at different stages of the cycle, but so far only for a few species of Protozoa. This provides a means for assessing the character of metabolism at every stage of the cycle of development of Protozoa.

In this respect the researches on parasitic Protozoa, such as the gregarines, Coccidia, blood Sporozoa, opalinids, and certain ciliates (*Balantidium*) are of special interest.

Among the Coccidia those of the fowl have been studied in greatest detail (Gill and Ray, 1954; Ray and Gill, 1954; Patillo and Becker, 1955; Tsunoda and Ichikawa, 1955), as well as those of rabbits (Chejsin, 1958, 1960; Bejer, 1960). Das Gupta (1959) provided some data on the changes of lipids, polysaccharides, and nucleic acids at different phases of the cycle of development of the malaria parasite, *Hepatocystis*, *Leucocytozoon*, and others.

In Coccidia, for instance, in *Eimeria magna* and *E. intestinalis* from rabbits, the schizonts and microgamonts contain hardly any glycogen at all; they draw their resources of energy from the cells of their host. At the same time the macrogametes accumulate a large amount of glycogen, together with lipids, which represent important reserves of food, utilized later by the zygote, under the cover of its thick membrane (oocyst), outside the organism of the host. Glycogen is also found in the merozoites, which can exist for some time extracellularly; therefore it serves as their inner source of energy, utilized in movement and penetration into the cells of the host. The sporozoites also contain a reserve of glycogen, which serves the same purpose as in merozoites.

All the growing stages, the schizonts and gamonts, are characterized by intensified protein synthesis; therefore they are rich in RNA, which is localized mainly in the cytoplasm. In the synthesis of proteins of the growing macrogametes an essential role is played by RNA of the large nuclear karyosome, while in microgametogenesis and schizogony the cytoplasmic is of greater importance. The synthetic processes terminate in the zygote and the amount of RNA decreases (Chejsin, 1958, 1960).

The sporozoites of the gregarines *Geneiorhynchus aeschnae*, like those of the Coccidia, have considerable reserves of glycogen. In the growing gamonts an accumulation of proteins and polysaccharides takes place at the expense of endosmotic nutrition; while both their cytoplasm and nucleioli contain large amounts of RNA. This ensures the subsequent large output of gametes. Active synthetic processes are absent in adult gamonts and the amount of RNA in the cytoplasm diminishes, falling to a minimum at the moment of the encystation. On the other hand, the amount of polysaccharides increases with the growth of the gamonts. The polysaccharides are used up during the process of sexual reproduction (Stein, 1960).

Sukhanova (1960) detected in *Balantidium elongatum*, *B. entozoon*, and *B. duodeni* from tritons and frogs an increase of basophilia in the cytoplasm at the expense of RNA during the process of division, in exconjugants and in cysts, which have the highest content of RNA. The changes in glycogen at different stages of the cycle was studied in the same species. In *B. elongatum* the highest content of glycogen was observed in the second half of summer, when the tritons emerge from the water, during the autumn, and at the beginning of winter. A decrease in the content of glycogen takes place during the second half of winter, which is associated with the period of starvation of the host. The content of glycogen is lowest in early spring. In the late spring, when the host begins to feed intensively, the content of glycogen begins to increase. The largest amount of glycogen accumulates in the precystic forms and in the cysts. When the glycogen content in *B. Elongatum* is high its fat content is low. Only in early spring, when all the glycogen is utilized by the starving ciliates, does fat accumulate. This is the so-called starvation fat. A similar phenomenon was described during the winter starvation in free-living ciliates, *Stentor, Paramecium, Frontonia, Loxodes* (Zhinkin, 1930; Barbarin, 1937*a, b*; Manusova, 1939; and others) and in *Opalina ranarum* (Sukhanova, 1953). In the last-named species the change in the amount of reserve nutritive substances is most closely associated with the alternation of different stages in the annual life-cycle.

Encystment

The majority of Protozoa have the ability, at the onset of certain conditions, to secrete around the body a special membrane, or to encyst themselves, thereby temporarily protecting themselves against the influence of the environment or at least reducing its effect. The greater the periodic changes to which the environment of the Protozoa is subjected, the more widespread and frequently is encystment encountered in these organisms. Therefore cysts are most commonly encountered in freshwater Protozoa, inhabiting shallow bodies of water, which readily dry out in the summer and are frozen through in the winter. For the same reasons, soil Protozoa have a tendency to encyst rapidly and frequently, their whole life consisting of frequent alternations of periods of encystment and transition to the active state. Very often, especially in parasitic Protozoa, encystment becomes strictly periodical, forming a definite phase in the normal life-cycle. In parasites encystment usually serves as a means whereby their transfer into the appropriate host is ensured.

The cysts of Protozoa may be divided into several categories according to their biological significance, the principal of which are the following:

1. *Resting cysts.* The great majority of cysts serve in one or another way for the protection of their contents from unfavourable conditions, but some of them are more specifically intended for prolonged rest. There are certain features that are especially characteristic of cysts of this particular type, although absolutely precise criteria peculiar to them alone are often absent. One of these indications is a more or less pronounced differentiation of many organoids: the protruding flagella or cilia are cast off and disappear, and food particles and excretory bodies (in ciliates) present in the body are ejected from it. At the same time the intensified work of the contractile vacuole serves to rid the body of an excess of water, thereby increasing the density of the cytoplasm. The decrease in the volume of the plasm during encystation is sometimes very considerable. Thus it was shown for *Vorticella microstoma* that the volume of the contracted, but not encysted, animal

is equal, on the average, to 58,000 cubic microns; whereas the cyst of this animal together with its membrane has a volume of only 29,000 cubic microns. As already stated, this contraction occurs as a result of the discharge of a very large amount of water, which in its turn leads to a decrease in the intensity of metabolism during the resting state. In resting cysts the membrane is often divided into two layers (ectocyst and endocyst) and sometimes even into three. The animals often rotate vigorously during the secretion of the membrane, which probably serves to smooth the inner surface of the membrane. In this way, for example, is carried out the encystation of the ciliate *Colpoda*, whose cysts may withstand desiccation for 14–16 months.

Another good example of a resting cyst is provided by the colonial ciliate *Zoothamnium arbuscula* (Fursenko, 1929). As early as from June onwards part of the large individuals, or macrozoids, which are formed on the colony and serve to found new colonies, settle on the substratum, excrete a stalk, and remain encysted on it right up to the following spring. These cysts have a double wall. The macrozoids do not undergo any special dedifferentiation, but this is due to its being to a great extent dedifferentiated already before encystation, its body being round and smooth, while its mouth and peristome are of miniature size. When the ciliate hatches, the vacuole increases considerably in volume; this evidently helps the cyst to rupture. When a slit is formed on the ectocyst, the mucilaginous endocyst comes into contact with the water and swells considerably, and as a result of this the macrozooid together with the mucilaginous mass is shot out, as it were, from the endocyst and drops not far away from it on the substratum. This is followed by the growth of the posterior ciliary circlet, and more than an hour after excystation the macrozooid swims away as a swarmer in order to settle down for good on the substratum and to produce by division a new colony.

Among the Sarcodina resting cysts are common among amoebae and freshwater Testacea. The cysts of the intestinal amoebae and of the rhizopod *Euglypha alveolata* (Fig. 254) may serve as examples.

The cysts of *Entamoeba histolytica* have a regular spherical shape and an elastic, smooth, transparent membrane $0 \cdot 5 \mu$ thick. The cyst of the amoeba is fully occupied by its plasmatic cytoplasm which contains in addition to one or more nuclei a considerable amount of reserve substances, viz. a glycogen vacuole and chromatoid bodies. In many Protozoa such an accumulation of reserve substances is characteristic of resting cysts.

The encystment of *Euglypha* is very interesting. First of all, before encystment it closes the aperture of its shell, which consists of siliceous plates, with a special plug secreted by the animal. In this manner the shell of *Euglypha* is transformed into an ectocyst. Then the animal loses a large quantity of water and shrinks within the ectocyst into a round lump. At the same time the reserve skeletal plates, present in large numbers in the body of the rhizopod, emerge on to the surface of the spherical body of *Euglypha* and form round it an endocyst separated from the ectocyst by a wide space.

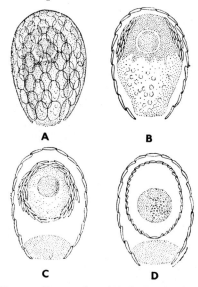

A   B

C   D

FIG. 254. Encystation of *Euglypha alveolata*.

(*A*) cytoplasm drawn into shell before encystment; (*B*) superposition of siliceous plates inside shell; (*C*), (*D*) formation of plug and of interior cyst from plates. (After Doflein and Reichenow, 1929.)

Among the resting cysts in flagellates one may take as an example the curiously formed cysts of the Chrysomonadida. In *Ochromonas crenata* (Fig. 255) the flagella of the vegetative individual are shed and a thick gelatinous layer is secreted. Then around the plasmatic body is formed the true covering of the cyst, consisting of silica. A narrow aperture is formed in the membrane after its secretion, through which a certain amount of cytoplasm flows out to the exterior, enclosing the cyst in a fine layer beneath the outer layer of gelatinous substance. At the expense of this peripheral plasma are secreted (*a*) the external sculpture of the siliceous cyst, (*b*) a special, projecting neck surrounding the aperture of the cyst, and (*c*) a special plug closing the neck of the efferent aperture. Thus the cyst of Chrysomonadida is formed to a certain extent endogenously within the cytoplasm and is distinguished by the presence of a preformed aperture. The external gelatinous substance is shed off from the surface of the cyst.

In the Sporozoa the formation of cysts is usually associated with the process of reproduction, so that the cysts are not purely protective but serve also for multiplication.

Resting cysts may have a dual origin. Some of them are produced asexually and can therefore be called vegetative, while the formation of the others results from the completion of a sexual process: those are sexual cysts. All the examples given so far represented vetetative cysts. As an illustration of sexual cysts, those of many volvocidae may be mentioned, especially in *Volvox*, where the zygote, rich in reserve nutritive substances, is invested in a compact, thorny membrane, and goes through a long period of rest. Among the ciliates a good example of encystment is provided by *Bursaria* (Poljanskij, 1934) with its two types of cyst (Fig. 256). Some *Bursaria* cysts are formed by neutral individuals, i.e. they are vegetative cysts possessing one long sausage-shaped nucleus. In addition, however, during starvation some of the exconjugants encyst even before the recon-

struction of the nuclear apparatus. Such cysts may be distinguished by
the presence in them, instead of one typical nucleus, of four Ma-Anlagen
(placentae), i.e. the primordia of future macronuclei. Therefore these

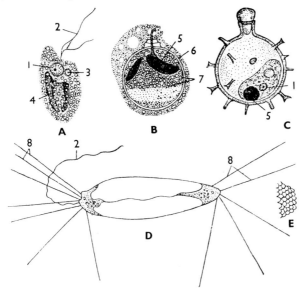

FIG. 255. Cysts of flagellates of the order Chrysomonadida.

(A), (C) *Ochromonas fragilis*; (C), (D) *Mallomonas litomesa*. (A) motile
form; (B) formation of cyst at the expense of cytoplasm emerging
through aperture to the exterior; (C) completed cyst; (D) an entire
flagellate; (E) part of body surface covered with siliceous scales. 1,
nucleus; 2, flagella; 3, contractile vacuole; 4-5, chromatophore;
6, cyst wall; 7, droplets of fat; 8, siliceous needles. (After Doflein and
Reichenow, 1929.)

cysts have been produced immediately after conjugation, and represent
sexual cysts.

Among sarcodina the best example of sexual cysts is provided by *Actinosphaerium*, in which several zygotes formed inside a common cyst are each
enclosed in a solid membrane, after which they enter into a long period of
rest. On hatching one heliozoan emerges from each zygocyst.

Sexual cysts are very common in Sporozoa and the formation of their
cysts is complicated by the formation of a supplementary system of membranes, which clearly indicate that they are protective membranes of the
type found in resting cysts. One type of such cysts in Coccidia is represented
by their oocysts. Chejsin (1935) has shown that the oocysts of *Eimeria* consist of two membranes, the outer of which, or ectocyst, is permeable and
serves as a protection from mechanical injuries, while the inner one is semi-
permeable, and protects its contents from damage by chemical agents.
Moreover, the protection of this sexual cyst is further enhanced by the
presence within the oocyst of spores, each of which, in its turn, possesses

a double membrane. Thus in Coccidia there is a system of intercalated membranes, with small cysts—for the spores are in fact cysts of the second order—inside larger cysts of the first order, or oocysts. The sexual resting cysts of *Eimeria* (Fig. 257) and other Coccidia can survive for many months outside the body of the host without perishing. The same system of inter-

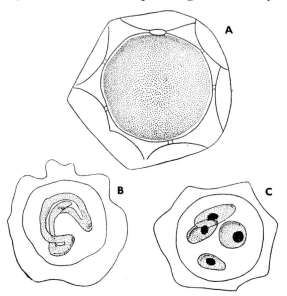

FIG. 256. Cysts of ciliate *Bursaria truncatella*.

(*A*), (*B*) resting cysts; (*C*) encysted exconjugant with 4 placentae.
(After Poljanskij, 1934.)

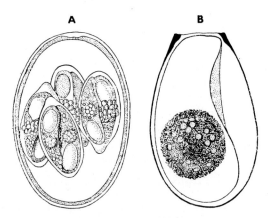

FIG. 257. Oocysts of coccidium *Eimeria*.

(*A*) oocyst containing 4 sporocysts, each with two sporozoites;
(*B*) oocyst of *Eimeria magna* in state of plasmolysis due to the
action of saturated solution of common salt. (After Wenyon,
1926, and Chejsin, 1935.)

calated membranes is also present in gregarines, where, however, gamontocysts function as cysts of the first order, while cysts of the second order are
represented by the so-called oocysts, which in their origin correspond completely to the oocysts of Coccidia since they are essentially zygotes. Some
cysts of gregarines from land arthropods have a special structure which
facilitates the emergence of sporocysts from the common cyst. Thus in

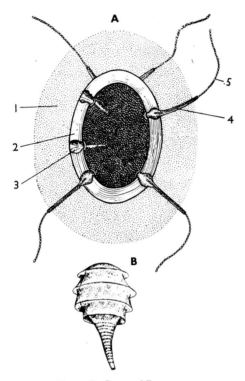

FIG 258. Cysts of Protozoa.

(*A*) mature cyst of *Gregarina blattarum* with partly
everted sporoducts (4), from which chains of spores
emerge (5). 1, gelatinous membrane; 2, cyst wall;
3, unextruded sporoducts. (*B*) cyst of suctorian *Podophrya fixa*. (After Lühe, 1913.)

Clepsidrina ovata from earwigs, in *Gregarina blattarum* from cockroaches
(Fig. 258) and others, the wall of the common cyst has several tubules—the
ooducts (=sporoducts)—which are inverted within it. When the oocysts
are completely ripe the ooducts are everted, like the finger of a glove, from
the cyst into the exterior, and the oocysts emerge through them in the
form of chains, and escape from the cyst. The eversion of the ooducts
is apparently caused by an excessive swelling of the large residual body,
which presses out the contents of the cyst.

In *Echinomera* this process is simpler: in this gregarine the oocysts take up approximately three-quarters of the cyst, the remaining quarter being occupied by a voluminous residual body. When the oocysts mature, this body swells and the mass of oocysts is vigorously pushed out through the fissure in the ruptured cyst membrane.

The duplication of the system of membranes—comprising the cyst with numerous oocysts inside it—is due to the following circumstance. Apparently, in parasites like the gregarines, with numerous oocysts, the common cyst ruptures outside the host and may in this way increase the scattering of the infective forms, which are represented by the oocysts.

The maximum periods of survival of resting cysts in a desiccated state are sometimes extraordinarily long. The length of this period is 2 years in the hypotrichous *Gastrostyla*, $5\frac{1}{2}$ years in *Oicomonas* (Protomonadida), 8 years in *Haematococcus pluvialis*, and finally even $16\frac{1}{2}$ years in *Peridinium cinctum*.

2. *Multiplicative cysts.* These cysts are very common in ciliates. Among the Holotricha whole families (for instance Ophryoglenidae) possess such cysts, and we find the same in Apostomata. In most cases before the formation of these cysts in ciliates a period of intensive feeding is observed and the animal grows in size. The ciliate is then surrounded by a fine, delicate membrane, and gives rise by repeated fission, without intervening periods of growth, to from 4 to 64 and even up to as many as 2,000 (*Ichthyophthirius*) minute products of division (in Chatton's terminology—tomites), which soon leave the ruptured cyst. The parasitic Apostomata possess cysts of two types, occupying a definite position in the life-cycle. One of the cysts behaves similarly to the reproductive cysts of Ophryoglenidae mentioned above, i.e. the tomites derived from it swim and then settle on suitable animals (marine crustacea and others) and form small solitary cysts on their integuments. This cyst belongs to the resting type; it is attached to the crustacean by a short gelatinous stalk, and remains on it until the crustacean is eaten by a predator. In the alimentary tract of the predator the small ciliate feeds and grows considerably; and is finally discharged from the alimentary tract of the predator with the faeces, and then forms a reproductive cyst.

Among the flagellates, *Euglena rubra*, for instance, forms on the one hand thin-walled, temporary reproductive cysts in which the protozoon divides into 2–4 individuals, and, on the other hand, resting cysts, which in addition to a tough membrane are coated on the outside by a gelatinous layer. The multiplication of this species takes place only inside the cysts.

The stages of development of the dinoflagellate *Dissodinium lunula* (Dogiel, 1906a) represent a kind of intermediate form between the reproductive and the resting cysts. This form is usually represented by a spherical cyst enclosing the cytoplasm with one nucleus and golden yellow chromatophores. This may possibly be the vegetative stage of *Dissodinium*. Under certain conditions the contents of the cyst divide successively into

16 parts which stretch out in the shape of a crescent, each secreting a cyst of the corresponding shape. Such 'horned cysts' have been known for a long time, but the fact that they belonged to dinoflagellates was unknown. The contents of all the 16 crescentic cysts undergo in their turn division into 8 parts arranged in a row and representing in structure miniature organisms of the dinoflagellate type. At first the crescentic cysts remain inside the common spherical membrane, but the latter soon ruptures and the horned cysts may then be encountered swimming freely in the plankton.

Some forms allied to *Dissodinium*, namely *Chytriodinium* (Dogiel, 1906*a*), are parasitic inside the large eggs of copepods swimming in the plankton. In the egg they have the appearance of common plasmatic mass, but during reproduction they leave the egg through a narrow aperture in the form of a very plastic, spherical cyst with very fine, delicate walls. The contents of this cyst emerge with difficulty from the egg into the exterior, and then it can be seen that it consists of a gradually increasing number of units (about 100). At the end of the period of reproduction these units acquire the appearance of small, naked swarmers, which escape from the cyst. Their further development is unknown. In this case, we have a typical multiplicative cyst, judging from the similarity of its development with that of *Dissodinium*. They differ, however, in that in *Dissodinium* the encysted phase lasts longer and also by the presence of coloured chromatophores in the encysted *Dissodinium*, which seems to point to their ability to feed in this state. Hence the intercalated cysts of *Dissodinium* combine the features of both resting and multiplicative cysts.

Multiplication cysts are encountered also in Sporozoa, where they are represented in many Coccidia by very fine membranes covering the segmenting schizonts.

3. *Cysts of other categories.* It might be possible to distinguish another small category of cysts—digestive cysts. Thus in the ciliate *Amphileptus* digestion of food is always associated with encystation. They are predators feeding on colonial Peritricha (especially *Epistylis*). They crawl on to the branched colonies of *Epistylis*, swallow the ciliates on the stalk itself, then encyst on the spot, together with the swallowed prey, and digest their food. Later the predator escapes from the cyst either in its former state or after one division. These cysts differ from the resting cysts in the absence of preparations for encystation, and in particular by the absence of a preliminary thickening of the cytoplasm. These cysts have a simple membrane.

Vampyrella spirogyrae encysts in a similar manner after the ingestion of abundant food.

Finally, the least differentiated and unstable cysts are formed by some ciliates from secretory tectin bodies or granules, produced by the ectoplasm of the animal (see p. 479). In many cases tectin serves also for the formation of more solid, typical cysts.

Recently another category has been distinguished, that of 'reconstructive cysts'. They are present in ciliates and serve for a periodical reconstruction of the nuclear apparatus. Fermor (1913) was the first to direct attention to such cysts: she found that in *Stylonychia pustulata* during encystation the former macronucleus degenerates, while the micronuclei fuse and recon-

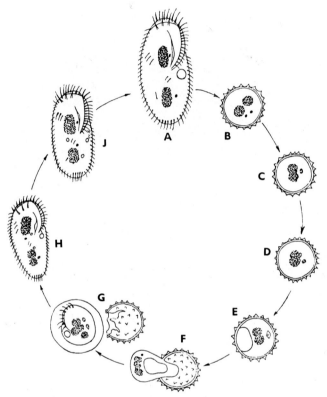

FIG. 259. Diagram of life-cycle of *Oxytricha hymenostoma*.

(*A*) active form; (*B*)–(*D*) cyst; (*E*) beginning of encystation; (*F*) emergence from ectocyst; (*G*) ciliate in entocyst; (*H*), (*J*) excysted ciliate and return to normal active state. (After Pomrjaskinskaja, 1940.)

struct the whole set of nuclei. Among other works devoted to such cysts that of Pomrjaskinskaja (1940) on *Oxytricha hymenostoma* (Fig. 259) deserves attention.

In an encysted ciliate, first all the organoids are resorbed, except the nuclear apparatus, which consists of two micronuclei and two macronuclei. Then both the macronuclei fuse together, and this is followed by fusion of the two micronuclei to form a single micronucleus with a double set of chromosomes. During excystation the macronucleus divides twice, after which the four products of division fuse in pairs. The micronucleus also divides twice, and as early as the first division the chromosomes are distributed evenly between the two daughter micronuclei, thereby restoring the diploid character of the micronuclei. Two of the four micronuclei are resorbed, while the two others, together with the two newly formed macronuclei, produce a normal nuclear apparatus in the ciliate that emerges from the cyst. Thus nuclear apparatus undergoes complete reconstruction during encystment.

The shape of the cysts is in the great majority of cases rounded. The cysts of the plankton Protozoa show a tendency to increase their surface: for instance the crescentic cysts of Dinoflagellata, the cysts of *Hydrurus* (Chrysomonadida), provided with a wing-like rim, are the cysts of some Lake Baikal pelagic ciliates. In *Podophrya fixa* (Fig. 258) the cyst is spindle-shaped. The caudate, anchor-like or rod-shaped spores (i.e. resting cysts in our interpretation) of many Myxosporidia and Actinomyxidia are also of the same significance, which probably drift in the water and are also equipped with special polar capsules that serve for attachment to the body or the walls of the alimentary tract of the host. The long, caudal appendages in the sporocysts of certain Coccidia (*Barrouxia*) and gregarines (*Urospora*, *Ceratospora*), which are parasites on marine animals, serve the same purpose. In general, an elongated form is characteristic of the sporocysts in the great majority of cases, while the zygocysts are usually rounded. The biological significance of this difference is not known.

4. *The factors promoting encystation* may be of a most diverse nature. Encystation may depend on temperature, on the concentration of substances dissolved in water, on the evaporation of the water, on the accumulation in it of harmful products of metabolism, on the deficiency of oxygen or food, or on a combination of several of these factors. In some cases a protozoon, for instance the ciliate *Colpoda cucullus*, encysts temporarily in order to go through the process of reorganization of its nuclear apparatus. One of the main factors controlling cyst-formation in free-living Protozoa is a deficiency of food in its environment. Under the conditions of the experiments carried out by a number of authors, none of the other above-mentioned factors had any effect on encystment. In a sterile medium free of bacteria, i.e. devoid of food, *Colpoda* encysted in a few hours. In a very rich culture (6 million ciliates per cubic centimetre) that is constantly supplied with food resting cysts are not formed, but multiplicative cysts are frequently observed.

In the hypotrichous *Uroleptus mobilis* studied by Calkins (1919a, b, c, 1920) in a series of works, the maintenance of mass cultures provided evidence of the dependence of encystation on the age of the culture. It was shown that during the first days (10–80) of cultivation the ciliates manifested a tendency to encyst; later, however, under similar conditions, instead of encystation an epidemic of conjugation was observed.

The direct dependence of encystment and excystation of Protozoa on changes in the environment has been demonstrated by a series of authors, among whom it is sufficient to name only a few.

For many years Beers (1925–30) observed the factors inducing encystation in the ciliate *Didinium nasutum*. He came to the conclusion that encystation of this ciliate does not depend on any inner factor, as suggested by Calkins, but is promoted entirely by changes in the environment.

First of all it is affected by starvation. If *Didinium* is given 6 or 9 paramecia per day as was done by Calkins, its vitality and its rate of division are lowered, while its rate of encystation increases. This led Calkins to the conclusion that encystation was an inevitable process arising periodically in the life-cycle. He came to this conclusion because he regarded such a ration as entirely sufficient and normal for *Didinium*. However, Beers has shown that not fewer than 12 paramecia per day are required for the normal diet of *Didinium*. When food was abundant, *Didinium* continued to live actively and to divide for an indefinite length of time without encystation and conjugation—actually up to 800 generations were recorded. When given 9 paramecia a day *Didinium* encysted after 113–165 generations, while on a ration of 6 paramecia a day the experimental lines encysted after 14–17 generations with, moreover, a delayed rate of reproduction. Hence Beers was correct in concluding that Calkins worked with animals on a deficient diet, which inevitably led to encystation. When food is abundant the process of encystation is omitted from the cycle. Thus starvation of these ciliates promotes the formation of cysts.

Beers further tested the influence on the behaviour of ciliates in culture of certain internal factors, namely, the interval of time since the previous encystment or conjugation. It was found that individuals derived from 750 divisions since the last encystment and those with only 10 divisions, when placed under identical conditions, behaved in exactly the same way in respect of encystation. Similar behaviour was observed in experiments both on a culture with 450 generations since the last conjugation and on a culture in which conjugation occurred 10 generations before the experiment. From these observations it follows that such internal facts as previous conjugation or encystment have no effect on the later processes of encystation. On the other hand, various environmental factors do have a very marked influence on encystment.

Thus encystation occurs most readily at a concentration of hydrogen ions in the liquid within the range from pH 6·4 to pH 8·4. Within these limits encystment is, as it were, a constant process, while encystation is inhibited by higher or lower concentrations. However, in *Colpoda steini* encystation takes place beyond concentrations of pH 4–pH 8.

In further experiments Beers studied the effect of the products of the vital activity of paramecia accumulating in their culture on the behaviour of *Didinium* in the absence of the paramecia themselves from the culture medium. He found that *Didinium*, starving in the cultural fluid from which the paramecia had been removed, lost their ability to encyst: of 2,000 *Didinia* placed under such conditions only 3 encysted, the rest perished without forming cysts. On the other hand, when *Didinium* were placed without food in a culture, in which their own products of metabolism had previously accumulated, Beers observed a tendency to intensified encystation. About 70 per cent. of the individuals in such a culture encysted, whereas in a control vessel with pure spring water, where another batch of *Didinium* was starved, only 45 per cent. encysted throughout the same period. These experiments demonstrated clearly that the presence in the medium of the products of metabolism of *Paramecium* inhibits encystation of *Didinium*, whereas encystment of a species of ciliates is accelerated by the products of metabolism of *Didinium* itself.

In addition to the diverse experiments of Beers, the data obtained by Breslau (1921) on *Colpidium colpoda* should also be noted. He found that rapid heating to 34–35° C., light pressure and centrifugation induce encystment in this ciliate. In parasitic Protozoa inhabiting the alimentary tract of the host, encystation usually takes place before the parasite is discharged into the external medium, and is probably controlled, as in free-living Protozoa, by external factors. However, it is difficult to say whether these external factors are unfavourable to the parasite. For example, the ciliate *Balantidium coli* always encysts in the large bowel of the pig, whereas in the alimentary tract of rat or man these ciliates lose their capacity to encyst. It is possible that certain conditions requisite for the process of encystation are absent in the medium of the alimentary tract of these hosts, which would therefore appear to be unfavourable for the parasites, since it prevents the development of one of the essential stages in the life-cycle of the ciliate in question.

B. elongatum from the alimentary tract of newts encysts in the external medium after the precystic stage leaves the host and gains entry into the water. Encystation takes place as a rule on the pellicles of the surface epithelium periodically shed by the newt, or on pieces of various detritus (Sukhanova, 1953).

Under cultural conditions encystation can be induced experimentally in certain parasitic Protozoa by various factors. For example, *Entamoeba histolytica* encysts rapidly on addition of starch to the culture medium (Balamuth, 1951), or if the oxidation-reduction potential is changed from −200 to −300 mV, and finally by changing the pH to 7·2 and higher (Chang, 1946). It is difficult at present to say whether the process of encystation is controlled by these factors, *in vivo*, but there is reason to believe that they play an important role in the life of *E. histolytica* in its natural habitat.

5. *The factors promoting excystation.* Excystation is also probably controlled mainly by the environmental factors. According to some data, certain free-living ciliates hatch when the cyst is placed in pure water. In this case the resumption of the activity of the contractile vacuole, which in ciliates usually ceases during encystation, plays an important role. When the work of the vacuole is resumed, water is first absorbed by the animal from

outside and then ejected by the vacuole under the membrane of the cyst, which finally is unable to withstand the pressure and bursts. However, many cysts possess special apertures closed by a plug, which falls out during excystation. We have already mentioned the existence of such plugs in Chrysomonadida.

It is possible also that the mechanism of excystation is associated with the secretion by the encysted organism itself of enzymes, with the aid of which the endocyst is digested. This was demonstrated by Goodey as early as 1913 for *Colpoda*, *Didinium*, and other ciliates. A clear analysis of the process of excystation is given by Beers (1948*a*) in the case of *Bursaria*. Having induced encystment of *Bursaria* towards the autumn by starvation, Beers at first unsuccessfully attempted to induce their excystation, but this became possible only after the cysts were allowed to rest for 11–13 months; by this time their contents had become slightly granular and semi-transparent. Under these conditions the cysts excyst readily in a decoction of salad, in peptone, and even in distilled water. Excystation takes place by rupture of a membrane covering the special efferent aperture, which is only 25 μ in diameter. The ciliate takes about an hour to hatch; during this process the encysted *Bursaria*, measuring up to 155 μ in diameter, is deformed to such an extent when emerging through the narrow pore that at first it is quite unlike the normal individual. Its body is at first irregular in shape, then becomes oval and devoid of a peristome, &c.

In general, Beers did not succeed in inducing excystation of the resting cysts of *Bursaria* in the autumn, and in his opinion the autumn cysts require long periods of rest.

However, encystment was readily induced in cysts of many other ciliates, first of all by raising the acidity of the medium. Thus Beers (1926) often activated the excystment of *Didinium* by placing the cysts in a decoction of timothy grass (*Phleum pratense*) from cultures of paramecia; Barker and Taylor (1933) found that various extracts of vegetable and animal tissues act as good stimulants for *Colpoda cucullus*; Haagen-Smith and Thimann (1938), continuing the previous experiments, have shown that the main active agent in such extracts are the potassium and sodium salts of a series of organic acids (fumaric, acetic, lactic, oxalic, and malic acids); moreover, these compounds act more strongly in a mixture than singly. In the opinion of some investigators, excystment is attained by a change in the amount of hydrogen ions in the medium.

Excystation of parasitic Protozoa takes place under the action of digestive enzymes. Excystment is not induced by pepsin, whereas the pancreatic juice of warm-blooded animals has a positive effect on the cysts both *in vivo* and *in vitro*. In this respect the oocysts of Coccidia have been studied in the greatest detail. According to Smetana (1933), Ikeda (1956, 1960), and others, trypsin is a specific enzyme promoting excystation of the oocysts of Coccidia. This enzyme causes the sporozoites of *Eimeria stiedae* from rabbits and *E. tenella* from fowls first to emerge from the spore, and then to escape from the oocyst through a micropyle, if it exists. Landers (1960), however, considers that the proteolytic enzymes (trypsin) are not the sole factor for the excystment of oocysts, since in the alimentary tract of myriapods, for instance, trypsin is absent, but nevertheless the oocysts of *E. schubergi* and of other Coccidia do invariably excyst.

The same observation applies to other Protozoa. Thus, excystation of *Entamoeba histolytica*, in cultures grown on different media, may be promoted by various factors but without the participation of specific intestinal enzymes. Excystation takes place when there is a decrease of the oxygen pressure in the medium, or on addition of live bacteria to the medium (Snyder and Meleney, 1941), or when the oxydation-reduction potential falls to -160, -200 mV (Jacobs, 1941), and under the influence of other factors.

IX

SOME PROBLEMS OF THE EVOLUTION
OF PROTOZOA

The concept of species and its constitution in Protozoa

THE problem of the nature of species, its limits and its constitution in Protozoa, represents part of the general biological problem of species in living organisms. Before turning to a consideration of the problem of species in Protozoa, it will therefore be necessary to deal briefly with its general biological aspects. Our analysis of this problem will be based on Darwin's theory of the laws governing evolution in the organic world.

The reality of species at all contemporary phases of evolution of the plant and animal world is accepted by the overwhelming majority of Darwinian biologists. In his book on species in plants Komarov states with remarkable clarity: 'A species is first of all a phenomenon of nature, one of its methods of translating life into reality. Those authors who have tried to define species as a method of classification, as something conventional, were quite wrong'[1] (Komarov, 1940). The recognition of the reality of species as a phenomenon with an objective existence in living nature also implies the existence of general features that characterize the biological category of species qualitatively at all phases of organic evolution.

The concept of species developed side by side with the development of biology as a whole. Darwin's theory, which was the first to view the problem of species in the historical aspect, was the turning-point in this development. It is well known that Darwin himself did not give a clear definition of the concept of species, which led to the unjustified accusation that he did not recognize its reality.

The present concept regarding the problem of species, reflecting Darwin's views on its reality and individuality, have found expression in the work of the Soviet botanist V. L. Komarov, who defined the species as follows: 'A species is a series of generations, descended from a common ancestor, and segregated by selection from the rest of the world of living beings under the influence of the environment and of the struggle for existence; at the same time a species is a definite phase in the process of evolution.'[2] This definition underlines the role of the basic factor of organic evolution, viz. selection in the process of formation of species as well as the close connexion of this process with the conditions of existence and the

---

[1] V. L. Komarov, *The Doctrine of Species in Plants*, p. 202, 1940. Published by the Academy of Sciences, U.S.S.R. [2] Ibid., p. 212.

external environment. Owing to its complexity and multiformity, any brief definition of the species concept inevitably covers only some of the aspects of this phenomenon. Therefore Komarov's definition is by no means exhaustive, but it does indicate the main characteristics of species as an objectively existing phenomenon of living nature.

Darwin's concept of species comprises not only the universality of this biological category, but also its qualitative peculiarity at different phases of the evolution of organisms, which is determined by the history of the species and its relationship to the abiotic and biotic conditions of the environment. From this point of view we believe that V. Poljanskij (1936, 1956) was right in proposing to distinguish two aspects of the problem of species; the general and the individual. The individual aspect is exhibited in the peculiarities of this category within diverse groups and at different phases of organic evolution.

The method of multiplication is of special importance in the determination of the peculiarities of a species. Sexual reproduction, which is inherent in the majority of organisms, and free interbreeding within the confines of the species lead to an enrichment of the genotype, to an increase of hereditary variability, to the production, on the basis of selection within the species, of local populations and geographical forms. Is sexual reproduction, however, an indispensable condition of the existence of species? Do species exist in forms reproducing exclusively by the agamous method? The answer to this question is of special importance for Protozoa, since by no means all of them possess a sexual process. According to some authorities the absence of a sexual process leads to the appearance of a multitude of distinct clonal lines, among which the limits between the species are indistinguishable; therefore in such cases one is forced to speak of an 'extraspecific form' of evolution (according to Hohlov's terminology, 1946). This point of view is most consistently maintained by Dobzhansky (1937, 1941, 1958) in his well-known book *Genetics and the Origin of Species*, and in a series of other works. Dobzhansky regards the species as a phase in the evolutionary process ' . . . at which the once actually or potentially interbreeding array of forms becomes segregated in two or more separate arrays, which are physiologically incapable of interbreeding' (Dobzhansky, 1937, p. 312).

Hence interbreeding is the only cause of delimitation of species, and this aspect of the problem (especially the question of the mechanism of isolation) is developed in Dobzhansky's book in detail and from abundant, chiefly genetic material. As regards agamous reproduction, and obligatorily self-fertilizing organisms, Dobzhansky makes the following observation: 'The modification of evolutionary patterns wrought by the obligatory asexual reproduction and self-fertilization manifests itself in the absence of a definite species category in such organisms' (Dobzhansky, 1937, p. 319). Hohlov (1946), who enunciated the theory of the 'extraspecific form of evolution' in plants with apogamous reproduction, maintains a similar point of view with regard to higher plants, in which the formation of seeds takes place without cross-fertilization (apomictic).

These two examples provide sufficient illustration, within the framework of this chapter, to characterize the views of those authors who connect the existence of the 'form of life on the species level' with the sexual process. However, in our opinion, this widely accepted point of view is erroneous, for both factual and theoretical objections can be advanced against it. First of all, it is not true that in agamously reproducing organisms species are, as a rule, delimited less clearly than in those with sexual reproduction, nor that an interspecific hiatus is absent in them. In support of this view, we may consider facts from the field of protozoology. The species of freshwater rhizopods producing asexually (genera *Difflugia*, *Arcella*, *Nebela*, and many others) are not less clearly delimited than, for instance, in *Chlamydomonas*, which have a sexual process. In many other Protozoa reproducing only by the agamous method, the species are also clearly delimited. As examples, species of the genus *Euglena* among the free-living forms, or those of the genera *Giardia* or *Trichomonas* among parasitic Mastigophora, may be mentioned.

Particularly convincing evidence of the reality of species in agamously reproducing organisms is furnished by flagellates of the group Hypermastigida, symbiotic in termites and certain cockroaches. Cleveland (1956) has shown that numerous species of Hypermastigida, parasitic in termites, reproduce themselves only by the agamous method. However, in flagellates from the cockroach *Cryptocercus* the sexual process takes place regularly. In spite of this difference, the delimitation of species and the presence of discontinuity between them is just as clear in Hypermastigida from termites and in those from *Cryptocercus*. Therefore, the species from the termites are no less 'real' than those from *Cryptocercus*.

V. Poljanskij (1956) gives numerous similar examples of the reality of species among the lower algae which reproduce asexually. It is true that in agamously reproducing Protozoa and algae, the discontinuity may be slight, and difficulties in the delimitation of species are frequently encountered. However, the same difficulties arise also among organisms reproducing themselves sexually, for specific status is basically determined not by the method of reproduction but by the degree of divergence during the process of speciation, since a species is always 'a phase in the process of evolution' (Komarov). Thus the available facts—at any rate as regards Protozoa (we do not undertake to express any opinion about the apomictic plants)—speak against the existence of an 'extraspecific form of life' in asexually reproducing organisms.

This approach to the problem is also not justified from the theoretical point of view, based on the Darwinian concepts of organic evolution. The fundamental factor of speciation is natural selection. At the basis of the delimitation of specific characteristics and of the origin of discontinuity between species lies natural selection, and, as a consequence of it, divergence. Therefore it is more correct to attribute 'the existence of life on the species level' to the action of specific biological principles, viz. natural selection and inheritable variability. The sexual process has probably arisen at a comparatively much later phase of evolution. It must have been preceded by differentiation of the nuclear apparatus, of the chromosome mechanism of localization, and of transference of genetic self-reproducing material. It should also be remembered that at the beginning the sexual process (isogamous copulation) was probably facultative, and under suitable environmental conditions agamous reproduction could proceed for an unlimited time. This 'optional' property of the sexual process is still encountered in many plant flagellates belonging to the Volvocales, as was shown by Hartmann (1921) for *Eudorina*.

There is an opinion (especially common among geneticists) that the absence of the sexual process in Protozoa and in some lower algae is a secondary phenomenon, due to the loss of a previously existing sexual process. In support of this point of view, it is usual to refer to bacteria, in which the existence of a sexual process is postulated, mainly on the basis of genetic investigations. However, this reasoning does not sound convincing to us. Even if there are some forms of sexual process in bacteria, it is by no means a proof of its obligatory existence in Protozoa. There are no grounds for assuming the existence of direct phylogenetic links between bacteria and Protozoa, and it is much more probable that the sexual process in bacteria (if it exists) arose independently. There are no convincing facts pointing to a secondary loss of the sexual process among recent Protozoa with an agamous reproduction.

However, the possibility of the occurrence of secondary loss of the sexual process in individual cases cannot be excluded; thus its absence in Hypermastigida from termites probably belongs to this category of phenomena.

The foregoing arguments provide sufficient evidence of the reality of species not only in Protozoa which reproduce themselves by the sexual method but also in agamous forms.

One of the characteristic peculiarities of species is its diversity, its polymorphism. Species exist in the form of genotypically and phenotypically distinct populations, adapted to definite ecological conditions or characteristic of definite geographical conditions. This biological differentiation of the species should be regarded as one of the most important characteristics of its existence, ensuring the adaptation of the species to certain conditions of life, as well as the possibility of its further evolution.

The problem of the polymorphism of species, of its constitution, and of its ecological and geographical divergence, has been thoroughly investigated during the last twenty-five years, both in the botanical and zoological fields. Even a very short review of research on this subject would have required a whole book. In the field of botany may be mentioned the works of Vavilov (1931), who discovered the fundamentally important laws of inheritable variability as the source of the genotypic polymorphism of species; of Turesson (1922, 1929), who created the theory of ecotypes; of Rozanova (1946), Sinskaja (1948), and many others. In the field of zoology the researches of Mayr (1947) on birds; of Schmidt, Heinke, Marti, and many others on fish; of Rensch on molluscs; of Goldschmidt and Dobzhansky on butterflies, beetles, flies, &c. The problems of intraspecific inheritable variation, polymorphism, and constitution of species in Protozoa have been studied immeasurably less. In fact, on this subject only isolated data are available. Nevertheless, during the last twenty to thirty years a quite considerable amount of material on Protozoa has been accumulated, enabling us to make certain deductions and generalizations, and to set a course for further investigation. In the development of the polymorphism of species, a great role is played by the environmental conditions, which to a considerable extent determine the direction of selection. This is particularly clear from a comparison of certain parasitic groups of Protozoa with free-living ones. As will be shown below, in tissue-parasites there arises a series of biological differentiations associated with the evolution of the parasite-host system and with the development of complex mutual adaptations between the components of this system.

We can now consider briefly some basic factual material on the problem of intraspecific differentiation in Protozoa. We shall first turn to the free-living rhizopods, which reproduce only asexually. There are several works on this subject, among which the extensive experimental investigations of Jennings (1916, 1929) on the freshwater rhizopods *Difflugia corona* are of particular importance. This rhizopod possesses a shell built of particles of sand, which encloses the greatest part of its protoplasmic body, and from the opening of which the pseudopodia protrude. During reproduction part of the cytoplasm emerges out of the opening and is invested in a new shell, while the nucleus undergoes mitotic division. In *Difflugia* there is considerable variation in a number of its characters; thus the number of spines of the shell varies from 0 to 14; the number of denticles round its opening from 9 to 21; the size and length of the spines also vary greatly, &c. As a result of a careful analysis by the method of individual cultures, of populations of *D. corona* taken from nature, Jennings succeeded in isolating the hereditarily constant lines (biotypes), differing clearly in a number of distinct morphological characters (Fig. 260), thus demonstrating the considerable polymorphism of the species in question. Jennings's observations on the problem of the origin of new biotypes in a population of *Difflugia* are most interesting. He succeeded in establishing two types of heritable modifications. On the other hand, there occasionally appear in lines of *Difflugia* sudden sharp changes, which proved to be hereditarily constant. But small, gradual changes, the accumulation of which leads to a progressive change of the genotype and, correspondingly, of the phenotype, are of much greater importance. Jennings proved the existence of such small step-by-step changes by selection within the clone (line), which produced positive results when carried out consistently and for prolonged periods.

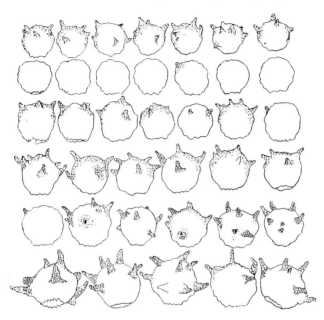

FIG. 260. Variation of form and size in 6 different biotypes of *Difflugia corona*. (After Jennings, 1916.)

Hegner (1919) carried out similar observations on another species of rhizopods, *Arcella dentata*. The results obtained by him fully confirm those of Jennings.

However, although the investigations considered above establish beyond doubt the existence of complex intraspecific polymorphism in freshwater rhizopods, they provide no information regarding the connexion of this variation with definite ecological conditions or about their geographical distribution.

A clearly defined intraspecific differentiation is observed in parasitic amoebae. In the dysentery amoeba *Entamoeba histolytica*, Wenyon and O'Connor (1917) and then Dobell and Jepps (1918) described five separate races differing in the size of their cysts. This question has been investigated many times. Certain authors (Matevosyan, 1951) are inclined to deny the existence of races among *E. histolytica*. However, there are serious factual data supporting the reality of the existence of races in the dysentery amoeba. In this respect a very convincing investigation was carried out by A. A. Filipčenko and E. M. Chejsin (1937), who demonstrated the constancy of the sizes of cysts in different 'races' of *E. histolytica* discharged from man in the course of many months.

The results of the measurements of the diameter of cysts of *E. histolytica* discharged by the same individual in the course of a year are given in the following table. These measurements are characterized by remarkable constancy. In cases when the cysts exhibit considerable variation, this probably depends on infection with several strains (biotypes).

TABLE I

Diameter of cysts of Entamoeba histolytica *(in microns) discharged by one individual during one year (Filipčenko and Chejsin, 1937)*

Date	*n*, number of measurements	Range	M–m
21.XI	250	8·5–14·5	11·34–0·064
15.XII	200	8·5–14·5	11·37–0·73
9.I	200	8·5–13·5	11·19–0·069
26.I	250	7·5–14·5	11·31–0·057
16.II	300	8·5–14·5	11·39–0·60
2.III	250	7·5–15·5	11·25–0·073
8.IV	200	8·5–13·5	11·36–0·070
12.V	200	8·5–14·5	11·42–0·071
8.XII	200	8·5–13·5	11·07–0·046
10.XII	500	7·5–14·5	11·26–0·052
14.XII	400	7·5–14·5	11·30–0·050

At present sufficient significant data have been accumulated, showing that different strains of *E. histolytica* vary in virulence. On this basis a hypothesis was advanced stipulating the existence of two independent species of *Entamoeba*, morphologically indistinguishable from each other: the non-pathogenic *Entamoeba dispar* and pathogenic 'true' *Entamoeba histolytica*. Brumpt (1925, 1949), the author of this hypothesis, had won the support of a number of protozoologists (Avakjan, 1955; Epstejn, 1941). However, further investigations of this problem support another, more probable hypothesis, according to which *Entamoeba histolytica* is a polymorphic species, comprising pathogenic and non-pathogenic races, the latter corresponding to Brumpt's *Entamoeba dispar*.

In a careful investigation of this question in England, Neal (1951, 1954, 1958) has shown that the pathogenic and non-pathogenic strains of *E. histolytica* have a different geographical distribution, the pathogenic race being restricted mainly to tropical latitudes, while the non-pathogenic race is prevalent in temperate northern latitudes. Neal's point of view on the nature of the polymorphism of *E. histolytica* has recently been supported by Hoare (1960b) in a special paper devoted to this question.

Thus the species *Entamoeba histolytica* is characterized by a fairly complex intraspecific polymorphism. On the one hand, there are races differing in the degree of their virulence and in their geographical range; on the other, there are smaller, hereditarily constant groups, differing from each other mainly in the size of their cysts, and probably corresponding to the biotypes of *Difflugia* described above.

Within the class of Mastigophora the available data on the problem of intraspecific groupings are based almost exclusively on the study of parasitic forms, which, like the amoeba, reproduce by the agamous method exclusively. Before turning to the factual material, it is necessary to make some general remarks regarding parasites. When considering the question of intraspecific differentiation among parasitic organisms, it is essential to bear in mind two special factors. These are, first, the transfer to a new species of host (final or intermediate), and, secondly, the change in localization of the parasite within the host or on it (change of the hostal biotype). The first of these factors usually leads to the isolation of the parasite population in the new host, comparable in this respect to geographic isolation of free-living animals (this comparison was first formulated by Semenov-Tjanj-Šanský, 1910), and also brings about a reconstruction of the complex biochemical bonds present in the 'host-parasite' system. These characteristics are especially well expressed in certain parasitic Mastigophora.

In trypanosomes the presence within the limits of a species of fairly numerous races (or strains), differing in their antigene properties, is an established fact. They are known, for instance, in *Trypanosoma rhodesiense* (Lourie and O'Connor, 1937) and in *T. gambiense* (Inoki, Kitaura, Kurogochi, Osaki, and Nakabayashi, 1952). These different antigenic hereditary properties of trypanosomes can be partially modified experimentally by passing them through various mammals. Apparently they have the characteristics of enduring modifications (see below, p. 493).

Some species of trypanosomes are characterized by extraordinarily pronounced morphological polymorphism. This is the case, for instance, for *Trypanosoma brucei*—the causative agent of nagana in cattle. Within this species several morphological forms are distinguished, differing from each other in the width of the body, the position of the nucleus, and the presence or absence of a free flagellum. Other species, on the contrary, show little variation (*T. suis*), while in *T. evansi* the causative organism of 'Surra', another disease of cattle, polymorphism is encountered only as an exception. However, morphological polymorphism of certain species of trypanosomes does not denote the presence of hereditarily constant biotypes, but is an expression of different physiological states of these flagellates and of the broad phenotypic plasticity of their variability. Side by side with it trypanosomes exhibit differentiation into numerous races within the limits of the species, which are associated with parasitism in distinct hosts, with different geographical distribution, and also with different relations to the intermediate hosts. In the case of *T. evansi* and some other species this problem has been studied most exhaustively and with great care by Hoare (1925,

492   SOME PROBLEMS OF THE

1956a, c, 1957, 1960a). He investigated in detail (morphologically and biometrically) more than thirty strains of *T. evansi* from the blood of various mammals (cattle, camel, horse, dog, guinea-pig, and others). As a result, Hoare demonstrated the existence of many races differing from one another, in particular in their dimensions. However, the differences among them are not sufficiently great to regard them as independent species or subspecies. Hoare suggests the use of the term 'deme'[1] for these intraspecific groupings (Gilmour and Gregor, 1939; Gilmour and Heslop-Harrison, 1954). According to the character of the difference, an appropriate prefix is combined with the deme: e.g. serodeme (denoting immunological differences), ecodeme (differences in the conditions of habitat), clinodeme (for geographical races), &c. The concept 'deme' has no taxonomic status and is actually close to the concept 'population'. The races or 'demes' of *T. evansi* should be referred to ecological forms that are associated in particular with parasitism in distinct hosts (xenodemes). It is of special interest that a definite geographical regularity has been detected for certain intraspecific groupings of *T. evansi*, which can thus be regarded as geographical forms or 'clinodemes'. In *T. evansi*, parasitic in horses, there is a gradual, clearly expressed increase of size from West to East. This increase in size is correlated with an increase of virulence of the strains in question.

Some intraspecific groupings in trypanosomes are determined by a change in their relationship to their vector and in the change of the method of transmission to the vertebrate host. As is known, some species of trypanosomes are transmitted through vectors, represented by blood-sucking insects. Two typical examples are *Trypanosoma gambiense* of man (causing sleeping sickness) and *T. brucei* of cattle (causing nagana).

The vectors of these trypanosomes are tsetse-flies (genus *Glossina*). In the vector trypanosomes multiply and undergo a fairly complex cycle of development. Only after completing this and reaching the stage of so-called metacyclic trypanosomes are they again capable of infecting the vertebrate host. In other species, as for example in *T. evansi*, no development takes place in the intermediate host and the vector transmits the infection purely mechanically; in this case the parasite merely survives for a certain time in the anterior of the alimentary tract of the vector. Thus *T. evansi* is transmitted mainly by horse-flies, in the proboscis of which they survive for some time. The horse-fly, to use the descriptive expression of Hoare, plays the part of a syringe. It has been found that within the limits of a species in some trypanosomes the mode of transmission of the infection may change, leading to the formation of different races, but without any morphological differences between them. In *Trypanosoma vivax* (parasitic in cattle and horses), for instance, the transmission from one vertebrate to another, within the habitat of *Glossina* in Africa, is affected by this

[1] From the Greek 'demos'—population.

vector, in which this trypanosome undergoes its normal cycle of development. However, the area of distribution of *T. vivax* is much wider than that of its intermediate host, *Glossina*. Thus, these trypanosomes are encountered in the islands of the West Indies, and in South America, where there are no tsetse-flies. In all these regions the vectors of *T. vivax* are Tabanidae, which act like a 'living syringe'. It has been shown by special experiments (Rouband, Colas-Belcour and Gashen, 1938) that *T. vivax*, occurring beyond the boundaries of the habitat of *Glossina*, had lost the ability to develop in their specific vectors, showing that profound changes in the cycle of the development of the parasite have taken place. Evidently, the *T. vivax*, which are unable to develop in *Glossina*, should be regarded as a special hostal race ('xenodeme'). The absence of any pronounced morphological differences between *T. vivax* in the habitat of *Glossina* and outside it does not justify the separation of this species into two.

Hoare (1956a, c) has advanced an hypothesis, which seems to us most probable, that the change in the life-cycle in the vector, as in the case of *T. vivax*, may be that starting-point of speciation. According to Hoare, *Trypanosoma evansi*, which is transmitted mechanically by horse-flies, originated in this way from *T. brucei*, which undergoes a complex cycle of development in *Glossina*. However, it would be wrong to assume that a change of the species of host always leads rapidly to a change in the characteristics of the trypanosomes and to a disturbance of the established 'host–parasite' relationship. From this point of view, the experiments carried out over many years in Tanganyika by Willet and Fairbairn (1955) on the causative organism of one of the forms of sleeping sickness in man—*Trypanosoma rhodesiense*—are very interesting. The question at issue in this investigation was the solution of the problem of the specific independence of *T. gambiense*, *T. rhodesiense* (both causing sleeping sickness in man), and *T. brucei* (causing nagana in cattle and other mammals), and in particular the experimental verification of the idea that *T. rhodesiense*, when passaged through sheep by *Glossina*, are transformed into typical *T. brucei* and lose their ability to infect man. A strain of *T. rhodesiense* isolated from man in 1934 was inoculated into a sheep through *Glossina*. In the course of $18\frac{1}{2}$ years it was passaged through 115 sheep by the vector. The number of agamous generations undergone by the trypanosomes during that period must have been stupendous. Their ability to infect men was periodically tested, and it was shown that it had not been lost after $18\frac{1}{2}$ years. However, during the period of the experiment there was a gradual lengthening of the incubation period of the infection in man, indicating a decrease of virulence. This prolonged experiment points to a considerable stability of the association in the historically established 'host–parasite' relationship, which is determined by complex biochemical, as well as immunological, factors.

Hoare (1954, 1960a) observed in *Trypanosoma evansi* the production by mutation of strains differing morphologically from the typical form, by a sudden loss of the kinetoplast. Such forms appeared spontaneously in two normal laboratory strains and were subsequently maintained for an unlimited time in the course of passages. It is interesting that similar akinetoplastic races were also discovered by Hoare among naturally infected camels in the Sudan. During the examination of the 300 infected camels Hoare found 5 cases in which the kinetoplast was absent.

A biological differentiation of the species has also taken place in another genus of flagellates, which is important from the practical point of view, namely in *Leishmania*. Since it is impossible to dwell on this problem, which has an abundant literature, only a few facts connected with it can be mentioned. Within the limits of the species *Leishmania tropica* (the cause of cutaneous leishmaniasis or Borovsky's disease) two distinct forms can be recognized: *Leishmania tropica minor* and *L. tropica major* (Latyšev, Koževnikov, and Povališina, 1958). These two forms (races) differ morphologically in the size of the cell of the parasite, and they are adapted to different biotypes. Thus *Leishmania tropica* f. *minor* causes disease of the 'urban type', mostly encountered in urban areas, while *L. tropica* f. *major* is responsible for the 'rural type' in rural localities. The source of human infection with f. *major* are rodents of the sandy desert, the disease being an obligatory transmissive disease with a natural focus (according to E. N. Pavlovskij's terminology). A different pattern is characteristic of f. *minor*, which under urban conditions is transmitted, as a rule, directly from man to man through sand-flies. There are also certain differences in the clinical course of the disease caused by these two forms. Within *L. tropica* there are also some other intraspecific groupings, in particular those connected with ecological and geographical features and associated with distinct vectors—sand-flies. Thus, for example, strains of *L. tropica* from Baghdad develop readily in *Phlebotomus papatasii*, while the Jericho strains develop with difficulty in this species of sand-fly (Adler and Theodor, 1929; Adler and Katzenellenbogen, 1952). A similar pattern of adaptations to different species of vectors, connected with the geographic factor, is also present in another species of *Leishmania—L. donovani*, the causative organism of visceral leishmaniasis.

The foregoing facts regarding intraspecific differentiation in parasitic Protozoa with agamous reproduction indicate the presence of two categories of phenomena in these organisms: (1) the objective reality of species and (2) the complex constitution of the species and its composition of populations distinguishable from each other.

The most complex pattern of intraspecific differentiation among the Protozoa is encountered among ciliates. Unfortunately the problem of the constitution of the species in them has not been sufficiently examined. However, the data already available point to the multiformity of intraspecific groupings among ciliates.

One of the causes of the complex intraspecific polymorphism in many ciliates is probably the occurrence in them of varied forms of reproduction and reorganization of the nuclear apparatus, giving rise to variation. Side by side with agamous multiplication they possess a peculiar sexual process —conjugation, during which karyogamy takes place. A new macronucleus, which is restored at the expense of the synkaryon, represents, according to modern concepts, a highly polyploid nucleus.

Apart from conjugation, the ciliates may also undergo autogamy (self-fertilization), which is also accompanied by reorganization of the nuclear apparatus. In some ciliates, endomixis, a reorganization of the nuclear apparatus not accompanied by karyogamy, is also observed. All these forms of the sexual process and nuclear reorganization represent a source of heritable variation and of the appearance of new biotypes; this has been proved experimentally for *Paramecium* and other species of ciliates (Jennings, 1911, 1913; Sonneborn and Lynch, 1932; Cohen, 1934; Caldwell, 1933, and others). Since the process of conjugation and autogamy is associated with chromosome reduction, preceding karyogamy, the increase of variability resulting from these processes should be regarded as a typical example of combinative variation (segregation).

Among individual examples of the constitution of species and of intra-specific polymorphism in ciliates, we may first of all consider representatives of the family Ophryoscolecidae, inhabiting the rumen and reticulum of ruminants. The polymorphism of the species in this group was studied by a number of Soviet protozoologists (Dogiel, 1927; Poljanskij and Strelkov, 1938*b*; Kil, 1940). The family Ophryoscolecidae is extremely rich in species. It includes the ciliates of the most complicated structure (in this case parasitism is not accompanied by a simplification of their organization), whose cytoplasm shows a pronounced differentiation into two and some-times three layers; their locomotor apparatus is highly differentiated, there is a system of digestive organoids, and various fibrillar structures, &c. The external morphology of the Ophryoscolecidae is also most varied, for many of its species possess various spines, processes, &c.

In brief, the main results of the works of the above-mentioned authors reveal the following complicated pattern of intraspecific polymorphism in-volving various morphological features. It was found, first of all, that the diversity of morphological forms in Ophryoscolecidae partly represents the phenomenon of modifications (mostly enduring modifications) within the limits of an exclusively wide standard of reaction. We have proved this in a most conclusive manner in the clones of several species, namely *Ento-dinium caudatum*, *Eudiplodinium neglectum* (Poljanskij and Strelkov, 1938), and *Diplodinium dentatum* (Kil, 1940). The amplitude of modification in *Entodinium caudatum* and *Diplodinium dentatum* is shown in Fig. 261. The variation affects chiefly the structure of the posterior end of the body—the number of spines and lobes, their relative dimensions, &c. It may be noted that in the case of *E. caudatum* the amplitude of variation in clones includes forms that had been previously described as independent species. Thus on Fig. 261 the fourth specimen (upper row from left to right) is identical with the former *E. lobosospinosum*, while the extreme right one, devoid of spines, is morphologically a typical *E. simplex*. Kil (1940) has demonstrated on clonal material the transformation of various forms of *Diplodinium*

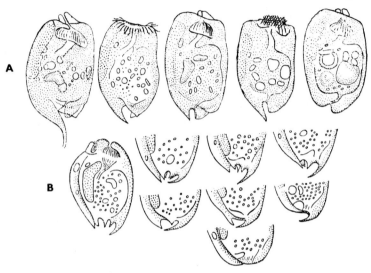

FIG. 261. Variation of the ciliates Ophryoscolecidae.

(*A*) *Entodinium caudatum* within a clone (after Poljanskij and Strelkov, 1938);
(*B*) *Diplodinium* (*Anoplodinium*) *dentatum* (after Kil, 1940).

dentatum (Fig. 261, *B*) into one another. Dogiel (1927) referred to these diverse morphological variants by the 'neutral' term of 'forms', while American authors (Kofoid and MacLennan, 1932) described all such forms as independent species; thus the amplitude of variation within the norm of reaction (on clonal material) embraced eight 'species' of the American authors. It has been demonstrated experimentally that the appearance of various forms within the range of variation is determined by the environmental conditions, and primarily by the nature of the food. By changing the diet it is possible for the experimenter to transform at will the form *E. caudatum* into the spineless '*E. simplex*', the six-spined *Diplodinium dentatum* into the spineless form '*anacanthum*', and vice versa. Thus the diversity of forms discussed above, leading to considerable morphological polymorphism within the limits of the species, does not, strictly speaking, represent polymorphism in the usual sense of this word, since this term usually denotes the presence of genotypically different groups within the species. In this case, however, there can be no doubt that we are dealing with modifications within the limits of a given genotype, since the experiments were carried out on clones. It is of interest that the exceptionally wide plasticity of some species of Ophryoscolecidae mentioned above is by no means a characteristic of all species of this family. A study of variation (in clones) of some other species (*Entodinium simplex*, *Eudiplodinium maggii*) revealed their stability and their narrow standard of reaction. It is noteworthy that at certain phases of their variation widely variable species as it were 'copy' other, slightly variable species. For instance, *E. caudatum* which had lost its dorsal spine and ventral lobes (Fig. 261, *A*), is phenotypically indistinguishable from *E. simplex*. Thus there exist, as it were, two *E. simplex*—the 'true' one and the spineless stage of *E. caudatum* 'simulating' it.

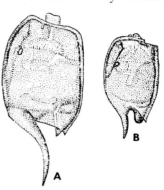

The wide amplitude of modifications does not exclude the presence in Ophryoscolecidae, within the limits of the species, of groups of genotypically distinct individuals. An examination of populations and clones in *Entodinium caudatum* has most clearly demonstrated the presence within this species of two races (Fig. 262). Race 'A' is noticeably larger than race 'B'; its caudal

FIG. 262. Biotypes of *Entodinium caudatum*.

(*A*) and (*B*) two races differing in body dimensions. (After Poljanskij and Strelkov, 1938*b*.)

spine grows to much greater relative length; moreover, these two races differ in their standard of reaction. Although each of them produces all the forms from '*caudatum*' to '*simplex*', nevertheless the smaller race 'B' is more readily transformed into the spineless state than race 'A'. Race 'A' possesses a more pronounced tendency to retain the spine. Within the races 'A' and 'B' there have been detected still smaller, apparently hereditarily stable forms which probably correspond to biotypes. They differ from each other in size, and in the nature of their reaction to the changes in environmental factors (order and character of the reduction of spines), &c.

Lubinsky (1957), who studied the ophryoscolecid ciliates from the stomach of the ruminants of Pakistan, likewise noted the wide morphological variability in the genus *Entodinium*. He gives a description of the range of variation in three species of this genus (*E. simulans*, *E. rectangulatum*, and *E. caudatum*) analogous to those discovered by Poljanskij and Strelkov in clones of *E. caudatum*.

Considerable differences have also been observed among the biotypes of *Diplodinium dentatum* in their ability to react to environmental changes (Kil, 1940). In one of the biotypes of this species, a change in the diet readily caused its transformation into a spineless form, or one with a small spine, while another proved to be much more inert, and could never be transformed completely into a spineless form. Divergences among the biotypes of Ophryoscolecidae are thus frequently expressed not so much by morphological differences as by the norm of reaction to changes in the environmental conditions.

The forms of intraspecific variability of certain Ophryoscolecidae considered above do not represent either geographical or ecological intraspecific groupings. However, in some cases geographical and ecological races do occur in them. Dogiel (1927a) gives examples of geographical variation in *Epidinium ecaudatum*. Populations of this ciliate in the southern regions of the U.S.S.R. are characterized, in contrast to those of northern areas, by thinner and more delicate spines. Dogiel notes distinct geographical forms also in some other species of Ophryoscolecidae (*Anoplodinium denticulatum, Entodinium furca*, and others). Finally, according to Dogiel, there also exist ecological forms of Ophryoscolecidae. They represent cases of morphological differences within the limits of a species, when it is parasitic in different hosts. For instance, the typical form *Eudiplodinium ypsilon ypsilon* is a parasite on cattle, whereas in the reindeer a special form of this species, *Eudiplodinium ypsilon magnum*, is encountered which differs in its dimensions and in certain morphological features. In the case of ecological and geographical forms of Ophryoscolecidae it is impossible to say, without a special experimental genetic investigation, whether we are dealing with groups genotypically differentiated by natural selection, with definitely directed modifications, or with enduring modifications. The first suggestion seems to us the most plausible.

A complex intraspecific polymorphism occurs also in parasitic ciliates of the genus *Balantidium* (Chejsin and Pick-Levontin, 1946).

An extraordinarily complex pattern of intraspecific differentiation was found in certain free-living ciliates. The study of these is concerned not so much with the morphological as with the physiological groupings within a species. Already half a century ago, in 1908, Jennings showed that in *Paramecium aurelia* and *P. caudatum* separate hereditarily stable biotypes, differing markedly both in morphological and physiological characters, could be separated from populations by means of selection.

The numerous experimental genetic investigations by American authors of the Jennings–Sonneborn school have demonstrated the presence of intraspecific groupings within the limits of species of the genus *Paramecium* (*P. aurelia, P. caudatum, P. bursaria, P. trichium*, and others), which have been called 'varieties' or 'syngens'. Sixteen such 'varieties' are known at present for *P. aurelia*. As a rule conjugation does not take place between ciliates belonging to different 'varieties': they cannot interbreed. Thus there is a physiological isolation between the 'varieties'. This isolation is not absolute, for in very rare cases a small number of pairings between ciliates belonging to different 'varieties' has been successfully obtained. However, the number of such pairs is always very small, and conjugation in most cases is not completed (to the formation of the synkaryon), while in the rare cases, when karyogamy does nevertheless take place, there is a very high mortality among the exconjugants. In their inability to interbreed, the separate 'varieties' are like independent species, comparable to the 'biological species' established by Cholodkovskij (1910) for plant lice.

Jennings and Opitz (1944) have shown that in *P. bursaria* in rare cases conjugation was observed between the 'varieties' 'R' (from the neighbourhood of Moscow) and other 'varieties' (from the U.S.A.), but it always leads to a fatal result—death of the exconjugants. Chen (1946), who studied the cytological aspect of this phenomenon, found that there was a pronounced disturbance in the course of the nuclear processes.

The differences between 'varieties' (syngens) were particularly thoroughly studied by Sonneborn and his school in *Paramecium aurelia* (Sonneborn, 1957). As already shown in the chapter on mating-types, each of the 'varieties' of this species contains two mating-types.[1] From the point of view of the problem regarding the nature of intraspecific differentiation, it is an interesting fact that among the 'varieties' of *P. aurelia* there is a divergence of their development in two directions. All the varieties fall into two groups, A and B, which, as we have seen above, differ essentially from each other in the determination of mating-types in the exconjugants.

Among the separate varieties of *P. aurelia* certain morphological and physiological differences have been observed.

Within a variety (the temperature and other conditions of the culture being equal) the dimensions remain very stable. Three varieties (1, 2, and 4) were studied for many years, and their sizes were found to remain surprisingly constant. This is illustrated by the following figures (length of *Paramecium* in microns), which are taken from Sonneborn's work (1957).

Authors	Variety 1	Variety 2	Variety 4
Sonneborn and Dippell, 1943 .	139	145	112
Powelson, 1956	131	149	112

The varieties differ also in various physiological characteristics, including resistance to heat and rate of division, and there are also quite essential differences among them as regards their life cycle. These differences concern the relative duration of separate phases of the cycle, namely that of immaturity, maturity, and ageing. In the varieties 4, 8, 10, and 14, for instance, a period of immaturity is completely absent—the exconjugants are capable of resuming the sexual process almost immediately after conjugation.

In other varieties the duration of this period may be variable. An extreme case is presented by variety 15, in which the period of immaturity lasts for half a year (Giese, 1957). Similar differences among the varieties have been

[1] The only exception apparently is the fifteenth variety which comprises four mating-types (Sonneborn, 1957).

noted also for two other phases of the life-cycle. It is interesting that the external conditions promoting the onset of conjugation or autogamy are not the same for different varieties. For instance, in varieties 2, 3, and 11 conjugation cannot take place at a temperature above 19° C. In contrast, in varieties 1, 4, 8, and 9 conjugation is possible even at much higher temperatures, up to 27° C. For certain varieties it has been established that the sexual process depends on illumination. For instance, in variety 3 the onset of conjugation is inhibited by light, whereas in the other, *P. aurelia*, this is not observed.

The distribution of separate varieties of *P. aurelia* is of interest, as it throws light on the geographical aspect of the constitution of this species. Sonneborn and his school have examined more than 260 samples of *P. aurelia*, collected in diverse regions of the world, and identified them according to the kind of variety to which they belong and type of mating. Unfortunately this abundant material provides data only for certain preliminary deductions regarding the geographical distribution of the varieties, owing to the fact that the localities from which *P. aurelia* was collected under natural conditions are very irregularly distributed. Of the 260 samples 200 were collected on the territory of the U.S.A., while the other 60 came mostly from Europe, Southern America, and Japan, and only isolated samples were obtained from other continents. Among the varieties studied some (1, 2, and 6) are apparently distributed throughout the world, while the other varieties have a much more restricted distribution. For instance, 3, 5, 7, 8, 10, 11, and 14 were discovered only on the territory of the U.S.A., 9 only in Europe. Finally, some have apparently a very restricted range; thus 12 were found only in Madagascar. In a number of cases there appears to be a definite correlation between the geographical distribution of certain varieties and their temperature requirements. Thus variety 6 is adapted to bodies of water in a hot climate, the same holds true but to a smaller extent for 7, 8, 10, and 14; other varieties (for instance 1, 2) do not show such a close connexion with the temperature factor.

Varieties of *P. aurelia* differ also in the form of their sexual process. In some conjugation is predominant and they are therefore outbreeders; in others the sexual process is accomplished by autogamy and conjugation within the limits of the karyonide (selfing): these forms are inbreeders. Finally, in the third kind conjugation and autogamy are represented to the same extent.

Varieties in which conjugation is the main form of sexual process (outbreeders) are usually characterized by a long life-cycle; they provide a good example of prolonged immaturity. This is probably associated with the necessity of finding a partner for conjugation. In contrast, the inbreeding varieties are characterized by a short cycle and a short period of immaturity (or its almost complete absence). These peculiarities of the sexual process are usually associated with the differentiation of local populations.

In recent years the American protozoological geneticists have made a very thorough study of the antigenic structure (serological properties) of *Paramecium aurelia*. The existence of antigens in *Paramecium* was first established by Rössle (1905, 1909); but the genetic aspect of this phenomenon has been studied by the school of Sonneborn (Sonneborn, 1943; Beale, 1954; Pringle, 1956; and others). The antigenic reaction is highly specific; it is carried out by introducing paramecia into the vein of a rabbit, in the blood-plasm of which there develops antibodies reacting with the antigen of *Paramecium*, and producing immobilization and death of the ciliates. This reaction is very sensitive and is effected at very high dilutions of the serum (1/800–1/3,200). However, antibodies formed against antigens of one line of paramecia do not react with other lines. Within one 'variety' it is possible to detect several types of antigens that are highy specific in evoking antibody response in the rabbit. The antigenic structure is hereditary. The mechanism of its inheritance has been established with some accuracy and it has also been shown that it is determined by both cytoplasmic and genetic factors. The manifestation of antigens depends largely on environmental conditions. The biological significance of the extraordinary heterogeneity of *Paramecium* as regards its antigenic structure remains unexplained. However, there is no doubt that it represents a form of intraspecific differentiation.

A complex intraspecific differentiation, similar to that observed in *P. aurelia*, is found also in other species of free-living ciliates, as has already been mentioned in the chapter on 'mating-types'.

Thus American and Japanese authors have described sixteen varieties (syngens) in *Paramecium caudatum* (Sonneborn, 1957). Moreover, Vivier (1960) found four varieties in France, two of which proved to be identical with the American ones, while six varieties of *P. caudatum* were isolated in our Leningrad laboratory from samples collected chiefly in the northern areas of the U.S.S.R. Their comparison with the American lines has not yet been carried out.

However, the pattern of intraspecific groupings of *P. caudatum* must differ from those of *P. aurelia*, since in the former species autogamy is either completely or almost absent, but 'selfing' clones are frequently encountered.

The characteristic peculiarities of intraspecific groupings are also encountered in a third species of *Paramecium*, *P. bursaria*. Here there are plural systems of mating-types, a comparatively smaller number of varieties than in *P. aurelia*, and outbreeding occurs almost exclusively.

We cannot within the scope of this book give a more detailed analysis of the problems of intraspecific differentiation in ciliates, but it is clear from what has been said that, apart from common characteristics, different species also possess minor peculiarities of their own.

The presence within the species *P. aurelia* of special strains of 'killers', first discovered by Sonneborn (1938), is of great interest. These races do not coincide with the varieties, but form a component part of the latter, and are encountered only among some of the 'varieties' known at present. This phenomenon consists in the following: when individuals belonging to a 'killer' strain are simultaneously present in a drop of water with ciliates of the same species but not of the 'killer' race (the so-called 'sensitives') the latter perish fairly quickly. Their death is due to the secretion by the 'killers' of a special substance of the type of the antibiotics, called 'paramecin', whose effect on the 'sensitives' is lethal, but is not harmful to the 'killers' themselves. There is yet another type of 'killer', the so-called 'mate-killers', first discovered by Siegel (1952). They kill the 'sensitives' only during conjugation. When the conjugating pair consists of a 'killer' and a 'sensitive', the exconjugant derived from the sensitive partner dies immediately after separation of the pair.

The characteristics of the 'killers' are hereditary. The genetic mechanism of the transmission of this characteristic has been very fully studied by American geneticists. This characteristic is genetically determined on the one hand by the nuclear dominant gene 'K', and, on the other, by special cytoplasmic factors (plasmogenes called 'kappa'). These may be recognized in the endoplasm cytologically in the shape of small round or oval bodies very rich in DNK (deoxyribonucleic acid). 'Kappa' particles are capable of self-reproduction. Without dwelling at greater length on the purely genetic aspect of these phenomena, it may be emphasized only that they are of great interest from the point of view of the problem of biological differentiation of the species and of intraspecific biological interrelations.

New data that have recently come to light make it necessary to reconsider the problem of the nature of 'kappa' (Sonneborn, 1959). It was found that there are several categories of self-reproducing particles in the endoplasm of *Paramecium aurelia*, only some of which produce the killer-effect. The rates of multiplication of these particles do not always coincide with those of ciliates themselves. During a high division rate of paramecia (which is readily produced at a suitable temperature) the particles cannot keep pace and divide as quickly, so that their number gradually decreases and they may completely disappear from the endoplasm. In contrast, when the rate of fission of the ciliates is slow, the particles may 'overtake' the ciliate and accumulate in the endoplasm in very large numbers.

On account of this many investigators regard 'kappa' particles and other reproducing endoplasmic particles of *Paramecium* as symbionts, whose nature, however, remains obscure. It has been suggested that they might be bacteria, rickettsias, or virus particles.

We do not propose to discuss here this very complex and still obscure question, for it is not directly connected with the problem under consideration. In any case, even if 'kappa' and similar particles are symbiotic organisms, their development in the endoplasm is determined by the genotype of *Paramecium*. As has been stated above, 'kappa' particles develop only in the presence of the dominant gene K. It is noteworthy that in homozygous individuals KK, about twice as many of them develop as in heterozygous Kk individuals. In many varieties 'kappa' particles do not develop at all. Consequently, even if the hypothesis of the symbiotic nature of 'kappa' particles is accepted, their relationship with *P. aurelia* may be regarded as one of the manifestations of intraspecific polymorphism.

The question of intraspecific geographical variability of different species of *Paramecium* was dealt with from a somewhat different point of view by Smaragdova (1941) in the U.S.S.R. She carried out a comparative study of *P. aurelia*, *P. bursaria*, and *P. caudatum* from the southern regions of the European part of the U.S.S.R., from the Moscow district, and from the northern regions. She detected definite differences in the temperature optimum between the Moscow and southern *P. aurelia* as well as between northern and southern *P. bursaria*, but no essential difference was observed in *P. caudatum*. The size of the body of *P. bursaria* changes from north to south (being larger in the north and smaller in the south); moreover, these differences are hereditarily fixed. Smaragdova interbred lines of different geographical distributions and found that the highest mortality among exconjugants occurred on interbreeding northern forms with Moscow or southern ones, and the lowest on interbreeding the Moscow *P. bursaria* with each other (Smaragdova, 1941, p. 83). What is the relationship of the geographical variability observed by Smaragdova to the 'varieties' of the American authors? Are these phenomena of the same order or not? Further comparative investigations are required in order to answer these questions.

It is evident from the short survey given above of the forms of intra-specific differentiation in free-living ciliates that the 'structure of species' in these organisms is extremely complex and original. It should be borne in mind that in the case of ciliates this problem has been investigated so far only in very few species, and it is evident that further study of it, based on broad comparative material with the application of genetic methods of investigation, is necessary.

We can now turn to a consideration of the structure of species and of polymorphism in parasitic Protozoa with complex cycles of development, with an obligatory sexual process, and sporogony. Let us take as an example *Plasmodium vivax*, the causative organism of benign tertian malaria in man, which has been fully and widely studied. Within this species, which, as is well known, has an extraordinarily wide geographical distribution, there is great diversity of strains (they should apparently be regarded as races or demes) differing in various characters (see Boyd, 1949). The differences between strains of *P. vivax* concern antigenic properties, pathogenecity for man, preference for different species of vectors (mosquitoes of the genus *Anopheles*), and the duration of the incubation period in man. Apparently in some series of *P. vivax* certain morphological differences can be detected. These differences, however, might possibly be regarded as pathological deviations caused by the action of special factors (Field, 1942). Many races of *P. vivax* are associated with a definite geographical distribution: the Madagascar strain, which is characterized by great virulence and a short incubation period, is a good example. Races of malaria parasites, with a long incubation period, are of great interest. This phenomenon was first noticed by Swellengrebel *et al.* (1929), and then studied in detail for many years by Nikolaev (1939, 1949) and others. Nikolaev demonstrated on abundant material that there are two types of incubation in benign tertian malaria: short (8–23 days) and long (7–12 months). In the second type there is a very considerable interval of time between the inoculation of man with sporozoites of *P. vivax* from *Anopheles* and the appearance of schizonts in the peripheral blood. In Nikolaev's opinion, strains with a long incubation period are characteristic of the northern regions of the distribution of *P. vivax*, while in the southern regions most of the strains have a short incubation period. Nikolaev explains the predominance in the north of strains with a long incubation as an adaptation of the parasite to an existence in northern latitudes. Owing to the shortness of the summer season, only one generation of *Plasmodium* is capable of developing in the mosquitoes, i.e. there is only one passage through the vector. If the schizonts, and later the gametocytes, appeared in the blood of man in 2–3 weeks after inoculation, which can take place only in the second half of the summer, then the parasites taken up by the mosquito again would not be able to complete the sporogony again, owing to the fall of the temperature of the air in the autumn (it has been established experimentally that the development of *P. vivax* in the mosquito does not proceed at temperatures below 16° C.). A prolonged incubation period enables *Plasmodium* to persist in man until the following spring, when the environmental conditions again become suitable for that part of the life-cycle of the parasite which takes place in the mosquito. We believe this to be the most plausible and most acceptable explanation. Nikolaev regards the strains of *P. vivax* with a long incubation as a separate subspecies; however, this question of nomenclature does not seem to us to be of much importance. We are concerned here not with the name to be used for uniting strains with a long incubation period, but with the fact that such strains really exist, and that they represent one of the forms of intraspecific differentiation.

The existence of intraspecific polymorphism has been discovered also in other species of the genus *Plasmodium*. However, in *P. falciparum* and *P. malaria* strains with a long incubation period have not been observed.

In our discussion of the problems of intraspecific variability in Protozoa we ought to mention the phenomenon of enduring modifications ('Dauer-modifikationen') first discovered by Jollos (1913, 1921, 1934) in the ciliates *Paramecium*. In contrast to ordinary modifications, the enduring ones do not disappear when the action of the factors that induced them is discontinued, but persist throughout a long series of agamous generations. Jollos obtained enduring modifications by increasing resistance to the effect of AS_2O_3 and to some other factors. Orlova (1941, 1947), Poljanskij and Orlova (1948), and Poljanskij (1957) obtained in *Paramecium caudatum* enduring modifications of an adaptive character to the changes in the content of salt in the medium and to higher temperature. The morphological changes in Ophryoscolecidae described above should, no doubt, be regarded, to a considerable extent, as enduring modifications (Poljanskij and Strelkov, 1938), since their characteristics are modified some time after changes in the environmental conditions had taken place. Enduring modifications have now been observed in many Protozoa: thus, Moewus (1934) studied them in chlamydomonads.

Variations in the antigenic structure in trypanosomes, arising in relapse strains as a result of adaptation to successive antibodies produced by the host, apparently represent enduring modifications (Hoare, 1956a). Thus one or another phenotype of a protozoon is determined not only by its genotype and the environmental conditions under which the phenotype is shaped in the process of multiplication and development of a given generation, but also by diverse 'after effects' of many factors, which acted upon it in the course of preceding agamous generations. This question is in need of further systematic investigations.

Is there any evidence for regarding the intraspecific groupings in Protozoa as the initial phases of divergence leading to speciation? In our opinion this question can be answered in the affirmative. Some factual material supporting this view has already been adduced above. Thus, in the case of trypanosomes, Hoare expressed the opinion that *Trypanosoma evansi* had probably originated from *T. brucei*. This process probably passed through phases similar to those through with *T. vivax* is passing at present after spreading beyond the boundaries of its vector *Glossina*. The contemporary species of *Leishmania*—*L. tropica* (the cause of cutaneous leishmaniasis) and *L. donovani* (the cause of visceral leishmaniasis)—represent the results of a comparatively very recent divergence, as may be judged by the complete morphological identity of the two parasites and by the ability retained in *L. donovani* to produce the cutaneous form of leishmaniasis under experimental conditions (in dogs). The process of formation of new forms within the genus *Leishmania* is probably still going on at present, as shown by the existence in *L. tropica* of distinct forms (evidently races)—*t. major* and *t. minor*—differing epidemiologically and in clinical pattern. It is evident from these examples that in a number of cases among Protozoa speciation has conformed to the classical Darwinian pattern and the varieties represent the initial phases of this process.

In parasitic Protozoa there are no factual data for the free-living Protozoa —speciation might also have proceeded in a somewhat different way. In this respect the pattern of the process of speciation in parasites which was proposed by V. B. Dubinin (1954) is fully applicable to Protozoa. According to his hypothesis, speciation in parasites may proceed in the form of either a fairly sharp 'jump' or of a slow accumulation of new properties in varieties. The former takes place when there are pronounced changes in the conditions of life (e.g. on transfer to a new host, a change in the localization of the parasite in the host, &c.). This type of divergence frequently leads to the formation of 'conjoint species' in Dogiel's (1949) sense. Among Protozoa, Coccidia may serve as a good example of the formation of 'conjoint species' (Chejsin, 1947, 1957). Several species of the genus *Eimeria* are parasitic in the alimentary tract of the rabbit. Each of these species (*Eimeria magna, E. media, E. irresidua, E. perforans*, and others) is characterized by a definite localization both along the alimentary canal and in the tissues of the intestinal wall (in the epithelium itself, in the sub-epithelial connective tissue, &c.). In this case it is conceivable that the process of speciation was directly associated with a change of localization in the intestine and that divergence led comparatively soon to the separation of 'conjoint species' of *Eimeria* in the alimentary tract of the rabbit.

'Conjoint species' are apparently widespread among parasitic Protozoa. They probably include *Trichomonas intestinalis* and *Trichomonas vaginalis*, various species of the genus *Trichodina*, some of which are parasitic on the gills, some on the fins, and others in the urinary bladder of fish.

The problem of speciation in Protozoa lies outside the scope of this book; therefore we shall not consider it in greater detail. It has been mentioned here merely to show the connexion between the intraspecific differentiation in Protozoa and the problem of speciation.

The following are some of the conclusions based on data considered in this chapter:

1. A 'form of life' on the species level is characteristic of all groups of Protozoa irrespective of their type of multiplication and the character of their life-cycle.

2. In all groups of Protozoa (both free-living and parasitic) there is a complex intraspecific differentiation, the type of which depends largely on the conditions of existence of the species, on their method of reproduction, and the pattern of their life-cycle.

3. The intraspecific groupings of Protozoa (biotypes, forms, races, and subspecies) are in certain cases connected with geographical and in others with ecological factors. However, it is by no means always possible to associate the intraspecific polymorphism of Protozoa with definite ecological and geographical conditions.

4. The distinction between the biotypes and races within a species of Protozoa may be based on various criteria. Sometimes they are represented by physiological and immunological characters, without visible morpho-

logical differences. Intraspecific groups frequently differ from each other by the standard of their reactions.

5. In some cases the existence of marked ecological and physiological differences have been demonstrated between intraspecific groupings which are separable by the absence of interbreeding between the 'varieties'.

6. The intraspecific groupings in Protozoa may be regarded not only as a form in which the species exists, but also as the initial steps in speciation, the primary phases of divergence. However, the process of speciation in Protozoa may apparently follow various patterns.

THE BIOGENETIC LAW AND PROTOZOA

The problem of the applicability of the biogenetic law in the interpretation of the evolution of the Protozoa has so far received little attention in textbooks on protozoology. However, a careful consideration of the comparative morphology and life-cycles of different groups of Protozoa reveals numerous and striking examples of the recapitulation of ancestral characteristics in the most diverse groups.

Severcev (1939) established three main modes of phylogenetic development: anabolism, deviation, and archallaxis. In most cases the characters of the ancestral adults, i.e. the last stages of their morphogenesis, are recapitulated. This represents the anabolic mode, i.e. phylogenetic development by superposition to the final stages of ontogenesis. Recapitulation of the early embryonic characters of the ancestor with deviations at later stages is characteristic of the mode of deviation: it is produced as a result of a change in the development during the middle stage of ontogenesis. Finally, in the third mode, i.e. archallaxis, the course of development deviates from the ancestral type already in the initial stages of ontogenesis, and in such cases recapitulation of characters is generally absent.

In Protozoa anabolism is encountered most frequently, signs of deviation are much more rare, while archallaxis is most pronounced in Sporozoa, where adaptation to a parasitic mode of existence, especially in combination with an alternation of hosts, frequently obliterates all ancestral characters.

The pattern of the recapitulation of characters is usually revealed during the course of ontogenesis of Protozoa, i.e. when tracing different stages of the life-cycle of Protozoa, or various phases of the growth of an individual. However, in some cases recapitulation is revealed either in certain peculiarities of nuclear division or under definite experimental conditions.

A prerequisite of the process of recapitulation in a recapitulating organism is the occurrence of stages of development on the one hand, and, on the other, a certain life-cycle involving the recurrence of stages of development in a definite order, so that on completion of a cycle certain stages serve as starting points of a new cycle.

We can now turn to the conditions under which the phenomenon of recapitulation in Protozoa is most frequently encountered. It is often observed in organisms during a change in their mode of life.

In free-living Protozoa the most common change in the mode of life is the transition from a motile to a sessile or attached existence. A whole subclass of ciliates, the Suctoria, may serve as the best example of this type. This is a large group of ciliates, which—apart from a few plankton or parasitic forms—has become permanently adapted to a sedentary mode of life.

The complete adaptation to the sessile state is manifested in the presence in Suctoria of a whole series of specialized structural features. The body of the majority of Suctoria is attached to a stalk and in many of them it is covered by a cup-shaped lorica; cilia disappear completely in all stages of life, except in one very short one. Furthermore, even the whole sexual process, i.e. conjugation, takes place in the fixed state. Finally, the ingestion of food in Suctoria is quite peculiar, since the mouth has disappeared and food is taken in by sucking tentacles. However, all Suctoria, in addition to monotomic fission of vegetative individuals, which proceeds without a sign of any recapitulation, multiply by means of exogenous or endogenous budding, the products of which become detached from the suctorian and are represented by ciliated swarmers. This ciliated stage indicates first of all a temporary reversal to the motile and ciliated ancestral form, some kind of free-living ciliates. The arrangement of cilia in the swarmers points to the origin of Suctoria from a definite group of ciliates.

Collin (1912) considered in detail the problem of the phylogeny of Suctoria and arrived at the following conclusion. The ciliary covering of the swarmers of Suctoria is, in the great majority of cases, composed of several circles of cilia, surrounding the body. In Peritricha the cilia are also arranged in circles; it is true that there is only one circlet, but it is composed not of cilia but of a row of membranelles, which had presumably been produced by the coalescence of several circlets of ordinary cilia. Moreover, Poljanskij has demonstrated the presence in *Polycycla*, a Trichodina-like peritrichous ciliate from holothurians, of as many as twenty circlets of cilia encircling the body. Besides, the stalk of Suctoria at the time when the swarmers become attached to the substratum has a longitudinally striated structure, as in the swarmers of Vorticellidae with a non-contractile stalk. Finally, at one pole of the swarmers there is a small bundle of cilia which Collin regards as a rudiment of the adoral zone of Peritricha.

Kahl (1931), however, tried to prove that the Suctoria originated from some primitive Holotricha through such forms as *Actinobolus* with prehensile tentacles. It may be added that *Enchelyomorpha*, a close relative of *Actinobolus*, and also equipped with tentacles, has several belts of cilia, resembling in this respect the swarmers of Suctoria, but the tentacles of *Actinobolus* have no opening at the end, and no lumen inside; the end of the tentacles is equipped with a bundle of trichocysts, therefore both the structure and the function of the tentacles is different from that in the suctorians. Guilcher (1951) and Corliss (1956, 1959) also suggested that the Suctoria had originated from the Holotricha (Gymnostomata). Their suggestion is based on the resemblance in the infraciliature of the swarmers of Suctoria and of some of the lower holotrichous ciliates.

Whatever the origin of Suctoria, it is evident that during their entogeny a recapitulation of the ancestral characters takes place, expressed in the formation of a ciliated free-living stage.

A somewhat similar phenomenon is observed in the Peritricha. Their motile 'larval' stage (telotroch) has a circlet or belt of cilia at the posterior end of the body. In this respect they somewhat resemble the Thigmotrichida ciliates. It is highly probable that it is precisely from them that the Peritricha take their origin (Fauré-Fremiet, 1950; Corliss, 1956), and the structural characters of the swarmers can therefore be regarded as ancestral.

According to Fauré-Fremiet, some of the Peritricha Loricata, for example *Vaginicola*, are interesting from the evolutionary point of view in that they produce swarmers of a different origin from those formed by the stalked Peritricha, since in *Vaginicola* swarmers are formed as the result of binary fission of the vegetative individual within the lorica. In the course of this process one of the daughter individuals retains its connexion with the lorica, remaining inside it, while the other swims away as a swarmer. In its significance the latter resembles the swarmers of Suctoria, and is of special interest since it points to the existence in this species of an obvious dimorphism of vegetative individuals. Its body has a somewhat different cylindrical shape, its mouth is very small and, to a certain extent, rudimentary, and in the anterior end of its body there is a special accumulation of opaque, black pigment. This black spot evidently plays the role of a sensory apparatus. Thus, although the *Vaginicola* swarmer possesses pronounced distinguishing characteristics, they are not ancestral. In fact, the rudimentary state of the mouth can hardly be regarded as characteristic of any ancestors of this form, but is simply an expression 'of the fact that the swarmer does not feed during the period of its motile life. Likewise, the pigmented 'eye' cannot be attributed to recapitulation of characters since it is an entirely original structure, not encountered in any other ciliates. The 'eye' is evidently a coenogenetic new structure developed in connexion with the free-living existence of the swarmer. After the swarmer settles on the bottom and the lorica is formed, the 'eye' is resorbed, and the oral apparatus is reconstructed, forming a widely open peristome.

This example is particularly interesting, since it emphasizes the caution required in interpreting the evolutionary significance of various characteristics in Protozoa.

According to Pascher (1917), *Dinamoebidium varians* is a splendid example of the influence of the transition to the creeping mode of life accompanied by recapitulation of the flagelloid form. *Dinamoebidium* is a marine form living on the bottom among dense growths of Schizophyceae together with small diatoms, unicellular green algae, and flagellates. It attains 40–60 μ in diameter, has short lobose pseudopodia, is very motile, and feeds on all the above-mentioned organisms, seizing them by means of its pseudopodia and digesting them in food vacuoles. In a word it is a true, purely hetero-trophic amoeba in its vegetative phase. Further observations, however, showed that *Dinamoebidium* represents a greatly modified representative of plankton Dinoflagellata, which, according to Pascher, should be separated into a special family Dinamoebaceae, establishing for it among the Dino-flagellata a special series of amoeboid forms under the name Rhizodininae, the sole member of which, so far, is *Dinamoebidium*. This nature of *Dina-moebidium* is clearly demonstrated by a series of stages in its life-cycle, which repeat the life-cycle of typical Gymnodiniaceae, but lead up finally to the formation of a prolonged amoeboid vegetative stage,. with which we began our description. Adult amoeboids may encyst, producing elongated 'horned' cysts, which are characteristic of Gymnodiniaceae. The contents of the cysts divide palintomically into four to eight parts, which are trans-formed into zoospores typical of naked Dinoflagellata, possessing longi-tudinal and transverse flagella and resembling individuals of the genus *Gymnodinium*. These cysts rupture and the flagellated swarmers escape out of them, but after a short free swimming period (not more than 15 minutes) they settle down on the bottom and acquire an amoeboid form. Thus the whole life-cycle of *Dinamoebidium*, except for the 15 minutes, is passed in the amoeboid state. The zoospores of Dinoflagellata (as may be seen in *Noctiluca* and certain parasitic dinoflagellates, *Coccidinium*) are probably gametes; in that case copulation in *Dinamoebidium* is probably accomplished in the amoeboid state, so that the recapitulation characters are represented by the formation of horned cysts, by palintomy inside them, and by the formation of flagellated gymnodiniid swarmers.

The transition to a pelagic mode of life, with the loss of any connexion with the land, also produces important modifications in the organization of Protozoa. In this case a number of recapitulations may be preserved as a reflection of the changes experienced. In this respect the subclass Radio-laria is especially instructive. All the Radiolaria are typical oceanic animals, characteristic inhabitants of the open sea. However, the mode of life in all of them is more or less alike, their environment—i.e. the mass of water of the world ocean—also changes to a much lesser extent than the coastal waters and the freshwater and terrestrial environments. Nevertheless, there is no other group of Protozoa which displays such a great variety of struc-ture and so large a number of species.

The extraordinary variety and multiplicity of Radiolaria in a comparatively uniform environment and mode of life still remain a riddle, but in this case we are interested in the fact that the great antiquity of the Radiolaria and the great plasticity of their structure make it possible to trace in them a certain series of forms, the higher members of which recapitulate in their ontogeny a whole series of stages which are characteristic of the structure of the adult individuals of those species that are found at lower levels of a given series of forms. Such series of forms, which developed progressively so far as their skeleton is concerned, were demonstrated very clearly and in great detail by Ševjakov (1926) in the order Acantharia because he had succeeded in following the whole life-cycle of these animals from the zygote to the adult vegetative stage.

The zygote of Radiolaria is produced by the fusion of two flagellated gametes with ancestral flagelloid characters. It is impossible to trace phylogeny down to some definite group of Mastigophora or Sarcodina. It can only be noted that the gametes of Radiolaria very closely resemble those of Foraminifera, so that the origin of Radiolaria from the latter group cannot be excluded. In that case the resemblance of their gametes to those of the Foraminifera can be regarded as the first sign of recapitulation. The zygote acquires the shape of a plasmatic sphere, from the centre of which radiates a bundle of spicules, characteristic of the so-called asteroid skeleton of Radiolaria. In the family Acanthometridae all the twenty spicules of the skeleton in typical cases have identical dimensions and shapes and are devoid of processes. Another family, the Lithopteridae is thought to have originated from the Acanthometridae, although the extreme, most highly specialized species of Lithopteridae, the genus *Lithoptera* for instance (Fig. 263), are completely different in their appearance. Sixteen of the twenty radial spicules of *Lithoptera* are more or less shortened and attenuated, in other words underdeveloped. On the other hand, the four remaining spicules lying in one equatorial plane are very strongly developed and are equipped with lateral processes in the shape of large, perforated plates. As a result of the development of these lateral apophyses, as they are called, the whole skeleton acquires the shape of a remarkably elegant fenestrated cross extended in the equatorial plane. In spite of the peculiar shape of its skeleton, *Lithoptera* originated from the family Acanthometridae. During the development and growth of *Lithoptera* the youngest stages possess a skeleton composed of twenty identical spicules devoid of any apophyses. This is as it were the acanthometrid stage. Only much later, when the central capsule, pseudopodia, and myonemes have become differentiated, transverse apophyses appear on four of the spicules, which are first simple and short, but later becoming two or three layers thick and at the same time perforated. In the course of this gradual hypertrophy of the four spicules, the young *Lithoptera* pass through a series of recapitulations. The separate stages of *Lithoptera* differ from each other so much that Haeckel regarded them as distinct forms. Thus, according to Ševjakov, *Lithoptera mülleri* goes through the *Xiphoptera* stages with one transverse trabecula on the equatorial spicules, through the *Lithopteranna* stage with two trabeculae connected by means of 4–7 cross-pieces, and through the

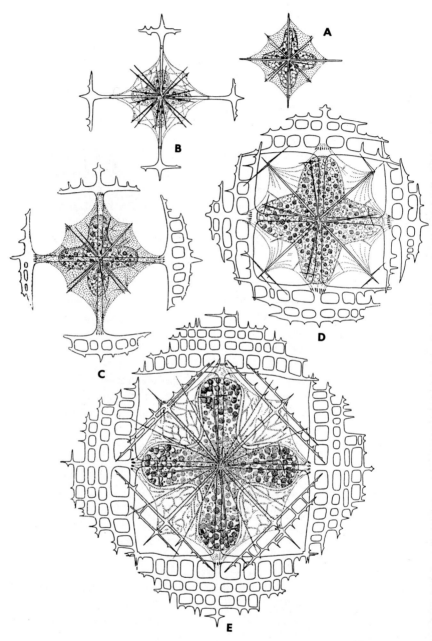

FIG. 263. Development of Strelkov Acanthometrid *Lithoptera mülleri.*

(*A*) young stage; (*B*) *Xiphoptera* stage; (*C*) *Lithopteranna* stage; appendages on equatorial spicules become 2-rowed and cribriform; (*D*) *Lithopteromma* stage; appendages on the equatorial spicules become 4-rowed; (*E*) adult animal. (After Ševjakov, 1926.)

Lithopteromma and *Lithopterella* stage with five trabeculae connected by 5–10 cross-pieces.

From the family of *Acanthometridae* also originates the family *Dorataspidae*, the skeleton of which has the appearance of a single fenestrated sphere, produced in such a way that from each spicule, at some distance

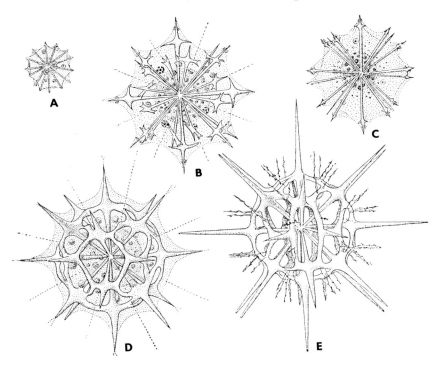

FIG. 264. Development of Acanthometrid *Pleuraspis costata*.

(*A*) young stage devoid of appendages on spicules; (*B*) *Lithophyllium* stage with two lateral apophyses on spicules; (*C*) *Phractacantha* stage; (*D*) *Phractaspis* stage; dichotomous, tangential apophyses fused into a cribriform sphere; (*E*) skeleton of adult animal; lateral dented spicules have appeared on cribriform sphere. (After Ševjakov, 1926.)

from its free end, there are formed first two transverse trabeculae, lying tangentially to the surface of the spherical body. Then each trabecula splits repeatedly, forming little dichotomous branches the ends of which come in contact with each other, with the result that a hollow fenestrated skeletal sphere is produced with the tips of the radial spicules protruding above its surface. The successive stages of the complication of the skeleton, and the increase in the number of nuclei and myonemes, have been fully traced by Ševjakov in *Pleuraspis costata* (Fig. 264), and proved to be similar in structure to the adult skeletons of certain genera with a simpler structure, namely *Lithophyllium* and *Phractacantha*. Thus the stages of development of certain genera recapitulate the structure of adult skeletons of others.

In a word, as may be seen from what has been said above, the *Acantharia* reveal several excellent phylogenetic series, based not only on comparative anatomy, but also on the ontogeny of the organisms supported, moreover, by many examples of clear recapitulation of characters.

It is natural that the peculiarities of a parasitic, and especially endo-parasitic, mode of life must have exerted a strong influence on such Pro-tozoa, and produced significant changes in them. However, examples of the recapitulation of the stages passed by them are not very numerous. Perhaps the cause of this is the fact that the great modifications undergone by them as a result of the parasitic mode of life has affected them more than other groups.

Among the parasites in which there is no alternation of hosts, one might mention the polycystid gregarines, which in the vegetative adult stage consist of two parts, the protomerite and the deutomerite, whereas the body of their young stages is simply undivided; in this they recapitulate to a certain extent the characteristics of the more simply constructed *Mono-cystidae* with their unsegmented body.

Among the masses of flagellates parasitizing the alimentary tract of termites there are two allied genera, *Oxymonas* and *Proboscidiella*, the second of which repeats the structure of the first in the course of its own development. *Oxymonas* has one nucleus, one axostyle, and four flagella, while *Proboscidiella* displays the same features only during its youth; in later stages *Proboscidiella* becomes multinucleate, and develops many sets of flagella and axostyles.

It may likewise be said that the higher representatives of *Opalinata*, namely the multinucleate *Opalina* and *Cepedea*, repeat in their development and growth the binucleate stage, which represents the final step of develop-ment in the more primitive genera *Protoopalina* and *Zelleriella*.

The phenomenon of recapitulation has been clearly demonstrated in various members of the family *Trypanosomidae* (Hoare, 1933, 1960), the cycle of development of which takes place either in one host (monogenetic *Trypanosomidae*) or with an alternation of hosts (digenetic), usually a vertebrate and an invertebrate.

In Hoare's opinion, the digenetic *Trypanosomidae* of vertebrate hosts originated from monogenetic flagellates inhabiting the alimentary tract of insects. This may have taken place in the following manner: the in-testinal flagellates of those insects that acquired blood-sucking habits found their way into the body of a vertebrate and gradually adapted themselves to the new habitat in another host, giving rise to leishmanias and trypano-somes, while the insects became vectors of these haemoflagellates.

In their vertebrate hosts members of the genus *Leishmania* are always represented by rounded leishmanial forms (2–$3\,\mu$ in diameter), while in the vectors, the sand-fly, they acquire the leptomonad form. This fact provides important evidence of their origin from the genus *Leptomonas*, in which leishmanial stage is transitory and serves for the transmission of the parasite from host to host. On the other hand, in the genus *Leishmania*, the leishmanial form becomes the main stage that predominates throughout the whole cycle of development, while the leptomonad one becomes subsidiary, serving for the infection of the vertebrate host. Hence the appearance in the cycle of development of *Leishmania* in the vector of the leptomonad form may be regarded as a recapitulation of the characters of the ancestors.

As regards the genus *Trypanosoma*, its members have stages of development similar to those of the genera *Crithidia* and *Herpetomonas*. Therefore it may be assumed that the trypanosomes originated from one of these genera (Hoare, 1948). In the alimentary tract of the vector the trypanosomes, ingested with blood, are transformed into crithidial forms and the latter are later again transformed into trypanosome forms, representing metacyclic trypanosomes. The latter represent the infective stage, serving for the transmission to new vertebrate hosts. Thus the crithidial stage, which is always present in the life-cycle of trypanosomes, recapitulates the original ancestral forms. This stage may disappear from the cycle, as for example in *T. equiperdum*, the causative organism of dourine in horses. In this case the insect vector is also eliminated from the cycle, and only the trypanosome form remains, which is transmitted from horse to horse by direct contact. From what has been said above about different types of gametes in Protozoa (see p. 322), there can be no doubt that the structure of gametes may frequently provide good criteria for the understanding of the ancestral forms of Protozoa, especially of those that have been altered beyond recognition by parasitism (*Blastodinidae, Haplozoon*, and others).

The group of ciliated Protozoa which is so rich in species provides only scanty data on recapitulation. The clearest indications of this phenomenon are provided by the behaviour of the macronucleus at different phases in the life-cycle of ciliates. Whatever shape the macronucleus may assume in the vegetative stages—and it varies considerably—the so-called 'placenta', i.e. the new macronuclei formed in exconjugants, always have a regular spherical shape. It would not be a strained interpretation to say that this constancy of the shape of the placentas should be regarded as a recapitulation of the spherical nucleus present in the majority of recent ciliates; while in a more distant past this might have been a recapitulation of the vesicular nucleus of the ancestors of all the ciliates in general.

Moreover, the behaviour of the macronucleus during the vegetative multiplication is most significant. At the beginning of division the macronuclei of any shape become either spherical or oval; therefore indications of recapitulation are also encountered in the modifications undergone by the macronucleus during vegetative multiplication. This recapitulation is especially pronounced in forms like *Urostyla* (Raabe, 1947), where the macronucleus is composed of hundreds of small, elongated nuclei. At each division they all fuse together into one huge division nucleus, which after fission breaks up again into a hundred small macronuclei.

Recapitulation of the structure of the macronucleus is especially clearly revealed in the ciliate *Tripalmaria dogieli* (Fig. 265) of the family *Cyclo-*

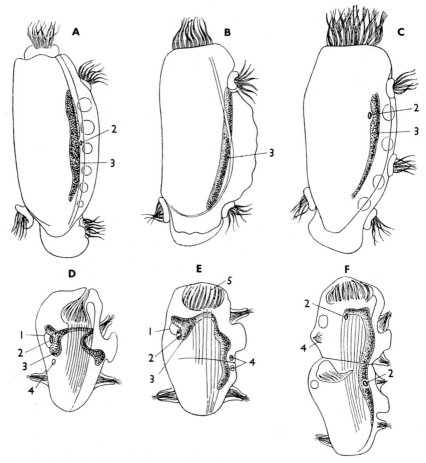

FIG. 265. Position of macronucleus and micronucleus in different Cycloposthiidae (*A*)–(*C*), and change in their position during nuclear division in *Tripalmaria* (*D*)–(*F*). All animals are orientated with their dorsal side to the right.

A, *Tripalmaria*; B, *Tricaudalia*; C, *Prototapirella*; D, *Tripalmaria*. 1, vacuole; 2, micronucleus; 3, macronucleus; 4, new primordial bundles of membranelles; 5, adoral spiral of membranelles. (Original.)

posthiidae. In one of its forms there occurs repeated recapitulation of both ancient and more recent—but still ancestral—characters. During conjugation the spherical form of the placenta of *Tripalmaria* repeats the type of spherical nucleus common to all ciliates, while during vegetative multiplication the nucleus first loses its peculiar branched shape and becomes elongated, then moves to the dorsal side of the body and repeats more concretely the shape of nucleus characteristic of the less specialized members of the family *Cycloposthiidae*. Thus in ciliates certain phylogenetic deductions can be made on the basis of the behaviour of their macronucleus.

PHENOMENA OF CONVERGENCE IN PROTOZOA

In considering the evolution of Protozoa the question naturally arises as to whether the peculiar phenomena of convergence, that are fairly frequently encountered among Metazoa, and have at times been a source of serious phylogenetic misinterpretations, have been observed in Protozoa.

Examples of far-reaching convergences are actually fairly widespread in the world of Protozoa. An analysis of the variety of converging characters shows that they may to a certain extent be subdivided into two main categories, one of which concerns the major architectonic characteristics of the animal, the other the minor, more detailed characteristics of the similarity between the animals compared. All the most pronounced examples of convergence among Protozoa concern coincidences of shape in the structure of the skeletons, whereas other systems of organoids converge much more rarely. Convergences are accordingly especially widespread among the *Sarcodina* equipped with a skeleton, i.e. in *Radiolaria* and *Foraminifera*. *Radiolaria* provide exceptionally rich material, which is understandable, since the extraordinary abundance of species in this group offers much scope for the evolution of the phenomena of coincidence of characters.

In the special literature devoted, the question of convergences in *Radiolaria* has been dealt with mainly by Haecker (1907–9) in the general part of his monograph on this group.

In our survey we shall also dwell first on *Radiolaria* (Figs. 266–76). It may be noted that convergence is observed in groups removed from each other in various degrees. Convergences in the structure of the skeleton (and in the case of *Radiolaria* we shall deal only with these) may develop among representatives of two different families, two different orders of *Radiolaria*, or, much more rarely, even in two different classes (namely *Radiolaria* and Ciliates). The analysis of cases of convergence among different genera of the same family is much more difficult, for in such cases it is sometimes very hard to decide which of the similar characters have evolved convergently, and which have arisen concurrently as a result of phylogenetic affinity between the genera.

Haecker dealt mainly with convergences within the limits of the order *Phaeodaria* (*Tripylea*), where this phenomenon is excellently exhibited in the form of coincidences in the structure of the skeleton among members of various families. On examining the structure of the skeleton in other orders we have found numerous further examples of far-reaching convergences (see also Table on p. 530).

First of all numerous cases of convergence are found in those elements of the skeleton which are of special significance as supporting and protective organoids, including those terminal extracapsular sections of the skeletal spicules whose function is to support and stretch the peripheral

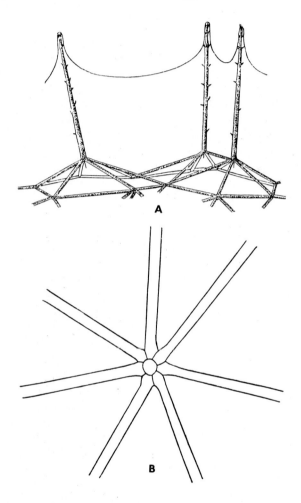

FIG. 266. Parts of skeleton of *Auloscena*.

(*A*) small superficial pyramids of skeletal spicules in *Auloscena pelagica*; (*B*) pyramid composed of trabeculae articulated with each other (fam. Aulosphaeridae). (After Haecker, 1908.)

layers of the delicate, extracapsular cytoplasm. The completeness of convergence is enhanced in these cases both by a complete similarity of function and by the same peripheral arrangement of the converging structures.

These relationships are well illustrated by three genera of Radiolaria: *Coelanthemum* (fam. *Coelodendridae*, order Phaeodaria), *Aulospathis* (fam.

Aulacanthidae, order Phaeodaria), and *Lychnosphaera* (fam. *Astrosphaeridae*, order Spumellaria). The central part of their skeletons is arranged quite differently: in *Coelanthemum* it is protected by a bivalvular, bilaterally symmetrical shell with radial spicules given off from its surface; in *Aulospathia* the skeleton consists of 40-50 radial spicules freely crossing each

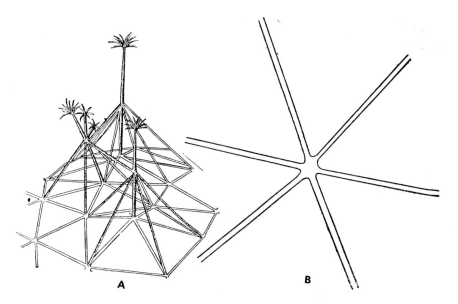

Fig. 267. Parts of skeleton of *Sagenoscena irmingeriana*.

(*A*) superficial pyramids of skeletal spicules; (*B*) small pyramids composed of trabeculae fused together (fam. Sagosphaeridae). (After Haecker, 1908.)

other in the centre of the spherical body, so that their central ends terminate in a simple tapering point; finally, the central skeleton of *Lychnosphaera* is a cribriform sphere with 12-16 radial spicules running from its trabeculae.

On the other hand, the peripheral skeletal structures show much resemblance to each other. In all the genera radial spicules produce, at some distance from their outer free end, tufts composed of 2-4-6 lateral branches disposed tangentially to the surface of the body, which may branch out further in the same plane (*Coelanthemum* and *Lychnosphaera*), in which case their secondary branches fuse into a peripheral, wide-meshed, skeletal sphere. The free ends of the radial spicules in all genera diverge in the form of a rosette consisting of 4-8 short branches terminating in minute denticles. In a word, the whole peripheral armature of the skeleton in the three genera is very similar.

Convergence in the peripheral skeleton is well known among members of two families of Phaeodaria, namely *Aulosphaeridae* and *Sagosphaeridae*. In both families the skeleton is situated entirely on the periphery; it is shaped either as a sphere, a sausage, or a pyriform aerostat; and is composed of triangular and hexagonal alveoles, which are separated from each other by a system of tangential trabeculae. Triangles outlined by the skeletal trabeculae are arranged in groups of six, which converge by their apices to one point. From this point a comparatively short radial spicule is given off to the exterior, and from its end is produced a bundle of short branches, which serve partly for the support of the extracapsular cytoplasm and partly to ensure a more uniform distribution of the pressure from the surrounding water on the surface of the cribriform skeleton. This system is complicated in both families by the projection of the six-fold groups of skeletal trabeculae in the form of hexagonal pyramids above the surface of the cribriform skeleton, while the apex of each pyramid is prolonged into the radial spicule mentioned above (Figs. 266–7).

As will be mentioned below, this increases the skeleton's resistance even more. The characteristics described, as well as some other details, may be duplicated exactly in members of both families, as for example in *Auloscena* and *Sagenoscena*. However, the structure of the elements composing the skeleton differs considerably in the two families. Thus in the *Aulosphaeridae* all the trabeculae and spicules of the skeleton are hollow and are articulated with each other, but not fused into one whole. In contrast, in the *Sagosphaeridae* the skeletal parts are massive and the skeleton forms one fused whole. While differing sharply in the physical structure of their skeleton, the two families nevertheless display many convergences in the arrangement of its parts.

It is noteworthy that an arrangement of the meshes of the cribriform skeleton closely resembling that of *Sagosphaeridae* is sometimes displayed also by representatives of other orders of radiolarians. Thus, among *Nasselaria* the lattice of the skeleton in *Tridictyopus* consists of sixfold groups of triangular meshes, although the shape of the whole skeleton is quite different and is typical of the given order.

Other elements arising by convergence in many families of Phaeodaria are the so-called 'anchor-filaments' representing a widespread peripheral component of the skeleton, which serve to support the extracapsular cytoplasm; they have the appearance of thin, delicate, siliceous filaments, provided at the tips with a group of small hooks. These anchor-filaments are attached to the coarser radial or tangential parts of the skeleton; they reach a luxuriant development in Phaeodaria *Cannosphaeridae*, *Planktonettidae*, and *Coelodendridae*. The anchor-filaments are attached either singly or in pairs, or in whole tufts (Fig. 268).

The peripheral apparatus in the shape of zigzag, curved filaments, the ends of which frequently form a lenticular plaque serrated at the edges and called spatilla, are similar in structure to the anchor-filaments. Among the Phaeodaria they are known in *Aulacanthidae*, *Cannosphaeridae*, and *Coelodendridae*; in addition to these, typical filaments with spatillae were found by us in Spumellaria (genus *Octodendron* of the *Astrosphaeridae*), while zigzag-shaped filaments without spatillae at the ends occur also in Spumellaria (*Drymosphaera* of the Astrosphaeridae), as well as in Acantharia (genus *Dodecaspis* of the fam. *Dorataspidae*, *Lychnaspsis*, and *Pleuraspis*).

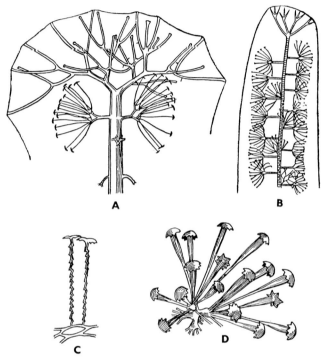

FIG. 268. Convergence in structure of the spicules in Radiolaria and sponges.

(*A*) terminal circlet of radial needle in phaeodarian *Coelodecas*; (*B*) terminal portion of the spicule of phaeodarian *Planktonetta*; (*C*) anchor spicules of phaeodarian *Coelodrymus*; (*D*) discohexaster of the Poriferan *Dictyocaulus*. (After Haecker, 1908.)

A typical and very far-reaching convergence can be detected in the structure of the peristome in certain *Tuscaroridae* and in *Challengeridae* (*Challengeron diodon*), i.e. among the members of two completely different families of Phaeodaria. The basket-shaped peristome of these forms acquires an extraordinarily similar structure (Fig. 269).

However, apart from all these examples given by Haecker and concerning chiefly the Phaeodaria, a large number of other not less interesting examples of convergence are known.

Thus, the general appearance of the skeleton of many *Cubosphaeridae* and *Liosphaeridae* of the order Spumellaria, closely resembles that in the family *Castanellidae* of the Phaeodaria (Fig. 270): namely, the skeleton is in the shape of a latticed sphere with rounded pores; pores are frequently of the same funnel shape in both families, or with sharp margins; the margins of the neighbouring pores are in contact with each other and have

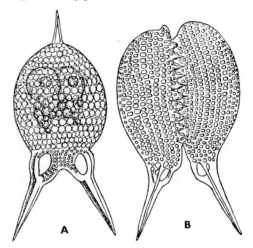

FIG. 269. Convergence in the organization of pylome and in the general shape of skeleton, with considerable difference in the basic pattern of skeleton.

(*A*) *Challengeron diodon* of fam. Challengeridae: entire skeleton sac-like; (*B*) *Conchoceras caudatum* of fam. Concharidae: skeleton consists of two valves united by serrated hinge. (After Haecker, 1908.)

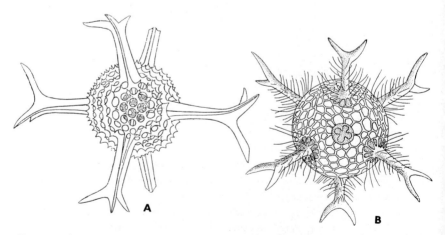

FIG. 270. Convergence of skeleton in two radiolarians belonging to different orders, expressed in spherical shape of body, perforated skeleton, and the ramification and number (6) of their spicules.

(*A*) *Hexancistra tricuspis* (Spumellaria); (*B*) *Circoporus sexfurcus* (Phaeodaria). (After Haecker, 1908.)

pointed ends, the points growing out into supplementary spicules—all these modifications take place concurrently in certain members of the three families compared. The skeletons of *Castanellidae* differ only in the presence of a pylome with a serrated margin, which is absent in Spumellaria.

Moreover, in some Spumellaria there are 3–4 radial spines on each of the tangential trabeculae of the latticed sphere. This adaptation is encountered in *Astrosphaera* (Spumellaria), a particularly interesting feature of which is the presence of centripetal 'guy-ropes' on its spicules.

However, among the Phaeodaria the spines of the trabeculae are characteristic of *Aulosphaeridae* and *Sagosphaeridae*, whereas the 'guys' are found only in the *Coelodendridae*. Thus *Astrosphaera* displays sculptural convergences simultaneously with two different groups of families of Phaeodaria.

Among *Cubosphaeridae* there are some forms (*Hexancistra*) in which the spherical shell of the castanellid type becomes even more like that in the genus *Castanopsis*, in that the radial spicules ramify at the ends into a tuft of short, thick branches.

The representatives of the orders Spumellaria and Acantharia exhibit a whole series of convergences in the development of sharp, longitudinal facets on the radial spicules (Fig. 271)—their serration or spiral twisting. These characteristics combined with the common latticed-spherical skeleton are due to more or less close convergences. Among Spumellaria spicules with four sharp facets are encountered in *Staurolonche* (Staurosphaeridae), three-faceted ones among *Rhizoplegma*, *Lychnosphaera*, *Astrosphaera*, and others. Three-faceted and serrated needles are found in *Drymosphaera*, *Hexacontium*, and others. Finally, three-faceted and at the same time spirally twisted spicules characterize certain Spumellaria, e.g. *Hexancistra*, *Hexastylum*, *Octodendron*, and others. At the same time among the Acantharia sharp-faceted spicules occur in *Acanthonia* and *Stauracantha*; while sharp-faceted and also serrated spicules are present in *Hylaspis*, *Pristacantha*, and *Stauracon*.

Side by side with these similar features the radiolarians also exhibit characteristics pointing to phylogenetic distinctions between the Acantharia and Spumellaria. As mentioned above, in Spumellaria the spicules are almost always three-faceted, whereas in Acantharia they are four-faceted. Moreover, the three-faceted spicules show a tendency to longitudinal spiral twisting, while in four-faceted spicules of Acantharia this twisting is never observed.

A most original convergence concerns one peculiarity in the arrangement of spicules in certain Spumellaria and Phaeodaria. Among the Phaeodaria, in a number of *Coelodendridae* and *Coelographidae*, the lateral transverse branches of the main radial spicules give off in a centripetal direction very fine, silicious filaments, which run parallel to the radial spicule and finally enter into the composition of the delicate network of skeletal fibrils that support the extracapsular cytoplasm. In their position they resemble the steel cables or shrouds running down from a ship's mast, the role of which is played by the radial spicule (Fig. 272). Identical, very fine 'cables' are stretched in a centripetal direction along the radial needles of certain Astrosphaeridae (*Rhizoplegma*, *Astrosphaera stellata*) of the Spumellaria.

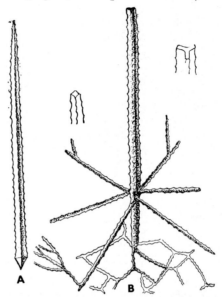

FIG. 271. Convergence in structure of spicules.

(*A*) *Acanthometra* (order Acantharia) and (*B*) *Drymosphaera dendrophora* (order Spumellaria). In both forms spicules consist of 3–4 sharp facets with irregular, undulating edge, but the method of attachment of the spicules to the body is different. (After Haeckel, 1862.)

The apertures in the walls of the spherical skeletons of Collosphaeridae (Spumellaria), which are edged by a circlet of denticles, closely resemble the pylome aperture of Castanellidae (Phaeodaria), but the convergence is even more marked between the single- or double-lattice spheres, a form of skeleton that is widespread among Spumellaria on the one hand and among Acantharia on the other. Such spheres are covered by radial spicules, and at first glance they are very similar, although their genesis is entirely different. In Spumellaria the first stage of their development is represented by a lattice sphere, from the walls of which is given off to the exterior a system of radial spicules, which therefore do not reach the centre of the animal. In Acantharia, on the contrary, the initial basis of the skeleton is formed by twenty spicules meeting in the centre of the body by their inner ends, while the latticed sphere is formed later at the expense of tangential processes of the spicules; these processes ramify repeatedly in the tangential plane, meet the tangential branches of the neighbouring spicules, and thus only secondarily form the latticed sphere round the body. A second sphere of a larger size may be formed later round the first one.

Thus there is a broad path for convergences from the spheroid skeletons to the astroid, or from the astroid to the spheroid. Apparently, a combination of both these types of skeleton is functionally the most advantageous, since

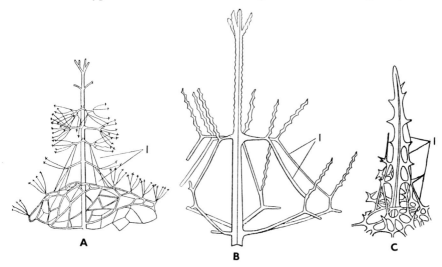

FIG. 272. Convergence in different radiolarians in shape of fine 'guys' running down obliquely from tip of spicules to their base.

(*A*) *Coeloplegma murrayanum* (Phaeodaria); (*B*) *Lychnosphaera regina* (Spumellaria); (*C*) *Rhizoplegma boreale* (Spumellaria); 1, 'guys'. (After Haecker, 1908.)

the spheroid one satisfies the requirements for the protection of the central capsule, while the astroid one increases its buoyancy. The skeletons of the spheroid Spumellaria accordingly tend to be modified towards the astroid Acantharia by developing a system of radial spicules, while the typically astroid Acantharia secondarily develop latticed spheres on the basis of their radial skeleton. Examples of such convergent evolution are very numerous in these orders. Convergence of the general shape may proceed even further in both orders, when a skeleton in the shape of two or more concentric spheres is produced during the process of individual growth.

The least number of convergences, as compared with other orders of Radiolaria, are encountered in the order Nassellaria. This is apparently due to the fact that the main type of the skeleton in Nassellaria is different. According to Jorgensen (1905) it is composed of one four-rayed spicule, three rays of which form a tripod encompassing the central capsule while the fourth is directed upwards as an apical spicule. The coincident features of the skeletal sculpture are represented only by the funnel-like or sharp-edged pores of the helmet-shaped skeleton of some Nassellaria (fam. *Podocyrtidae*, resembling the skeletons of Spumellaria and certain Phaeodaria (*Castanellidae*).

A more pronounced convergence is encountered in some representatives of the family *Phormocampidae* of the Nassellaria, for example, in *Stichocapsa*, and especially *Artocapsa*, which closely resembles the Spumellaria,

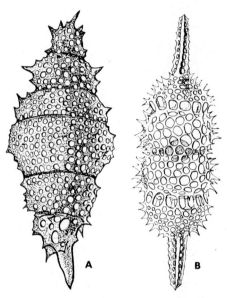

FIG. 273. Convergence of general shape of body in representatives of different orders of Radiolaria.

(*A*) *Artocapse spinosa* (Nassellaria); (*B*) *Panarium tubularium* (Spumellaria). (After Haeckel, 1887.)

such as *Panarium tubularium* (Fig. 273), *Desmartes larvalis* of the Zygartidae, *Tetrapyle* of the Pylonidae, or *Amphimenium* of the *Porodiscidae*. An external examination of both the *Phormocampidae* and the above-mentioned Spumellaria reveals their spindle-shaped form; the skeleton, pierced with pores, bears on its surface several slight, transverse constrictions and tapers at both poles. Their similarity is great not only as regards the common type of structure, but also in its outer sculpture. There is even a greater similarity between such forms as *Pipetta fuscus*, among the Spumellaria, and *Eusyringium macrosiphon*, among the Nassellaria (Fig. 274).

Many of the convergences in Radiolaria discussed above can be conveniently summarized in the form of a table given on p. 530.

Convergences of certain Nassellaria with members of another class of Protozoa, namely with the loricas of the planktonic ciliates Tintinnoinea, are of special interest. The Tintinnoinea are small ciliates with an adoral spiral of membranelles at the anterior end, and an elongated body. Their whole body is hidden in a sac-like chitinous shell, from the aperture of which the anterior end of the ciliate projects. *Tintinnoinea* swim vigorously among the marine plankton by means of their spiral of membranelles. When the *Tintinnoinea* are compared with certain Nassellaria, namely with the members of the family *Theomitridae*, a clear convergence in the shape of the shell strikes the eye, which is particularly significant in view of the

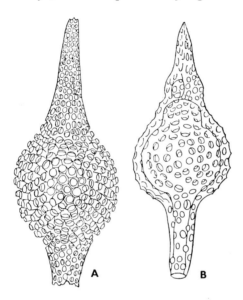

FIG. 274. Convergence in structure of skeleton in representatives of two different orders of Radiolaria.

(*A*) *Pippetta fuscus* (Spumellaria); (*B*) *Eusyringium macrosiphon* (Nassellaria). (After Haeckel, 1887.)

passive floating mode of life of Nassellaria and the free-swimming mode of life of *Tintinnoinea*. The greatest similarity is observed between the shells of the nassellarian *Cycladophora* and the ciliate *Dictyocysta* (Fig. 275). In both organisms the shell consists of two parts—a narrow neck, or collar, the walls of which are perforated by large rectangular apertures, and a wide cup-shaped basal part closed at the bottom. The only difference is that the deep, cup-like part of the shell of dictyocysts is intact, whereas in the radiolarians it is pierced by several rows of round pores. Another example is provided by some species of the genus *Undellopsis* among the *Tintinnoinea* and *Lithomitra nodosaria* among the Nassellaria. In both genera the shell looks like a small pail with constrictions in four places and a slightly convex bottom; while in the radiolarians the shell bears several transverse rows of apertures. The genus *Amplectella* of the *Tintinnoinea* and the genera *Theocampe* and *Tricolocampa* of the nassellarians have the same appearance, but their body is constricted into three transverse zones. As to convergences between different radiolarians, in Haecker's opinion convergence in the general shape of the body is observed mainly between groups living in similar areas of the sea. Thus the *Aulosphaeridae* and *Sagosphaeridae*, which show a tendency to mutual convergence, converge in the same direction within the same areas of the sea: in the surface layers of the warm

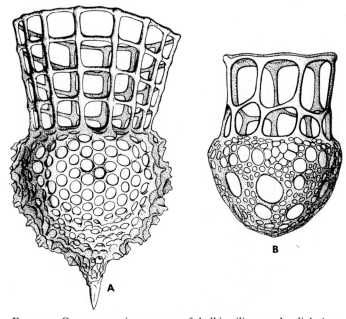

FIG. 275. Convergence in structure of shell in ciliates and radiolarians.

(*A*) radiolarian *Cycladophora pantheon* (order Nassellaria); (*B*) ciliate *Dictyo-cysta mitra* (order Oligotricha). (After Haeckel, 1887.)

seas both families are represented by small round forms; in cold waters they tend to be pyriform. Likewise there is a most striking convergence between the deep-water representative of *Concharidae*, *Conchellium tridacna*, and the *Castanellidae* caught in the same antarctic stations, in respect of their dimensions, external pores, and the character of the shell walls.

Among Foraminifera there occur several parallel lines of development: there are parallel series among forms that are arenaceous and calcareous, perforated and imperforated, rod-like, uniserial, diserial, and spiral, all of which provide abundant material for convergences. However, in view of the very great uniformity of structure of the plasmatic body and nuclear apparatus of Foraminifera, as compared with the Radiolaria, it is difficult to decide where we are dealing with convergence and where with direct phylogenic affinity. Therefore we shall abstain from consideration of the phenomena of convergence based on examples from Foraminifera.

Among Mastigophora we have detected the only evidence of convergence among Dinoflagellata. The free-living armoured flagellate *Acanthodinium* (Fig. 276) closely resembles radiolarians of the group Spumellaria. From its spherical body are given off in all directions numerous radial processes (up to twelve) which are shaped more like long, regular, polyhedra than spicules. This shape of the processes is due to the fact that they are covered

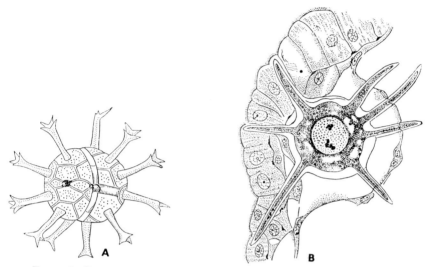

FIG. 276. Convergence between planktonic and endoparasitic dinoflagellates.

(*A*) planktonic dinoflagellate *Acanthodinium caryophyllum*; processes in armour serve to facilitate flotation in water; (*B*) endoparasitic dinoflagellate *Actinodinium apsteini* from the body cavity of Copepoda; processes on body serve to increase absorption surface of body. ((*A*) after Doflein-Reichenow, 1929; (*B*) after Grassé, 1952.)

by rectangular plates of cellulose, which, as in other Dinoflagellata, form the outer skeleton of *Acanthodinium*. Functionally these processes correspond to the radial spicules of radiolarians, since, like these, they serve to increase the surface of the body and to decrease its specific gravity. Hence in this case the similarity with the radiolarians is determined by the identical, planktonic mode of life. (See Table overleaf.)

It is much more difficult to explain the analogous shape of the body of certain endoparasitic Dinoflagellata, namely *Actinodinium apsteini*, described by Chatton and Hovasse (1937), in the body cavity of the marine copepod *Acartia*. *Actinodinium* has a spherical body, covered with a delicate membrane and equipped with approximately ten radial processes, in the form of horns or needles pointed at their ends. At the point of contact of one of the processes with the intestinal wall of the copepod the process protrudes into the lumen of the intestine, into which the contents of the horned parasite escape in order to be discharged from the host. Within the body of *Actinodium* lies a large nucleus whose structure is characteristic of

Dinoflagellata. In *Actinodinium* we have a case of convergence with *Clado-pyxis* (*Acanthodinium*) (Fig. 276) caused, curiously enough, by completely different conditions of life. This apparent incongruity finds its explanation in the completely different purposes served by the convergent characters (radial processes). The processes of *Actinodinium*, it is true, also increase the total surface of the body as in *Acanthodinium*, but they are utilized not for reducing the specific gravity of the animal but for increasing the surface for absorption by the parasite of the nutrient substances from the body of its host.

SCULPTURAL COINCIDENCES IN RADIOLARIANS

Characters	Spumellaria	Nassellaria	Phaeodria	Acantharia
1. Serrated margins of pores	Collosphaeridae Cubosphaeridae		Castanellidae	
2. Centripetal 'guys' on radial spicules	Lychnosphaera Astrosphaeridae		Coelodendridae	
3. Spatillae with two hooks or without hooks	Octodendrum spathillatum Lichnosphaera regina Drymosphaera		Aulacanthidae Coelodendridae Cannosphaeridae	Dodecaspis
4. Spines on trabeculae of sphere, and centripetal 'guys'	Astrosphaera stellata		Aulosphaeridae Coelodendridae	
5. Funnel-like spiny pores	Cubosphaeridae Liosphaeridae	Alacorys bismarcki	Castanellidae	Acanthaspis
6. Spicules with a basal system of supports	Rhizosphaera serrata Haliomma macrodoras		Aulosphaeridae Sagosphaeridae Circoporidae	
7. Castanelloid type of spheres with main spicules ramifying at their tips	Cubosphaeridae (Hexancistra)		Circoporidae (Circoporus sexfurcus)	
8. Radial spicules with longitudinal serrated spiral margins	Staurolonche Hexastylus Astrosphaerus			Xiphacantha

Our knowledge of convergence within the class Cnidosporidia is equally meagre. The only indisputable case of coincidence of characters is found in the spores of three different genera of Myxosporidia—*Henneguya, Myxo-bylatus,* and *Agarella* (Fig. 277). All the three genera inhabit various organs of fish (gills, subcutaneous connective tissue, kidneys, testes, and cavity of the urinary bladder). The spores of Myxosporidia, which in this group represent the most important taxonomic character, are enveloped in a bivalve membrane; the two valves meeting in a so-called sutural plane. Within the spore, usually at one end of it, are situated two to four polar capsules, the extrusive filaments of which serve for attachment to the animal host. The three genera mentioned belong to two different families, *Myxosomatidae* (Agarella) and *Myxobolidae*, and differ in important characters, though the general outer appearance of the spores is identical. The spores are considerably elongated in the form of a spindle, while the posterior end of the spore extends into two fine filamentar tails, corresponding to the two valves. The similarity of the external appearance of the spores is so great that until quite recently

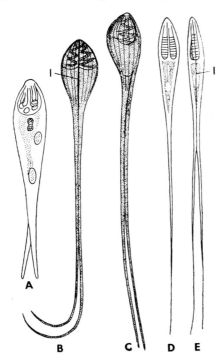

FIG. 277. Convergence in the form of spores in three genera of Myxosporodia belonging to different suborders.

(*A*) *Agarella*; (*B*), (*C*) *Myxobilatus*; (*D*), (*E*) *Henneguya*. 1, suture line. (Original.)

the representatives of both genera *Henneguya* and *Myxobilatus* were classified in one genus. As a matter of fact, all these genera can be easily differentiated, thus the genus Agarella possesses four polar capsules and is devoid of the special iodophile glycogen vacuole, characteristic of the family *Myxobolidae*, whereas both the other genera have two polar capsules in the spore and a distinct iodophile vacuole. The genera *Henneguya* and *Myxobilatus* are clearly distinguished from each other by the fact that in *Henneguya* both polar capsules are situated in the sutural plane of the spore, while in *Myxobilatus* they are in the plane perpendicular to this plane, i.e. they lie on both sides of the sutural plane. This case presents a clear example of complete convergence in the whole external appearance coupled with a marked divergence in the arrangement and number of the internal structural details.

A considerable convergence of the exterior form of the body is observed in certain gregarines, which are not closely related to each other. One example of it is *Pterospora* from the body cavity of marine Polychaeta and *Aikinetocystis* from the coelome of Burmese earthworms. Both gregarines are characterized by a multiple dichotomy at one end of the body, producing eight to sixteen branches, the function of which is apparently to increase the absorption by the parasite of nutrient substances from the body of the host. The spores in both genera are quite different: in *Aikinetocystis* they are simple, biconical; in *Pterospora* one end of the spore is drawn out into an elongated trihedral tail, while at the other the membrane forms a high collar or funnel.

A second, most interesting, example of coincidence of the external shape of the body in gregarines is encountered in the genera *Ancora* from the alimentary tract of Polychaeta and *Enterocystis*, described by Cvetkov (1926) from the intestine of *Caenis* larvae (Ephemeridae). As it grows, *Ancora* produces from the sides of its body two blunt plasmatic processes, which give the animal the appearance of an anchor and serves for a better attachment of the adult gregarine in the lumen of the intestine when it breaks away from its epimerite. In *Enterocystis* the body of the adult gregarine has a simple, elongated shape, but, when two gregarines unite to form a syzygy, one of the syzygites presses itself into the end of the body of the other and forces this end of its partner to open up in a transverse direction, forming as it were two elbows protruding to the sides. Hence, the two united syzygites form a kind of anchor or cross, as in the case of *Ancora*. Thus, the same pattern, and for the same purpose, is produced in *Ancora* from one and in *Enterocystis* from two individual gregarines (see Fig. 12).

Within the class Ciliata the number of cases of convergence is not very great, but some of them are undoubtedly interesting.

The clearest instance, and, moreover, one which concerns a whole suborder of ciliates is the group of ciliates devoid of a cystosome, the Astomata. At present most authors regard this suborder as being a collective group that has arisen as a result of the convergent evolution of several branches of the genealogical tree of ciliates in the direction of the loss of the mouth and the acquisition of certain general characters peculiar to endoparasitic ciliates. Certain undoubtedly convergent features have developed in two different suborders of the spirotrichous ciliates, namely in Entodiniomorpha from the alimentary tract of ungulates and rodents, and in Ctenostomata which are sapropelic in freshwater lakes.

A factor uniting these two suborders is their habitation in a dense medium, poor in oxygen but rich in vegetative particles or vegetative detritus. Against this ecological background both suborders have acquired the following common features, while retaining a sufficient number of special characters to distinguish them as two independent suborders: strong solidification of their cuticle, reduction of the ciliary covering, leaving only an adoral spiral and a few separate zones or bundles of membranelles, the formation of the body of transverse cuticular ridges and on the posterior pole of an armament consisting of various numbers of caudal spines. The convergent nature of many characters of these groups is clearly visible (Fig. 305).

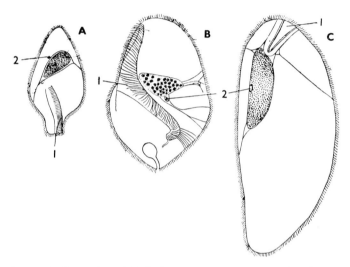

FIG. 278. Formation of fibrils for suspension of macronucleus (karyophore).

(A) *Clevelandella panesthiae* from the gut of a cockroach; (B) *Nyctotherus piscicola* from the gut of fish; (C) *Isotricha prostoma* (Holotricha) from the stomach of cattle. 1, mouth; 2, micronucleus. (After Ten Kate, 1927.)

Another group of convergent characters has evolved in many endoparasitic ciliates from the alimentary tract of herbivorous animals (Fig. 278). In a whole series of ciliates living under such conditions—and only in them—are encountered in different combinations two morphological and one physiological characters: a special suspension apparatus for the macronucleus, a concrement vacuole, and a simple reconstruction of the nuclear apparatus in exconjugants (usually only one, more rarely two, divisions of the synkaryon). However, simple nuclear reconstruction also occurs in some free-living ciliates.

These three characteristics are combined in different representatives of the biological group of ciliates in question in various ways, not always corresponding in this respect to the taxonomic position of the ciliates. This situation is best illustrated by the accompanying Table.

Name of genera	Order	Suspension of nucleus	Concrement vacuole	Simple nuclear re-construction
Didesmis	Gymnostomata	I	I	?
Bütschlia, Poly-morpha, and other Bütschliidae			I	I
Isotricha Dasytricha	Trichostomata	I		I
Paraisotricha			I	I
Ophrysoscolecidae	Entodiniomorpha			I
Cycloposthiidae				I
Balantidium Nyctotherus	Heterotricha	I		I
Clevelandia Paraclevelandia		I		

As is shown by the Table, such an original organoid as, for example, the concrement vacuole arises convergently in the suborders Gymnostomata and Trichostomata; and the suspension apparatus for the macronucleus appears independently in intestinal Gymnostomata, Trichostomata, and in Heterotricha, whereas it is completely absent in free-living ciliates. Finally, the tendency to simplification (secondary) of the reconstruction of the nuclear apparatus is generally widespread among intestinal ciliates of herbivorous animals, though it may be encountered also in free-living ciliates. From all this it follows that the intestinal ciliates tend to converge with each other; moreover, the convergent characters are either correlated with each other or do not show such a connexion.

In conclusion one more extremely significant convergence should be mentioned. It concerns the polar capsules or nematocysts found in different classes of Protozoa. Among Dinoflagellata well-developed nematocysts are present in *Polykrikos* and *Nematodinium*; among the Cnidosporidia all Myxosporidia, Actinomyxidia, and Microsporidia have polar capsules. Moreover, in Myxosporidia the capsules vary considerably in structure: their shape may be regularly spherical, or pyriform, or in the form of elongated spindles. Their number varies from one to four in Myxosporidia or to three in Actinomyxidia. The presence of such highly specialized structures in several groups differing in their mode of life (planktonts and parasites) is of great interest, the more so since the method of formation of polar capsules in Dinoflagellata and Cnidosporidia is apparently quite different. In Dinoflagellata the capsule originates inside the cell of the flagellate, with the aid of the centriole, from two primordia, and is preceded by the formation of a cnidoblast. In Myxosporidia the details of the formation have not been exactly elucidated, but it is well known that each capsule is formed at the expense of a special capsulogenous cell, the nucleus of which undergoes pycnotic degeneration after the formation of the capsule.

Separate organoids of Protozoa, i.e. parts of the unicellular organism, may in some cases repeat the structure of the cells of certain Metazoa or of the products of the secretion of certain cells, or even of whole groups of cells of multicellular organisms.

A. *Convergence between entire organisms of Protozoa and whole cells of Metazoa*

1. *Choanoflagellates (Craspedomonadina) and choanocytes of Porifera.* As early as 1924 Hirschler noted the presence at the base of the flagellum of the choanocytes of sponges of a small vesicle with osmiophile walls, which he considered to be homologous with contractile vacuole of flagellates. Later Duboscq and Tuzet (1934) found at the base of the flagellum of the blastula cells of calcareous Porifera, in addition to the basal grain, a typical parabasal apparatus suspended from the latter by means of a rhizoplast. It is lamelliform and its outer surface is covered by a thick layer of osmiophile substance, while the rhizoplast extends beyond the limits of the parabasal apparatus to the nuclear membrane as in the case of some flagellates. If we add to this the small cytoplasmic collar encircling the base of the flagellum in a choanocyte, then it will be seen that the choanocyte of Porifera possesses the complete set of organoids characteristic of an individual choanoflagellate, including an entire whole kinetid. In this case convergence extends very far.

2. *The organization of flagelloid gametes of Protozoa and of typical spermatozoa of Metazoa.* In the section on the gametes of Protozoa attention was drawn to a comparison of flagelloid gametes, especially in certain gregarines, with the spermatozoa of Metazoa. We regard the similarity of the spermatozoa of Metazoa as being not so much due to their phylogenetic affinity with the flagellates, but as the result of far-reaching convergence caused by the identity of function of the spermatozoa and the male gametes.

3. *Convergence of the organization of certain Trichonymphidae with that of aberrant spermatozoa of crustaceans and with the cnidocysts of Polykrikos.* Dogiel (1920) compared the organization of such trichonymphids as *Pseudotrichonympha introflexibilis* with the spermatozoa of decapod crustaceans, which consist of the head and the so-called caudal capsule, with the cnidocysts of the dinoflagellate *Polykrikos*. The similarity between the two structures can be seen from the accompanying figures (Fig. 279). It is

evident in the close resemblance of the structure of the cnidocyst of the caudal capsule of the spermatozoa of *Eupagurus* and of the so-called cephalic organ in certain representatives of *Trichonymphidae*. In all three cases there is a chitinous two-layered capsule (the cnidocyst capsule with its ampulla, the caudal capsule of the spermatozoon with its internal canal, and the two-layered tube of the cephalic organ). In all cases the cavity of

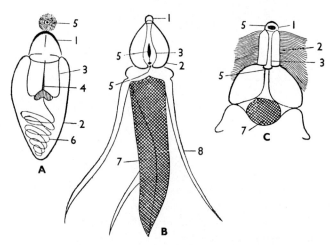

Fig. 279. Convergence between: (*A*) cnidocyst of dinoflagellate *Polykrikos*; (*B*) spermatozoon of crustacean *Eupagurus*; and (*C*) cephalic organ of trichonymphid *Cyclonympha strobila*.

1, cuticular cap; 2, outer wall of capsule, wall of cephalic organ; 3, ampulla, wall of canal of capsule or tube of cephalic organ; 4, striker; 5, centriole or centrioles; 6, nematocyst; 7, nucleus; 8, processes of spermatozoon. (After Dogiel, 1920.)

the capsule or tube communicates with the outer medium (the upper aperture of the capsule in *Polykrikos*, the opening of the canal of the capsule in the spermatozoon, the upper aperture in the tube in trichonymphids). This aperture is invariably closed by a cap which falls off. Finally, in all three cases, the centriole, which is situated in different ways, takes part in the formation of the organoid. In *Polykrikos* there is one centriole at the bottom of the ampulla, i.e. of the invagination of the capsule, while another lies in front in a special mucous sphere. The spermatozoon has two centrioles within the canal of the capsule; in *Trichonympha* one centriole lies at the upper aperture of the canal of the two-layered tube, while the other is apparently situated at the base of the tube. Finally, all the three structures possess one important, common physiological trait. They all serve for the discharge of part of their contents through the upper aperture of the organoid. In *Polykrikos* it is the polar filament lying on the bottom of the capsule that is voided; in the spermatozoon it is the 'explosive substance' inside the capsule which readily swells up; in trichonymphids it is a dense accumulation of special granules situated at the base of the tube of the cephalic organ. In the genus *Cyclonympha* Dogiel saw specimens with an extruded clump of such grains.

The marked convergence of the organoids described above has a twofold basis. In the first place, it is due to a certain identity of the mechanism governing the function of the organoids, although their biological function is quite different.

All the organoids described execute a movement in the form of a single, abrupt thrust: in *Polykrikos* it is the discharge of the polar filament, in the spermatozoon, the explosion of the capsule, and in *Trichonympha*, the extrusion of the swollen clump of grains. It is true that the ultimate result of the thrust is different: viz. protection from enemies and attack in *Polykrikos*; fusion with the ovum in the case of spermatozoon and an unknown third function in *Trichonympha*. However, the difference of purpose produced by an identical mechanism of action, does not preclude the development of convergence.

An identical morphological substratum provides the second basis for the development of convergence. All the structures compared are cells, and accordingly the construction materials from which these adaptations evolved are similar—centrioles playing an important part in their formation. The combination of identical functions with a similar substratum leads to convergence. The occurrence of such far-reaching coincidences in such distinct animal groups points, among other things, to a certain limitation of the courses of morphogenesis within the animal kingdom.

B. *Convergence of organoids of Protozoa with those of individual cells of Metazoa*

1. *Convergence of individual skeletal spicules of Radiolaria with simple spicules of Porifera.* Numerous examples of such spicules are found in Spumellaria, Nassellaria, and especially Phaeodaria. The similarity of their needles with the spicules of Porifera is so great that certain types of them are comparable to definite categories of spicules that serve as diagnostic characters in the classification of Porifera. Thus the radial needles of Aulacanthidae are structurally similar to the needles of the tylostyle type in Porifera; the tangial needles of *Aulacanthidae* resemble most closely the rhabda in Porifera; finally, in many *Aulacanthidae* the radial needles diverge at the free end at an angle of 120° into three rays, i.e. are built like a triaene. Apart from Phaeodaria, convergence with the spicules of siliceous Porifera is observed also in Nassellaria and Spumellaria. In Nassellaria one tetra-radial spiculum, in other words one triaene, is even regarded as the basic form of the skeleton: the skeleton acquires other additional elements and becomes considerably complicated only as a secondary process.

Among members of the family *Thalassosphaeridae* of the Spumellaria numerous small needles of different forms are scattered in the extracapsular plasma. *Lamproxanthium* possesses spicules of the type of tetraradial triaenes and diplotriaenes. In the latter three lateral rays are given off from both ends of its main axis. They are comparable to two triaenes attached to each other by the ends of their main ray. Apart from triaenes, there are also monaxonic rods similar to the microrhabs of siliceous sponges. Diplotriaenes are also encountered in *Sphaerozoum* and microrhabs in *Thalassoplancta* and others.

Thus in *Thalassosphaeridae* there is a whole series of needles that are identical with the spicules of Porifera, as well as some other types of needles, not represented among sponges.

It should be noted that needles resembling the spicules of siliceous sponges are found only in radiolarians with a siliceous skeleton. On the other hand, Acantharia, whose needles are composed of strontium sulphate, do not show this resemblance.

2. *Convergence between nematocysts and polar capsules of Protozoa and stinging cells of Coelenterata* is quite pronounced, mainly as regards their function, although the nematocysts of Protozoa and those of Coelenterata differ essentially from each other in details of structure.

C. *Convergence of organoids of Protozoa with those of Metazoa that have a multicellular origin*

1. *Convergence of skeleton of Radiolaria with complex spicula of Porifera.* This case concerns chiefly the peripheral parts of the skeleton of some Phaeodaria, Spumellaria, and Acantharia on the one hand, and the floricomes and discohexasters of glass sponges (*Hyalospongiae*) (Fig. 268) on the other. Many members of the Phaeodaria, belonging to different families, develop in addition to their main skeletal framework, a system of fine, delicate secondary processes situated on the surface of its spicules. They are either single or arranged in bunches, or in the form of anchor-threads and other extremely delicate, threadlike siliceous structures. They show a close resemblance to the so-called microscleres of glass sponges. Thus, there is a remarkable similarity between the bunches of anchor-threads on the radial needles of *Coelodecas* and the discohexasters of the sponge *Dictyocaulus*. The spatillae of Phaeodaria reproduce in detail the structure of the so-called clavules of Porifera, while the minute, free tangential needles of *Cannoraphis* imitate certain needles of *Euplectella*. The candelabrum-shaped ends of radial needles in many Aulacanthidae remind one vividly of a separate bunch of branches of the discohexaster in Porifera, while the peripheral verticillate branches of the lattice skeleton of *Aulosphaera* strongly resemble the small, elegant pinules of glass sponges attached to the skeleton at their base. Finally, in a whole series of species of Acantharia, the zigzag-shaped microspicules running from the surface of the latticed sphere are closely analogous to the microscleres of Porifera which lie freely in the mesogloea.

In the case of the spicules of Porifera, it should be emphasized that each floricome, every discohexaster, is formed not from one cell but as the result of the activity of an entire cellular syncytium which surrounds the spicule secreted by it. Here the secretory activity of a single protozoon is contrasted with the activity of numerous multicellular complexes in the body of the sponge. In accordance with its multicellular origin, each spicule is merely a miniature organ of the sponge, whereas each independent part of the radiolarian skeleton is only an organoid of the cell.

The diverse types of convergence in Protozoa with different structures in Metazoa are of special interest, because they help to elucidate the morphophysiological significance of the protozoal organism. From the survey of the categories of convergence, established by us, it is evident that some of them, namely those in categories A and B, indicate that the Protozoa correspond to a part of the individual metazoan cell. As to category C, it points to a correspondence between the organoids of Protozoa, namely of every separate part of the skeleton of Radiolaria, to a separate organ of Metazoa, hence it follows that an aggregate of organoids of the same type is represented in Metazoa by a definite system of organs; while the entire protozoon corresponds not to an individual cell of Metazoa but to the entire multicellular organism. The dualism of the organization of Protozoa is clearly reflected here; from the morphological point of view a typical Protozoon is a cell, while from the physiological point of view it is a complete, fully valid organism.

It is possible that this dualism is partly due to the fact, already mentioned above, that the term 'Protozoa' refers to organism at different levels of organization. According to whether they are monoenergid or polyenergid they may correspond either to one metazoan cell or to an entire multicellular organism. This view is supported to a certain extent by the fact that among Protozoa examples of convergences of group C have so far been found only among the polyenergid forms, namely Radiolaria.

AROMORPHOSES AND IDIOADAPTATIONS

When discussing the courses of morphophysiological evolution in Protozoa the question naturally arises whether the regularities, so brilliantly worked out by A. N. Severcev (1931, 1939) in his investigation of the evolution of vertebrates, may be fully applied to a group of organisms which are in the first stage of development of the animal world. Severcev established two main types of changes affecting the organization of animals in the course of morphophysiological progress. One of these types is aromorphosis, which comprises those modifications in the organization and function of animals that raise the energy of the vital activity of the organisms of animals. In Severcev's opinion aromorphoses are modifications in those systems of organs which are directly or indirectly connected with the metabolism in the organism and concern especially the respiratory circulatory and digestive organs. However, all the progressive modifications of the organs of locomotion, of higher senses, and of the central nervous system are also indirectly associated with metabolism. In a word, aromorphoses are modifications of a universal character. The second type of change is idioadaptation which is characterized by the fact that it does not reinforce or raise the total energy of the vital activity of the organism, but produces particular and mostly special modifications of the organization, adapted to definite environmental conditions. Aromorphoses are a characteristic of large taxonomic groups of animals, while idioadaptations occur in smaller animals.

Aromorphoses

In Protozoa it is most natural to seek variations of the aromorphoses type by comparing separate classes. However, it should be noted that the concept of Protozoa as a single phylum of the animal kingdom, corresponding in systematic position to any phylum of Metazoa, is erroneous, since Protozoa exhibit a degree of diversity far beyond the concept of a phylum. On account of this, the classes of Protozoa accepted in the modern classification represent taxonomic units of very high order and should, strictly speaking, be referred to as superclasses. There are all the more reasons therefore to seek in the classes of Protozoa distinguishing features representing aromorphosis.

If we take as a starting-point the class Mastigophora, and compare them with ciliates, it will be seen that the latter show some indubitable signs of morphophysiological progress, accomplished by modifications of the type of aromorphosis. On the one hand, the differences between them and the flagellates are very great; on the other, many of them are undoubtedly progressive. In this connexion we may consider the main physiological functions of ciliates and their morphological basis.

Movement. The ciliates move with greater speed than the Mastigophora and all other Protozoa; their locomotion is the most rapid and most varied. The rate of locomotion of flagellates varies between 30 μ and 235 μ, while in the ciliates it reaches 310 μ to 2,647 μ per sec. Such rapid movement greatly increases the capacity for seeking food, for in cases where food (e.g. bacteria) is uniformly distributed in the surrounding medium, rapid movement allows the animal to capture more of it. Finally, speed enables the animal to avoid places where the environmental conditions are becoming unfavourable and to travel towards places with more favourable conditions.

The advantage of rapid locomotion can be observed very well in such predators as *Didinium*. In a culture with *Paramecium* it can be clearly seen how *Didinia*, swimming about rapidly among the Paramecia, which are also moving swiftly, are able to intercept the latter and to devour their prey. If the locomotion of the two species were slower, the frequency of the meeting of *Didinia* with their prey would have been considerably reduced.

Finally, the locomotion of Hypotricha is even more varied owing to the presence of cirri on their ventral side.

Capture and digestion of food. In Mastigophora the flagella very rarely undergo any special changes which convert them into specialized organoids for the capture of food. In ciliates, on the contrary, as a rule a definite proportion of cilia 'go over to the service' of the digestive system and become connected with the buccal apparatus. Moreover, many Holotricha possess a special rod-like apparatus of the pharynx, and in many Entodiniomorpha the pharynx acquires an unusually complex structure, with a system of special filaments, skeletal plates, &c. Special organoids for the capture of food, like the pharyngeal rods in *Entosiphon* and certain others, are very rare in Mastigophora.

A very important progressive moment in the process of the digestion of food by ciliates is, in our opinion, development of intensive endoplasmic cyclosis. We think that the circulation of the food vacuoles which is associated with cyclosis, facilitate the digestion of food in the cytoplasm. The development of a special anus, and sometimes (Entodiniomorpha) of a true 'hindgut', represents a further step forward in progressive development of a digestive system. In a word, the modification of the whole digestive system in ciliates represents a true aromorphosis.

Excretion and osmoregulation. The organoids ensuring these two functions are constructed according to the same plan in both the groups compared; but in ciliates they are both better developed and more complex in structure.

Sensory organoids and the system of conductive filaments

Sensory organoids in flagellates and ciliates are on approximately the same level of development. It is true that in Phytoflagellates there are primitive photoreceptor apparatus; on the other hand, in ciliates the organoids of the sense of balance are sometimes developed (*Paraisotricha, Bütschlia,* and others), while the tactile organoids are incomparably better developed, in the form of special sensory bristles, usually tactile, but sometimes apparently playing the part of chemoreceptors.

The system of fibrillar structures (supporting, contractile, conductive) is in flagellates at best only rudimentary, but in ciliates it reaches a high level of development; this indicates a higher degree of perfection of the regulatory apparatus and of the aromorphosis undergone by the ciliates in this respect.

Nuclear apparatus. Although the ciliates represent the highest degree—albeit a blind alley—in the development of Protozoa, the differentiation in them of two nuclei with different properties is an important advance in the distribution of functions between the various components of the nuclear apparatus.[1] According to the latest data the macronucleus is a

---

[1] It is difficult to agree with the views lately expressed on the origin of multicellular organisms from the lower ciliates (Hadzi, 1953; Hanson, 1958).

highly polyploid nucleus, containing a large quantity of nucleic acids and capable of supporting a high level of metabolism in the cell. It is an example of true aromorphosis.

Sexual process. We do not possess any convincing evidence as to whether conjugation in ciliates has any advantages over copulation in flagellates, but the wide distribution of the ciliates in nature, at all events, does not indicate that this characteristic, i.e. conjugation, might be a sign of regression. Moreover, the capacity of the conjugants to continue their vital activity immediately after conjugation is an advantageous feature. In Mastigophora copulation is usually followed by encystment, i.e. by a temporary interruption of their active life.

Consequently there is in general a whole series of very important differences between the flagellates and ciliates, indicating changes in the ciliates leading to a complication of the organization and an intensification of functions; taken together, these changes conform to the pattern of typical aromorphosis.

Apparently, the formation of the flagellum and of other elements of the kinetid in the Flagellata may likewise be regarded as an important acquisition in the course of morpho-physiological progress, which augments considerably the general vital activity of the organism in comparison with their probable ancestors, the Sarcodina, which are endowed with amoeboid movement.

Regress in the class Sporozoa

According to present views, the class Sporozoa originated from Mastigophora and its evolution undoubtedly followed the course of morpho-physiological regression or general degeneration. Severcev included under this term such adaptational changes that lead to a lowering of vital activity, although the morpho-physiological changes lead to a biological progress in the given group of organisms.

A general regression of organization in the Sporozoa is clearly seen: thus many coelomic gregarines, Coccidia, and others are as a rule slightly motile in the adult state; their mode of nutrition is saprozoic, special organoids for the capture of food being absent, nor are there any excretory osmoregulatory organoids or organoids of sense and a system of conductive fibrils. As in the examples given by Severcev to illustrate the general degeneration in Metazoa, 'the function of locomotion and of active dispersal is transferred from the adult forms to the free-swimming larvae', or in our case to different stages of multiplication (sporozoites, merozoites, sporokinetes, ookinetes, &c.).

The only organoids that undergo a clear and diversified complication are the different protective adaptations, which enable the progeny of the Sporozoa to accomplish safely the transfer from one host to another. For this purpose a system of interpolated membranes (cysts with spores inside them) has developed in gregarines and Coccidia, while in certain gregarines there are special sporoducts of complex structure. According to Severcev, these developments are also characteristic of general degeneration. 'In the course of which', writes Severcev, 'organs with active functions are usually reduced, while organs which are passive but of importance for the animals develop progressively.'

Idioadaptations

There is no necessity to go into details of the idioadaptations undergone by individual groups within every class of Protozoa in the course of their adaptation to various more special environmental conditions and divergence from an original common root, for in some cases it is difficult to establish the course of development of such idioadaptations, while in others a description of them is given in various chapters of this book.

It is sufficient to say that a whole series of idioadaptations can really be traced. We are in a position to point out the kind of adaptations that had taken place, to enable the animal to live in the plankton as well as the groups of Protozoa in which they occurred; which features developed in ciliates inhabiting the sapropele; what modifications were undergone by Protozoa on their transition to a parasitic mode of life in general and to various types of parasitism in particular (ectoparasitism, blood parasitism, &c.).

In the problem of morphophysiological regularities governing the evolution of Protozoa, it is not these points that are of special interest, but those peculiarities in the development of adaptations in certain groups which are, apparently, characteristic of Protozoa alone.

We have in mind the idioadaptations of certain Protozoa to an endoparasitic mode of life, in particular within the intestine. In our discussion of the evolution of the Sporozoa we have already noted the simplifying effect on the organization produced by the endoparasitic mode of life. But in addition to these patterns of extreme general degeneration, some groups of endoparasitic Protozoa reveal quite an opposite phenomenon, viz. an extreme complication of structure and functions. Therefore, in these cases there is clearly evidence of morphophysiological progress, displayed not by isolated, random species, but by hundreds of species forming whole orders.

This phenomenon of morphological progress due to parasitism is observed first of all in intestinal ciliates of the order *Entodiniomorpha*, and in the order *Gymnostomata* of the subclass *Holotricha*. The structural complication is especially striking in *Entodiniomorpha*, the cytology of which is so complicated that they can be regarded as the most highly organized ciliates. The locomotor apparatus of *Entodiniomorpha* consists of large, powerful cirri, and is differentiated into several groups of these structures which have different physiological functions. The external form of the body varies greatly, and shows a fine development of spines, processes, &c. *Entodiniomorpha* are the only ciliates provided with a well-developed special internal skeleton consisting of platelets. Their digestive apparatus is also the most complicated among all the ciliates. It is composed of a pharynx consisting of two parts, of a clearly defined mid-gut (endoplasmic sac) and of a thick-walled rectal canal. Finally, the body of *Entodiniomorpha* contains a well-developed system of fibrils of supporting, contractile, and perhaps also regulating nature. The development of the entire group *Entodiniomorpha* is associated with herbivorous mammals, ungulates, more rarely rodents, proboscidians, chimpanzees, and gorillas. Thus, the complication, or at all events a great structural complexity in this group, which consists of several hundred species, is displayed in almost all the systems of organoids. It should also be noted that these organoids include those which perform active functions, such as the locomotor and digestive systems.

Among the parasites living in the same medium as Entodiniomorpha, i.e. in the digestive tract of herbivorous mammals, are the Gymnostomata, (*Bütschlia, Didesmis, Paraisotricha*, and others), a group composed of more than a hundred species. These ciliates reveal not a general but a partial complication of organization; namely, in the majority of them there is a very peculiar structure, 'the concrement vacuole', which plays the role of a very complex sensory organ of equilibrium. This development of sensory organoids on transition to an endoparasitic mode of life is of special interest.

In our attempts to explain these exceptional phenomena, we find the only plausible interpretation to be as follows. All these ciliates live in the voluminous parts of the alimentary tract: the rumen in ruminants, and the caecum and larger intestine in perissodactyls. The capacity of these organs is measured by buckets of their contents. In other words, the ciliates in such large containers find conditions differing but little from those in some small natural body of water, for instance a deep pool, which is moreover filled with a huge quantity of nutrient substances. These conditions are so similar to the external medium that, as is known, the ciliates were followed into the alimentary tract of ungulates by some of their ectoparasites, namely suctorians of the genus *Allantosoma*. In fact, the alimentary tract of the herbivores represents a small but peculiar body of water, in which the ciliates continue to lead the life of free-living Protozoa, but in the presence of more abundant food.

An entirely analogous situation is encountered in those orders of *Mastigophora* which have established themselves in the alimentary tract of termites, namely Polymastigida and Hypermastigida; the former includes some free-living representatives, while the latter comprises parasites only, and had probably originated from the first order. These peculiar flagellates, feeding exclusively on bits of wood, underwent in the course of their evolution within the termites extensive changes of structure of a progressive nature.

All the phenomena typical of morphophysiological progress such as the increase in size, polymerization of organoids, appearance of new organoids, and intensification of the functions of organoids, are clearly displayed in both orders inhabiting the termites, which comprise several dozen genera and more than 200 species. We can find no explanation of the intensive development and structural complication in the Polymastigida and Hypermastigida from the alimentary tract of termites. However, we may note certain features which are common to the Entodiniomorpha and to the above-mentioned flagellates. All these forms live in the alimentary tract of herbivorous hosts; they all feed on formed particles of the host's food (bits of grass and leaves, fragments of wood); and they all live under conditions of extraordinary abundance of food.

Such are the conditions under which groups of Protozoa, adapted to a mode of life within the intestine, had—contrary to all theoretical premisses—developed extremely complex structural changes bearing all the characteristics of morphophysiological progress. In this respect the evolution of certain groups of Protozoa presents some peculiarities that are not encountered among endoparasitic Metazoa.

Finally, the same entodiniomorphous ciliates, which have just been mentioned, illustrate another peculiarity in the evolution of certain Protozoa, namely an extremely wide range of morphophysiological complications observed in one comparatively small taxonomic unit. This suborder includes the family Ophryoscolecidae, consisting of comparatively few genera (about ten) which comprise a large number of species.

While the limits of this family are well defined, the different genera of the family present a series of very clear gradations of gradual polymerization and of complication in several systems of organoids (Fig. 280).

The first phase in the development of the family is represented by the genus *Entodinium*; it consists of small forms (20–60 μ), provided with one simple adoral zone of membranelles, one contractile vacuole, and a simple oval macronucleus; the posterior end of the body is simple and rounded, but occasionally it may carry one to four caudal spines. The entodinia feed on bacteria, spores of fungi, and particles of detritus. It has no skeletal plates.

The second phase is represented by the genus *Anoplodinium*. The dimensions of species belonging to it vary between 35–200 μ; a second, dorsal zone of membranelles is detached from the adoral zone, whereby the progressive locomotion of the animal is increased; a second, posterior vacuole is added to the anterior one; the macronucleus is frequently bent in the shape of a hook; the posterior end of the body is either simple or it bears one to six caudal spines. Fairly large bits of grass serve as food for members of this genus. There are no skeletal plates.

The third phase of the development is represented by the genus *Eudiplodinium*. On the whole it is close to the preceding one, but on the left side of the body, between the pharynx and the right side of the body, there

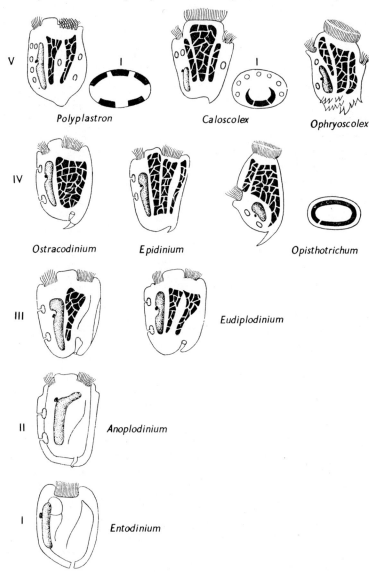

FIG. 280. Scheme of gradations of morphological complication in genera of ciliates of the family Ophryoscolecidae, illustrating also their evolution in time. The two lowest phases presumably belong to the Eocene; the third from below corresponds to the Oligocene; the fourth Oligocene and Miocene; the fifth corresponds to Pliocene. I, transverse sections through body of the ciliates. (After Dogiel, 1946.)

are one or two narrow skeletal plates consisting of one layer of polygonal prisms set perpendicularly to the surface of the body. The appearance of this characteristic marks an important progressive step in the organization of the animal. Its skeletal plates serve not for the protection of the body from outside, but especially for the support of the pharyngeal walls, to prevent large bits of grass entering the pharynx from tearing the thin right side of the pharynx. Owing to this modification of the pharynx, the animals are capable of swallowing much greater, sometimes huge, bits of cellulose over which their bodies become stretched in the form of a thin, plasmatic film. The function of feeding is thus considerably intensified. The size of the animals varies from 75 μ to 500 μ.

The next stage of evolution is represented in three genera (*Ostracodinium*, *Epidinium*, and *Opisthotrichum*). Their progressive development finds expression mainly in the strengthening of their internal skeleton, which forms either one or three plates, but it is so broad that it covers either the entire right side of the pharynx, or even bends round the whole of it, leaving uncovered only a narrow, longitudinal slit. Besides this, in the genus Opisthotrichum the dorsal zone of membranelles is removed somewhat backwards. This strengthens the effect of this zone during the forward propulsion of the animal. These forms have two to four vacuoles. Their sizes are 120–230 μ.

Finally, the culminating point of development is reached by the genera *Polyplastron*, *Caloscolex*, and *Ophryoscolex*. In these genera the number of skeletal plates is three to six, the number of vacuoles increases from nine to fifteen; moreover, they surround the body in the form of one or two semi-circlets, while the dorsal zone of membranelles encircles the body, leaving only the right third of the surface of the body free of membranelles. The posterior end of the body of the most highly organized representative (*Ophryoscolex*) is armed not with one but with three or four circlets of spines, the foremost one of which consists of six complex 2–4-branched spines. This complication of the armament represents a progressive character, since the spines, when spreading out sideways, may help the animal in its progression through the contents of the rumen.

Thus, within the limits of one family, the *Ophryoscolecidae* go through a very long evolutionary course, involving the acquisition of a new system of organoids (skeletal plates), a strong intensification of the digestive function, a reinforcement of the excretory apparatus, and a considerable strengthening of the caudal equipment associated with an intensification of locomotion.

What is the length of time required for the production of such significant changes? The *Ophryoscolecidae* provide a rare case among the Protozoa where it is possible to give an answer to this question. Owing to the fact that there is a comparatively complete palaeontological record of the hosts of *Ophryoscolecidae*, i.e. the ruminants, and because various genera of this family are more or less specific for individual groups of ruminants (Dogiel, 1947), we can to a certain extent establish the time when various genera of this family made their appearance. It has thus been possible to establish that the most primitive representative of the family, i.e. the genus *Entodinium*, as well as the genus *Anoplodinium*, had probably arisen in the Eocene; the genera *Eudiplodinium* and *Epidinium* appeared in the Oligocene; other genera, representing further stages of evolution, became differentiated in the Miocene, and finally the group of the most highly organized genera (*Polyplastron*, *Caloscolex*, and *Ophryoscolex*) emerged in the Pliocene, during the period when the groups of camels, deer, antelopes, and musk-oxen became differentiated. Thus a period from the lower Eocene to the middle Oligocene was required for the *Ophryoscolecidae* to develop their peculiar character, namely the skeletal plates. Hypothetically a series of specially characteristic species may be referred to the Pleistocene.

It is noteworthy that the evolution of the Entodiniamorpha and of the parasitic flagellates from termites shows a rigidly directed trend. This tendency towards an increase in size, polymerization, and the complication of structure proceeding in a definite direction is particularly striking in the *Ophryoscolecidae*, but it is also clear in the Polymastigida, where the basic type of the structure seen in the genus *Trichomonas* undergoes complication, mainly along the line of an increase in the number of flagella and complication of the parabasal apparatus.

Thus in Protozoa the general course of evolution may proceed both by aromorphosis and idioadaptations, and by general degeneration. These adaptations of organisms to the changing environmental conditions are, according to Severcev, achieved in Metazoa by phylogenetic modifications of the structure and function of individual organs. Several categories of such phylogenetic modifications of organs have been established. The first is represented by those types of evolutionary changes, in which the main function of the organs remains qualitatively unchanged, but increases quantitatively; to the second category belong types of evolutionary changes, in which the main function of the organ is altered qualitatively. According to Severcev, all these modifications are based on the fact that every organ is multifunctional, i.e. a fundamental property of the organism is that each part of it is endowed not with one function but many, one of them being the main function, while the others are secondary and not always used by the organism.

The question arises whether these principles of phylogenetic modifications are applicable also to the unicellular organisms. No detailed investigations have been carried out on this problem and only J. Gelei (1950) made an attempt to apply it to the ciliates. He noted, for instance, an intensification of the functions correlated with the development of protective adaptations in ciliates. In free-living forms the pellicle is usually thin, whereas in the parasitic Entodiniomorpha it increases in thickness and density, so that something like an external 'skeleton' is produced. An intensification of the locomotor functions is manifested in ciliates by an increase in the number and length of the cilia. For instance, in some rapidly swimming ciliates a thickening of the ciliary cover is observed at the anterior end and on the abdominal side (for instance, in *Loxocephalus* and others). In many Spirotricha long cilia united into complexes—sincilium, cirri, membranes, and membranelles—are formed. This increases not only the locomotor function but also that of food capture.

The principle of a functional substitution of organoids was demonstrated by Gelei in the case of the Suctoria, in which the oral aperture has disappeared and the function of food ingestion has been taken over by the formation of suctorial tentacles.

A change of functions is effected by differentiation of the cilia, which perform locomotor and sensory functions. The former function is the primary one, but sometimes it may weaken and then the secondary, sensory, function comes into play. This takes place, for instance, in the rows of cilia at the anterior end of the body of *Spathidium* and in other ciliates. The broadening of functions is associated with qualitative changes in the cilia. In addition to the swimming function, cilia united into cirri acquire a new function—movement along a solid substratum ('walking').

As regards other phylogenetic modifications noted by Severcev in Metazoa, such as the loss of intermediate functions, decrease in the number of functions, fixation of phases, activation of functions, immobilization of functions, &c., so far they have not been found to be applicable to Protozoa, and the examples adduced by Gelei cannot be regarded as convincing.

POLYMERIZATION AND OLIGOMERIZATION IN THE EVOLUTION OF PROTOZOA

In 1929 Dogiel suggested that one of the important principles of progressive evolution in Protozoa is the polymerization of their organoids. By polymerization is meant in this case the development in an individual protozoon of many homologous and equivalent organoids or whole complexes of organoids. These organoids include in the first place nuclei, contractile vacuoles, skeletal elements (spicules, plates), chromatophores, parabasal bodies, &c.; as well as the polymerization of flagella organoids that are usually present in a definite number. As will be shown below, the evaluation of the number and of the polymerization of cilia is more difficult.

Dogiel (1936, 1947, 1954) later returned again to the problem of polymerization and oligomerization in the evolution of both Protozoa and Metazoa. According to his views polymerization is a characteristic trend in Protozoa, whereas in a great majority of groups of Metazoa the opposite trend predominates, namely the oligomerization of the organs which is effected either by the loss of some of the homologous organs or by their fusion with each other.

In considering the phenomenon of polymerization in Protozoa we should start from their simplest structural types. Haeckel (1868) described under the name 'moneres' amoeboid organisms devoid of a nucleus. It was later shown that all Haeckel's moneres possessed nuclei and this category of organisms was abolished. However, theoretically speaking it might exist and in that case it would be regarded as the first step in the evolution of Protozoa, namely the prenuclear phase of their evolution. The second phase of evolution is represented by typical unicellular organisms, which in their morphological significance correspond to the concept of a single energid. This term was proposed by Sachs (1892) for every cell nucleus together with the part of the cytoplasm that surrounds it and is under its control. A cell with one nucleus is monoenergid; with many, polyenergid. In the case of Protozoa, all uninucleate or multinucleate species were therefore monoenergid, while organisms which are multinucleate, but not separated into cell compartments, were polyenergid. Hartmann (1911), who regarded this definition as insufficient and too physiological, used the term 'energid' in the morphological sense and considered it from the point of view of the physiology of development. Under the name energid he designated the nucleus or part of a nucleus, which after isolation (natural, as the result of division, or artificial, i.e. when the animal is dissected) is capable of forming, together with a certain portion of cytoplasm, a typical complete organism.

Doflein and Reichenow (1929) defined the concept of the energid even more precisely, regarding it as a portion of the cytoplasm, together with a nucleus containing one complete set of chromosomes. An amplification of this concept was necessitated by the fact that there exist Protozoa whose single nucleus contains several sets of chromosomes, so that in the course of division it breaks up into as many nuclei and energids as the number of sets of chromosomes in it. Hence some Protozoa are unicellular but nevertheless polyenergid (e.g. many radiolarians).

Finally, according to Zachvatkin's definition (1949), the basic criterion of 'true unicellularity' should be not the 'monoenergid' constitution alone, in the abstract sense, as understood by Sachs, but a combination of the uninucleate structure with the presence of a complete, single complement of permanent cellular organoids. Evidently Zachvatkin understands by the term 'uninucleate' structure one nucleus with one complete set of chromosomes.

The phenomenon of polymerization of organoids by no means always depends on the polyenergid organization of the animal, just as this is not always reflected, apart from the nucleus, in the other organoids. In those cases when a group of Protozoa is composed of a series of forms whose structure gradually becomes more complicated, polymerization progresses with the development of complication, embracing more and more organoids.

We can now consider examples of polymerization first in the typical unicellular and monoenergid Protozoa. The simplest form of polymery is a gradual increase in the number of any single type of organoids, while the others remain unaffected by polymerization. A good example of this is provided by the polymerization of flagella in a series of Polymastigida. The genus *Bodo* (Fig. 281) (belonging to the order Protomonadida), provided with one anterior and one trailing flagellum, is regarded as a primitive

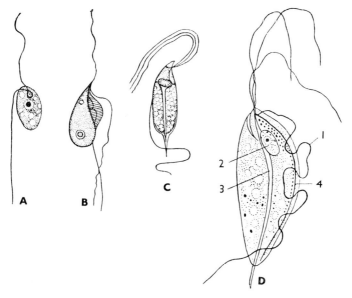

FIG. 281. Various flagellates.

(*A*) *Bodo edax*; (*B*) *Trimastix marina*; (*C*) *Foaina nana*; (*D*) *Trichomonas*. 1, undulating membrane; 2, nucleus; 3, axostyle; 4, supporting fibril of membrane. (From Dogiel, 1951, after many authors.)

form of parasitic Polymastigida. The lower representatives of Polymastigida, which are still free-living, already possess three flagella (*Trimastix, Dallingeria*). The transition to parasitic Polymastigida is effected by four-flagellate forms like *Chilomastix mesnili* or *Tricercomitus* and others, in which three flagella are directed forwards, while the fourth trails behind the body. The same type of structure is found in the family *Trichomonadidae*, except that in its representatives the trailing flagellum is attached to the body and forms part of an undulating membrane. Many Polymastigida retain the same number of flagella, which form a tetrad, consisting of three anterior (a triad) flagella and one posterior flagellum. At the same time, in *Trichomonas* certain species already possess four anterior flagella (*Trichomonas vaginalis* and others) instead of three or even five (*Pentatrichomonas hominis*).

The above examples of polymerization of flagella belong to the category of simple polymerization, which affects only one system of organoids, whereas in regard to the structure of their nucleus the animals remain monoenergid. The other category is composed of monoenergid Protozoa which display polymerization of two or more organoids. Examples of such polymerization, which may be called complex-monoenergid, are found among the Polymastigida from the alimentary tract of termites and cock-roaches (Fig. 282). For example in *Parajoenia grassii* the number of flagella,

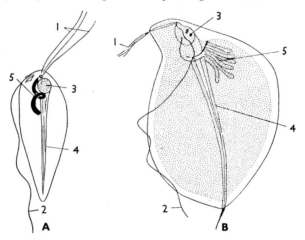

FIG. 282. Polymastigida from termites. (Grassé, 1952.)

(*A*) *Devescovina* with three anterior (1) and one trailing (2) flagella, with nucleus (3), axostyle (4), and sausage-shaped parabasal body (5); (*B*) *Pseudodevesovina uniflagellata* with three anterior flagella, one trailing flagellum, nucleus, axostyle, and cluster of parabasal bodies.

as in *Trichomonas*, is increased to four, but in addition to this, the para-basal apparatus suspended from a group of basal granules, from which the flagella arise, is not simple, but is composed of a pair of sausage-shaped structures; while in *Pseudodevescovina*, with the same structure of the flagellar apparatus, the parabasal apparatus is composed of seven to nineteen sausage-shaped bodies.

   In all the cases enumerated the polymerization of organoids is effected within the limits of one simple uninucleate and monoenergid cell, and is accomplished either by fission or new formation of organoids in which the nuclear apparatus takes no part. Apart from this course, another method of multiplication of organoids within one common plasmatic body occurs in Polymastigida and Hypermastigida. In such cases the polymerization of organoids is also effected by fission, but in the course of it a whole series of organoids of the animal, even including the nucleus, is multiplied n times, whereas the plasmatic body of the organism itself remains undivided. As a result of this process, there is produced not a simple, unicellular organism, nor a colony of these, but a peculiar, in some respects intermediate, stage of organization, to which the term 'somatella' was applied by Kofoid and

Swezy (1922). They were the first to apply this term to intestinal flagellates of many vertebrates, namely to the genus *Giardia* (order Polymastigida). In this genus the whole set of organoids (nucleus, axostyle, four flagella) possessed by the genus *Trichomonas* is strictly duplicated, so that both complexes are arranged symmetrically inside the body, as mirror reflections of each other. The permanence of the number of components, and the strict correspondence of the number of cytoplasmic organoids to the number of nuclei, indicate that in *Giardia* the polymeric (dimeric) structure has apparently arisen as the result of uncompleted division, i.e. of suppressed vegetative multiplication.

The genus *Hexamitus* possesses a similar organization, and some of its species have still retained a free mode of life, suggesting that the transition from the *Trichomonas* state to that of a somatella had been accomplished before these flagellates adopted a parasitic mode of life.

The evolution of the somatella from a simple unicellular organism is well illustrated in two families of *Polymastigida*: the *Oxymonadidae* and *Polymonadidae*. The genus *Oxymonas* represents a uninucleate flagellate with a peculiar digitiform process (rostellum) at their anterior end, with a supporting axostyle passing in the shape of an axial rod through the entire body (as in *Trichomonas*): the trailing flagellum of the trichomonads is here apparently reduced, but the anterior triad of flagella is doubled, forming two triads instead of one. The number of basal granules of the flagella is also doubled in *Oxymonas*. The next member of the series of polymerized forms of Oxymonadidae is represented by the genus *Proboscidiella*, which is already in transition to the stage of a somatella. Like *Oxymonas*, the genus *Proboscidiella* possesses an anterior attachment process, the rostellum, an anterior triad of flagella and a rod-like axostyle, but the number of sets of different organoids in *Proboscidiella* is subject to considerable individual variation. In the simplest cases the animal has only one nucleus, but several (2–13) triads of flagella and axostyles. From the morphological point of view, such individuals correspond to a mono-energid unicellular organism, but with an increased number of organoids. Side by side with such individuals are encountered others, in which the multiplication of the number of locomotor and supporting organoids corresponds to that of the number of nuclei (sometimes up to thirty-four); the number of the supporting-locomotor apparatus is usually greater than that of the nuclei, i.e. polymerization of the nuclei and that of the supporting-locomotor apparatus proceed at different rates, without harmony. However, the fully defined form of the body of *Proboscidiella* remains unchanged— in other words the animal has been converted into a somatella.

In *Calonympha* (family *Calonymphidae*) polymerization has proceeded even further, being accompanied by considerable regulation of the position occupied by the complexes of the supporting-locomotor organoids in the body of the animal. The complete set of organoids, or 'working unit', in the body of *Calonympha* consists of a nucleus, of a group of basal granules with a tetrad of flagella, of a parabasal apparatus, and an axostyle. Such a complex is named 'karyomastigont'. Karyomastigonts (up to fifty) form several circlets round the anterior end of the animal, but the extreme parietal region is occupied by several dozens of such complexes, but they

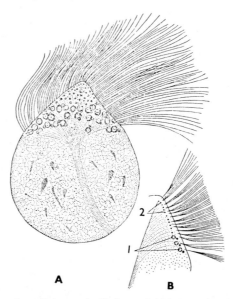

Fig. 283. Flagcllate *Calonympha* (Polymastigida) from the alimentary tract of termites.

(*A*) whole animal; (*B*) part of the anterior portion of body showing karyomastigonts (1) and akaryomastigonts (2). (After Janicki, 1915.)

are devoid of nuclei—these are akaryomastigonts. The axostyles of all the sets of organoids are collected inside the body into one common bundle.

The concealed meaning of the phenomenon of polymerization in Protozoa is revealed in such organisms as *Proboscidiella* and *Calonympha*. The delay in the rate of polymerization of the nuclei, lagging behind that of the supporting-locomotor apparatus, indicates that in these cases the increase in the number of organoids is directed not towards vegetative multiplication and the separation of its products, but only towards a functional intensification of the resulting complex structure—the somatella. The necessity for this functional intensification is very probably due to the increase in the volume of the plasmatic body under the conditions of intestinal parasitism which are extremely favourable for this.

A comparison between the genera *Torquenympha* and *Coronympha* (Fig. 284), belonging to different families, shows the extent of variation in polymerization observed in parasitic flagellates from the alimentary tract of termites. They display a similarity in general architectonics and a similar multiplication of the number of organoids, but differ in one essential feature. Both parasites have a pyriform shape of the body, the anterior widened end of the body bears a circlet of eight triads (*Torquenympha*) or sixteen tetrads (*Coronympha*) of flagella with rod-like axostyles running backwards from their bases, and with a number of parabasal apparatus corresponding to the number of triads or tetrads. These pyriform apparatus form within the anterior end of the body a peripheral circlet.

However, when we turn to the structure of the nuclear apparatus, we find in *Torquenympha*, inside the circlet of parabasal apparatus, a single mono-energid nucleus, whereas in *Coronympha* there is in the same place a circlet of sixteen nuclei, corresponding to the number of supporting-locomotor apparatus. Therefore, *Torquenympha* is a typical unicellular protozoon, while *Coronympha* is a multinucleate organism, representing a higher structural stage— the somatella.

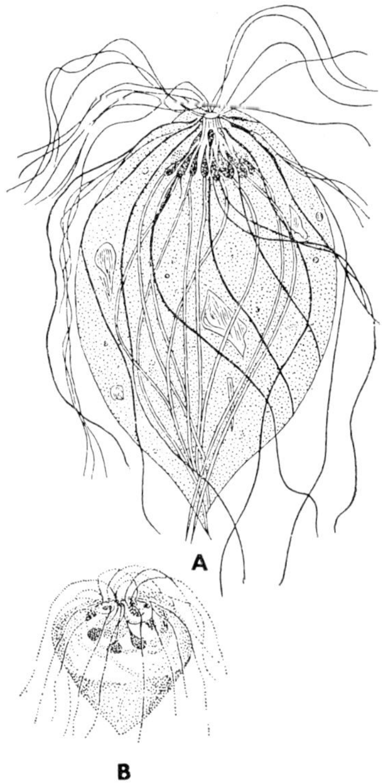

Polymerization is also encountered in polyenergid multinucleate Radiolaria, the best illustration being provided by the 'myophrisks', i.e. muscle fibres connecting the ectoplasm of the radio- larians Acantharia with their radial spines. According to Ševjakov (1926), in the most primitive family of Acantho- plegmidae the number of myophrisks on each spine is restricted to 2–4; in Con- aconidae and Gigantoconidae, which originated from this family, their number increases to 6-8, while in the even more

B

FIG. 284. Polymastigida from alimentary tract of termites.

(*A*) *Coronympha clevelandi* (after Kirby, 1929) with circlet of 8–16 karyomasti- gonts, from which a common bundle of axostyles is given off; (*B*) *Torquenympha octoplus*: at the anterior end of the pyri- form body there is a single nucleus surrounded by a circlet of 8 parabasal bodies and a circlet of flagella. (After Brown, 1930.)

differentiated descendants of the *Acanthoplegmidae* it is 8–16 (reaching in the genus *Heliolithium* even 24–32).

The family *Acanthometridae*, which is more highly developed than all the foregoing, possesses 24–40 myophrisks on each spine, and in the most highly organized families, the *Phyllostauridae* and *Dictyacanthidae*, the number of myophrisks on a spine reaches the maximum, namely 50–60. Thus in the course of evolution of the suborder Acantharia the number of myophrisks per spine rises progressively from 2 to 60.

It is noteworthy that parallel with this there has also been an increase, though less regular, in the number of pseudopodia in each of the twenty areas on the surface of the body of the Radiolaria, which surround the points from which the twenty spines emerge.

Evidence of further evolution is provided among the Foraminifera by the multilocular forms that have undoubtedly evolved from the unilocular ones, and in Radiolaria Spumellaria by the latticed skeletal spheres that are fitted into each other (up to four, one inside another); such modifications of the skeleton are caused by a periodical growth of the cytoplasm of these forms.

Finally, among the Dinoflagellata an interesting organization of the species *Polykrikos* should be noted. In this genus, incomplete division has led to an increase in the number of nuclei, from one, which is normal for Dinoflagellata, to two in *P. schulzei*, and four in *P. schwartzi*, and to a corresponding multiplication of the number of flagella, vacuoles, parabasal apparatus, &c. The general cigar-shaped body, adapted to swimming, gives *Polykrikos* the appearance of a single individual, although in fact it is a somatella, similar to *Giardia*, but with an increased number of organoids not in the transverse but in the longitudinal direction.

Polymerization is widespread in ciliates. The best example is provided by ciliates of the family *Ophryoscolecidae*, the general outline of whose phylogeny has been established, while its polymerization is extremely varied. The gradual complication finds expression in the progressive increase of the number of homologous components in different systems of organoids. The increase in the number of skeletal platelets, contractile vacuoles, caudal spines, and ciliary arches during the evolution of the family is clearly shown in the accompanying Table.

GRADUAL COMPLICATION OF THE ORGANIZATION OF GENERA OF FAM. OPHRYOSCOLECIDAE

Stage	Genera	Skeletal platelets	Vacuoles	Spines	Ciliary arches
V	Polyplastron, Caloscolex, Ophryoscolex	3-5	7-15	0-15	2
IV	Epidinium, Ostracodinium, Opisthotrichum	1-3	2-4	0-6	2
III	Eudiplodinium	1-2	2	0-6	2
II	Anoplodinium	..	2	0-6	2
I	Entodinium	..	1	0-4	1

In another family of the same order Entodiniomorpha, namely in *Cycloposthiidae*, the process of polymerization is revealed only in the number of vacuoles (from 2–9) and of the bundles of membranelles (from 2–4).

The initial number of contractile vacuoles in ciliates is undoubtedly one; their number increases only in the course of further evolution. A concrete example of this is provided by the family *Ophryoglenidae*, whose primitive, free-living forms usually have only one vacuole. On the other hand, the larger *Ichthyophthirius multifiliis*, a parasitic in the skin of fish, has a large number of vacuoles (over thirty). This species is especially interesting because its young individuals have at first only one vacuole, like the free-living *Ophryoglenidae*.

In ciliates of the order Astomata, from the alimentary tract of oligochaetes and turbellarians, there is an evident increase in the number of contractile vacuoles proceeding from their simpler representatives to the more specialized and complicated ones. There is a whole series of gradations from species with one vacuole (certain *Anaplophrya*, *Dogielella*) to those with a longitudinal row of vacuoles (many *Mesnilella*, *Radiophrya*), and in individual cases even with two parallel rows of vacuoles (*Radiophrya limnodrili*, and others).

Some Astomata also provide instances of polymerization of the skeletal attachment rays or spicules, which is especially clear in the genus *Mesnilella* (Chejsin, 1930, 1947). The most primitive species of the genus possess only one longitudinal skeletal ray on the lower side of the *M. rostrata*; in other species Chejsin traced an increase in the number of rays up to 2 (*Mesnilella bispiculata*), 3 (*M. trispiculata*), and 4–8 (*M. vermicularis, M. depressa, M. maritui, M. multispiculata*), and finally in the most complex *M. radiata* up to 15–28.

Among ciliates of the genus *Trichodina*, which is parasitic on the body of fish, the most ancient and primitive species are undoubtedly those that are ectoparasitic on the gills and skin of the host, while the species which had penetrated into the urinary bladder of fish and have become endoparasitic are of later origin. It appears that in the ectoparasitic forms of *Trichodina* the number of hooks in the attachment disk is not great (from 15 to 30), but in *Trichodina* from the urinary bladder their number rises to 50 and more. In certain other Peritricha, as in *Polycycla*, discovered by Poljanskij (Fig. 285), the number of ciliary circlets increases from one to forty.

The process of polymerization of the nuclear apparatus in ciliates is most unusual, owing to their characteristic nuclear dualism. It is expressed in a morphological and functional differentiation between the macronucleus and micronucleus, on account of which all the ciliates may be referred to the category of heterokaryotes, without, however, attaching a taxonomic significance to this term. In contrast to this category, the other Protozoa should be referred to homokaryotes (Grell, 1950; Biocca, 1957). However, among the Foraminifera in *Roteliella heterocaryotica*, *Rurbatella intermedia*, and *Glabratella sulcata*, according to Grell (1954, 1958), there is a clear differentiation into somatic and generative nuclei, i.e. like the ciliates, these forms can also be referred to the category of heterokaryotes. On the other hand, among the lower ciliates *Stephanopogon* (Lwoff, 1936) does not possess a nuclear dualism, but has one or several identical nuclei. Hence it may be concluded that nuclear dualism was evolved within the class

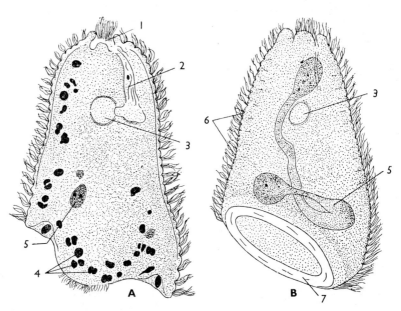

FIG. 285. *Polycycla* (Peritricha) displaying polymerization of the ciliary circlets on the body.

(*A*) longitudinal section; (*B*) general view. 1, mouth; 2, vestibule; 3, contractile vacuole; 4, food particles; 5, macronucleus; 6, ciliary circlets; 7, attachment disk. (After Poljanskij, 1951.)

Ciliata, the process of polymerization playing an essential role in its development. Rajkov (1957) and Poljanskij and Rajkov (1960) have expressed the opinion that the complication of the nuclear apparatus was associated with an increase of the size of the body and an intensification of metabolism. As a result, in the first stage of the evolution the nuclear apparatus underwent polymerization and forms with a greater number of identical nuclei were produced (for instance, the vegetative stage of *Stephanopogon*). This process was later followed by their differentiation. In connexion with the intensification of functions some nuclei, that had arisen by additional divisions, became more active physiologically. In such modified nuclei, representing macronuclei, RNA is accumulated and the DNA content is small, but the latter is not synthesized within them, with the result that they lose their capacity for division. During fission of the ciliates the macronuclei are distributed among the daughter individuals, while the micro-nucleus undergoes mitotic division. The number of macronuclei is restored at each division of the ciliates at the expense of the micronuclei. It may be assumed that the multiple macronuclei in such ciliates are probably diploid, as are the micronuclei. Some lower holotrichous ciliates—*Trachelocerca*, *Loxodes*, *Geleia* (Rajkov, 1958, 1959)—are in this stage of development.

The subsequent phylogenetic modification of the macronucleus proceeded by polyploidization, resulting in their transformation into a massive nucleus rich in DNA. This was associated with a further intensification of the functions of the nucleus and the acquisition of the capacity for division. Poljanskij and Rajkov (1960) regard polyploidization as a manifestation of the process of polymerization. In this case polymerization is not expressed in an increase of the number of identical, probably diploid, nuclei, as in the initial stages of the evolution of nuclear dualism, but in the multi-plication of whole chromosome sets in the macronuclei from the diploid state to polyploid.

As already noted in the chapter on the nuclear structure of Protozoa, the macronucleus of most ciliates is polyploid. During restoration of the macronucleus from its diploid primordium endomitotic polyploidization occurs, i.e. repeated autonomous divisions of the chromosomes, as a result of which the polyploidy of the macronucleus attains a high level.

The polymerization of chromosome complexes in the macronucleus, leading to the formation of a polyploid macronucleus, brought with it a general intensification of functions and a heightening of the level of morphological differentiation. Apparently, the formation of a polyploid macronucleus was followed by an increase in its size and a complication of its shape. The emergence of polyploidy in the macronuclei opened the way to the oligo-merization of their number, as a result of which the number of nuclei was reduced to one macronucleus and one micronucleus, as is observed in the majority of Ciliata. The primary multinucleate condition of ciliates should be distinguished from their secondary one, produced as a result of seg-mentation of the single macronucleus after division or conjugation. Such forms as *Dileptus*, *Urostyla*, and others belong to this category of multi-nucleate ciliates.

Of course, polymerization and the opposite phenomenon, i.e. oligo-merization or a reduction in the number of homologous organoids, are governed not by mathematical laws but by biological rules, and are subject to exceptions. Thus among Protozoa there occur, side by side with numer-ous examples of polymerization, individual cases of oligomerization. Such examples are found in many specialized ciliates, in which the number of locomotor elements or kinetids is decreased. This is accomplished simply as the result of disappearance of cilia on a large part of the surface of the body (Peritricha, Entodiniomorpha, Oligotricha).

A second example, in astomatous ciliates, can be regarded rather as pseudo-oligomerization. The contractile vacuoles in Astomata develop by polymerization from a single primary one into a longitudinal row of rounded vesicles. However, in certain species of the family *Haptophryidae* the row of vacuoles is replaced by one pulsating canal with many excretory pores. Hence it may be concluded that the canal is a secondary structure produced by fusion of a row of vacuoles. In some Acantharia there are cases of complete reduction of some of the skeletal spicules. Among Myxosporidia of the genus *Myxobolus*, it may be assumed that the spores of some species lost one of the two polar capsules and became unicapsular.

However, such cases are so rare that they are literally lost in the multitude of examples of the predominant phenomenon of polymerization.

The polymeric organs in Metazoa may display either a metameric or an antimeric arrangement, the antimerism being either bilateral or radial.

The same categories of polymerism are observed also in Protozoa. Thus the arrangement of chambers in Foraminifera is longitudinal, while a similar distribution of vacuoles in many ciliates and of concrement vacuoles in *Loxodes* also point to metamerism.

The mouth of the ciliate *Pycnothrix* is differentiated into a longitudinal row of small apertures, and in Hypermastigina of the genus *Cyclonympha* the body is girdled by a series of flagellar circlets.

As to antimeric polymerization in Protozoa it should be noted that bilateral antimerism is a very rare phenomenon: it is encountered only in the flagellate *Hoplonympha natator*, parasitic in the alimentary tract of termites, in flagellates of the family Hexamitidae (*Giardia* and others), and in some Radiolaria of the group Phaeodaria possessing a bivalve shell.

Radial antimerism is encountered much more frequently among Protozoa. It is seen mostly in the arrangement of the skeletal spicules of many Radiolaria, in that of the contractile vacuoles of certain Ophryoscolecid ciliates (*Ophryoscolex*, *Caloscolex*), and in the arrangement of flagellar bundles in some Hypermastigida (four bundles in *Staurojoenia* and *Staurojoenina*, forming a cross). In Polymastigina of the genera *Calonympha* and *Stephanonympha* the complexes of organoids are arranged in circlets around the longitudinal axis. Many other examples could be given.

The investigation of the causes and process of polymerization is of great interest. It has been found that polymerism arises in different ways in various groups of Protozoa.

In a whole series of cases polymerization of organoids is the result of uncompleted vegetative multiplication by fission; this can be seen in the antimeric polymerization of *Giardia* and the metameric in *Polykrikos*. In *Polykrikos* the groups of four united individuals are extraordinarily similar to temporary chains of individuals of *Ceratium* and other Dinoflagellata; however, these eventually always break up into separate individuals. In other flagellates (for instance *Proboscidiella*) and in all the ciliates from the alimentary tract of ruminants, multiplication of their homologous organoids takes place independently of reproduction.

Some systems of homologous organoids are formed by division of an originally large apparatus into several homologous parts of smaller size. This pattern is observed in some genera of the family *Cycloposthiidae* from the alimentary tract of perissodactyls, and in *Troglodytella* from anthropoid apes, when from the end of the originally whole, long adoral zone of membranelles are detached several portions which are transformed into independent zones or bundles of homologous membranelles. Apparently this arrangement, resulting in the shifting of some of the membranelles towards the posterior end of the animal, is the most expedient, for the posterior arches or bundles of membranelles in these ciliates serve to propel the animal through the dense mass of food particles.

In the case of some intestinal Protozoa that attach themselves to the intestinal walls, metameric polymerization is induced by their existence in a constant stream of food passing by. The metameric arrangement of the flagella of *Cyclonympha strobia*, a flagellate from the alimentary tract of termites, is clearly indicated by constrictions and annular circlets. Likewise the body of the gregarines *Taeniocystis mira*, *Metamera schubergi*, and others (see Fig. 313) is divided into a considerable number of metameric sections by plasmatic transverse partitions.

Finally, in a whole group of intestinal Dinoflagellata of the genus *Haplozoon* the body consists of one cephalic cell and metamerically arranged generative cells, or rows of cells.

One of the most important causes of polymerization is probably also a progressive increase in the size of the animal, not accompanied by a corresponding growth of its individual organoids. In such cases a corresponding improvement in the efficacy of the organoids may be attained by an increase of their number. An excellent confirmation of this is the increase in the number of contractile vacuoles in various genera of the family *Ophryoscolecidae* corresponding to the progressive increase in the size of the ciliates starting from the genus *Entodinium* (not more than 60 μ) to the genera *Diplodinium* and *Ophryoscolex* (up to 100–300 μ). The extremely large number of flagella in such forms as *Trichonymphidae* is probably explained by a similar growth in size of the Hypermastigida.

Both polymerization and oligomerization predominant among the Metazoa have this in common, that while arising in different ways, they both appear parallel in diverse groups. In our opinion the variety of the means by which the same final result, i.e. polymerization (in Protozoa) or oligomerization (in Metazoa) is attained, bears witness to the biological importance of these processes in the course of evolution.

The process of oligomerization is correlated with the morphological and physiological concentration of organs and functions. At the same time, in a multicellular organism considered as a whole, oligomerization represents a series of successive steps of integration, i.e. of the subordination of parts to the whole. In complete contrast to oligomerization, polymerization represents, from the point of view of the organism as a whole, a process of decentralization. The organoids of Protozoa multiply in number and are widely distributed throughout the body, thereby reducing to a certain extent the controlling unity of the organism. This process proceeds furthest in those somatellas in which whole complexes of organoids are multiplied, including the nucleus. Such examples reveal also the general tendency of the whole phenomenon polymerization in Protozoa—that of gradual disintegration of the unicellular organism as it becomes more complex.

This tendency may be associated to some extent with the following points. Polymerization of organoids is usually correlated with a complication of the organization of Protozoa, while the latter is to a certain extent linked with an increase in the size of the body (Entodiniomorpha, flagellates from termites, and deep-water Radiolaria with an extremely complex skeletal structure). In contrast, a decrease in the size of the body in Protozoa is associated rather with a simple organization (Silicoflagellata, small Chrysomonadida, piroplasms, malaria parasites, *Leishmania*, and others). This simplicity is apparently an unavoidable consequence of the impossibility of distributing the sets of complex organoids in the limited space of a microscopic body (compare bacteria).

With an increase in the size of the body the activity of the organoids formerly present in the animal has to be intensified in order to satisfy the new requirements of the enlarged organism. The required intensification of the functions of the existing organoids may be effected by two main methods: (1) by an increase in the size of the organoids, without an increase in their number, or (2) by an increase in the number of organoids, while retaining their original size.

The first type of intensification of the efficacy of the organoids occurs, for example, in the heterotrichous ciliates (*Stentor, Spirostomum, Bursaria*) which attain 1–2 mm. in length. In these ciliates (*Stentor, Spirostomum*) the contractile vacuole remains single, but expands considerably; the macronucleus is single but extremely elongated. Some flagellates from the alimentary tract of termites, like *Gigantomonas*, retain the same set of organoids as their ancestors, the small trichomonads, but the size of their body and the length of their flagella are much greater. However, this method of intensification of functions is effected comparatively rarely. In the great majority of cases it proceeds by the second method, i.e. by polymerization of the organoids. It is difficult to determine definitely why this method predominates, but the life-cycle of Protozoa contains a feature which to some extent guides them in this direction. This is due to the fact that vegetative multiplication by fission is an essential part of the cycle of Protozoa, so that at each division the number of organoids is doubled even before the complete separation of the daughter individuals, a feature that is especially evident in flagellates. In our opinion, the behaviour of the organoids when the size of the animal increases without multiplication is determined to some extent by a similar premature multiplication of the number of organoids during division. This view is supported also by the fact that the polymerization of organoids in flagellates proceeds in a plane parallel to the longitudinal axis of the animal, i.e. in the same direction in which the organoids multiply during division of the organism. Hence it would seem that the phenomenon of polymerization of organoids is based on the nature of the evolutionary course of Protozoa.

The process of disintegration, which originally (in Protozoa) led to multiplication of the organisms, eventually (in Metazoa) resulted in a complication of their organization in the course of transition to a multicellular state. This phase was a turning point affecting the direction which changes in the number of homologous organs had taken in different groups of animals. When the structure of the body became differentiated into tissues, accompanied by multiplication of the cellular composition of the body and the emergence of new structures (multicellular organs, instead of organoids), a new principle of further evolution was established, which had an opposite tendency, being manifested by oligomerization of homologous organs, and this predominates in Metazoa. When viewed from this point of view, the predominance of polymerization in Protozoa and of oligomerization in Metazoa finds a ready explanation and is not contradictory.

Summarizing all that has been said about the process of polymerization, we arrive at the following phases of complication in the structure of Protozoa, based on the concept of an energid.

1. Animals with one monoenergid nucleus and one set of organoids. These are typical unicellular organisms, for which the concept 'cell' fully corresponds to the concept 'individual'.

2. Animals with several uniform monoenergid nuclei, not accompanied by a corresponding multiplication of the organoids. This category may be called multinucleate cells or, better still, plasmodia. Apart from the typical plasmodia—multinucleate amoebae, Foraminifera, *Acanthometridae*, plasmodia of Myxosporidia—certain unicellular Radiolaria (Phaeodaria, Nassellaria) possessing a single but—as is shown by its capacity for division—polyenergid nucleus should also be referred to this group.

3. Animals with one monoenergid nucleus and several sets of all organoids (*Oxymonas*); in spite of polymerization of their other organoids (not the nucleus) such animals may still be regarded as true cells.

4. Animals with many monoenergid uniform nuclei and with the other organoids multiplied more or less in accordance with the number of nuclei, forming as regards their external form and structure of the body one common whole; such animals may be called somatellae; they represent a transition to multicellular organisms.

5. Animals with one or several monoenergid nuclei and one or several

vegetative polyenergid nuclei: they represent polyenergid heterokaryotes, to which the Ciliata belong.

6. The spores of Myxosporidia form a completely separate category: their vegetative stages belong to the type of Plasmodia, but their spores undergo a process of cellulation, forming multicellular complexes that are also heterocellular, i.e. consist of different cells, the vital centre of which is represented by single or several reproductive cells (so-called amoeboids).

7. Finally, the last form of complex individualities among the Protozoa is represented by colonies, which may be the result of vegetative multiplication either of typical cells or of Plasmodia (certain Radiolaria, for instance *Collozoum* and allied forms), or heterokaryotes (colonies of the Ciliata Peritricha). All those Protozoa that are on a higher level than a single cell Zachvatkin sets apart under the name 'supercellular'.

All the supercellular Protozoa, whatever their mode of origin, illustrate the tendency to transition to the multicellular state common to diverse groups of Protozoa. However, most 'attempts' remain as blind-alleys leading nowhere: only the single path of evolution, through the spherical hollow colonies of Mastigophora, has led to the formation of a new category which eventually flourished luxuriantly—the multicellular animals or Metazoa.

STRUGGLE FOR LIFE AND NATURAL SELECTION IN PROTOZOA

The Protozoa furnish good material for the study of the struggle for existence and natural selection. The small size of Protozoa, their ability to multiply rapidly, the ease of growing both mass cultures and clones, the possibility of growing them under quite uniform conditions (such as the same pH, feeding them on a single species of bacteria or even in a bacteria-free medium); all these factors favour considerably experiments under laboratory conditions carried out on a sufficient number of living and very uniform initial material.

Gause (1932–9) carried out important experimental investigations of this nature on yeasts and ciliates. We may consider some results of this work, in which he threw light on the interspecific relationships in different ciliates. Their populations were secondary, since the ciliates lived in them by feeding on the primary population of bacteria. This represents an elementary food-chain: bacteria—ciliates, in which a culture of *Bacillus subtilus* in a decoction of oat-flour was used as nutrient medium. In the first series of experiments the growth of an equal number of *Paramecium caudatum* and of *Stylonychia mytilis* was compared separately and in a mixed culture; while the liquid in the culture was not changed.

A comparison of pure and mixed cultures revealed first of all that in a mixed population both species of ciliates, especially *Paramecium*, show a considerable fall in the number of individuals as compared to the curves of growth of these same species in pure cultures. The coefficient of the effect of *Stylonychia* on *Paramecium* was found to be 5·5 while the coefficient of the effect of *Paramecium* on *Stylonychia* was only 0·12. This indicates that *Stylonychia* influences *Paramecium* greatly, each individual *Stylonychia* occupying space sufficient for 5·5 Paramecia. The cause of such difference between the two species could not be determined. To make his experiments even more precise, Gause took two ciliates of the same genus, *Paramecium caudatum* and *P. aurelia* (Figs. 286, 287), and grew pure and mixed populations of them together with *Bacillus pyocyaneus*, cultivated, for complete uniformity of conditions, on a solid medium of peptone, glucose, agar-agar, &c. The nutrient medium for the bacteria was thus standardized. For further standardization of the conditions the ciliates were cultivated in Osterhaut's standard saline solution, to which food for the ciliates, in the form of one evenly filled platinum loop of fresh bacteria, was added daily per 10 c.c. of Osterhaut's medium. This solution was prepared afresh every day, and centrifuged ciliates were transferred into it. In this type of experiment all the properties of the medium are brought to a permanent 'standard condition' every twenty-four hours.

Under such conditions it is possible to discover whether in such a biocenosis, in which the store of energy is kept at a definite level, two species can exist for a long period of time, or whether in the end one of them would displace the other.

In order to study the process of competition it was also essential to pass from counts of the number of individuals of both species to an estimate of their biomasses, since the two species of *Paramecium* differ considerably in volume. Assuming the form of both species to be a regular ellipsoid of rotation and taking the volume of *P. caudatum* as equal to one unit, we obtain for *P. aurelia* from Osterhaut's medium a volume which is equal on the average to 0·39 of the volume of *P. caudatum*.

In order to pass from the number of individuals of the two species of *Paramecium* (which cannot be compared, owing to their different sizes) to an increase in their volume, it is sufficient to leave the number of individuals of *P. caudatum* unchanged, and to decrease in all cases the number of individuals of the smaller *P. aurelia* by multiplying it by 0·39.

As is shown by the curves of growth of each species in mixed and in pure cultures, the process of growth in mixed population is divided into two periods. During the first period (up to the eighth day) the species grow and compete with each other for the capture of the energy that is still unused by either (food stores). Once both species in the mixed population have multiplied to such an extent that the feed contained in one loopful of bacteria cannot satisfy all the ciliates in the culture for twenty-four hours, the problem resolves itself only to a redistribution of energy between the two species, i.e. to suppression of one species by the other, as can be seen from the curve for this experiment (Fig. 287). Furthermore, it was discovered that the process of competition under these conditions always proceeds until one species is completely displaced by the other, thus confirming the theoretical postulates. In the given example *P. caudatum* is gradually displaced.

Another series of experiments was carried out in order to determine the exact mechanism of competition. For this purpose a medium entirely

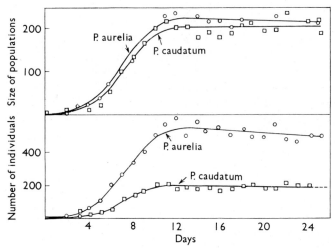

FIG. 286. Increase in number of individuals and of size of populations in *Paramecium caudatum* and *P. aurelia*. (After Gause, 1935a.)

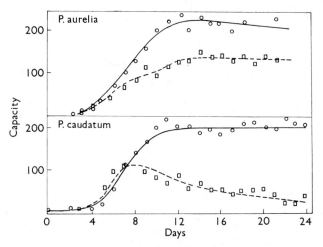

FIG. 287. Selection in Ciliates under various conditions.

(*A*) growth of mixed population of *Paramecium caudatum* and *Didinium* in oat-medium with precipitate; (*B*) interaction between *Paramecium caudatum* and *Didinium* in oat-medium without precipitate. (After Gause, 1935a.)

favourable to *Paramecium* was employed, but the amount of bacteria serving as their food was halved. Furthermore, Osterhaut's medium was buffered. This provided an opportunity to examine in a pure state the competition of two species for a common food supply. This last series of experiments on two species of *Paramecium* confirmed the conclusions drawn from the preceding series (see above). The mechanism of competition itself could be reduced in this case mainly to a greater coefficient of multiplication of one of the species (*P. aurelia*) in a mixed population.

The following correction should be introduced into all the results obtained in the works of Gause: while the general assessment of these series of experiments, i.e. their qualitative evaluation raises no doubts, it should be borne in mind that the correctness of the quantitative side (calculations of the coefficients of competition, &c.) applies only to the author's experiments themselves, since they cannot be exactly repeated. The quality of the substances used for the media (for example, oat-flour and others), the nature of the strains of bacteria, the peculiarities of different clones of the ciliates, represented, for example, by the energy of phagocytosis, by their rate of multiplication, &c., in different lines, might vary so much, that under certain conditions the very nature of the dominant species might prove to be different, so that in certain cases *P. caudatum* might win. However, the rule according to which one species is completely displaced by the other invariably remains in force. An excellent example of this is provided by the investigations of Gause, Nastjukova, and Alpatova (1934), providing further data on *Paramecium*. Under certain conditions *P. caudatum* is dominant over *P. aurelia* in its coefficient of multiplication, but the latter is superior to *P. caudatum* in its resistance against the products of metabolism. In this connexion, when rapid capture of food is the decisive factor, *P. caudatum* is the victor, but when resistance towards the accumulation in the medium of products of metabolism is all important, it is *P. aurelia* that survives.

Later Gause demonstrated (1934) the extermination of one species by another in a mixed population of two ciliates, *Paramecium caudatum* and *Didinium nasutum*, representing respectively the bacteriophagous form and the predator feeding on it (Fig. 288). The purpose of this investigation was to verify the theoretical assumption, advanced by mathematicians, that a population consisting of homologous victims and homologous predators, inhabiting a limited microcosm, where all the environmental factors remain strictly constant, should, according to mathematical theory, show periodical fluctuations in the numbers of the two species. These fluctuations are 'natural periodical fluctuations', since they are based on the properties of the system prey-predator itself.

The first series of experiments consisted in the introduction of a known number of *Didinium* into a population of *P. caudatum* living in a culture with *Bacillus pyocyaneus* in a liquid oat medium (free of precipitate). The results obtained were always the same: the numbers of Paramecium begin to decrease after the introduction of the predators, which multiply intensively, devour all the Paramecia and then die out. The destruction of Para-

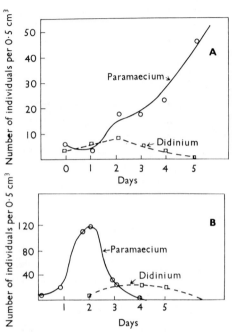

FIG. 288. Growth of biomass of *Paramecium caudatum* and *P. aurelia* in pure (continuous line) and mixed populations (dotted line). (After Gause, 1934a)

mecia cannot have been caused by a shortage of food, since bacteria were constantly added to the culture. Therefore, when the concentration of the first link of the food chain bacteria→*Paramecium*→*Didinium* is artificially kept at a certain level eventually the two last components disappear completely from the chain. Thus in a homogeneous nutrient medium kept under constant environmental conditions the system *Paramecium–Didinium* does not show any of its own periodical fluctuations that had been postulated on theoretical grounds by mathematicians. Consequently the relationship between the increment in the number of predators per unit of time and the density of the population of the prey, as well as the correlation between the number of prey destroyed and the density of the population of predators, is more complex than had been assumed theoretically.

The simple pattern of the process described may easily change if the conditions of the experiment become more complicated. Thus, wishing to imitate natural conditions, Gause provided in the experimental vessels a 'shelter' in which *Paramecium* might hide. For this purpose a dense oat medium with a precipitate was chosen. Observations have shown that Paramecia, penetrating into this precipitate, are out of reach of the predators, since the latter swim about only in the liquid part of the medium; furthermore, *Didinium* do not pursue individual Paramecia, but come in contact with them only by chance. Similarly, the Paramecia do not take refuge in the precipitate in order to escape from the predators, but find themselves there by chance, since penetration into the precipitate occurs both in the presence and in the absence of *Didinia*.

In cultures having a shelter the following takes place in a mixed population: when both species of ciliates are introduced simultaneously into the medium, the number of predators increases somewhat at first, but since the main mass of the prey is in the shelter the predators die out completely and an intensive multiplication of the Paramecia begins. However, when a shelter is provided the process does not always terminate in this manner. In a large number of vessels, with a shelter and a mixed population, the results may vary in different cases. Thus in 55 microcosms into which 5 *Paramecium* and 3 *Didinium* were introduced simultaneously the following results were obtained after periods from 2 to 6 days.

In 8 vessels all the Didinia died, in 4 all the Paramecia disappeared, while in the remaining 43 vessels both species of ciliates were present in different combinations of numbers. This led Gause to the conclusion that it was impossible to predict accurately the course of development of a mixed population for any given case under conditions approximating to natural ones, since the struggle for existence is then regulated by too great a number of factors.

Thus in pure experiments with the food chain bacteria→*Paramecium caudatum*→*Didinium*, Gause obtained results which contradicted the occurrence of their own periodical fluctuations, postulated by mathematicians. However, it appears that in certain combination of organisms such fluctuations do indeed take place. This was observed by Gause (1935) in mixed populations of *Paramecium bursaria* with the yeast *Schizosaccharomyces pombe* and *P. aurelia* with *Saccharomyces exiguus*.

Observations on the changes in the number of Paramecia and of the yeast cells showed clearly that there were two periodical waves of fluctuation with an approximately constant period of fluctuation, in which the rise of the wave of the producer (i.e. yeast) every time preceded that of the consumer (i.e. *Paramecium*).

A comparison of the behaviour of a mixed population of *Paramecium* with yeast and that of a population of *Didinium* and *Paramecium* (without a shelter) shows in populations of one species of consumer with one species of producer that the result may be twofold. If the numerical strength of the predators is considerably greater than that of their prey, then on a definite territory they usually completely destroy them (*Didinium* and *Paramecium* without a shelter). This type of interaction between species leads to so-called relaxation fluctuations of the numerical strength of the populations. But if the ability of the predators to destroy their prey is not so highly developed then a type of periodical fluctuation of the numerical strength of the population is established on the defined territory, in which a certain number of the prey constantly escape destruction (*Paramecium* and yeast). Thus differences in the dynamics of the population may create different conditions of natural selection, and consequently direct the evolutionary process in one direction or another.

Gause further examines those differences in the fate of mixed populations which are associated with the extent to which both species cultivated together possess completely identical food requirements, &c. (for example, *Paramecium caudatum* and *P. aurelia*), when they occupy the same 'ecological niche', or belong to different niches. In the first case the result is obvious: only one of the coexisting species, namely the one best adapted to life under the given conditions survives, while the other perishes, so that the population becomes pure.

An example of the second combination given by Gause is a mixed culture of *Paramecium aurelia* and *P. bursaria* on a mixed diet of bacteria and yeast. The mixed diet is important here because *P. aurelia* prefers bacteria, while *P. bursaria* feeds on the yeast-precipitate from the bottom of the culture; hence in this experiment there is a mixed population with two different food niches. In these cases the experiments resulted in a lasting stabilization of a mixed culture of two species of ciliates, occupying two different food niches within the given microcosm.

In cases when *P. bursaria* was mixed not with *P. aurelia* but with a closely allied species, *P. caudatum*, the equilibrium was maintained with a strong numerical preponderance of *P. caudatum*, but it was disturbed in cases of excessive increase in the numbers of individuals of *P. bursaria;* the cause of this was found to be a specific sensibility of *P. caudatum* to the products of metabolism of *P. bursaria; P. caudatum* is completely unable to multiply in dense populations of *P. bursaria*. These experiments show clearly the great significance of different specific peculiarities of the animals used in the experiment in the results obtained.

One of the most spectacular examples of the struggle for existence and of natural selection in Protozoa was provided in the experiments of Poljanskij and Strelkov (1937) on the interaction between two representatives of the genus *Entodinium* in the rumen of artificially infected goats. One of the species, *Entodinium caudatum*, is small (29-37 μ in length), and consists of several 'forms' differing in the greater or smaller development of the caudal spines. The other species, *E. vorax*, is much larger (60·8–92·8 μ in length) and more bulky. In contrast with other species of *Entodinium*, *E. vorax* readily swallows smaller species of the same genus, and is thus a facultative predator. In mixed cultures of the above-mentioned two species it was observed that *E. vorax* eat *E. caudatum* selectively, namely, if the population of *E. caudatum* in the experimental goat consists, as is usual, of a mixture of 'forms' specific to it, i.e. of individuals with large spines (class I), with gradually diminishing spines (classes II–V), and devoid of spines (class VI or form 'simplex'), individuals of the class V and VI are preferably eaten. This is due to the fact that the spined forms are much more difficult for the predators to swallow, with the result that classes V and VI disappear completely from the population, while the long-spined forms of class I become dominant. These experiments were repeated many times, and under conditions which usually facilitated the development of the spineless forms (comparatively scanty nutrition only on grass and hay): nevertheless, the introduction of *E. vorax* into the experimental goats invariably produced the same results. In order to determine whether *E. vorax* exercised any specific influence, *Eudiplodinium neglectum*, which develops a tailless form and forms with one and two caudal lobes, was added to the culture. *Eudiplodinium neglectum* is larger than

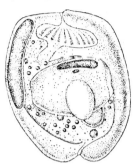

FIG. 289. *Entodinium vorax* with ingested individual of unarmed *Entodinium caudatum*. (After Poljanskij and Strelkov, 1938*b*.)

Entodinium vorax and therefore does not serve as a prey for the latter. In such cultures, composed of three species of ciliates, the population of *Eudiplodinium* showed no changes, whereas in the population of *Entodinium caudatum* the long-spined forms always became predominant after the addition of *E. vorax*. This is clearly illustrated in the Table (p. 572) of Poljanskij and Strelkov, representing in figures the effect of the addition of *Entodinium vorax* to the initially pure culture of *E. caudatum*. The great effect of an admixture to this culture of *E. vorax* on the composition of the population of *E. caudatum* is clearly seen from this Table.

In proportion as the composition of the population of *Entodinium caudatum* changes in the direction of an exclusive proliferation of class I with strongly developed spines, the number of *E. vorax* with ingested *E. caudatum* goes on decreasing, until they all gradually become vegetarians owing to the absence of spineless *E. caudatum*.

The interspecific struggle for existence, and the survival of the fittest (i.e. *E. caudatum* equipped with spines), are clearly demonstrated in the foregoing example.

Very little is known about the behaviour of other parasitic Protozoa in mixed infections. However, trypanosomes provide examples of competition or antagonism between two species inhabiting the same individual host. In such cases there may be an inhibition or suppression of one species by another. Thus *Trypanosome congolense* can be inhibited by *T. brucei* (Tseng, 1935) or by *T. vivax* (Roubaud, 1951), and the latter by *T. uniforme* (Wilson, 1949). The incompatability of two species in a mixed infection is

TABLE 22

Variations of E. caudatum *in goat No. XXXVII before and after introduction of* E. vorax *into stomach of goat*

Dates of taking of samples	Classes of E. caudatum, *percentage of individuals*						Remarks
	I	II	III	IV	V	VI	
17.VIII	..	4	6	..	4	86	..
23.VIII	1	1	4	..	9	85	..
29.VIII	1	..	..	..	1	98	..
5.IX	..	2	1	..	3	94	..
11.IX	..	..	1	..	4	95	Appearance of E. vorax
17.IX	96	4	22	..	8	37	..
23.IX	22	11	..	..	..	..	..
29.IX	100	..	..	..	..	..	..
5.X	100	..	..	..	..	..	..
11.X	100	..	..	..	..	..	..

revealed by the appearance of only one of them on subinoculation of the mixed strains into a susceptible host. This phenomenon may be due either to selective susceptibility of the recipient host or to alteration in the periods of predominance of the two trypanosomes in the blood of the donor.

Furthermore, in a mixture of two trypanosomes, or of one trypanosome with another micro-organism, the virulence of the trypanosomes may also be affected. Thus the virulence of *T. brucei* is considerably reduced when it is associated with *T. vivax* (Curasson, 1943), and a similar change is undergone by pathogenic trypanosomes in mixed infections with spirochaetes or spirilla (cf. Tate, 1951). This effect is attributed to the destruction of numerous trypanosomes during the acute phase of the disease caused by the heterologous micro-organism, as a result of which the dead trypanosomes act antigenically, stimulating the production of specific trypanocidal antibodies by the host.

CHAPTER X

ECOLOGY OF PROTOZOA

THE extremely wide distribution of Protozoa in nature is promoted by their minute size, which facilitates their dispersion by various agents, as well as by their ability to multiply rapidly and also the formation by them of very variable resting stages. They represent organisms which live in vast numbers in a great variety of habitats.

An essential condition for their existence in the active state is water. Therefore bodies of fresh and salt water are their main habitats. However, some Protozoa have adapted themselves to life in the soil, in its moss cover, in the snow of glaciers, in the water reservoirs of insectivorous plants, &c. Finally, a considerable number of Protozoa have adopted the parasitic mode of life within animals or, much more rarely, in plants.

Under such different conditions of the external medium Protozoa frequently display most diverse and delicate adaptations to their environment.

These adaptations may find expression both in the morphological characters of the Protozoa, and in their physiology and life-cycles.

Under various ecological conditions different groupings of Protozoa have evolved, sharply distinguished from each other both quantitatively and qualitatively. Thus, it may be said that the marine fauna of Protozoa differs from the freshwater fauna not less than the marine ichthyofauna differs from freshwater fishes. The parasitic Protozoa form a still more distinctive and original group.

The four main ecological groups of Protozoa are represented by organisms living in the seas, in fresh waters, in the soil, and in or on the bodies of other organisms, i.e. leading a parasitic mode of life. In addition to these there are also some smaller individual groups, which will be dealt with separately.

FREE-LIVING PROTOZOA

Marine Protozoa. It is well known that the marine fauna as a whole is much more varied than the freshwater and terrestrial ones.

The distribution of orders of free-living marine and freshwater Protozoa is as follows.

The class Mastigophora contains 10 orders, most representatives of the latter being free-living Protozoa. Of these 1 lives only in the sea, 7 only in freshwater, and 5 are encountered in both habitats.

The class Sarcodina, consisting of 11 orders, contains 6 orders peculiar to the sea, 5 which live in both habitats.

Finally the class Ciliata, consisting of 10 free-living orders, has 1 purely freshwater suborder and 9 common to seas and bodies of fresh water.

We do not take into account the class Sporozoa, since it consists of endoparasites only, which have no direct connexion with the external medium.

In all 7 orders are restricted to the sea and 5 to fresh water, while 19 are common to both habitats.

As regards the number of species, the marine fauna of Protozoa is also the richest: out of approximately 20,000 species in this division of the animal kingdom, 15,500 lead a free mode of life, while the rest are parasites.

Among the free-living forms, such abundant groups as the order Foraminifera, containing approximately 1,000 species, as well as the subclass Radiolaria, composed of 6,000 species, are purely marine. Among the ciliates the group Tintinnoidea with 800 species lives almost exclusively in the seas. Among the flagellates the order Dinoflagellata, with several hundreds of marine species, is prevalent chiefly in the seas: thus one tribe, Gymnodinioidea, has up to 300 species and 30 genera, of which only one-tenth are encountered in fresh water. A second tribe, Peridinioidea, also consisting almost exclusively of marine forms, contains no fewer than 800 species.

Thus out of 15,500 species of free-living Protozoa about 9–10,000 are purely marine forms.

All aquatic Protozoa can first of all be divided into two large categories, namely the planktonic and benthonic. Those Protozoa which remain suspended or in an active motile state within the column of water are called planktonts; while the inhabitants of the sea bottom are known as benthonic Protozoa. The column of water, i.e. the area of distribution of the planktonts, is known as the pelagial, while the whole area of the bottom of the basin inhabited by the benthonic forms is the benthal.

On the basis of their motility the Protozoa of these two regions are divided into free-living and attached or sessile forms.

The attached species of the benthos either settle down at the bottom or on various bottom-living organisms. The attached forms of planktonts settle down either on various floating objects: floating timber, the bottom of boats, &c., or on other planktonts.

Planktonic Protozoa. The great majority of Protozoa of the plankton are free-living. Among them only a few epibionts belonging to the Suctoria lead an attached mode of life. Attached epibionts are represented also by some marine Peritricha and marine representatives of the ciliates belonging to the order Chonotricha (*Kentrochona, Kentrochonopsis* on the crustacean *Nebalia*). Finally, a very few planktonic Flagellata of the order Chrysomonadida are attached to the substratum.

The total number of such epibiotic forms is limited to a few dozen.

It is noteworthy that while the mechanism of attachment to the substratum is the same in planktonic and benthonic animals, its biological significance in these two groups is quite different. Namely, in planktonic Protozoa attachment assists in the passive dispersal over a wider area of distribution, especially when the Protozoa are attached to organisms that are actively motile, for example, to planktonic crustaceans. However, the main significance of attachment is probably to facilitate flotation in water without either wasting their own energy for this purpose or developing floating devices. The best illustration of this tendency is provided by a representative of marine planktonic tintinnionean ciliates, *Tintinnus inquilinus* (Fig. 49). Like other Tintinnionea, *T. inquilinus* secretes around its body a cylindrical lorica, from the aperture of which the anterior pole of the animal with its ciliary apparatus protrudes. This ciliate attaches itself to a unicellular diatomous alga *Chaetoceros* by the lateral side of its lorica. The alga is not larger in size than the ciliate, and it is immobile, so that the ciliate drags it along when swimming. Therefore, the alga cannot serve for widening of the area of distribution of the ciliate, but it possesses several long radial processes, which enlarge its surface considerably. In this unusual association the ciliate uses a morphological characteristic (the processes) of *Chaetoceros* to increase its ability to float in the water.

In the great majority of planktonts the same adaptation is attained by the development of appropriate morphological features by the planktonic organism itself, as in the case of Radiolaria, Heliozoa, Dinoflagellata, and others, whose skeletal structures were described above. The important role played by the skeletal processes in increasing the surface of the body of planktonts is evident from the fact that the few representatives of the order Foraminifera, which had changed from the benthonic mode of life peculiar to their order to a planktonic existence, have developed a multitude of long radial spines on their shell. Among such Foraminifera are *Globigerina* (Fig. 290), *Orbulina*, *Hastigerina*, and others, altogether about ten genera allied to each other, with about thirty species.

The significance of the size of the body surface of the planktonts and of the internal friction of water is evident from the following examples. The internal friction of water increases with the fall of temperature, while the surface of the body (its form remaining the same) decreases proportionally with the increase of the size of the animal. In accordance with this, a most interesting vertical distribution of species is observed in Radiolaria of the family *Challengeridae* (Fig. 291). In the warmer surface layer of water only the small species of *Challengeridae* are encountered, while in the depths with colder water, which has a higher coefficient of friction, the species are much larger.

Thus *Challengeria xiphodon* (Fig. 291), *swixei*, and *harstoni* from a depth of 50–400 m. measure 0·10–0·11 mm.; *bethelli*, *slogetti*, and *tixardi* from a depth of 400–1,500 m. reach 0·21–0·28 mm., and finally *thomsoni* and *naresi* from depths of 1500–5000 m. are 0·38–0·58 mm. long. In precisely the same way the Radiolaria *Aulacantha* (Fig. 292) of another group of the order

Phaeodaria shows analogous differences in size at different depths, even within the same species: the small *Aulacantha scolymantha typica* inhabits the upper layers; whereas the much larger *A. scolymantha bathybia* dwells at greater depths.

A greater buoyancy is sometimes attained without the production of special processes, by a change in the shape of the body, which becomes flattened (Fig. 293). *Leptodiscus* and *Craspedotella* of the cystoflagellata

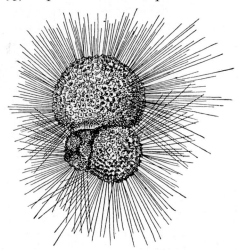

FIG. 290. Planktonic foraminiferan *Globigerina bulloides*. (After Doflein-Reichenow, 1929.)

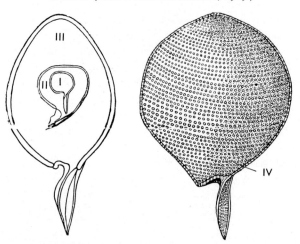

FIG. 291. Increase in size of allied species of Radiolaria, according to depth of their habitat.

I, *Challengeria xiphodon*; II, *C. slogetti*; III, *C. naresi*, at same magnification; IV, *C. naresi*, showing sculpture of shell. (After Haecker, 1908.)

provide the best examples of this: their body has the appearance of a disk which is slightly concave at the side that is normally directed downwards. On account of this their body has the shape of a medusa, with its exumbrella and subumbrella. The shape of a disk or a plate is also acquired by the skeleton of some Radiolaria Spumellaria (*Discoidea*) and Acantharia (*Lithoptera*). The effect of the general shape of the body is here associated with the additional influence of the radial spicules of the skeleton.

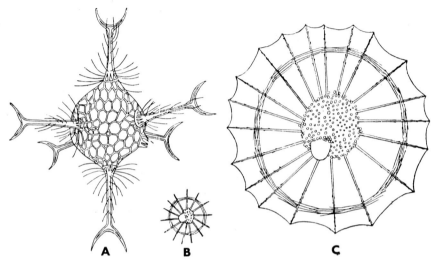

FIG. 292. Various Radiolaria Phaeodaria.

(*A*) *Circopurus sexfurcus*; (*B*) *Aulacantha scolymantha cathybia* (deep-water form); (*C*) typical shallow-water form *A. scolymantha* at same magnification. (After Haecker, 1908.)

Frequently special morphological or structural adaptations of planktonts, which facilitate their buoyancy in water, are replaced by some changes in their metabolism, which reduce the weight of the body. Namely, in a whole series of planktonts the reserve nutrient substances, accumulated in the body, are converted into fatty inclusions, facilitating buoyancy. Among the flagellates numerous droplets of fat of different sizes accumulate in the body of *Noctiluca miliaris* and of many Dinoflagellata; in the body of the Radiolaria Spumellaria, &c., large drops of oil have the same significance.

The vacuolated outer layer of cytoplasm in many radiolarians (Spumellaria and Acantharia), filled with large vacuoles containing a gelatinous substance, might play a similar role. Some authors believe that the alveolar walls of the delicate lorica of such typical planktonts as the ciliates Tintinnoinea contain in their alveoles a substance of a lower specific gravity, facilitating flotation of these animals in the column of water.

Finally, in many radiolarians of the order Phaeodaria, in *Aulacantha* and many others, the spicules of siliceous skeleton are hollow; therefore the weight of the skeleton is reduced, and their buoyancy is increased. The

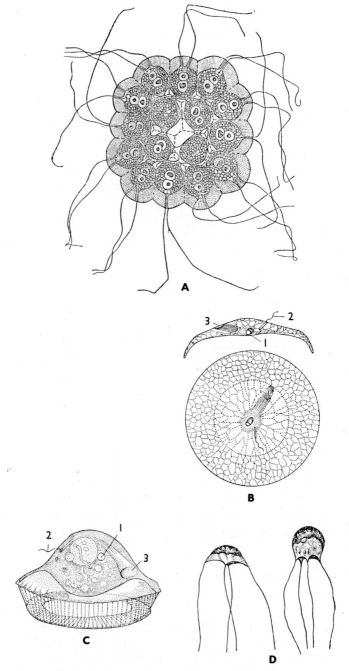

FIG. 293. Lamelliform and umbelliform types of planktonic Protozoa.

(A) *Gonium pectorale* colony (Phytomonadida); (B) cystoflagellate *Leptodis-cus*, side and surface views; (C) cystoflagellate *Craspedotella*, lateral view; (D) *Medusochloris* (Phytomonadida), in contracted and expanded states. 1, nucleus; 2, flagellum; 3, invagination of cytoplasm. (From Dogiel, 1951, after various authors.)

discontinuous porous or latticed character of the skeleton in many plank-tonic Protozoa has the same significance. Thus the spherical skeletons of diverse radiolarians are not continuous, but latticed, which reduces their weight. The arrangement of the skeletal elements follows a definite pattern which ensures that the delicacy of the airy skeletal structures is associated with sufficient solidity to enable the body to withstand fracture and great pressure.

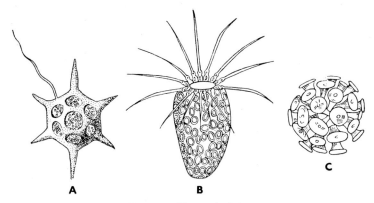

FIG. 294. Nannoplanktonts.

(*A*) *Distephanus speculum* (Silicoflagellata); (*B*) *Michaelsarsia splendens* (Coccolitho-phoridae), shell composed of coccoliths; around the aperture there is a circlet of three-segmented coccoliths; (*C*) *Syracosphaera apsteini* (Coccolithophoridae) with a shell of goblet-shaped coccoliths. (After Doflein and Reichenow, 1929.)

In the Radiolaria Phaeodaria of the family *Circoporidae*, and especially in Sagosphaeridae, during mechanical jolts, the bases of the radial spicules of the latticed, i.e. the light spherical, skeleton are supported by systems of six converging trabeculae of the sphere. In some of the Ciliata Tin-tinnoinea (for example, *Ptychocyclis*) a system of narrow thickening, re-sembling the veins on the wings of dragon-flies, runs over the surface of the extremely delicate cap-shaped lorica. It is known that such a structure of the lorica makes it as solid as if the entire wall were of the same thickness as the veins intersecting it.

Hydrobiologists divide the planktonic organisms according to their size into mesoplankton, microplankton, and nannoplankton.

The first include forms more than 1 mm. in diameter, the second forms from $50\,\mu$ to 1 mm., and the third dwarf forms of less than $50\,\mu$ in diameter. According to this classification, the main mass of protozoal plankton falls into the category of microplankton; only certain colonial radiolarians (Sphaerozoum, Collozoum—sausage-shaped colonies up to 6 mm. in length), and among the solitary radiolarians a few members of the Spumellaria, like *Oroscena*, reaching 4·5 mm. in diameter, can be referred to mesoplank-ton. The minute representatives of the nannoplankton (Fig. 294) are more numerous among the marine planktonts, which include two families of *Chrysomonadida*, namely *Silicoflagellidae* and *Coccolithophoridae*, as well as certain small Dinoflagellata and some individual members of other groups of flagellates. Nannoplankton remained practically unknown for a long time, and became accessible only after special methods of research had been applied, namely sedimentation or centrifugation of the water examined.

Vertical range of distribution of planktonts. In some marine Protozoa this sort of vertical zonal distribution is particularly pronounced, as, for example, in the whole order Radiolaria. Haecker (1908) even attempted to stratify the vertical mass of sea water according to this criterion, since definite forms of Radiolaria are always found at certain depths. Thus, he called depths from 400 to 1,000–1,500 m. the layer of Tuscaroridae, while the depths from 1,000–5,000 m. were referred to the region of Pharyngellidae. Haecker's later scheme was somewhat more precise. For example, two ecological groupings of Radiolaria were established for the Kurilo–Kamchatka depression of the Pacific Ocean, viz. stenobathic forms strictly adapted to a definite horizon and eurybathic forms either associated with several horizons or distributed throughout the whole mass of water in the ocean (Reshetnjak, 1955). The main mass of the species is composed of members of the order Phaeodaria, while Spumellaria and Nasselaria are encountered in smaller numbers. A graphic representation of the distribution of various species of Radiolaria according to depth zones is given in Fig. 295. About 45 per cent. of all the species are stenobathic, the great majority of them (32 per cent.) being adapted to depths from 1,000 to 2,000 m., while a comparatively small number of species was found even at a depth of 8,000 m. Although the eurybathic Radiolaria are distributed throughout the whole mass of water, they reveal a certain predilection for definite horizons, being encountered more frequently and in larger numbers in some than in others. This phenomenon is illustrated in Fig. 295. The most specific diversity of Radiolaria and greatest actual number of them are found among species of the middle depths and in bathypelagic forms (200–2,000 m.).

Ševjakov (1926), who studied the order Acantharia in a restricted area of the sea (the Bay of Naples) during different seasons of the year, made the following observations about their distribution. Acantharia are predominantly surface planktonts of the open sea, dwelling at depths down to 200 m. After abundant rain the Acantharia disappeared from the upper layers, moving down to depths of 100–200 m., but 1–2 days after a rain they accumulated again at the surface. The Acantharia are even more sensitive to sea swell, for they move to a depth of 5–10 m. even when the waves are of medium strength, but when the swell is strong they accumulate at 50–100 m. During the cold months of the year from October to May the Acantharia also leave the surface layers and move into the zone 50–200 m. deep, whereas during that period Spumellaria and Nassellaria gather in

HORIZONS	STENOBATHIC FORMS	EURYBATHIC FORMS
0–50 metres surface		
50–200 metres subsurface		
200–1000 metres medium depth		
1000–2000 metres bathypelagic		
2000–4000 metres 4000–8000 metres		

large masses in the 1–50 m. layer. Thus Acantharia are driven away from the surface layers by unfavourable conditions. It may be added that there are several 'winter' species of Acantharia in the Mediterranean, which appear and multiply in considerable numbers in December–January (Šev-jakov, 1926) at a comparatively low temperature of the water.

In general, the Acantharia depend on the depth less than the Phaeodaria, for practically the same forms as at the surface were observed not only at depths up to 200 m. but even down to 500–800 m. (at the outlet from the Bay of Naples into the Tyrrhenian Sea). Although the number and diversity of forms diminish as the depth increases, representatives of some primitive families of Acantharia were encountered at depths of 300–800 m. in comparatively larger numbers than at the surface. Moreover, in the deep-water forms zooxanthellae were always absent, evidently owing to the complete absence of light and the destruction of these algae at such great depths. The complete absence of pigment specimens taken at great depths, but belonging to species which on the surface have a reddish-brown or cerise colour due to the presence of a granular pigment (*Acanthostaurus purpurascens* and others), is explained by the same cause.

The temperature undoubtedly plays a decisive role in the vertical distribution of planktonic Protozoa. Furthermore, it should be borne in mind that the surface layers of water down to 100–200 m. exhibit particularly great temperature variations, both permanent and seasonal, in different regions of the world ocean. Deeper down the temperature remains constant, gradually dropping with depth to $4°$, $2°$ C. and less. Only in the Arctic and Antarctic does the temperature rise somewhat with depth, so that the negative surface temperature (slightly below $0°$ C.) is replaced deeper down by low positive temperatures (slightly above $0°$ C.).

The influence of temperature on the vertical distribution of protozoal (and also multicellular) planktonts at any given point is manifested first of all in a decrease of the total mass of plankton.

If we take the mass of nannoplankton (composed exclusively of unicellular organisms) in the upper layers of water, both in the cold regions and in the tropics, as 100, the further distribution of nannoplankton according to the depth is represented by the following figures:

Depths	o m.	50 m.	100 m.	200 m.	400 m.
Cold waters	100%	27%	9%	1·5%	0·5%
Tropical waters	100%	92%	32%	8%	3%
Temperature in tropics (Guinea current)	26·6°	..	14·5°	12·3°	7°

Of course not all the changes in the mass of plankton given in the Table are due to the effect of temperature, since decrease in the vegetative part of the nannoplankton especially at depths below 100 m. is due to disappearance of light.

In the region of great depths (below 1,000 m.), or the so-called abyssal plain, the identity of the conditions obtained there (even temperature, complete absence of swell and light) causes many deep-water forms to be distributed uniformly throughout the abyssal plain of all the oceans. In general, the Protozoa prevalent in the abyssal region are represented almost exclusively by various Radiolaria, especially of the order Phaeodaria. In the Kurilo–Kamchatka depression of the Pacific Ocean the abyssal Radiolaria are adapted to the sea-bed mass of water with a temperature of 1·5–2·0° C., the bathypelagic to the deep waters with a temperature of 1·7° C., and the middle-depth radiolarians are distributed in the warm mass of water with a temperature of 3·5° C., while, on the contrary, the sub-surface ones inhabit the cold-water layer with a temperature of 0·3° C. and the surface ones are adapted to a temperature of 2·6° C.

The horizontal distribution of planktonic Protozoa. From the part played by the temperature of water in the distribution of planktonic Protozoa it can be inferred that the same factor must also influence their horizontal distribution in the world ocean. As has been shown above, the main mass of planktonts dwell at comparatively low depths of 0–100–150 m., i.e. at depths that are most subject to the warming or cooling effect of differing meteorological factors. In accordance with this, five basic thermal regions are distinguished in the world ocean, differing from each other in the composition of their population. These regions are as follows: tropical or equatorial; two adjacent to the poles, Arctic and Antarctic; and two intermediate ones, the boreal in the north and the notal in the south. The presence of continents cutting across the ocean, and of powerful warm and cold marine currents, which often also flow in a southerly meridional direction, interfere with the schematic regularity of the distribution of thermal zones, and create within the world ocean a series of definitely circumscribed areas which are more or less constant and can be distinguished by their fauna. A rough division of the protozoal plankton into planktons of tropical and cold-water seas reveals the following distinctive features in the horizontal distribution of marine Protozoa. Radiolaria are predominant in warmer seas, the number of their species diminishing towards the north. This pattern of the distribution holds true only for Radiolaria dwelling in the surface layers of the ocean, i.e. mainly members of the order Acantharia. In the case of the Atlantic Ocean, for instance, it is known that the number of species of the order Acantharia in the equatorial zone is ten times greater than that of the northern regions (Popofsky, 1904). The same situation was observed in the northern part of the Pacific Ocean, where the number of species drops sharply as compared with the equatorial waters (Dogiel and Rešetnjak, 1956), while in the Arctic seas the number of species is still lower: thus not more than fifteen species of Radiolaria are known from the Kara Sea (Bernstein, 1932).

As regards the deep-water forms the difference between the zoogeographical regions of the world ocean almost disappears, owing to the similarity of hydrological conditions at great depths, both in the tropics and in the moderate zones.

Purely thermophilic, almost exclusively tropical forms are represented by planktonic foraminifera (only 2 species out of 30 penetrate into cold waters). *Coccolithophoridae* are encountered in cold currents only in small numbers; whereas the warm currents, on the contrary, are characterized by an abundance of *Coccolithophoridae* (almost exclusively the genus *Syracosphaera*) and Dinoflagellata.

Although the cold-water plankton comprises a small number of species and less variety among them, it is represented in both hemispheres by great abundance of individuals, especially in certain Dinoflagellata. The planktonts of cold and warm waters reveal certain characteristic peculiarities of structure associated with the greater viscosity of cold and lesser viscosity of warm waters. The viscosity of water at 25° is half that at 0° C., and therefore—other conditions being equal—an organism sinks in water twice as quickly at 25° as at 0° C.

In cold water members of the same group are more buoyant than in warm ones, when their size increases, and accordingly we find, for example, that the common marine species *Ceratium tripos* attains the size of 560 μ under Arctic conditions, and only 300 μ in the North Sea, with an identical shape of body. On the other hand, as is clearly seen in the same Dino-flagellata, Protozoa inhabiting warm waters develop in connexion with the lower viscosity of the water a tendency to form particularly long and ramified processes, spicules, &c., which increase their surface and diminish their specific gravity. This feature is common to the complex of warm-water plankton in general and is especially pronounced in some widespread individual species in various parts of their range of distribution. Thus *Ceratium reticulatum* and *C. palmatum* from the Indian Ocean have incomparably longer and more palmate horn-like appendages than the same species from the eastern Atlantic, i.e. from a region of colder water (Fig. 296).

Planktonic Protozoa as a source of geological deposits (pelagic sediments). The calcareous and siliceous skeleton of planktonic Protozoa, accumulated in large numbers at the bottom of the ocean, may serve for the formation of massive eupelagic deposits. The so-called 'Globigerina ooze' is of special importance in this respect: 53 per cent. of it consists of the shells of planktonic *Globigerinidae* (Fig. 297). In accordance with the predilection of these Foraminifera for warm waters, it occupies huge areas of the bottom (more than half of the Atlantic and Indian Oceans and a narrower strip in the Pacific).

The role of pelagic Foraminifera in the formation of marine deposits is exceptionally great. It is especially noteworthy that this ooze is, apparently, an entirely recent deposit. In the northern and Antarctic seas Globigerina oozes are absent. Radiolarian ooze, containing more than 20 per cent. of siliceous skeletons of radiolaria and diatoms, is not so widespread. Strips of Radiolarian ooze are scattered in regions of warm waters of the Pacific and Indian Oceans. In contrast to globigerines, the Radiolaria played a

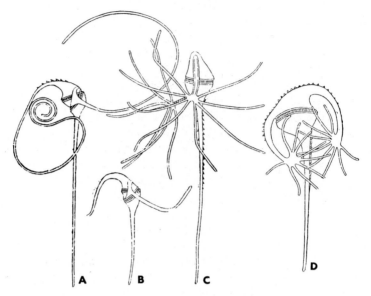

FIG. 296. Changes in *Ceratium* in cold and warm waters.

(*A*) *Ceratium reticulatum* from Indian Ocean; (*B*) *C. reticulatum* from Atlantic Ocean; (*C*) *C. palmatum* from Indian Ocean; (*D*) same species from Atlantic Ocean. (After Doflein and Reichenow, 1929.)

part in the formation of deposits also in earlier epochs, beginning from the lower horizons of the Palaeozoic era.

A brief description of the planktonic Protozoa of the Soviet Seas.

The bordering and inland seas of the U.S.S.R. can be arranged in the direction from west to east into two parallel chains—northern and southern. The northern chain comprises the Barents Sea (western and eastern region), White and Kara Seas, the Laptev Sea, and the Chukotsk Sea. The southern chain consists of the Black Sea, Sea of Azov, Caspian and Aral Seas.

A gradual impoverishment of different groups of plankton from west to east is observed in both chains, although the causes of such parallelism are entirely different. In the northern chain it is determined chiefly by the transition from the more favourable temperature conditions of the boreal zone to the harsh ones obtained in the Arctic.

In the southern chain there is a gradual transition from the high salinity of the Mediterranean to a decreasing salinity, then to freshening of water and to a substitution in the water of chlorides by sulphates. These data are given in the following Table (p. 585).

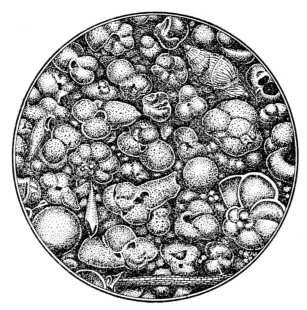

FIG. 297. Globigerina ooze from the Indian Ocean. (After Dogiel, 1951.)

NUMBER OF SPECIES OF PROTOZOA IN DIFFERENT SEAS
(Zenkewitch, 1947)

Name of Sea	Dinofla- gellata	Other flagel- lates	Silico- flagel- lata	Radio- laria	Ciliata	Plank- tonic Fora- minifera	Benthonic Foramini- fera
Barents Sea	69	2	6	11	21	2	190
White Sea	29	5	2	27	27	27	42
Kara Sea	20	2	2	12	41	1	126
Laptev Sea	5	..	6	..	5	..	55
Black Sea	73	..	3	..	..	..	9
Sea of Azov	52	2	9	..	16	..	..
Caspian Sea	28	17	17	..	..	..	9
Aral Sea	8	..	3	..	2	..	2

'*Blooming*' *in water basins.* By this phenomena is understood such a mass development of planktonic organisms (most frequently Phytomastigina) in the surface layers of the water that it noticeably changes its colour and transparency. Among the Protozoa various *Cryptomonadida* and *Chrysto-monadida* (*Phaeocystis* and others) and especially various Dinoflagellata are able to produce a blooming on water. In the seas, for example, off the coasts of California and Japan, as well as in the Black Sea, outbreaks of 'red water', caused by luxuriant development of the dinoflagellates *Gony-aulax*, *Gymnodinium*, and *Cochlodinium*, have frequently been observed. In such cases a layer of water one metre or more thick becomes brownish-red or blood-red and almost opaque.

The mass destruction of such Protozoa, accompanied by decay and the liberation of hydrogen sulphide, may cause the death of fish and other marine animals over large areas. This phenomenon has been frequently observed along the coasts of the Pacific in the U.S.A., where it was caused by the destruction of the dinoflagellate *Gonyaulux*.

Water blooming also occurs in freshwater basins, being caused by very intensive multiplication of *Chrystomonadida* and some species of *Euglena*.

The coloration of water, usually visible only in day-time, is quite frequently observed also at night, owing to the capacity of many marine Mastigophora, especially Dinoflagellata (*Ceratium*, *Noctiluca*, and others), for luminescence. In Protozoa the capacity for luminescence is usually associated with the presence of small, oily droplets in their cytoplasm. Therefore, in *Noctiluca*, for instance, the entire organism is not luminescent but only minute microscopic points in its body. Light is emitted by these organisms only when irritated (for instance along the wake left by a moving ship, by the beat of the oars, or on the breaking crests of waves), their luminescence being either bluish, greenish, or bright silver-white. The physiological nature of luminescence has not yet been fully elucidated. It has only been established that luminescence is associated with the process of oxidation, and that it does not take place in the absence of oxygen. Two substances have been extracted from some multicellular organisms—luciferase (probably a substance of the type of the ferments) and luciferin. On their combination luciferase catalytically promotes the oxidation of luciferin, thereby producing luminescence. These substances have so far not been detected in Protozoa; it is likewise difficult to explain the biological significance of the luminescence for the Protozoa themselves.

Benthonic Protozoa. The bottom-living marine Protozoa show less diversity than the planktonic ones. The leading group among them are the Foraminifera, which are rich in species (not fewer than 1,000), while the rest are comparatively insignificant.

In the coastal region the thickets of marine seaweeds are the favourite habitat of Foraminifera. The off-shore Rhizopods, for instance Miliolidae and Peneroplidae, are distinguished by comparatively thick, solid shells, adapted to an existence exposed to the action of waves. In spite of this, the shells of coastal Foraminifera frequently bear traces of injury, such as holes, showing regeneration of shell-substance. In contrast to these, the walls of the shells of Foraminifera living at considerable depths are delicate and thin.

Foraminifera of the neritic region, accumulated in larger numbers, play a considerable part in the formation of littoral deposits. In some places the coastal beaches consist mainly of the shells of rhizopods washed out of seaweeds. In the sand from Gaete near Naples as many as 5,000 Foraminifera shells are contained in 1 mg. of sand. The same condition is found in the coral sands of the shores of Australia, the Bermuda Islands and others.

The abyssal silts also contain a considerable number of Foraminifera. Thus the light-blue mud taken from a depth of 300 m. off the shores of Norway contains numerous *Uvigerina pygmaea*; the rhabdammine clay of the Arctic Ocean is filled with the rod-shaped shells of *Rhabdammina*, while in the North Sea, the red-brown biloculine clay lying at a depth of 1,500–2,000 m. got its name from the genus *Biloculina*.

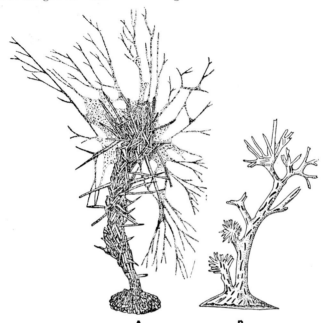

A **B**

Fig. 298. Attached Foraminifera with skeleton consisting of a layer of sponge spicules and other extraneous particles.

(*A*) *Haliphysema* extending upwards a network of pseudopodia; (*B*) *Dendrophrya arborescens* with apertures at tips of branches. (After Lankester from Doflein and Reichenow, 1929.)

The majority of Foraminifera crawl slowly over the substratum with the aid of a dense network of fine thread-like pseudopodia. Their shells have accordingly acquired flattened 'recumbent' shapes: lamellate, plate-like, stellate, or spiral, resembling the shells of the bottom-living gastropod molluscs which also crawl about on the sea-bottom.

The attached mode of life is fairly widespread among the benthonic Protozoa. Thus among Foraminifera there is a considerable number of forms that are attached to the ground, the majority being attached to the substratum (very often to seaweeds) by their flat side, e.g. many *Rotalidae*, *Saccamminidae*, and *Hyperamminidae*. Much more rarely (*Haliphysema*, *Dendronina*, and *Psammatodendron*) attached forms of the family Hyperamminidae form a vertical tubular shell, which attaches itself by means of a flat base, whereas the opening is directed upwards; the vertical part of the tube may be branched, in which case the branches terminate in apertures (Fig. 298).

To the chitinous base of such shells adhere particles of sand, sponge spicules, &c. In such form their attachment to the ground apparently serves for raising their capturing apparatus, i.e. mouths, above the sea-bed to enable them to catch their prey from the layers of water near the sea-

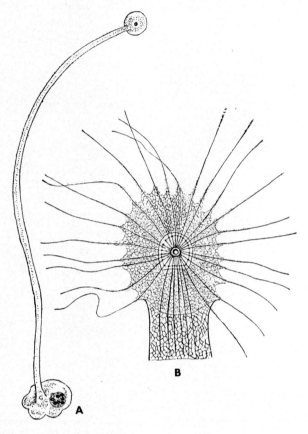

FIG. 299. Heliozoon *Wagnerella borealis.*

(*A*) entire individual, with centriole in the head and nucleus in the base; (*B*) head of *Wagnerella* at high magnification, showing centriole, axopodia, and their axial filaments. (After Zuelzer, 1909.)

bottom. It is interesting that, among typical planktonic groups of Sarcodina, there are sometimes observed immigrants into the sessile benthos of the same type of structure as *Haliphysema.* Among the marine Heliozoa the genus *Wagnerella* belongs to this category; it was discovered by Merejkovsky in the White Sea, but is apparently widespread, since much later it was encountered also in the Mediterranean. *Wagnerella* (Fig. 299) has the appearance of a vertical tube with widened ends; the lower end forms the base, in which the nucleus lies, while the upper, club-shaped end sends out in all directions a multitude of axopodia which converge in the centre of the club containing the centrosome. The body is surrounded by an organic sheath with minute siliceous spicules scattered in it; while long and radial spicules are given off from the club-shaped head. Finally, Schröder (1907) has described among the Radiolaria (Acantharia) an unusual sessile form, *Podactinelius sessilis* (Fig. 300).

From the centre of the body of *Podactinelius* as many as 400–500 spicules run out in all directions, while one bundle of them which is directed downwards is particularly long and serves as a stalk.

FIG. 300. Sessile Radiolarian *Podactinelius sessilis* (Acantharia).

(*A*) adult individual with numerous radial spicules; (*B*) basal part of the stalk; (*C*) free-swimming young stage. (After Schröder, 1907.)

All these sessile Sarcodina provide an example of convergence of ecological origin.

The distribution of Foraminifera in depth varies considerably. The majority of them are encountered in the neritic region, i.e. in comparatively shallow water (up to 200 m.); they are numerous in the bathyal region (up to 1,000 m.); as regards the abyssal fauna of rhizopods, it is extremely poor. The deep-red clay is inhabited only by some agglutinating siliceous forms; and a series of forms inhabiting the neritic regions of cold seas are encountered in the abyssal of the warm seas.

We have already mentioned the great influence upon animals of their descent to great depths. In such cases, the low temperature affects the dimensions of a whole series of Radiolaria. Exactly the same increase in the size of a species in cold waters, as compared with its thermophilic representatives, is exhibited by Foraminifera. Thus in the Antarctic the arenaceous *Astrorhiza granulosa* reaches a length of 14·7 mm., while in medium latitudes it is only 6 mm.; the corresponding measurements for *Tholosina laevis* are 2·1 mm. and 0·7 mm., and for *Rheophax cylindrica* 10 mm. and 3·6 mm. Similarly, *Miliolina tricarinata*, which in the Mediterranean is 1 mm. long, reaches 5 mm. in Spitsbergen. The geographical distribution of Foraminifera is also especially strongly affected by temperature. On this basis Cushman distinguishes the cold-water and warm-water forms. The cold-water forms of Foraminifera have a more or less bipolar distribution. According to Cushman (1948), the warm-water benthonic Foraminifera belong to four large zoogeographical regions, Mediterranean, West Indian, East African, and Indo-Pacific (Fig. 301). This last has certain peculiar features: its fauna has much in common with the Eocene fauna of the West Indies and Europe (*Operculina*, *Siderolites*, and *Calcarina*) and is apparently the result of the migration of the European fauna eastwards during the Tertiary period. The quantitative composition of the fauna of Foraminifera in the seas of U.S.S.R. is shown in the Table on p. 585.

A definite zonality, depending on temperature conditions, depth, and partly on the salinity of water, is observed in the distribution of benthonic Foraminifera. This has been demonstrated by many authors for different parts of the world ocean. The data of Stschedrina (1953, 1956) for the Far Eastern seas of the U.S.S.R. and the northern part of the Pacific Ocean can serve as examples. In the littoral zone, with its pronounced fluctuations of temperature and salinity, are encountered various species of Ephedium and Quiquelculina. In the sublittoral zone (up to 50 m.), where changes of temperature are also observed but salinity is more constant, there is a characteristic complex of species, some members of which are depicted in Fig. 302, *A*. The pseudoabyssal zone (50—200 m.) is characterized by a cold-water group of species (Fig. 302, *B*) capable of living at a salinity of 3·35 per cent. In the bathyal zone (200–2,000 m.), where the temperature of water fluctuates from 0° to 2·4° C. and salinity from 3·37 to 3·45 per cent., is found another complex of rhizopods (Fig. 302, *C*, *D*), and finally in the abyssal zone (2,000–5,000 m.), at a temperature of 1·8–2·3° and a salinity of 3·47 per cent., *Reophax distans, Astrozhiza crassatina, Rhabdammina*

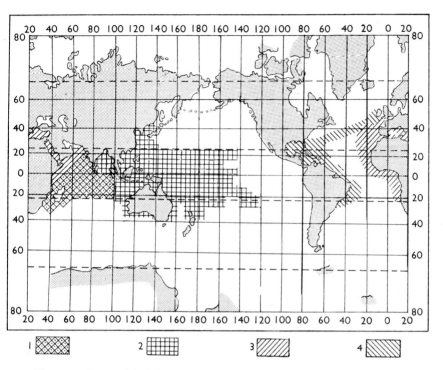

FIG. 301. Geographical distribution of warm-water benthonic Foraminifera.

1, East African province; 2, Indo-Pacific province; 3, Mediterranean province; 4, West Indian province. (After Cushman, 1948.)

linearis, Trochammina globiriniforms and other forms are common. Below 5,000 m. a superabyssal zone is distinguished, with *Reophax bacillari Hormosina globulifera* and others as characteristic forms.

In tropical and subtropical regions zonal distribution of Foraminifera according to depth is more pronounced than in the Arctic and boreal ones; this is connected mainly with greater changes of temperature at different depths (Norton, 1930; Natland, 1933; and others).

The Flagellata and Ciliata occupy a modest place in the benthonic marine fauna. Free-living benthonic marine forms of Ciliates are represented by various Hypotricha. Some of them belong to genera widespread in fresh water (for instance *Euplotes charon*); others are specifically marine and moreover are closely associated with benthos: e.g. *Euplotidium* on sponges, *Paraeuplotes* on corals in Florida. More similar forms will probably be discovered by detailed investigation in the warm seas. Among Holotricha representatives of the genus *Trachelocerca* are widespread in the seas.

Sessile benthonic forms of Ciliata belong mainly to the Peritricha and Suctoria, and most lead an epibiotic mode of life. Such is the order Chono-

FIG. 302. Complexes of benthric Foraminifera from various depth zones in Far Eastern seas.

(*A*) Foraminifera of the sublittoral zone (down to 50 m.): 1, *Ammofrondicularia arctica* (Brady); 2, *Elphidium oregonense* var. *recens* Stschedrina; 3, *Ammobaculites cassis* var. *inflata* Stschedrina; 4, *Verneuilina advena* (Cushman); 5, *Hippocrepina indivisa* Parker; 6*a*, *Cibicides lobatulus* (Walker and Jakob) from dorsal side; 6*b*, same from ventral side (species 3–5 are encountered also in the pseudoabyssal). (*B*) Foraminifera of pseudoabyssal zone (50–200 m.): 7, *Alveolophragmium orbiculatum* Stschedrina; 8, *Nodosaria scalaria* (Batch); 9*a*, *Reophax bacillaris* (Brady), megalospherical form; 9*b*, microspherical form of same species; 10, *Lagena acuticostata* (Reuss); 11, *Bulimina auriculata* (Bailey). (Species 9 also enters the bathyal zone, and species 11 the abyssal region.) (*C*) Foraminifera of upper part of bathyal zone (200–750 m.); 12, *Karreriella baccata* (Schwager); 13, *Triloculina tricarinata* var. *convexa* (Cushman); 14, *Cassidulina californica* (Cushman); 15, *Uvigerina peregrina* (Cushman); 16, *Robulus orbignyi* (Bailey); 17, *Sigmoilina sigmoidea* (Brady); (species 15–17 appear in lower part of pseudoabyssal; species 12–16 enter lower part of bathyal zone). (*D*) Foraminifera of lower part of pseudoabyssal zone (750–2,000 m.): 18*a*, *Eponides tenerus* (Brady) from dorsal side; 18*b*, same view from ventral side; 19, *Bolivina* (*Grammostomum*) *subspinescens* (Cushman), 20; *Cyclammina cuncellata* (Brady); 21, *Pyrgo murrhina* (Schwager); 22*a*, *Chilostomellina fimbriata* (Cushman) from oral side; 22*b*, same lateral side. (Species 22 appears in pseudoabyssal, species 19–21 in the lower part of upper bathyal, species 18 extends up to upper abyssal.) (After Stschedrina, 1953.)

tricha, members of which live on marine and also on freshwater crustaceans. Among the Peritricha some species of *Zoothamnium*, *Lagenophrys*, and *Folliculina* belong to this category. Among the Suctoria the genus *Ophryodendron* of the family *Ephelotidae* is especially common on marine animals and plants.

Marine relicts. Applying the concept of relicts, forms which have survived in isolated parts of their former area of distribution (recent or geological), we can distinguish a considerable number of marine relicts among the Protozoa. The majority of them belong to a category of adaptive relicts, i.e. those which live at present under conditions that are not characteristic of them, but to which they adapted themselves since the nature of their original, more spacious habitat had changed.

Marine relicts inhabit either seas, left over from the time when the particular marine basin had quite a different character, or in less salt waters, or even in fresh water, provided they are of some remote marine origin.

A member of the Dinoflagellata, *Pyrophacus horologium*, which is encountered, apart from the White Sea, in the Baltic, but is absent in the immediate neighbourhood of the White Sea—the Barents Sea, may apparently be referred to marine relicts of the White Sea. Apparently this is a relict of the post-glacial warming of the White Sea (the so-called 'Littorine period').

There are a number of relicts in the Caspian Sea, such as nine species of Foraminifera, some Tintinnoinea (*Codonella relicts*, *Tintinnus mitra*, and others), and certain Dinoflagellata.

According to Gaevskaja (1933), Lake Baikal provides an example of marine relicts in a true freshwater basin. Gaevskaja identified 17 marine relicts among 192 ciliates of Lake Baikal. In the first place, there are members of *Tintinnoinea*: apart from two usual freshwater species, she discovered in Baikal 7 species of *Tintinnopsis* and one species of *Coxliella* (Fig. 303) with marine characters. The majority of them represent brackish forms encountered within estuarial waters of rivers. Apart from Tintinnoinea, Gaevskaja refers to forms of marine origin 5 species of Suctoria, among which 3 are new and 2 have already been described from littoral marine habitats. In addition, Lake Baikal contains one purely marine species of *Vorticella* (*V. sertularium*) and 2–3 species of Holotricha of the marine type.

In shallower lakes marine relicts were discovered long ago in certain Hungarian lakes, especially in Lake Balaton. These are two species of *Tintinnopsis* and one Foraminifera (*Entzia tetrastomella*).

Brady has found in one completely freshwater lake of Ireland *Elphidium striato-punctatum* and *Nonion*, which are true marine Foraminifera. Finally, in one of the lakes near Borovoe, in Kazakhstan, Schmalhausen discovered the foraminiferan *Elphidium*, a form allied to the Balaton one.

Freshwater Protozoa. Ecology. Freshwater habitats of Protozoa are

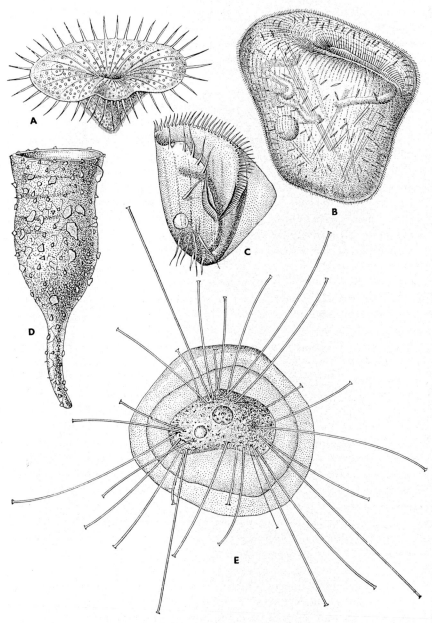

FIG. 303. Ciliates characteristic of Lake Baikal.

(A) *Liliomorpha*; (B) *Marituja pelagica*; (C) *Euplotes baicalensis*; (D) shell of *Coxliella*; (E) suctorian *Mucophrya pelagica*. (After Gaevskaja, 1933.)

extremely varied, for, in addition to the smallest and temporary accumulations of rain water, such as puddles, ditches, &c., Protozoa are widespread in all rivers and lakes. In most cases the fauna of lakes and rivers is contrasted with marine under the names limnetic and potamic; moreover, each of these consists, as in the seas, of benthos and plankton. The benthal region of fresh water is divided into three zones: the littoral up to the boundary of submerged vegetation; the sublittoral from there to the point where the physical conditions are more or less stable, i.e. to the lower limits of the variation of temperature; and the abyssal, i.e. the deepest zone, where the temperature is constant.

The pelagic zone of freshwater basins is divided horizontally into the neritic region, lying above the littoral and sublittoral, and the true pelagic, above the abyssal zone.

In very shallow bodies of water all these zones are not well demarcated, all the zones being reduced to the littoral, and its whole population being benthonic, since the existence of all the animals is more or less associated with the bottom, which is situated at a depth of a few centimetres.

But even in larger bodies of fresh water the size of the zones does not correspond to their extent in marine basins. Thus the littoral of Central European lakes does not usually go deeper than 3–7 m., and the sublittoral to 10–12 m. However, in the large lakes of the U.S.S.R., such as Onega, Ladoga, and Baikal all the divisions of the freshwater fauna are fully represented.

Various types of bodies of water also differ from each other considerably in many conditions of their existence. Thus the quantity and quality of different inorganic components varies greatly: there are ferrous waters, hard or calcareous waters, waters with a high content of calcium and magnesium sulphates; in addition, there is a variety of organic compounds (products of decomposition of plants, for instance in peat-bogs and lakes, &c.). The amount of gas, especially oxygen, dissolved in water also varies. In a cold climate during winter, the ice-cover prevents oxygen from entering the water from the atmosphere; at the same time hydrogen sulphide produced by decomposition of vegetable remains accumulates in frozen bodies of water.

The difference in the above-mentioned factors also affect the concentration of hydrogen ions which have a great influence upon the distribution of Protozoa. In accordance with the diversity of the conditions in bodies of water they are represented by several types distinguishable by their fauna. The classification of bodies of water based on the degree of their pollution, i.e. according to its content of organic admixtures, is of great practical importance. On this basis, waters are divided into the purest or katharobic, and then—with the gradual increase of admixtures—into oligosaprobic, mesosaprobic, and polysaprobic. Each type of waters is characterized by a definite group of organisms, which serve as indicators of the degree of pollution of the water. Mesosaprobic bodies of water have the richest protozoal fauna.

As examples, we may mention such Protozoa as *Dinobryon, Ceratium, Gonium, Eudorina, Volvox, Lacrymaria olor, Frontonia acuminata,* and *Ophrydium,* which represent oligosaprobic forms.

Mesosaprobic waters abound in coloured flagellates (*Cryptomonadida, Chlamydomonads,* and others), and contain a number of colourless Mastigophora, such as *Bodo, Tetramitus, Peranema, Chilomonas,* and *Antophysa;* Heliozoa *Actinophrys* and *Actinosphaerium;* and ciliates *Colpoda, Colpidium, Paramecium caudatum, Coleps, Spirostomum, Stentor, Stylonychia,* and others.

In waters particularly rich in decomposing organic matter, in sewage affluents, &c.—i.e. in polysaprobic conditions—the following forms are especially characteristic: *Oicomonas mutabilis, Polytoma uvella, Paramecium putrinum, Vorticella putrina,* as well as the free-living *Entamoeba moshkovskii.*

But even within the limits of a single small body of water slight differences are observed in the distribution of individual species of Protozoa, even among closely related forms. Such differences in ecological preference are well illustrated by Deflandre in the case of various species of *Arcella.* One of the species inhabits the body of water itself; a second is encountered in the same locality but chiefly near the banks on littoral vegetation; a third occurs in damp moss-cushions on the land; while a fourth lives even on the bark of trees along the bank (Fig. 308).

In spite of such diverse habitats, the fauna of freshwater Protozoa, as stated above, varies less qualitatively and does not contain as many species as the marine. The predominant dwellers in fresh water are coloured Mastigophora and Ciliata. Moreover, some orders and suborders of Mastigophora are known only from fresh waters (Rhizochrysidida, Chrysocapsina, Phytomonadida, Chloromonadida, and the free-living Polymastigida). The exclusively freshwater order Testacea (containing approximately 400 species) represent a more modest parallel to the marine Foraminifera, while the infinitely varied subclass Radiolaria is to some extent replaced in fresh water by the predominantly freshwater and subclass Heliozoa.

Many freshwater Protozoa have developed devices, similar to those of marine forms, but not so pronounced, for the increase of their surface by formation of long processes. Such processes are encountered in the genus *Ceratium* (*C. hirundinella*); in a few *Phytomonadida* (*Brachiomonas* with four little, short horns); in certain *Euchrysomonadina* (spherical colonies of *Chrysosphaerella* with numerous radial spicules running from the gelatinous matter, the solitary *Mallomonas,* which is covered with siliceous spicules, protruding from the surface of the body); in Helizoa with their radial spicules, or elastic axopodia which may serve the same purpose.

An increase of buoyancy effected by a change of the shape of the body is observed in flat, lammeliform colonies of certain Volvocidae (*Gonium pectorale*, Fig. 293, *A*). A medusoid, convex-concave body is encountered in the miniature *Medusochloris* (Fig. 293, *D*) and in the original Baikal ciliate *Liliomorpha* (Fig. 303, *A*) described by Gaevskaja (1933).

Flotation by means of inclusions which lessen the specific gravity of the body is observed in certain *Testacea*, for example in *Difflugia hydrostatica*, which produce in their cytoplasm bubbles of gas, which play the part of a swim bladder.

Owing to the comparatively small depths of most bodies of fresh water, the vertical zonal distribution of freshwater Protozoa has not been sufficiently studied. There are some data on the distribution of Rhizopods (*Testacea*) in the Swiss lakes, e.g. the deep Lake of Geneva (Penard, 1922). Zshokke (1889), an investigator of the Swiss lakes, came to the conclusion that, in contrast to the Rhizopods, the depths of fresh water have no special abyssal fauna of ciliates. Gaevskaja checked these data in the Lake Baikal, which provided excellent conditions for such an investigation, since it attains a considerable depth. She succeeded in investigating depths up to 1,320 m., and obtained the following results:

The total number of species of ciliates in Lake Baikal was found to be 192. Among them 130, i.e. 68 per cent., are encountered only at depths not exceeding 10–12 m.; the remaining 62 species are found up to a depth of 300 m.; while only 29 species descend lower. The deepest layers examined, 1,320 m., contained a fauna composed of only 12 species, i.e. 6 per cent. of the total number of ciliates. Thus the number of species of Ciliata decreases sharply with depth. It is mainly the pelagic ciliates that are confined to the open part of Lake Baikal, which descends to a depth of 300 m. Some pelagic endemic forms of Baikal, such as *Sulcigera*, *Mucophrya*, and *Marituja* (Fig. 303), go farther down, to 500 m. Epibiotic benthonic ciliates, which are attached to the gammarids, descend deeper than the pelagic ones, so that, apart from *Marituja*, all the 25 species encountered below 500 m. belong to this category.

Finally, the attached forms that reach the maximum depth (1,320 m.), viz. *Lagenophrys labiata, Carchesium spectabile, Vorticella crassicaulis, Dendrocometes paradoxus, Tokophrya cyclopum, Spirochona gemmipara,* and others, represent species which are encountered outside Lake Baikal in very shallow bodies of water.

Thus specifically deep-water forms were not found among the ciliates of Lake Baikal.

It is noteworthy that no morphological differences between the deep- and shallow-water forms of the same species were noticed. Gaevskaja only mentions a tendency for some slight decrease in size in the deep-water forms, which is contrary to the increase in size of the marine forms of deep-water Protozoa as compared with the shallow-water ones, described above. Since we associated with temperature the increase in size of marine forms with depth, this discrepancy might be due to the fact that in Lake

Baikal the temperature of the water drops very slightly with depth: for example, on 22 June, when Gaevskaja carried out her main observations on *Marituja*, the temperature of the water at the surface was 3·7° C., while at a depth of 1,300 m. it was 3·36° C. On the other hand, in the lakes of Central Europe the temperature at the surface is considerably higher than in the deep parts. The data for such lakes indicate that the length of certain rhizopods, for example, *Cyphoderia ampulla*, is twice as great in the depth than in the shallows (200 μ instead of 100 μ).

On account of the pronounced differences between freshwater basins mentioned above, on the one hand, and also because of considerable seasonal changes in the bodies of fresh water of the temperate zone in the course of the year, in many freshwater planktonts there occur first of all numerous local variants or morphae, and secondly, seasonal variations undergoing transitions from one to another even in the same body of water. Both are especially pronounced in rotifers and lower crustaceans, but they also occur in a number of Protozoa. They are especially well defined in some freshwater Dinoflagellata (Fig. 304), possessing such pronounced morphological characteristics as horns, spines, &c. Schröder (1914) discovered no fewer than nine local forms of *Ceratium hirundinella*, differing from each other in the size, situation, and even number of horn-like processes (some with 3, others with 4): all these forms are characteristic of various lakes in Central Europe.

Chlamydomonas debrayana is represented by many races, differing in shape, size, and structure and encountered in various localities. Moewus (1934) succeeded in producing these variations in the laboratory by changing the environmental conditions.

Seasonal variations, or cyclomorphosis, represent a phenomenon in which organisms belonging to the same species and same race exhibit at different seasons of the year a different external form. This phenomenon may also be illustrated by *Ceratium hirundinella* (Fig. 304), which in different lakes, but during the same seasons, displays analogous features as regards the degree of development of its processes.

Opinions regarding the significance of cyclomorphosis in the life of planktonts differ. At first it was thought that the smaller size and greater number of processes represent an adaptation for improving the buoyancy of the organisms in the warm summer water. According to Woltereck (1913), the processes developing in summer in planktonic organisms do not increase friction, but serve as rudders or stabilizers. Their purpose is to facilitate the direction of locomotion, with less deflexion to the sides, when the organism is in its normal physiological state.

In Woltereck's opinion these rudders are especially needed in summer, since then the food of planktonic organisms is disposed in the water in horizontal layers, whereas in winter it is distributed much more evenly in the column of water.

However, Woltereck's views are not sufficiently convincing, for some planktonts which possess cyclomorphosis, as for example *Ceratium*, feed holozoically.

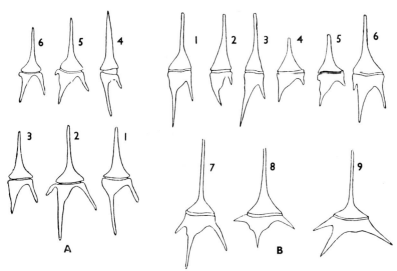

FIG. 304. Seasonal and geographical variation in *Ceratium hirundinella*.

(*A*), seasonal variations: Lake Foure, Lake Copase; (*B*), nine types of *Ceratium* from different European lakes. (After Schröder, 1914.)

Probably the direct cause of intensive development of the processes in summer is the more favourable conditions of nutrition (and in the case of holophytes also of illumination in its connexion with nutrition).

Owing to considerable climatic changes taking place in bodies of fresh water, definite dynamical seasonal changes of the fauna are observed in freshwater Protozoa, as reflected in the frequency in which its individual members are encountered.

Thus, in the case of Beloye Lake in the Moscow region, Zernow (1934) found the following succession of Protozoa in the course of the year—summer forms: *Ceratium hirundinella*, *Peridinium* sp.; spring–autumn forms: *Dinobryon sertularia*; winter: *Dileptus*.

We have clearly observed the winter complex of the ciliates *Stentor coeruleus*, *Dileptus anser*, *Loxodes rostrum*, and *Nassula* in ponds from the neighbourhood of Leningrad. These forms appeared in large numbers in late autumn and survived very well under the ice.

In summer coloured flagellates (*Dinobryon*, *Ceratium*, and other Dinoflagellata, and some Euglenida) multiply especially intensively, and may produce the phenomenon of 'water-bloom', after which they frequently die off in masses.

The inhabitants of organic slime, which covers the bottom of many lakes with a thick layer, or of the sapropel, form a special group of freshwater Protozoa. This ooze is devoid of oxygen and contains reducing substances (H_2S, NH_3, hydrocarbons). Life in it proceeds under anaerobic conditions; moreover, on account of the physical structure of the slime, which consists of a colloidal, fatty, and soft mass, rich in organic detritus, life in it resembles an existence in a water medium as much as in moist soil. Dried layers of the sapropel resemble dense, earthy plates.

These unusual conditions gave rise to the development of an original protozoal fauna first discovered by Lauterborn (1908). Side by side with multitudes of bacteria and blue-green algae some amoebae and other rhizopods (*Pelomyxa, Pamphagus armatus*) also inhabit the sapropel; however, the particularly characteristic representatives of the sapropel fauna are the ciliates which are numerous and specific to this medium (Fig. 305).

Most of these ciliates belong to the family *Ctenostomidae*, which Kahl (1932) raised to the rank of suborder Ctenostomata of the order Spirotricha. Kahl refers to this suborder approximately thirty species of ciliates of the genera *Epalxis, Pelodinium, Saprodinium, Discomorpha,* and *Mylestoma*. Moreover, certain Holotricha (genera *Legendrea* and *Dactylochlamys*) and some Heretricha (genus *Caenomorpha*) form part of the sapropel fauna of ciliates. It is thus seen that the ciliates that had settled in the sapropel belong to three different groups which are not closely related to each other. It is therefore all the more interesting that they all exhibit certain common morphological characters, which are evidently convergent adaptations to a life in such a peculiar biotope as the sapropel. Almost all these ciliates have a compact cuticle, forming at the posterior end of their body sharp spines and processes to which the animals owe their fantastic shape. This armour of the sapropelic ciliates closely resembles the analogous armour of ciliates of the suborder Entodiniomorpha (Fig. 305) which live in the stomach and alimentary tract of ungulates.

The resulting similarity of the external habitus is so great that certain genera of sapropelic ciliates have their counterparts among genera of the suborder Entodiniomorpha. Thus, *Saprodinium mimeticum* from the sapropel closely resembles *Anoplodinium denticulatum* from the rumen of cattle, while in external appearance the sapropelic *Discomorpha pectinata* and *Caenomorpha medusula* are exact replicas of *Triadinium caudatum* and *T. elongatum* from the large bowel of the horse. However, the inner structure and the position of the contractile vacuoles and nuclei in the two cases are quite different. These cases provide an excellent illustration of a type of convergence which is limited entirely to the external structure. The impulse to convergence is undoubtedly due to life under comparable conditions: the Entodiniomorphous ciliates live in a dense mass of minute nutrient particles, while the sapropelic ones inhabit the dense sapropelic ooze; moreover, both are anaerobes.

The last biotope, which can be distinguished for freshwater Protozoa,

is the miniature accumulation of water on the surface of some terrestrial
plants and animals. These are first of all the so-called epiphytic collections
of water. Some tropical plants have either sacculate (*Dischidia*) or urceolate
(*Nepenthes*) leaves in the cavity of which rain-water accumulates. In this
water a small aquatic fauna of its own develops. Among the European

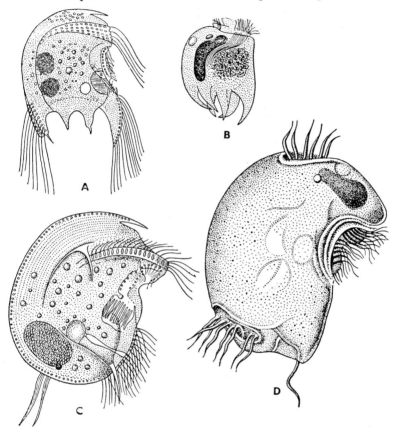

FIG. 305. Convergence in shape of the body and in the appendages of sapropelic ciliates and ciliates from the alimentary tract and stomach of ungulates.

(*A*) sapropelic ciliate *Epalxis*; (*B*) *Anoplodium denticulatum* from the stomach of cattle;
(*C*) sapropelic ciliate *Discomorpha pectinata*; (*D*) ciliate *Triadinium* from the large bowel
of the horse. (*A*) and (*C*) after Wetzel, 1928; (*B*) after Dogiel, 1928; (*D*) after Strelkov,
1939.)

plants in the umbelliferous *Angelica* the sheaths of the leaves clasp the stem
in such a way that they form a small reservoir into which water runs from
the surface of the leaves along a special groove, and is retained there for a
long time. Although the capacity of the reservoir is only 2–3 c.c., it contains
a whole small biocoenosis of rhizopods, ciliates, and even multicellular
animals (rotifers, tardigrades, and larvae of diptera).

The receptacles in the leaves of the above-named tropical plants harbour an even richer fauna; moreover, some of the insect larvae encountered in them are specific to the given biotopes.

Much more rare are miniature water receptacles which might be called epizoic. They have so far been found only on the body of terrestrial crustaceans, namely woodlice. Within the gill cavity of woodlice between their lamellate ventral legs thin layers of water, some tenths of a millimetre

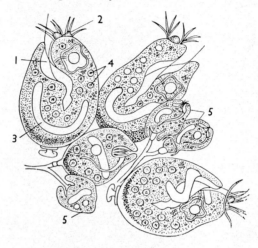

FIG. 306. Group of Peritrichous ciliates *Ballodora*, living on surface of the ventral legs of woodlice.

1, gullet; 2, adoral spiral of membranelles; 3, nucleus; 4, food vacuoles; 5, microzooids. (After Dogiel and Fursenko, 1920.)

thick, accumulate from night dew and from other sources. In spite of the negligible sizes of these 'reservoirs', Dogiel and Fursenko (1920) have established in them the presence of small peritrichous ciliates, *Ballodora* (Fig. 306), which are found to be strictly specific for this environment. These ciliates form pedunculate bushy colonies, with the separate individuals disposed on their branches. *Ballodora* feed on bacteria present in great numbers in the fluid between the gills. Thus they represent as it were 'lodgers' of woodlice. Apart from *Ballodora* the same biotope may be shared by small holotrichous *Chilodon*: the species was not identified. Thus a whole bioceonosis of organisms, of aquatic origin comprising bacteria, *Ballodora*, and *Chilodon*, find shelter between the gill-plates of woodlice.

From the foregoing account it may be concluded that everywhere on earth, where there is water, Protozoa are also present.

Geographical distribution of freshwater Protozoa. The most interesting point in this connexion is the generally cosmopolitan distribution of the great majority of freshwater Protozoa. 'The same ciliates, rhizopods, flagellates', writes Dofflein (1909), 'which are encountered in our pools are also present in India, Africa, South and North America, Siberia, Australia,

Greenland and Terra del Fuego.' Ehrenberg (1838) was the first to note this fact, but this problem was fully worked out by Ševjakov (1892) on the basis of abundant material. Ševjakov produced a comprehensive review of the subject and analysed all the main causes of the widespread distribution of freshwater Protozoa.

According to Ševjakov, the following conditions favour the universal dissemination of Protozoa.

1. Their capacity for extremely rapid and intensive multiplication.

2. The ability of the majority of freshwater Protozoa to form resting stages, namely the encystment, coupled with the fact that cysts can be transferred from one body of water to another by different means.

3. Diverse means of dispersal such as:
   (a) By currents of air.
   (b) By water currents.
   (c) Transportation by birds of motile or encysted stages.
   (d) Transportation by means of flying insects.
   (e) Transportation of Protozoa for short distances by amphibia and certain mammals.

Since the cysts of many Protozoa can withstand prolonged and complete desiccation (some for 5-8 years), they remain viable after the drying up of small bodies of water, pools, &c., and in the dry mud which has turned into fine dust. The abundance of cysts in the mud is evident from our own experience, when dried mud sent to our laboratory from different parts of the Soviet Union yielded cultures of great variety of Protozoa.

Moreover, dust from the bottom of dried-up bodies of water when taken up by the wind, may be carried away by air currents for hundreds of miles and deposited in suitable new bodies of water, into which the dust from the air sinks down with the protozoal cysts. Puschkarev (1913) demonstrated that in the high layers of the atmosphere there are comparatively few cysts of Protozoa, their number increasing only in dry weather and sufficiently strong winds. Thus on the average there are about two cysts of Protozoa per 1 m.^{3} of air. He has succeeded in obtaining in cultures from the air only thirteen species of Protozoa, including *Amoeba*, *Vahlkampfia*, *Bodo*, *Monas*, and, among the ciliates, species of *Colpoda*. In view of this, Puschkarev thinks that transportation by wind must play only an insignificant part in the dissemination of Protozoa. However, the absence of cysts in the upper layers of the atmosphere does not exclude the possibility of gusts of wind catching up and carrying away just above the ground not only dust but also bits of plants, straw, leaves, &c. which contain cysts.

The dissemination of Protozoa and their cysts by currents of water, especially along large rivers, needs no explanation. In Ševjakov's opinion, in this way islands even far removed from the shores may become populated by freshwater Protozoa from the floating bark, wood, &c. That such islands are in fact inhabited by the ordinary continental Protozoa was demonstrated by Sandon (1927) and Cutler in the case of Protozoa collected from the isolated islands of the Atlantic (St. Helena, St. Paul, Tristan da Cunha, South Georgia, and others).

The part played by birds in the dispersal of Protozoa was first observed by Guerne (1888). He obtained, from small lumps of earth and clay adhering to the plumage, beaks, and legs of wild ducks, cysts of ciliates and rhizopods (*Trinema enchelys*).

On a smaller scale and for smaller distances the same role is also played by insects, especially the amphibiotic ones. Migula (1888–9) found that cultures grown on a film of slime removed from the surface of the body of water beetles (*Dytiscus* and *Gyrinus*) produced not only unicellular algae but also a number of Protozoa (*Eudorina, Pandorina, Chlamydomonas*).

The variety of habitats of freshwater Protozoa and the many ways by which they are disseminated produce a curious zoogeographical pattern. Within the same country or region various biotopes contain different sets of Protozoa; but in different countries and even on different continents, as well as on isolated islands, identical biotopes are populated by approximately the same protozoal fauna.

However, it may be questioned whether in fact the cosmopolitan distribution of freshwater Protozoa is as wide as is usually assumed. Some recent works indicate that there are certain limits to this universality. The best example of this is provided by Lake Baikal. The protozoal fauna of this lake is most peculiar. First of all it should be noted that the shallow lakes, 'sory', which are directly connected with Lake Baikal, contain the usual Protozoa, whereas in Baikal itself such a rich group of benthonic Protozoa as the testaceous rhizopods are absent. The Baikal ciliates are most varied, containing a whole series of endemic forms (Svarchevsky, 1928; Gaevskaja, 1933). Among the 192 Baikal ciliates Gaevskaja described 42 new species, some of which were shown to belong to 3 new families and 10 new genera (Fig. 303). The author thought, however, that some of them might eventually be encountered in other localities as in the case of some species of Protozoa which for a long time were wrongly believed to be strictly endemic. However, one group of these organisms is undoubtedly restricted to Baikal. They represent a group of typical pelagic ciliates, living only in the open water of this immensely deep lake. Of the 24 species of this group 13 proved to be new species belonging to 6 new genera. Many of them had also acquired the characteristics of certain pelagic Protozoa. For example, the delicate *Liliomorpha* and the curious planktonic suctorian *Mucophrya* have a concave-convex medusoid shape of the body. Even the cysts of *Mucophrya* have the shape of a parachute facilitating flotation in the water, while certain species of the pelagic group (a pelagic species of *Euplotes* and others) possess processes which increase the surface of the body. Moreover, the investigations of Svarchevsky (1928) indicate that a small group of epibiotic Ciliata (mainly Suctoria) attached to gammarids of Lake Baikal contains a number of new species. Unfortunately this work was carried out on material fixed with formalin and is therefore not quite convincing.

Even so, the Protozoa of Lake Baikal undoubtedly possess original and peculiar features.

On the basis of his own observations in different parts of the U.S.S.R. and of results of a survey of rhizopods (*Testacea*) carried out throughout the world, Basin (1945) came to the conclusion that the distribution of about 30 per cent. of the genera and of more than 50 per cent. of the species of all Testacea is restricted to definite zoogeographical regions. These facts were advanced by him as evidence that the distribution of all the testaceous rhizopods was not cosmopolitan.

Basin even established within different regions groups of forms that are restricted to even narrower areas of distribution. Thus in the Palaearctic there can be distinguished a complex of transpolar forms, in the Swiss lakes another complex of forms, and a complex of insular forms in Great Britain. There are altogether 91 endemic forms in the Palaearctic. However, the number of endemic forms which Basin established for other regions was not at all great, viz. 11 species for the Nearctic region, 6 species only for the Neotropical region, 16 for the Ethiopian region, 27 for the Australian region; and finally in the Indo-Malayan region among 80 species of *Testacea* so far encountered none was endemic. Basin believed that further investigations would provide more evidence of a restricted distribution of some of the *Testacea*, but in our opinion they will also result in a diminution of the abnormally large number of endemics in the Palaearctic. After studying the African fauna of freshwater rhizopods, Decloître (1954) also came to the conclusion that there were geographical differences in the distribution of these Protozoa. Summing up all that has been stated regarding the cosmopolitan distribution of freshwater Protozoa, it must be concluded that in general the view according to which they have an extremely wide distribution is correct, but exception must be made for some groups of Protozoa and for certain peculiar bodies of water (Lake Baikal).

As regards marine Protozoa the widest, frequently cosmopolitan distribution has been established mainly for the deep-water planktonts, especially the abyssal Radiolaria, while the distribution of benthonic Protozoa, for example Foraminifera, is associated with definite zoogeographical regions of the world ocean. In connexion with the wide geographical distribution of freshwater Protozoa, many species are able to populate the most varied biotopes. Thus, in the bodies of water of Mexico, Panama, and Colombia *Tetrachymena pyriformis* is encountered in ditches, ponds, streams, rivers, and lakes situated in valleys at sea-level and at altitudes up to 3,000 m. (Elliot and Hayes, 1955), at a temperature range from 8° C. to 35° C. The same can be said about *Paramecium caudatum* and other ciliates. This points to a wide adaptability of Protozoa to the changing environmental conditions. Moreover, this is frequently due to individual adaptive variability associated with a wide norm of reaction. In the case of rapid agamous multiplication, the adaptations that had developed do not disappear, but are retained in a series of succeeding generations (Poljanskij, 1957, 1959).

Protozoa of brackish waters and salt-water lakes. Bodies of water with a salinity of from 0 to 5 per cent. are regarded as freshwater, while those with a salinity of 16 to 47 per cent. are marine. Bodies of water with an intermediate salinity are known as brackish. The fauna of some 'seas' considered by us above (Sea of Azov, Caspian Sea, and Sea of Aral) belong to the brackish form. A characteristic feature of this fauna is a mixture, on the one hand, of marine species or marine relicts adapted to the decreased salinity of these bodies of water, and, on the other hand, of freshwater species which can withstand a certain degree of salinity. The estuaries of large rivers, where conditions are particularly suitable for the mixing of fauna, owing to a gradual decrease of salinity proceeding from the sea towards the estuary, also belong to the bodies of brackish water.

However, there are very few typical brackish Protozoa. Among these may be mentioned the silicoflagellate *Ebria tripartita*.

Whereas the salinity of the bodies of brackish water is below that of the seas, there are numerous salt-water lakes and pools partly isolated from the sea and in a state of intensive evaporation which are frequently many times more salty than marine basins. The salinity of such waters may reach 250–280 g. per litre (Lake Elton and Lake Baskunchak), while in lakes with Glauber salt (Na_2SO_4) it may even reach 347 g. per litre (Tambukansk Lake in the Caucasus), i.e. these lakes sometimes represent even supersaturated salt solutions. Such hypersaline or ultrahaline bodies of water have a very scarce fauna which also contains some Protozoa, chiefly certain flagellates of the order Phytomonadida. First of all there is the biflagellate *Dunaliella salina* which forms a haematochrome and loses its chlorophyl in strong saline solutions; then the tetrahedral *Tetraptera halophila* and *Asteromonas gracilis*, equipped with six processes.

According to Gaevskaja (1924, 1925), some ciliates can withstand a high degree of salinity, for example *Cladotricha koltzowi* (Fig. 307) and *Palmarium salinum*, which live in lakes with a salinity of 2 to 23 per cent. Only *Dunaliella* and *Asteromonas* survive in the most ultrahaline lakes (Lake Elton).

According to Gaevskaja's observations and experiments, in basins of high salinity *Cladotricha* undergoes considerable changes in structure. With the increase of salinity the size of its body diminishes, the posterior spine disappears, while its bundle of locomotor cilia at the anterior end becomes relatively larger, owing to the difficulty of swimming in dense solutions. Finally, with the increase of salinity up to 22–23 per cent., the cytoplasm of *Cladotricha* becomes denser, ceases to move, and sinks to the bottom. It lies there in a state of saline anabiosis until the salinity of the environment decreases, when it resumes its active life.

In addition to these two species of flagellates, Krapin (1929) discovered in Lake Elton shells of the foraminiferan *Trochammina* sp. and *Cyclammina* sp., without, however, any signs of living protoplasm.

The population of hot bodies of water. In the previous paragraphs it was shown that under natural conditions Protozoa adapt themselves to different

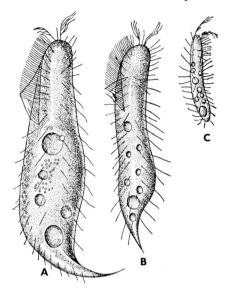

FIG. 307. Changes in size and shape of body of ciliate *Cladotricha koltzowi* under influence of increasing salinity of water from 5 per cent. (*A*) to 23 per cent. (*C*). (After Gaevskaja, 1925.)

degrees of salinity. We shall now discuss briefly the adaptation of Protozoa to extreme temperatures.

Basins of water and springs with a very high temperature are most frequently encountered in volcanic localities: they are known in Italy, Iceland, Japan, Kamchatka, &c. The temperature in these waters varies within wide limits from 20 to 100° C. The extreme temperature for living organisms is 89–90° C. (some non-chlorophyllous algae). However, the temperature for animals is much lower, usually not more than 52–55° C.

Among Protozoa in hot springs the forms most frequently encountered are the testaceous rhizopods *Centropyxis*, *Difflugia*, *Trinema*, *Quadrula*, and others (up to 40–45° C.); the ciliates *Frontonia acuminata* (at 49–50° C.); *Nassula elegans* (at 50–52° C.); *Cyclidium glaucoma* (up to 51° C.); the rhizopod *Hyalodiscus* (even at 54° C.). Finally, it is known that in the springs of Ischia (Bay of Naples) Protozoa were found even at 53–64·7° C.

In the Japanese hot springs the following species were noted: *Amoeba verrucosa*, *Chilodonella* sp., *Lionotus*, *Paramecium caudatum* at 36–40° C ; *Oxytricha fallax* at 30–50° C. It is obvious that many Protozoa—including such highly organized forms as Ciliata—can survive at very high temperatures. However, no Protozoa are so specifically adapted to high temperatures that they canot exist under other conditions.

Judging by laboratory experiments, many Protozoa may become accustomed to increases of temperature (Poljanskij, 1957, 1959). Under natural conditions, when hot bodies of water and springs made their appearance, the presence of Protozoa in them and their adaptation to the new environment was apparently accidental. However, their speciation under such extreme conditions has so far not been observed.

The minimum temperature required for the active life of Protozoa in nature is about 0° C. In winter a rich protozoal fauna continues to live directly under the ice of fresh water, especially in ponds; thus some species of ciliates live and multiply under the ice in great numbers.

On the snow of glaciers, at great heights, especially during slight thaws, some phytomonadine flagellates undergo, under the effect of the sun's rays, massive proliferation, resembling the 'bloom' on the surface of water. *Chlamydomonas nivalis*, which is rich in haematochrome, is particularly well known in this respect, causing the appearance of the so-called 'bloody' or 'red' snow, when a considerable part of the surface of the mountain snow is covered with a film of these minute organisms.

Soil Protozoa and the occupation by Protozoa of terrestrial territories. Like many other aquatic groups of animals, Protozoa proved to possess to a certain extent the capacity for transition to a life on the land; however, in all cases such transition becomes possible only when the soil or land plants are sufficiently saturated with moisture.

The transition to life on land or in it was accomplished by Protozoa in various ways.

First of all it could have happened as the result of irradiation from the shores of the bodies of water on to adjoining areas of land. In lakes, and especially in marshes, where water is to a certain extent mixed with earth and the mossy hillocks rising above the water level are impregnated with moisture, immigration by diverse Protozoa could have proceeded most easily. It was probably followed by occupation of the off-shore moss growths, whence such forms spread from the shore to the moss cushion growing in the shadow of woods and not directly connected with water (Fig. 308).

In fact, it is well known that the best places for collecting many forms of testaceous rhizopods are sphagnous peat mosses, which are inhabited by a whole small fauna of some dozens of original species of Testacea. In forest mosses this fauna is poorer, containing only about ten species, instead of which there is a biocoenosis of ciliates. Penard found up to thirty-six species of ciliates, which he had not encountered anywhere else but in mosses. These include *Balantidiopsis muscicola*, *Euplotes terricola*, and a good many species of *Cothurnia*, *Cothurniopsis*, and *Vorticella*.

In contrast to this, in the higher swamplands the mosses are inhabited, as in the sphagnum bogs, by a rich fauna of Testacea, whereas the ciliated occupy a second place.

The second type of immigration of Protozoa to land is exemplified by the psammitic biocoenosis. The term 'psammon' is used for the microscopic fauna sheltering in the spaces between the grains of littoral sands and composed mainly of unicellular algae and ciliates. The psammon develops on

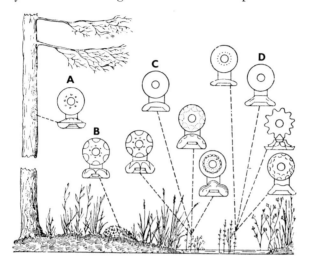

FIG. 308. Distribution of different species of *Arcella* in various micro-biocenoses.

(*A*) in moss on tree trunk; (*B*) in ground-moss; (*C*) in coastal growths; (*D*) on water plants. (After Deflandre, 1928.)

the banks of rivers and in the sand-bars above water-level. The closer to the river the richer is the psammon, but it may extend to a distance of 24 m. from the river bank with a depth of ground water of 24 cm. Sand containing the psammon is composed of several layers, running deep down from the surface of the sand. The thin so-called green horizon, lying under the very surface at a depth of 0·3–0·5 cm., is the most populated layer (0·1–0·5 cm. thick). In this layer several species of Testacea and about forty species of ciliates have been encountered.

However, the psammon comprises the common freshwater Protozoa, i.e. riverine species, but no specific forms are found in it.

Comprehensive investigations of the psammon were carried out in 1927 on the banks of the River Oka by Sassuchin, Kabanov, and Neizvestnova.

It is noteworthy that psammon was found not only along the river banks, but also in the vast, barren sandy regions between the Rivers Volga and Ural. Here, however, the green layer lies considerably deeper than on the river banks—at depths of up to 15 cm. The survival in the desert of diatomous and protococcal algae, which impart to the psammonitic layer a green colour, is due to intensive isolation of the earth surface under desert conditions and the penetration of the sun's rays into the soil.

Some authors extend the concept 'psammon' also to microscopic marine organisms living in sand.

Lately, detailed studies have been performed on the fauna of marine and brackish water sands. These sands proved to be abundantly inhabited by diverse fauna, the representatives of the latter dwelling in the water-filled spaces between sand grains. This fauna, called interstitial or psammophilic, is composed of representatives of many animal groups, including a great number of species of *Ciliata*. A considerable number of investigations deal with this peculiar protozoan fauna (Fauré-Fremiet, 1950; Bock, 1952, 1953; Dragesco, 1960; Raikov, 1960, 1962; and others). Its species composition is very rich. Raikov (1962) points out that the number of already described species of psammophilic ciliates exceeds 300. Taking into account the fact that this fauna has been studied only incompletely, Dragesco (1962) suggests that the total number of species could be evaluated with a figure near to 600.

The systematic composition of the psammophilic ciliate fauna is characterized by a large number of species of *Holotricha Gymnostomatida*, by a much smaller proportion of *Trichostomatida* and *Hymenostomatida*, and by a considerable number of *Heterotricha* and *Hypotricha*. *Peritricha* and suctorians are completely absent.

The psammophilic ciliates form a quite characteristic ecological group and exhibit many special adaptations to sand dwelling. Fauré-Fremiet (1950) and Dragesco (1960) show that the size of sand grains is the main factor determining the species composition of the fauna and the adaptive peculiarities of the characteristic species. These authors distinguish between *microporal* fauna, characteristic for sands with average grain size 0·1–0·4 mm., *mesoporal* fauna (grain size 0·4–1·8 mm.), and *euryporal* fauna, inhabiting fine as well as coarse sands. Adaptations to interstitial habitat are more clearly expressed in representatives of the microporal fauna.

Let us consider now some of the characteristic structural features of the psammophilic ciliates. Most of them are fairly large, and some even very large ciliates (up to 1 mm. and greater). A strong stretching of the body, leading often to vermiform (nematomorph) outlines, is characteristic of these forms. This peculiarity should be obviously considered as an adaptation to moving in narrow spaces between the sand grains. Together with elongation of the body, a flattening of the latter is peculiar to many psammophilic infusorians (*Kentrophoros*, *Tracheloraphis*, *Trachelonema*, *Geleia*, *Remanella*, and others). As a result, some species acquire a band-like body form.

Simultaneously with body flattening, a reduction of ciliary apparatus on one of the body surfaces is observed in some cases, especially in *Holotricha Gymnostomatida*. Such a series of gradual flattening of the body and partial reduction of the ciliature can be traced, for example, in the genera *Trachelo-cerca*, *Tracheloraphis*, and *Trachelonema*. A strongly expressed thigmotaxis is also a characteristic biological peculiarity of many psammophilic ciliates. They adhere by means of their cilia to surrounding sand grains, and it is often difficult to separate them from the latter. This peculiarity is also an adaptation, which prevents the ciliates from being washed out of the sand by water currents.

An abundant fauna of psammophilic ciliates develops in sands that are comparatively rich in organic matter in the presence of bacteria and algae, both of which serve as food for the infusoria. However, in sands with very much mud and organic detritus, decaying with hydrogen sulphide production, the ciliate fauna becomes poor and is represented only by few species specific for this medium.

It is an interesting peculiarity of marine psammobiotic ciliate fauna, that it contains, among the *Holotricha*, a considerable proportion of forms with primitive nuclear apparatus—with diploid Macronucleus, which are incapable of dividing (genera *Trachelocerca*, *Tracheloraphis*, *Trachelonema*, *Remanella*, *Kentrophoros*, *Geleia*). It has already been pointed out earlier (Chapters II and IX) that such type of the nuclear apparatus should be considered as a primitive one—as one of the early stages of phylogenetic development of the nuclear dualism in ciliates. This peculiarity could hardly be a character adaptive to dwelling in sand. In our opinion the mentioned features of the nuclear apparatus should be regarded as an evidence of the existence, among the psammophilic ciliates, of a rather numerous group of representatives of a very ancient and primitive ciliate fauna, these representatives having elaborated a number of adaptations to the peculiar conditions of life in spaces in the sand (idioadaptations, after Severtzoff's terminology—see Chapter IX). These adaptive characters could allow them to survive until recent times.

Together with this ancient ciliate group, the interstitial fauna includes many phylogenetically younger elements, which probably became psammo-philic ones only secondarily. These are, for example, psammobiotic *Hetero-tricha* and *Hypotricha*.

It is still difficult to judge definitely of the geographic distribution of the psammophilic ciliates, because they were not yet studied in the majority of regions of the world. However, a fairly great coincidence of the species composition of the faunas of the English Channel, Mediterranean, Barents Sea, White Sea, and Japan Sea[1] beaches witness to their very wide geo-graphical distribution. It is probable that the majority of these ciliates are even cosmopolitic species.

A very interesting discovery of typical marine multilocular Foraminifera was made by Brodskij (1929) in Central Asia, in an environment close to that of the psammon. They were found in ground waters at the bottom of

---

[1] Data on the Japan Sea are given after Raikov (in press).

salt wells of the Kara-Kum desert, at a distance of 250 km. from the Caspian Sea and 1000 km. from a true sea. These Foraminifera are represented by more than a dozen species of the common marine genera *Lagena*, *Nodosaria*, *Spiroloculina*, *Globigerina*, and others. Brodskij suggested that they were relicts of the Miocene sea which once covered the present Kara-Kum. Brodskij's pupil, Nikoljuk (1948), examined wells of the Kara-Kum, and on the whole confirmed his data. In 27 groups of wells he collected about 300 specimens belonging to 3 species of Foraminifera (*Miliolina oblonga* var. *arenacea*, *Spiroloculina turcomanica*, and *Fischerina sp.*). They were all characterized by an extremely thin-walled shell and by their dwarf size. The shells were filled with plasma, and only megalospherical forms were encountered. The ground waters of Kara-Kum were found to be very similar to sea water in their content of both salts and oxygen. In the central part of the territory examined the ground water resembles the water of the Mediterranean.

From the psammonitic Protozoa, which are spatially more or less associated with the nearest bodies of water, there is an easy transition to the Protozoa which exist everywhere in the soil, and have no genetic association with any definite bodies of water or their shores.

It has been known for a long time that abundant cultures of Protozoa appear in infusions of water prepared from samples of soil. This is due to the fact that the cysts of Protozoa that are present in the soil hatch in the water and give rise to a culture.

However, Russel and Hutchinson (1909) expressed the opinion that Protozoa are present in the soil not only in the encysted, i.e. passive state, but also as an active form. Furthermore, according to Russel and Hutchinson the activities of the soil Protozoa have a serious effect on the bacterial flora, since the Protozoa devour various bacteria, including the nitrifying ones.

Thus the intensive development of Protozoa in the soil must have a harmful effect on the nitrifying bacteria in that they diminish the amount of nitrogen produced by the latter, thereby indirectly influencing the fertility of the soil. Russel's conclusions were based mainly on the results of his experiments on partial sterilization of the soil either by toluene or by heating it to 60° C. The sterilization must have killed the Protozoa, retaining in the soil the more heat-resistant bacteria. These experiments demonstrated that partial sterilization of the soil leads to a rich development of the bacterial flora, which Russel attributed to the absence of Protozoa destroyed by sterilization.

The data obtained by Russel and his associate Hutchinson (1913) attracted much attention, and soil Protozoa became the subject of investigations in many countries. In the Soviet Union soil protozoology began to develop after 1917. Among the Soviet authors who worked in this field the following may be noted: Novikov (1922), Dogiel (1926), Strelkov (1930),

Lozina-Lozinskij and Martinov (1930), Rammelmejer (1930), Nikoljuck (1956).

The main data on soil Protozoa obtained up to the present may be summarized as follows.

Qualitative composition of soil Protozoa. The evaluation of the composition of soil Protozoa should be approached with great caution, since the soil always contains cysts of most diverse Protozoa, so that when preparations are moistened with water—without which observations *in vitro* are impossible—there is always the danger that some of the active Protozoa seen under the microscope may in fact have been in the soil in the encysted state, and have hatched when already under observation. Therefore, certain precautions against such errors are taken. Novikov (1922) gave a list of active soil Protozoa composed of 10 species of Mastigophora, 9 species of Sarcodina, and 20 species of Ciliata. Later Sandon (1927), who gave a detailed review of soil Protozoa, listed a much greater number of species, viz. more than 300 species of Sarcodina, Mastigophora, and Ciliata. Most of them are minute flagellates (*Bodo, Monas, Oicomonas,* and others), a series of amoebae and testaceous rhizopods (*Difflugia, Arcella, Trinema,* and others), and certain small ciliates (*Colpidium, Colpoda,* and others). These forms may be regarded as true active inhabitants of the soil; as regards many other species found in the soil, especially Heliozoa, *Vorticella,* and other large Ciliata, it can be definitely assumed that they were in the soil in the form of cysts. Those authors who took the necessary precautions when examining samples, e.g. Strelkov (1930), Brodskij and Yankovskaja (1929), found in the soil mostly the small forms mentioned above.

Thus the number of true soil Protozoa is probably comparatively small and consists of small forms, frequently measuring only 15–20 μ, which had adapted themselves to life in the thin, inner layers of moisture separating the solid particles of soil or on their surface. These forms are able to encyst rapidly when the soil dries, and to hatch as rapidly from the cysts. According to some data certain species of flagellates are most frequently encountered in the soil. However, the composition of species, even among the true soil Protozoa, does not represent anything specific, since the same forms are encountered not only in the soil, but in fresh water as well.

The number of Protozoa in the soil. This is a cardinal point in the assessment of the practical importance of soil Protozoa. They can inhibit the bacterial flora only when their numbers are excessive. However, the method of calculation of their numbers in the soil is still most unsatisfactory. The usual method of calculation consists in the addition of water to one gramme of soil, followed by inoculation of samples in varying dilutions on nutrient media in Petri dishes. The extreme degree of dilution at which Protozoa can still be obtained in culture serves as an indication of the number of Protozoa present per gramme of soil. Thus the presence of *Colpoda* in a

1 : 1000 dilution of one gramme of soil indicates the occurrence of 1,000 individuals of this ciliate per gramme of soil.

Brodskij (1929) used for the detection of Protozoa in soil a 'capsule' trap with moist cotton wool, into which the Protozoa penetrate actively from the soil, after which their number was calculated by means of an ocular micrometer.

Calculations carried out in different countries by numerous authors produced extremely varied results. The figures obtained by different authors varied from 10,000 to 100,000 and even to several million per gramme of soil. Of this number the majority belong to flagellates, amoebae, and rhizopods occupying the next place, while ciliates are the fewest.

The number of Protozoa present in the soil depends on a number of conditions, the chief being the depth from which the sample was taken. Most authors believe that Protozoa are encountered in the topmost 15–20 cm. of the soil; at a depth of 30 cm. their number does not exceed a hundred per gramme of soil, while still deeper Protozoa are not encountered at all. However, Brodskij (1937) thought that they penetrate much more deeply. Thus he considered that in the Kara-Kum desert the layer containing the densest protozoal population lies at a depth of 20–30 cm., and in some kinds of soil even at a horizon of 60–80 cm. According to Brodskij, the flagellates penetrate to the greatest depth (down to 2 m.); next come the amoebae (down to 90 cm.), and still nearer to the surface is the limiting horizon for the ciliates (at a depth of 60 cm.). Such depths of penetration have not been established by other investigators. Nikoljuck (1949, 1956) examined Protozoa in the soils of the artificial irrigated fields of Uzbekistan, in soils under a cotton-lucerne rotation of crops, and obtained the following main results. The root system of these plants exerts an attraction on Protozoa, their content in the rhizosphere being 2–3 times higher than in the soil taken at some distance from the roots—the only organisms not showing this effect being the flagellates. The concentration of Protozoa is due to the presence in the rhizosphere of certain groups of bacteria, which serve as food for Protozoa.

The seasonal dynamics of the Protozoa are characterized by a pronounced increase in the number of ciliates and flagellates in October–November (up to 25,000 per gramme and more), while amoebae reach their highest development in July–September. This fluctuation is determined mainly by the moisture and temperature of the soil. Thus in summer the moisture is reduced and the temperature rises; this has an unfavourable effect on the ciliates and flagellates, whereas the amoebae are able to withstand a considerable fall in moisture, so that they are able to develop in summer. The largest numbers of Protozoa accumulated in the soil under the cotton plants of the first year (after the ploughing in of the lucerne) reaches up to 100,000 per gramme. Their number falls sharply during the second year (down to a few thousand) and then rises gradually during the third year of cultivation. The density of the protozoal fauna on lucerne is higher than on cotton plants, except for cotton plants of the first year. The abundance of Protozoa on cotton plants of the first year is due to an increase of organic substances in the soil and the intensive proliferation of bacterial flora during the ploughing in of lucerne.

Nikoljuck obtained a 23–31 per cent. increase of the fixed nitrogen by growing *Azotobacter* in the presence of Protozoa, in mixed cultures of *Azotobacter* with *Colpoda* or of *Azotobacter* with *Amoeba*. However, no increase in the amount of nitrogen was obtained in cultures of *Azotobacter* with flagellates. It is noteworthy that the process of nitrogen fixation is activated not only by living Protozoa but also by suspensions of organisms killed by heat. Therefore, in Nikoljuck's opinion the stimulating effect of Protozoa upon bacteria is produced by some active substances discharged by the ciliates and amoebae into the surrounding medium.

The nature of the soil also affects the number of Protozoa inhabiting it. In general, apparently, light soils that are rich in humus represent more favourable habitats for Protozoa than heavy soils poor in humus; thus the number of Protozoa is greater in soils of greenhouses and hotbeds than in the open fields. Sandy soils contain scanty Protozoa; nevertheless, they have been found even under desert conditions (North Africa, Kara-Kum). According to some investigators Protozoa reach their maximum abundance in summer, according to others in winter. Sandon (1927) found considerable numbers of Protozoa (16,000 per gramme of soil) even in frozen soil. However, in all the above-mentioned cases the presence of active Protozoa in the soil remained doubtful.

Proof of the existence of active Protozoa in the soil was provided in the ingenious experiments of Lozina-Lozinskij and Martinov (1930) on the rate of their dispersion in it. A drop of a mixed culture of bacteria (*Bacillus radicicola*), amoebae (*Vahlkampfia*), and ciliates (*Colpoda*) was placed in the centre of a Petri dish containing sterilized earth. During the next few days samples were taken from the dish at different distances from the centre. It was found that, at a moisture content of 25–35 per cent., the bacteria moved 4–5 cm. from the centre of the dish towards the edge on the second day, while on the third day they reached it, the radius of the dish being 8 cm. The amoebae and ciliates progressed much more slowly: the amoebae began to spread only on the 5th day, and on the 8th day (by the end of the experiment) they had only reached a zone 4 cm. from the centre of the dish; the ciliates began to spread only on the 6th day and at the end of the experiment they had succeeded in occupying only a zone of 1 cm. around the centre. The rate of dispersion depended also on the size of the particles of soil; in a soil with larger particles (up to 0·5 mm.) the Protozoa spread and reached the edges of the dish much more quickly. At a lower moisture content the Protozoa inoculated into the soil migrated much more slowly.

There can be no doubt that Protozoa feed on soil bacteria, including the nitrifying bacteria. None the less opinions regarding the influence of Protozoa on soil bacteria still differ.

The British school, which developed the study of soil Protozoa, firmly maintains that the Protozoa destroy bacteria and thus have a harmful effect on the fertility of the soil, while partial sterilization of the soil, which kills the Protozoa but has no effect on bacteria, increases the amount of nitrogen produced by the bacteria. These data were confirmed by Cunningham (1915) and others by calculating the number of bacteria in sterilized and unsterilized soil in relation to the Protozoa. However, Waksmann (1916), though recognizing the inhibiting effect of Protozoa on bacteria, held that nitrification is not diminished by the presence of Protozoa. As an explanation he suggested that possibly the Protozoa feed not on nitrifying but on some other soil bacteria.

Many American authors, though not denying that Protozoa might have an effect on soil bacteria, note that they have not observed a decrease in the number of bacteria as a result of the activity of Protozoa. Among the English authors, Goodey (1912) expressed similar views.

However, Koffman (1931, 1934) definitely denied that Protozoa played any essential role in the life of the soil. In a series of experiments, in which as far as was possible a direct calculation of Protozoa in the soil was made under a microscope, he showed that the number of free and active Protozoa in the soil is so small, while the quantity of bacteria and their biomass is so great, that this alone indicates that the part played by Protozoa in the destruction of bacteria must be insignificant.

Moreover, it was pointed out (Alekseev, 1925) that, owing to the liability of the soil Protozoa and their high mortality, the destruction of bacteria by them is balanced by the enrichment of the soil with nitrogen, liberated by decomposition of dead Protozoa.

Among Russian investigators, Brodskij and Nikoljuck are of the opinion that in the complex soil microbiocoenoses Protozoa form a natural and essential link, which takes an active part in the biodynamic processes. Other investigators (Alekseev, 1935; Strelkov, 1950) consider that the problem of the part played by soil Protozoa remains unsolved, and it is doubtful whether they play any important role in agriculture.

PARASITIC PROTOZOA

Parasitism is widespread among Protozoa. All the classes of the phylum contain numerous representatives that have adopted this mode of life, while the classes Sporozoa and Cnidosporidia are composed of parasites exclusively. The parasites are those Protozoa whose habitat is represented by another living organism, on or in which they find shelter and food. Owing to their microscopic size, Protozoa find such conditions not only in various, even very small, Metazoa, but also within other Protozoa or in individual cells of their multicellular hosts.

The ability of the majority of free-living Protozoa to form resting cysts facilitates, on their transition to parasitism, the transmission of the infection to other host individuals. Finally, the rapid rate of multiplication of Protozoa is a further guarantee of their successful adaptation to parasitism, since in parasites the preservation of species can only be ensured by intensive proliferation. The capacity of all Protozoa for asexual reproduction also works in this favourable direction. Among the Protozoa there are parasites of both animals and plants.

The prevalence of parasitism within the phylum of Protozoa. A list of parasitic Protozoa arranged according to their groupings is given in the Table below.

APPROXIMATE DISTRIBUTION OF PROTOZOA IN DIFFERENT ENVIRONMENTS

Name of class	Total number of species	Sea	Fresh water	Parasites	Percentage of parasites
Mastigophora	3,500	1,300	1,300	900	25·7
Sarcodina	8,000	7,300	600	100	1·25
Ciliata	6,000	1,500	3,500	1,000	16·6
Sporozoa	1,100	..	..	1,100	100
Cnidosporidia	900	..	..	900	100
Total	19,500	10,100	5,400	4,000	20·5

Parasitic forms are present in all classes of Protozoa. Among the Mastigophora parasitic forms are found in the orders *Dinoflagellata, Euglenida,* and *Protomonadida,* but *Polymastigida, Hypermastigida,* and *Opalinina* are all parasites. The *Dinoflagellata* are represented chiefly by free-living planktonts, but among them there is a fairly large (more than sixty species) group of peculiar parasites belonging to the specialized family Blastodinidae, which are parasitic on the surface of the body, in the body cavity, the alimentary tract or in freely floating eggs of different planktonic animals, as well as in the gut of some bottom-dwelling *Polychaeta* (genus *Haplozoon*).

Within the order Euglenida, about ten species inhabiting the alimentary tract of *Turbellaria, Cyclops,* and amphibian tadpoles have adapted themselves to endoparasitism. It is particularly interesting that in this case not only the colourless forms which had lost their chlorophyll (*Astasia captiva* from the Turbellarian *Catenula, Astasia mobilis* from *Cyclops, Hegneria leptodactyli* from the gut of tadpoles), have become parasites, but also *Euglenamorpha* and one species of *Euglena* from the hindgut of tadpoles, which have retained their chlorophyll and stigma. The retention of chlorophyll is explicable by the semi-transparence of the body walls and alimentary tract of tadpoles. Adaptation to parasitism was probably facilitated by the food habits of tadpoles, since they readily feed on flagellates, which remain alive for a long time in their hindgut. Evidently some species of *Euglenida,* having found themselves under such conditions, managed to adapt themselves to them and were transformed from prey into parasites of the animals that had ingested them.

In *Astasia mobilis*, in addition to typical individuals, forms devoid of flagella are frequently encountered, the loss having probably been caused by the transition to a parasitic mode of existence.

Parasitism is much more widespread within the order of uniflagellated and colourless *Protomonadida*. Wenyon (1926) gives a list of about 300 species, including more than 70 species of *Trypanosoma*. Since then some species, especially in this genus, have been reduced to synonyms, though new ones have been discovered instead, so that for this order the figure of not fewer than 350 species of parasites can be accepted.

The composition of the orders *Polymastigida* and Hypermastigida has been studied much better. Among the *Polymastigida* more than 100 species are parasitic in various vertebratae and invertebratae hosts (*Trichomonas, Devescovina, Parajoenia, Oxymonas*, and others). Numerous members of the order *Hypermastigida*, whose host range is restricted to termites and 2–3 species of cockroaches, have adapted themselves to the same habitat. Although the Protozoa of termites have not yet been thoroughly investigated, more than 140 different species of *Polymastigida* and 100 species of *Hypermastigida* have already been described, though of the 400 species of termites only 150 have so far been examined by parasitologists. Finally, the subclass Opalinina, comprising 150–170 species from the alimentary tract of amphibians, represents another larger group of parasitic flagellates.

Thus, it may be accepted that not less than 900 parasitic members are known at present for the class Mastigophora. In the class *Sarcodina* the Amoebina contain a large group of parasites. According to Kudo (1954) the order Amoebina contains at least 100 parasitic species. On the other hand, the order Heliozoa contains only 2–3 parasitic forms (*Pseudospora, Nuclearia*), while the orders Testacea, Foraminifera, and Radiolaria do not contain any true parasites at all. Thus the class Sarcodina contains about 100 parasites or a little more.

In the class Ciliata the suborder *Entodiniomorpha* is totally parasitic, with its 200 species from the intestine and stomach of ungulates and more rarely of rodents. In the order *Holotricha* all the parasitic forms are concentrated mainly in the 5–6 groups. About 100 species live together with the *Entodiniomorpha* in the intestine and stomach of ungulates and rodents. Another group (order *Apostomata*) consists of up to 40 species of marine forms, parasitic anemones and crustacea. A third group comprising about 180 species (order *Astomata*) mostly inhabits the alimentary tract of rainworms; a fourth group belonging to the orders Holotricha and Oligotricha contains 50 species inhabiting the alimentary tract of sea-urchins; and finally the fifth (*Thigmotricha*) contains up to 80 species living on the gills of various molluscs.

At present more than 80 parasitic species are known from the order *Heterotricha*, while the order Hypotricha includes only about 10 parasitic species (*Korona* from the body of *Hydra* and some others). Among the *Peritricha*, parasitic forms are confined almost exclusively to just over 80 species (*Trichodina* and others) of the family Urceolaridae. Finally, in the subclass *Suctoria* there are about 50 species that are parasitic on crustacea, the gills of fish and turtles, as well as within *Peritricha* (*Endosphaera*, see Fig. 319) or in the alimentary tract of ungulates (*Allantosoma*, see Fig. 317). It is reckoned that there are about 1,000 species of parasites among the Ciliata.

The greatest number of parasites are found in the classes of Sporozoa and Cnidosporidia, which are represented by parasitic forms exclusively.

The subclass Gregarinida contains about 500 species; in the subclass Coccidiida the genus *Eimeria* alone contains up to 350–400 species, while the whole subclass comprises about 600. The suborder Haemosporidia and other groups of blood parasites of uncertain nature (*Piroplusmoidea, Theileriidea*) contain about 200 species. In the class Cnidosporidia, the order Microsporidia contains more than 200 species from arthropods and fish, the order Actinomyxidia contains probably 20–30 species from Oligochaeta and some marine vertebrates, while the order Myxosporidia has more than 700 species, and their number is still growing. Thus the class Sporozoa comprises considerably more than 1,100 species, and Cnidosporidia approximately 1,000 species. On the whole, out of the estimated total of 19,000–20,000 species in the phylum Protozoa about 4,000 species are parasites.

Thus the occurrence of parasitism in different classes of Protozoa varies considerably. This is particularly clear if the number of parasites is compared to that of free-living species within each class and with that of the total number of species in a given class (see Table on p. 617).

This calculation is not only interesting in itself, but it also enables us to make a better evaluation of those morphological features of Protozoa which promote or prevent their transition to a parasitic mode of existence.

First of all, it may be assumed that in general a strongly developed skeleton hinders the transition to parasitic life. Thus in the immense class of Sarcodina, the majority of whose groups (*Testacea*, Foraminifera, Radiolaria) possess a well-developed, often mineral, skeleton, the number of parasites is insignificant, and only in groups either devoid of a skeleton (*Amoebina*) or with a weak one (2–3 in *Heliozoa*) does their number increase slightly. Similarly, in the Dinoflagellata parasitism has developed only in some of the naked *Gymnodinioidea*, but not in the *Peridinioidea*, which are invested in a cellulose armour. Furthermore, chlorophyll-bearing Protozoa, i.e. in particular the coloured Mastigophora, have no tendency to parasitism, since their holophytic nutrition provides sufficient food resources. Only a few species of coloured Euglenida have become parasites, but among Dinoflagellata all the parasitic forms are devoid of chromatophores.

The complexity of the organization does not affect the tendency to parasitism; thus, there are practically no parasites among the Sarcodina, which are simply organized as regards the plasmatic structures, whereas among the most highly organized Protozoa, namely the Ciliata, 27 per cent. are parasitic.

A calculation of the numbers of parasitic Protozoa living in marine, freshwater, and terrestrial hosts reveals curious and rather unexpected results.

It is a difficult calculation and its results are of course only approximate, but the pattern obtained is sufficiently clear (see Table below).

DISTRIBUTION OF PARASITIC PROTOZOA ACCORDING
TO THE ECOLOGY OF THEIR HOSTS

Name	In marine hosts	In freshwater hosts	In terrestrial hosts
Euglenida	..	10	..
Dinoflagellata	60	..	..
Protomonadida	25	55	250
Polymastigida	..	40	100
Hypermastigida	..	..	100
Amoebina	10	20	85
Opalinina	..	150	..
Holotricha	60	55	100
Astomata	20	120	20
Apostomata	40	..	..
Heterotricha	..	20	60
Entodiniomorpha	..	..	200
Peritricha	20	30	5
Suctoria	25	20	5
Gregarinida	175	75	250
Coccidiida	50	50	300
Haemosporidia, Piroplasmoidea, Theileriidea	25	25	150
Sarcosporidia	..	..	40
Microsporidia	20	100	80
Myxosporidia	200	500	..

The Table shows that parasitic Protozoa comprise about 800 marine, about 1,000 freshwater, and about 1,800 terrestrial species.

These figures are striking, for there are rather fewer parasitic species of Protozoa in aquatic animals than in terrestrial ones, in spite of the fact that the former can be more readily infected, since their medium is water, which is so essential for Protozoa. This is most evident in the case of the marine fauna abounding in multicellular hosts differing widely in their bionomics and systematic position. Nevertheless, only three large groups of parasitic Protozoa comprising more than 50 species are encountered in the sea:

Blastodinidae, Gregarinida, and Myxosporidia. In fresh waters the large groups are represented by *Protomastigida, Opalinina, Astomata, Gregarinida,* and Myxosporidia. However, there are twice as many large parasitic groups on land, represented by *Trypanosomidae,* intestinal *Protomastigida, Polymastigida,* and *Hypermastigida* of termites, *Holotricha* and *Entodiniomorpha* of ungulates, *Coccidiida* (especially *Eimeriidae*), *Sarcosporidia, Haemosporidia, Piroplasmoidea,* and *Theileriidea,* and finally *Gregarinida* of insects. What can be the cause of this interesting fact? In our opinion it is due to two main causes. In the first place, the terrestrial fauna of vertebrates, for which all parasites including Protozoa show a special predilection, is much more varied, and the sea is inhabited mainly by fish; while amphibia and some reptiles are added to them in fresh waters, on land all classes of vertebratae, except fish, are abundantly represented. It is noteworthy that such large groups of parasitic Protozoa as *Entodiniomorpha* together with *Holotricha,* inhabiting the alimentary tract of mammals, as well as *Trypanosomes, Coccidia,* and *Haemosporidia* are abundantly represented chiefly in birds and mammals.

Another reason is that another group of potential hosts of Protozoa, namely the class of insects, is represented by a vast number of species differing widely in bionomics and living mainly on the land. In fact, a very substantial proportion of the terrestrial parasitic Protozoa are parasites of insects: more than 200 species of *Polymastigida* and *Hypermastigida,* more than 200 species of Gregarines, and numerous Protomonadida. Since in the active state Protozoa require a liquid or moist environment and cannot endure desiccation, they find suitable conditions on land only when they establish themselves in the alimentary tract, blood, or even tissues of various animals.

Evidence of this relationship is provided by the mode of transmission of Protozoa in terrestrial hosts. In many of them transmission takes place directly by contact between donor and recipient hosts, so that the parasite is transferred from one moist medium to another, independently of the terrestrial environment. Thus in species of *Polymastigida* and *Hypermastigida* from the hindgut of termites the infection is transmitted when termites lick up the liquid faeces protruding from the anus of infected termites. Species of *Entodiniomorpha* from the stomach of ruminants and probably from the alimentary tract of other ungulates are also transferred by contact. It has been demonstrated that neither these ciliates nor the Holotricha associated with them produce cysts, so that infection takes place when the cud regurgitated through the mouth, together with ciliates, is licked off by other hosts, or when they drink from a common trough, &c.

In other Protozoa from terrestrial vertebrate hosts the part of a moist vehicle of transmission is played by intermediate hosts or vectors, which ingest Protozoa into their alimentary tract when sucking the blood of animals infected with blood parasites and transmit them later to other vertebrate hosts when feeding again. Infection is transmitted in this way by *trypanosomes*, Haemosporidia, and by *Piroplasmoidea*. In these cases active parasitic Protozoa from the blood of one host are transferred into the intestine of another, and thence again into the blood of the first host, remaining all the time within the body of their hosts, i.e. in a moist medium. Hence it is evident that of the 1,800 terrestrial parasitic Protozoa no fewer than 700 species are transmitted directly by the contact method or by means of a blood-sucking vector. In the remaining species inhabiting the alimentary tract of terrestrial hosts transmission is effected by the formation of cysts of spores equipped with solid protective membranes, which are practically impermeable by water, such as, for example, the cysts of amoebae and of certain ciliates, the oocysts of *Coccidia* and gregarines, and the spores of Microsporidia. If we turn to the parasitic Protozoa living in fresh and sea water, it will be seen that in both groups only certain Protozoa are transmitted by blood-sucking vectors (thus trypanosomes are transmitted by leeches). All the others are transmitted either by ingestion of their cysts by the host or by migration of their active phases through the surrounding medium. All these facts confirm the correctness of our view regarding the significance of the parasitic mode of life in the occupation of land by the Protozoa.

The hosts of Protozoa. Owing to their minute size and their universal distribution Protozoa have adapted themselves to life in the most varied groups of hosts. In addition to being parasites in all types of Metazoa, down to such small forms as the rotifers (Haplosporidian *Bertramia* in the rotifer *Euchlanis*), some Protozoa parasitize their own kind, i.e. other Protozoa.

As a rule the endoparasitic Metazoa are free of protozoal infection. However, a whole series of cases are known of parasitism of Protozoa in certain parasitic worms. Thus the Microsporidia are apparently not very discriminating in their choice of hosts. Some of their members were discovered in the parenchyma of trematode metacercariae (*Nosema legeri* in *Gymnophallus somateriae* and others), in tapeworms (in the parenchyma and gonads of *Taenia bacillaris*, *Moniezia expansa*, and others), and in nematodes (*Nosema mystacis* in the gonads of *Toxocara mystax* from the cat, *Thelohania reniformis* in *Protospirura muris* in mice, &c.). In these cases there can be no question of an accidental infection of the helminths by Microsporidia encountered normally in its host, since the mammals (for instance cat, mouse) never act as hosts of Microsporidia.

Flagellates are also sometimes hyperparasites of parasitic worms. Thus Hunninen and Wichtermann (1938) discovered that the intestinal flagellate of marine eels, *Hexamita*, is frequently (in 20 out of 35 fish opened) encountered in the uterus, oviducts, and ova of the trematode *Deropristis inflata*—numbering sometimes 20 per ovum.

The flagellate *Histomonas meleagridis*, which is parasitic in the alimentary tract of fowls and turkeys, where it is frequently encountered together with the nematode *Heterakis gallinae*, is particularly interesting in this respect. Graybill and Smith (1920) have shown that this flagellate may not only be a parasite of *Heterakis*, but also frequently penetrates into the ova of this nematode. When discharged with the faeces the ova may serve as a source of infection not only by nematodes but also by the flagellates. The invasion by *Histomonas* leads to serious and even mortal disease in poultry.

Localization of parasitic Protozoa and its effect on their morphology and biology. Protozoa may attack the most diverse organs and tissues of their hosts. However, according to their localization, it is possible to distinguish several large groupings of Protozoa, since the site occupied by them is reflected in their specific organization.

One large group comprises parasites of various cavities, such as the alimentary tract and its appendages (including the ducts of the liver and of the gall-bladder), the urinary bladder, the body cavity, and the circulatory system, i.e. blood-vessels and the heart. The second large groups are constituted by tissue parasites, which may be situated either intra- or extracellularly. Among the intracellular parasites we shall consider separately the category of Protozoa parasitic in other Protozoa. Finally, the large group of ectoparasitic Protozoa must also be considered separately.

However, this division is to a certain extent conditional. In fact very many parasitic Protozoa change their localization—sometimes more than once—during the period of their life spent within their host. Thus, the human malaria parasites commence their life-cycle in the liver cells; later they develop in the erythrocytes of the blood, and their sexual process takes place in the lumen of the stomach of the mosquito; the ookinetes then penetrate the stomach wall of the mosquito and the sporozoites are discharged into its body cavity, whence they find their way into the cells of the salivary glands. Thus the malarial plasmodium is in turn an intracellular tissue and blood parasite (in the vertebrate); then again (in the mosquito) it inhabits first the body cavity and afterwards becomes an intracellular parasite.

Protozoa of the body cavities. As stated above, these include parasites of different kinds of cavities, among which three different types may be distinguished according to their organization and the character of their protozoal population. The first type is represented by the cavity of the alimentary tract, of its appendages, and of the urinary bladder. The second type: the primary or secondary cavity of the body; the third: the cavity of the circulatory blood system.

These cavities differ first of all as regards their relation to the outer world. The cavity of the alimentary tract is merely an extension of the external environment into the body of the organism; this cavity is in broad communication with the outer environment either at one or more frequently at both of its ends; finally, the contents of this cavity resemble in many respects certain bodies of water, namely in the abundance of bacteria and vegetative remains, and in anaerobic conditions it resembles certain oozes; pH in different parts of the alimentary tract also varies, and there is a permanent movement of the contents in one direction as a result of peristalsis of the alimentary tract.

The primary and secondary body of cavities are cavities of the internal medium, which in the great majority of cases have no direct connexion with the outer world. The best evidence of this is the absence in them of any micro-organisms, even in cases where the secondary cavity of the body opens to the exterior by means of the metanephridial ducts. Moreover, the fluids of these cavities do not display the intensive chemical processes of fermentation and fermentative digestion observed in the cavity of the alimentary tract.

Finally, the cavity of the blood system, which reveals some similarity to the body cavity, since it is a cavity of an internal environment, has the following properties. Though cut off from the external environment its cutaneous capillaries approach the surface of the body very closely, while its fluid constituents are in permanent circulation, part of them flowing through canals of a very narrow gauge (the fine capillaries).

The great diversity in the position and contents of the various types of cavities is reflected in a number of morphological and biological differences displayed by the protozoal fauna of the different cavities. These differences affect the methods of infection, the means of leaving the body of the host, and finally certain features of the life-cycle.

Intestinal Protozoa form a very large group comprising not less than half of all the parasitic Protozoa. The first common feature of all intestinal Protozoa is their method of finding their way into the host and of leaving it: penetration is through the mouth and escape is through the anus, except in the case of hosts (Coelenterata, Turbellaria) which have no anal aperture, when the parasites both enter and leave their host through the mouth (*foettingeriidae* ciliates parasitic in anemones).

In the majority of cases the Protozoa enter the alimentary tract in the form of a resting cyst, which hatches in that part of the alimentary tract that provides a suitable habitat. Protozoa also leave the alimentary tract as resting cysts. Encystment is essential for intestinal Protozoa in two respects: first of all in order to survive the critical period outside the body of the animal host, when the parasites are in danger of perishing owing to different hydrochemical conditions of the medium or (in the case of terrestrial hosts) from desiccation. Moreover, the encysted state protects many intestinal Protozoa from the harmful effects of the stomach content of the host. Since the majority of the intestinal Protozoa inhabit sections of the alimentary tract with either a neutral or a weakly alkaline medium, their passage in an active state through the cavity of the stomach with its acid reaction entails a mortal danger for them.

The cysts of many intestinal Protozoa are very resistant and can survive for a long time outside the organism of the host. Thus the cysts of *Chilomastix mesnili* can survive outside the alimentary tract for up to 232 days, the cysts of *Giardia intestinalis* up to 70 days, the cysts of *Entamoeba histolytica* survive in distilled water at a temperature of 12–22° C. up to 210 days, while the cysts of *Balantidium coli* remain viable for at least 60 days in most medium. Oocysts of *Coccidia* (*Eimeria*) can live up to 2 years in a medium rich in oxygen (for instance in 2 per cent. $K_2Cr_2O_7$), but perish rapidly in a putrefying medium, since bacteria consume the oxygen necessary for the normal existence of the oocysts. Furthermore, the presence in the environment of a large number of bacteria has a very harmful effect on the viability of the cysts, since the cysts of *Entamoeba* in faeces diluted with water (not distilled) survive only 35 days.

The large genus *Trichomonas* represents a puzzling exception among the intestinal flagellates, since cyst-formation is quite unknown among them. It is highly probable that trichomonads are transmitted through the mouth in the active vegetative state which remains viable in water for a short time. Apparently the successful passage of the active *Trichomonas* through the acid gastric medium may be explained in the same way as in the case of the numerous *Polymastigida* and *Hypermastigida* from the hindgut of termites. Dogiel (1916 and 1922) has shown that these flagellates possess very peculiar devices, which permit them to pass through the entire alimentary tract of the host right up to the hindgut without resorting to encystment. This is due to so-called mummification. In *Polymastigida* this is effected by the protozoon eliminating all the food from the cytoplasm as well as part of the cytoplasm itself, while the remaining cytoplasm with the nucleus is rounded into a sphere (without encystment) and becomes denser. In *Hypermastigida* the numerous long flagella form a fairly thick matted coat around the body. Dogiel has always observed in the hindgut of the termite *Hodotermes mossambicus*, in addition to the normal individuals, a small percentage of such mummified flagellates. Evidently when a termite licks off the drops of faeces from the anus of another individual, the normal flagellates are digested by the termite, while the mummified ones pass down to the hindgut unharmed and infect the new host.

As stated above, the ophryoscolecid ciliates (*Entodiniomorpha*) living in the stomach of the ruminants are transmitted in the active state by direct contact. In this case the active stages are able to pass to their habitat owing to the fact that the *Ophryoscolecidae* inhabit only the two anterior parts of the stomach of ruminants (the rumen and reticulum) where the medium is slightly alkaline, but not the abomasum with its peptic glands. Consequently the ciliates do not have to pass through an acid medium on their way to the site of their habitation. On the other hand, those *Ophryoscolecidae*, which are daily carried away by the current of food into the intestine, perish in the abomasum, where they are digested.

One of the peculiarities of the bionomics of Protozoa in the lumen of the alimentary tract is their existence in a stream of food moving always in the same direction. Owing to this the intestinal Protozoa must be able to attach themselves as firmly as possible in the intestine, so as not to be ejected out of the alimentary tract or be carried to a part of the intestine unsuitable for them. As a result, the intestinal parasites, like many ectoparasites, have developed various organoids and methods of attachment which are absent

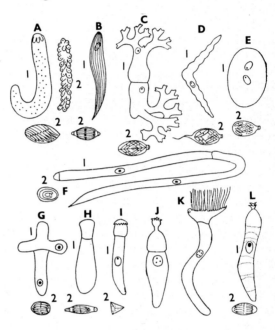

FIG. 309. Various forms of gregarines (1) with their attachment apparatus
and oocysts (2).

(A) Schizocystis gregarinoides; (B) Monocystis striata; (C) Pterospora ramificata;
(D) Urospora travisiae; (E) Diplodina gonadipertha; (F) Porospora gigantea;
(G) Enterocystis ensis; (H) Gregarina blattarum; (I) Tetraedrospora sciarae;
(J) Corycella armata; (K) Grebniciella gracilis; (L) Taeniocystis mira. (After
various authors, from Dogiel, 1951.)

as a rule in blood, tissue, or intracellular Protozoa, as well as in those inhabiting the body cavity. These organoids of attachment are usually represented by hooks and suckers.

Among the intestinal Protozoa hooks are present in the gregarines (Fig. 309) and ciliates. Among the gregarines hooks, and processes of the epimerite resembling them, are formed mainly in the suborder Polycystidea, which are widespread especially in the alimentary tract of arthropods. They take the form either of a circlet of typical hooks, or of leaflets or of palmate leaves encircling the epimerite, which are inserted into the intestinal epithelium of the host. In other cases the hooks are elongated into a bundle of long filaments, inserted between the cells of the intestinal epithelium.

In *Siedleckia*, belonging to the order *Schizogregarinida*, Dogiel (1907) described also at the anterior end a circlet of clip-like hooks with which the parasite surrounds the tip of one epithelial cell.

The astomatous ciliates from the alimentary tract of *Oligochaeta* also possess well-developed hooks; thus, for example, in some species of the genus *Radiophrya*, on the ventral side of the anterior end of the body there is one mobile hook which serves for implantation into the epithelium.

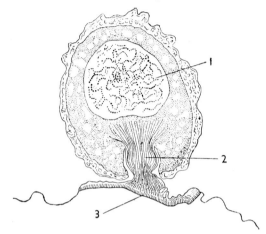

FIG. 310. Ectoparasitic *Oodinium frittilaria* (Dinoflagellata Blastodinidae) from skin of tunicate *Oikopleura*.

1, nucleus of the parasite; 2, stalk; 3, attachment disk. (After Chatton, 1920*b*.)

Attachment by hooks is very similar to that by means of a stalk (Fig. 310), a method especially widespread among intestinal flagellates of the orders Polymastigida and Dinoflagellata. In *Oxymonas*, *Pyrsonympha*, and others the anterior end of their body is prolonged in the form of a long spear-shaped process which wedges itself into the wall of the alimentary tract of the host. Among the intestinal Dinoflagellates, species of the genus *Haplozoon*, a parasite on polychaetes, have a stalk. At the anterior end of *Haplozoon* there is a small aperture through which protrudes a bundle of long filaments, resembling pseudopodia, which penetrate deeply into the intestinal epithelium (Dogiel, 1910). Furthermore, *Haplozoon* has also at the anterior end a mobile chitinous stylet, which can thrust itself into the epithelium, or be withdrawn into the body of the parasite.

Finally, in some gregarines the epimerite extends in the form of an immobile spear thrust into the epithelium, i.e. it also becomes a stalk. A modification of this type is represented by a kind of anchoring attachment in which the end of the body serving for attachment penetrates into the tissue of the host, and then becomes inflated, thereby ensuring a very stable and, as it were, irreversible attachment to the host. The epimerite of some gregarines undergoes such a modification.

Suckers (Fig. 311) are known in a number of intestinal flagellates and ciliates. Thus in the genus *Giardia* the ventral part of the body is concave,

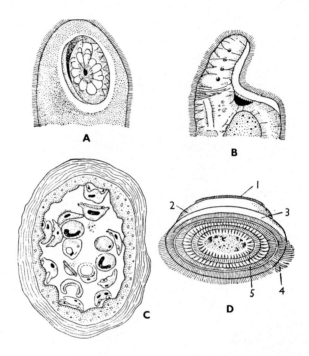

FIG. 311. Sucker-like attachment apparatus of parasitic ciliates.

(*A*), (*B*) *Haptophrya michiganensis* (Astomata); general view and sagittal section through anterior end of the body; (*C*) section through ureters of pike *Esox niger* with *Trichodina renicola* attached to the walls; (*D*) general view of this ciliate. 1, adoral spiral of cilia; 2, body of animal; 3, sucking disk; 4, lower circlet of cilia; 5, circlet of hooks. (After various authors, from Dogiel, 1951.)

forming a small depression encircled by a supporting filament. By means of this depression the parasites attach themselves temporarily to the ends of intestinal cells directed towards the lumen of the intestine. In many astomatous ciliates (*Radiophrya*, *Mrazekiella*, and others) one side of the body, which is concave and spoon-shaped, functions as a sucker. A series of longitudinal cuticular ribs, evidently aiding the attachment, run along this side of the ectoplasm of the ciliate. A sucker provided with fibrillar structures is also present in the ciliates *Hysterocineta* and *Ptychostomum*, parasitic in the alimentary tract and mantle cavity of some molluscs and the gut of oligochaetes. The most highly developed suckers are found in *Trichodina* and in the peritrichous ciliate *Polycycla* discovered by Poljanskij (1951) in the intestine of the holothurian *Cucumaria* in the Sea of Japan, the lower end of the body of which is taken up by a powerful sucker, bordered by a thick frame of elongated lamellated chitinous segments (see Fig. 285).

There are also simpler methods of attachment not requiring the development of any special organoids (Fig. 312). Thus in the gregarine *Ancora sagittata* from the alimentary tract of *Capitella* the body forms a pair of cross-bars, which enable the parasite to retain a hold in the lumen of the

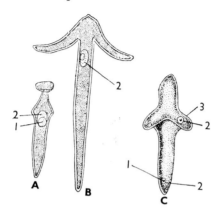

FIG. 312. Gregarines with appendages in shape of cross-bars.

(*A*), (*B*) *Ancora sagittata*, young and adult individual; (*C*) *Enterocystis ensis*, paired individuals: 1, karyosome; 2, nucleus; 3, primite or anterior individual of pair. ((*A*) and (*B*) after Watson, 1922, (*C*) after Cvetkov, 1926.)

alimentary tract without any direct attachment to its walls. The interesting gregarine *Enterocystis ensis* (Fig. 312) is retained in the intestine in the same manner, but in this case only the anterior segment of the conjugating couple of gregarines, or the primite, forms on the sides of the body a pair of 'elbows', whereas the posterior partner, the satellite, retains the vermiform shape typical of gregarines.

Finally, an excellent method for remaining inside the alimentary tract is used by the young stages of growth of many gregarines, which penetrate completely into the intestinal cell and protrude from it into the lumen of the gut only when their attachment epimerite is fully developed.

Apart from the development of organoids of attachment in some intestinal Protozoa another feature developed as a response to their localization in the gut, namely an extension of the body in length accompanied by a tendency for segmentation of the body into parts by transverse plasmatic septa. Such forms are represented by some gregarines. In the first place, in the majority of intestinal gregarines the body is divided by a septum into an anterior, short protomerite and a posterior, long deutomerite, which contains the nucleus. In some species this process goes further, and the deutomerite is divided by less pronounced septa into a series of metameric parts. To such forms belong *Taeniocystis mira*

(Fig. 313), certain species of *Merogregarina* from the alimentary tract of crabs, and also the interesting form, *Tricystis*, found in crabs of the Sea of Japan. The same type of structure is found in the peculiar member of *Hypermastigida*, *Cyclonympha strobila*, from the gut of termites. The body of *Cyclonympha* is divided by a septum supporting the nucleus into a kind of protomerite and deutomerite, while the deutomerite is further

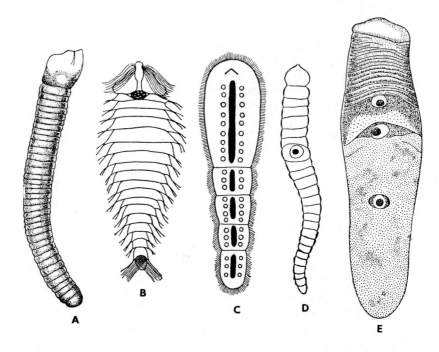

FIG. 313. Extended and segmented shape of body of many intestinal Protozoa.

(*A*) *Haplozoon* (Dinoflagellata); (*B*) *Cyclonympha strobila* (*Hypermastigina*); (*C*) *Radiophrya* (Astomata); (*D*) *Taeniocystis mira* (Gregarinida); (*E*) *Tricystis plicata* (Gregarinida). (After various authors, from Dogiel, 1951.)

subdivided into segments by rings of flagella. In the parasitic flagellates *Haplozoon* and a number of astomatous ciliates this type of structure is associated with the multiplication by constrictions of terminal buds or reproductive cells. In the vegetative stage the transverse septa in all the above-named forms apparently protect the long, thin body from rupture.

Another characteristic feature of intestinal Protozoa is their tendency to form in some hosts, especially in herbivorous ones, complexes varying in the specific composition and abundant in the numbers of individuals, giving rise to characteristic parasitocoenoses of Protozoa in such hosts. They are exceptionally pronounced in the rumen of the ruminants, in the large intestine of the perissodactyls, and in the hindgut of termites. Thus the rumen of every adult cattle is literally packed with innumerable ciliates.

The number of them is so large that 1 gm. of chyme from the rumen of an ox frequently contains up to one million ciliates, represented by up to 93 varieties, or 'forms' belonging to no fewer than 45 good species. The majority of these ciliates belong to the family *Ophryoscolecidae* (*Entodiniomorpha*) but 12 forms belong to the Isotrichidae and *Bütschliidae* (*Holotricha*). The number of forms encountered in one individual host may reach 25–30. Furthermore, 4 species of flagellates inhabit the rumen of cattle.

The number of forms of ciliates reported in sheep is 35, from reindeer 23, from camels 24, &c. Such assemblages of Protozoa are characteristic also of wild ruminants, such as antelopes, wild African buffaloes (up to 25 different ciliates), &c.

In perissodactyls similar assemblages are encountered in the large intestine and caecum of horses, where there are 1 species of flagellate and 53 species of ciliates of the family *Cycloposthiidae* (*Entodiniomorpha*), several families of *Holotricha*, and even four species of suctorians of the genus *Allantosoma*, first discovered by Gassovskij (1918), that have adapted themselves to parasitism on intestinal ciliates.

The majority of ciliates of the above-mentioned assemblages feed on particles of the food of their hosts, i.e. scraps of grass, while others feed on each other.

Thus the alimentary tract of ungulates contains a whole small world (parasitocoenosis) of Protozoa which the remote ancestors of modern ungulates obtained from watering places as free-living inhabitants of these basins, and these adapted themselves to existence in the alimentary tract of this group of mammals, and underwent corresponding changes. This world is composed mainly of ciliates, which not only become adapted to their new ecological niche, but evolved there a great number of new species, and had even unintentionally carried away with them some of their parasites, for example the Suctoria, which had formerly parasitized on free-living Ciliata, and now became hyperparasites of intestinal parasites.

The large group of 'thermitophilic' intestinal Mastigophora reveal as complex a pattern and extremely complicated host-parasite relationships. It is surprising how some two dozen species of Mastigophora, represented by numerous individuals, find enough room within the insignificant space of 5–6 cubic millimetres provided by the hindgut of a single termite. Smaller and less characteristic complexes of Protozoa are encountered in the hindgut of sea urchins and in the rectum of frogs.

Another characteristic of intestinal Protozoa is the tendency to increase the size of their body. The majority of free-living ciliates are 50–100 μ long (a few Heterotricha reach 1–2 mm.). Among *Entodiniomorpha* from the alimentary tract of ungulates a whole series of forms measure 200–300 and even 500 μ in length (*Eudiplodinium neglectum giganteum*); *Elephantophilus* from the intestine of the elephant reaches almost 300 μ, while *Pycnothrix*, an intestinal parasite of hyraxes, even reaches 3 mm. in length.

The same pattern is observed in Mastigophora from the alimentary tract of termites. Their ancestral forms were doubtless the trichomonads (*Trichomonas*) allied to those of many vertebrates. The length of typical trichomonads (among them some species from the intestines of termites) fluctuates within the range known also for a few free-living Polymastigida, viz. 15–20 μ.

However, under the conditions of life in the alimentary tract of termites the modified descendants of these flagellates reach a length up to 70 μ (*Gigantomonas*), while their more distant descendants—Hypermastigida—even a length of 250 μ (*Joenia*) and 450 μ (some *Trichonympha*). Gregarines from the alimentary tract of the lobster (*Porospora*) may also be longer than 1 mm. in length. Apparently the unlimited amount of readily digestible food, especially of vegetable nature, that is available for the parasites, frequently leads to an increase of the size of intestinal Protozoa.

Finally, the last general feature characterizing the intestinal Protozoa is a tendency to complicate their structure. It may be emphasized that none of the free-living ciliates and flagellates have developed such complex structures of their systems of locomotion, digestion, and support as those of *Entodiniomorpha* and *Hypermastigida*. The blood parasites, i.e. Protozoa inhabiting the blood-system of vertebrates, form a much smaller and less varied group than the previous one. It comprises first of all the numerous trypanosomids inhabiting the blood-plasma and some of the tissue cells; then the entire order Haemosporidia and the group of *Piroplasmidea* of unknown origin. Blood Protozoa differ markedly from intestinal ones in many morphological and biological features.

While the intestinal Protozoa are characterized by a tendency to increase their size, the blood parasites belong to the minutest Protozoa. This is partly due to the fact that the majority of them are endoglobular parasites within the blood-cells of their host—a factor which naturally limits their size. However, even trypanosomes moving freely in the blood do not usually exceed 25–35 μ in length. Only *Trypanosoma ingens* (70–120 μ) from antelopes, some trypanosomes from the blood of elasmobranch fishes, and some species from reptiles (e.g. *T. grayi* from crocodiles) reach a length of 70 or even 100 μ.

The malaria parasites measure 5–10 μ, while the piroplasms are even smaller: 1·5–4 μ.

Again in contrast to intestinal Protozoa, blood parasites usually have a very simple structure. This applies not only to blood Sporozoa—belonging to a class, with a widespread simplification of the organization—but also to blood flagellates, such as *Trypanosoma* and *Trypanoplasma*.

Finally, the almost complete absence of reserve nutrient substances in the body of blood parasites is a feature distinguishing them from intestinal Protozoa, which have abundant accumulations of glycogen and fat formed in the cytoplasm. In very small amounts such reserves are apparently present in the macrogamonts of Haemosporidia, but they are practically absent in trypanosomes, trypanoplasms, and piroplasms. This absence may be partly connected with the specific nutrient medium represented by blood.

The biology of blood parasites is determined by the character of their localization in a closed blood-system with no open communication with either the outer medium or the inner organs. This circumstance affects two important moments in their life-cycle: the method of penetration of the parasite into the organism of the host and that of its exit from it. Owing to a complete absence of communication with the outer world, the process of transmission of the infection from one host to another takes place by means of a special category of hosts called vectors, which are represented only by some kind of blood-sucking invertebrates. When sucking the blood of an infected host, the vector takes up into its alimentary tract, together with the ingested blood, the parasite. The vector thus becomes infected, and the infection is either restricted to its alimentary tract, or it passes also into other organs, including sometimes the sex organs. The infection is transmitted further either by the same individual vector or, as in certain ticks, by transovarial transmission of the infection to the next generation of the vector, through the bites of which the infection is finally transmitted into the blood of the vertebrate host. The vectors of blood parasites are most commonly blood-sucking insects: mosquitoes, sand-flies, and bugs (*Triatoma megista* and other species in the case of Chagas' disease in man). Blood-sucking ticks are vectors for *Piroplasmoidea*, while leeches of the family Ichthyobdellidae and *Glossosiphonidae* serve almost exclusively as vectors for trypanosomes of aquatic animals, i.e. fish and amphibia. Thus the piercing proboscis of insects and other blood-suckers can be compared to a syringe which injects the parasite directly into the cutaneous capillaries of the vertebrate hosts.

The transmission of the parasites takes place directly from the body of its vertebrate host into that of its vector and back, so that the blood Protozoa do not pass any stage of their life-cycle in the external environment outside the body of one of their hosts. This circumstance is closely connected with another important phenomenon in their cycle, namely encystment is absent in blood flagellates, while in Haemosporidia the stage of spore formation which is characteristic of all the Sporozoa is eliminated. This demonstrates the great influence exerted by the peculiarities of the localization on the life-cycle of parasites.

There are not many parasites of the primary body cavity (coelome, schizocoel) and they are encountered almost exclusively in invertebrates, in spite of the great opportunities which are apparently offered to them by the voluminous body cavity of vertebrates.

Among the aquatic animals they are represented chiefly by cavitary gregarines; among the terrestrial blood-suckers there are certain stages of development, for example the sporozoites of the Sporozoa. Occasionally ciliates are encountered in the coelome (in Chaetognatha, in the larvae of insects, *Lambornella*), as well as amoebae (*Paramoeba* in Chaetognatha); finally, the schizocoel of marine copepods is inhabited by about twenty peculiarly modified dinoflagellates, and some certain species of Microsporidia (*Glugea* and others) are encountered in the body cavity of some insects and fish. However, these Microsporidia are not specific for the body cavity, but are disseminated also in the tissues.

Cavitary Protozoa do not possess any general specific characteristics. Their sizes vary from very minute (Microsporidia) to fairly large. The shape of the body varies from the compact and spherical, as in the cavitary gregarines of certain insects (*Diplocystis*) and worms (*Choanocystis* from the rainworm *Pheretima*), to the extraordinary ramified shape found in *Urospora maldaneorum* from the marine annelids and *Aikinetocystis singularis* from the coelome of the rainworm *Eutyphaeus*.

The method of penetration of cavitary parasites into the host is apparently the same everywhere, viz. through the mouth. This has been definitely proved for some forms (gregarines, Microsporidia) and can be assumed for the others.

The infective stages leave the host from different places. In some cases (some Polychaeta, for instance, apparently in *Lagis koreni*, and in Gephyrei) the parasites, namely cysts with spores of the gregarine *Urospora*, emerge through the natural efferent apertures of the host, through its metanephridia. In rainworms cavitary parasites, including the cysts of gregarines, are driven out of the seminal vesicles through the apertures in the intersegmental septa together with various excreta into the posterior segments of the body, which are periodically discarded and rot away, thereby liberating the spores of the parasite. The same mechanism takes place in apodal holothurians, for instance in *Chiridota pellucida*, which easily discards the posterior third of its body, thus releasing from the body cavity into the exterior the cysts of the gregarine *Urospora chiridotae*. Finally, parasites frequently emerge only at the death and decomposition of their hosts. Thus cysts of the gregarine *Diplocystis* from the body cavity of *Phryganea grandis* are released only when the female caddis-flies lay their eggs in water and themselves perish when they fall into it. In the water the spores from the cysts are eaten by the larvae of *Phryganea* together with their food. Caterpillars of silkworms (Bombyx), overfilled with the spores of *Nosema bombycis*, perish, and the spores from their body fall on the mulberry leaves and are ingested together with the food by other caterpillars of this moth. The cysts of another microsporidian, *Glugea*, from the body cavity and tissues of young fish, are also liberated after the death of the host, since the fry are not long-lived.

There are only a few cases of parasitism of Protozoa in the urinary bladder and in the cavity of the sexual glands. The urinary bladder of fish frequently harbours plasmodia of Myxosporidia. The genera *Myxidum*,

Ceratomyxa, Leptotheca, and *Hoferellus* are most frequently encountered in the urinary bladder. Furthermore, ciliates of the genus *Trichodina* are also found in the bladder of fish; they commonly occur on the skin and gills of different fish, but now and then settle in the urinary bladder. Apparently Myxosporidia find their way into the urinary bladder through the alimentary tract, the blood-system, and then the kidneys, but there can be no doubt

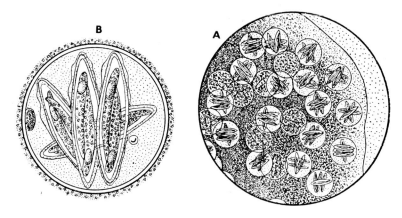

FIG. 314. *Eimeria sardinae* (Coccidia) from the Far East pilchard.

(*A*) oocyst; (*B*) part of testis of pilchard infected with numerous oocysts. (After Wenyon, 1926.)

that *Trichodina* became differentiated from the cutaneous species of the same genus, having penetrated through the outer urinary apertures into the urinary bladder, and undergone modifications under the new conditions of existence.

Parasitism in the genital system is a rare phenomenon among Protozoa. Such are, for instance, the flagellates *Trichomonas vaginalis* in man and *Trichomonas foetus* from the vagina and uterus of cattle, and allied forms of the trypanoplasm *Cryptobia* in the genital system of snails and leeches; the gregarines *Diplodina gonadipertha* parasitic in the sexual glands of the holothurian *Cucumaria frondosa*, the ciliates *Orchitophrya stellarum* from the testis of starfish, and certain others. In these cases the infective stages escape through the sexual aperture and this process is sometimes associated with the sexual cycle of the host. Such is undoubtedly the method of liberation of the oocysts of *Eimeria sardinae* (Fig. 314), a coccidian which frequently produces mass infection of the testes in several species of herrings. This form is interesting also in that its parasitism is restricted to one sex of the host, namely male (as in *Orchitophrya*).

The Protozoal fauna of the cavity of the gall-bladder, in spite of the genetic and topographical association of this organ with the alimentary tract, resembles most closely that of the urinary bladder. Evidently, the cause of this is to be sought in the similarity of the histological structure and of the contents (in both cases a liquid medium free of mechanical admixtures) of both these organs.

As in the case of the urinary bladder, the most frequent and numerous inhabitants of the gall-bladder are the Myxosporidia, which are largely represented there by the same genera as those in the urinary bladder.

According to Kudo (1954), scores of species of Myxosporidia of the genera *Ceratomyxa*, *Leptotheca*, *Myxoproteus*, *Sinuolinea*, *Myxidium*, *Myxobilatus*, and others, are encountered in the gall-bladder as well as in the urinary bladder and canals of the kidneys of marine and freshwater fish. The Myxosporidia of the urinary and gall-bladders are characterized, in contrast to the allied forms living in the tissues, by the formation of mobile plasmo-podia equipped with pseudopodia.

Apart from Myxosporidia, some intestinal Protozoa sometimes find their way and establish themselves in the cavity of the gall-bladder. In fish the gall-bladder is inhabited by the flagellate *Octomitus truttae* (Polymasti-gida).

The parasites of the cavities considered by us in this section either swim freely in the cavital liquid (trichomonads, some Myxosporidia) or adhere to the epithelial walls, thereby coming into closer contact with the tissues of the host.

Tissue and intracellular parasites. Protozoal tissue parasites come into the closest contact with the cells of different tissues of their host. They are represented by many Myxosporidia and Microsporidia and all the Sarco-sporidia. The ciliates (*Ichtyophthirius*, *Amphileptus branchiarum*) or Mas-tigophora (*Histomonas* and others) adopt tissue parasitism much more rarely. The Cnidosporidia in most cases assume the shape of rounded or elongated cysts, or they infiltrate the tissues, acquiring a shape corresponding to that of fissures and cavities between the tissue elements.

It is interesting that tissue parasites invade even such dense tissues as cartilage and bone (e.g. the myxosporidian *Lentospora*, which attacks the cartilages of young Salmonidae; Fig. 315). On the other hand, nervous tissue is also invaded, as, for example, the bundles of nerve fibres of trout by the microsporidian *Myxobolus neurobius*, and the peripheral nerves of the fish *Lophius* by the microsporidian *Nosema lophii*.

Tissue parasites find their way into the organism of their terrestrial hosts through the mucous membranes of the alimentary tract, and of their aquatic hosts either similarly, especially through the epithelium of the gills (in fish), or through the integuments (ciliates). In those cases when the young stages do not remain at the site of penetration, as in the case of gill microsporidia and in ciliates from the skin of aquatic animals, the infective stages ap-parently reach their place of final localization through the circulatory system. The ultimate destination of the parasites may be muscles (in some of the Myxosporidia and all Sarcosporidia), the sub-cutaneous connective tissue (Myxosporidia, ciliates), and the parenchyma of the kidneys (Myxosporidia) as well as other organs.

Many tissue parasites are intracellular. However, it is very difficult to distinguish them as a group since, on the one hand, many members of other

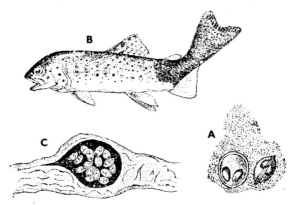

FIG. 315. Myxosporidia of fish.

(*A*) section of plasmodium of *Lentospora cerebralis* with two spores; (*B*) trout suffering from 'twist disease', curvature of the spine and darkening of posterior part of its body as a result of infection by *Lentospora*; (*C*) cyst *Myxobolus neurobius* in nerve of fish. (After Dogiel, 1951.)

categories begin their life with an intracellular stage, while others (many blood parasites) remain within the blood-cells practically all their life. On the other hand, some intracellular Protozoa (for instance, Coccidia inhabiting the liver and intestinal walls) are biologically much closer to cavitary and particularly intestinal parasites. Each intracellular parasite usually inhabits the cells of one definite tissue.

The intracellular parasites are most frequently harboured by cells of various epithelia: of the alimentary tract, of the kidneys, liver, peritoneal epithelium, &c. Such a localization is characteristic of the majority of Coccidiida, which are parasitic in many invertebrates and vertebrates.

Some Coccidia are not strictly confined to one tissue but, like *Klossia mesnili*, parasitic in the moth *Tineola biselliella*, may be encountered in the cells of different organs and tissues such as the fat bodies, Malpighian tubes, muscles, and hypoderm. In others, on the contrary, the localization is even more narrowly restricted. Thus their cycle of development may take place inside the nucleus of a host cell (*Cyclospora caryolytica*, Fig. 316, from the intestinal epithelium of moles, *Caryospora simplex* from the intestinal epithelium of *Vipera aspis*). Many Microsporidia are also intracellular.

The species of *Leishmania* are localized in the cells of the reticulo-endothelial system. This flagellate is also interesting because it clearly demonstrates the simplifying effect of intracellular parasitism on Protozoa. In fact, in its intracellular stage *Leishmania* loses the most essential characteristic of Mastigophora, namely its free flagellum, of which there remains only the basal granule and the kinetoplast associated with it. However, when leishmanias enter the alimentary tract of the sand-fly vector together with the blood, they assume there the leptomonad form, producing a flagellum and moving about in the contents of the insect gut.

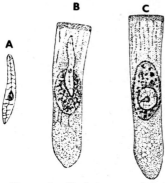

FIG. 316. *Cyclospora caryolytica* (Coccidia) from the intestinal epithelium of the mole.

(*A*) sporozoite; (*B*) its penetration into nucleus of cell; (*C*) schizont in nucleus of cell. (After Schaudinn, 1900.)

The above-mentioned simplification of the organization is displayed in all Coccidia and Microsporidia by the loss of all those organoids with which freely moving parasitic Protozoa are equipped.

The last group of intracellular parasites to be considered is represented by some forms encountered in the female sexual cells of various animals. A number of Myxosporidia are regularly parasitic in the eggs (roe) of fish, which are destroyed by them. They are *Henneguya oviperda* in the ovaries of the pike, and certain species of *Myxobolus* from the roe of roach. Among Myxosporidia, *Nosema bombycis* attacks, in addition to other tissues, also the gonads of silkworms. Slightly infected caterpillars survive and produce fertile butterflies, whose eggs are already infected by the spores of *Nosema*, and therefore serve to disseminate the most dangerous disease of silkworms—pebrine.

The motile stages of development (club-shaped forms) of Piroplasmoidea penetrate into the eggs of the female tick-vector of piroplasmosis, infecting the next generation of this tick and facilitating the spread of the disease among the ungulate hosts. Parasitic Dinoflagellata—*Chytriodinium roseum, Ch. parasiticum,* and others—often choose as their habitat the eggs of copepods floating in the plankton (infection probably occurs while the ova are still within the egg-sac in the body of the mother), and completely destroy the contents of the eggs (Dogiel, 1907).

The ciliate *Protophrya ovicola* (Astomata) lives in the uterus of *Littorina*; while single individuals may find their way into the ova of the molluscs between the ootheca and the ovum, so that the embryo emerging later from the ovum is already infected by the ciliates. The same may be said of *Histomonas.*

Protozoal parasites of Protozoa. There are now so many examples of this category that it deserves a special consideration. However, we can only consider here the most interesting cases of such parasitism, and those where the taxonomic position of the parasite is well known. As in the case of Protozoa parasitic in Metazoa, this small category contains both ectoparasites and endoparasites.

The ectoparasitic flagellate *Bodo perforans*, which possesses two unequal flagella, is encountered on the common saprozoic inhabitant of stagnant water, *Chilomonas paramecium*. This *Bodo* possesses a long, fine rostellum by which it attaches itself to the anterior end of *Chilomonas* at the base of its flagella. Although the length of the *Chilomonas* itself does not exceed 20–40 μ, it sometimes harbours 2–3 *Bodo*.

D. Sokolov (1933) found numerous flagellates, named by him *Euglena parasitica*, attached to colonies of *Volvox* by an anterior conical process.

Several species of the peculiar apostomatous ciliates of the genus *Phtoro-phrya*, which are parasitic on ciliates of the genera *Gymnodinioides* and *Vampyrophrya*, are of special interest. Young individuals (phoronts) of *Phtorophrya* settle down on the cysts of their hosts, become invested in their own cyst membrane, and then emerge from it and penetrate into the cyst of their host, where they proceed to devour the body of the *Gymno-dinioides* by means of their protruding mouth until its cyst is emptied. Then the parasite, occupying its host's place, grows considerably and divides successively into eight young phoronts, which escape from the cyst of their host in search of new victims. According to Chatton and Lwoff (1935), among the characteristics of *Phtorophrya* distinguishing it from the non-parasitic ciliates is the ability of the pharynx of *Phtorophrya* to evert itself through the mouth, forming a sucking protuberance on the body, and also the occurrence inside the cytoplasm of *Phtorophrya* of 4–5 nematocysts, capable of turning inside-out as in *Polykrikos*. The cysts of the host of this ciliate, *Gymnodinioides*, are attached to the legs of the amphipod *Coro-phium*, so that *Phtorophrya* is a hyperparasite.

Members of the genus *Hypocoma*, which are found on marine Peritricha (*Zoothamnium*) and on Suctoria, are also ectoparasites of ciliates. The parasites attach themselves firmly to the body of their host and gradually suck out all its contents by means of a special proboscis.

A number of suctorians attach themselves on other Suctoria or on *Peritricha* and *Heterotricha* and suck them out (*Pseudogemma*, *Tokophrya quadripartita*, and others).

The biology of suctorians of the genus *Allantosoma* (Fig. 317), discovered by Gassovskij (1918) in the alimentary tract of the horse, and studied in detail by Strelkov (1939), is still more interesting. This suctorian is encountered in the lumen of the intestine in a free state, but frequently it adheres by its tentacles to the body of the intestinal ciliates of the horse, including the Entodiniomorpha (*Cycloposthium*) and *Holotricha*. *Allantosoma* has a sausage-shaped body provided with two bundles of tentacles, each consisting of 1–6 tentacles (in different species) situated at opposite ends. *Allantosoma* is the only genus of Suctoria which has established itself in the alimentary tract of vertebrates as a parasite (hyperparasite) of parasitic ciliates.

Examples of endoparasitism in other Protozoa are also fairly numerous.

Among Mastigophora our attention is first of all drawn to a whole series of parasitic Dinoflagellata inhabiting other Protozoa. Up to the present parasitic dinoflagellates have been recorded in such minute hosts as the marine Tintinnoinea (genus *Duboscquella*), according to Chatton (1920*a*, *b*), in

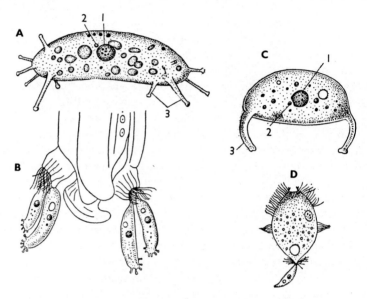

FIG. 317. Suctoria parasitic intestinal ciliates of horse.

(*A*) *Allantosoma intestinalis*; (*B*) *A. cucumis* on caudal bundle of *Cycloposthium*; (*C*) *A. dicorniger*; (*D*) *A. brevicorniger*, attached to *Blepharazoum* (the larger ciliate). 1, macronucleus; 2, micronucleus; 3, sucking tentacles. (After Gassovskij, 1918.)

dinoflagellates themselves (genus *Coccidinium*, according to Chatton and Biecheler, 1934, in *Peridinium* and others), and finally in various Radiolaria, genus *Merodinium* (Chatton, 1920*a*, *b*).

Doflein noted as early as 1909 that *Stentor coeruleus* frequently contains a multitude of very small Mastigamoebae; furthermore, if the infection is heavy, the infected ciliate shrivels and even bursts.

There is also evidence of hyperparasitism of amoebae in the body of different *Zelleriella* (Fig. 318), *Cepedea*, and *Opalina*, in the cytoplasm of which minute amoebae of 5–14 μ diameter, belonging to the genus *Entamoeba*, are often encountered in large numbers. Amoebae have also been encountered inside the cysts formed by the opalinids. This circumstance explains the ease with which amoebae are disseminated and the high degree of infection: in some individuals of frogs 100 per cent. of the opalinids were found to be infected. Carini and Reichenow (1935) suggested that this amoeba is *Entamoeba ranarum*, a parasite in the alimentary tract of amphibia, which might possibly pass over to parasitism on opalinids.

Protozoa are most frequently parasitized by Myxosporidia and Haplosporidia, which are quite often hyperparasites of parasitic Protozoa. Thus four species of *Nosema* have been described from the Myxosporidian *Ceratomyxa*, from *Balantidium* of frogs, and from two species of gregarines.

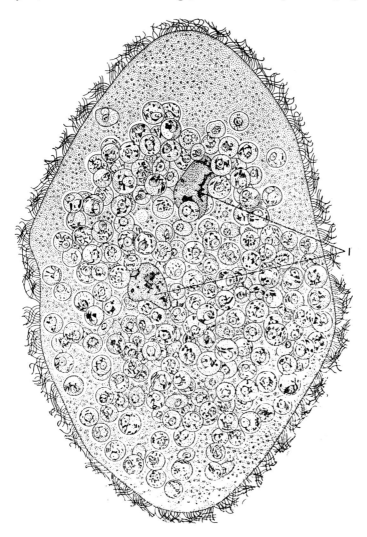

FIG. 318. *Zellerie la* (Opalinata) infected with amoebae *Entamoeba ranarum*. The entire cytoplasm is filled with encysted amoebae. I, nucleus of *Zelleriella*. (After Carini and Reichenow, 1935.)

Dogiel (1906*b*) described in the gregarine *Urospora chiridotae* the parasite *Hyalosphaera gregarinicola*, which he referred to the Coccidia. Haplosporidia of the family Metchnikovellidae have been repeatedly recorded in different gregarines from annelids. These parasites form in the body of

T t

the gregarines minute, mostly elongated cysts containing several uni-nucleate bodies.

Among the ciliates only Suctoria are capable of endoparasitism in other Protozoa. These are represented mainly by members of the genera *Sphaero-phrya* and *Endosphaera* (Fig. 319).

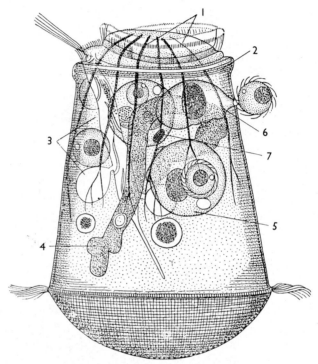

FIG. 319. *Opisthonecta* (Peritricha) infected with *Endosphaera* (Suctoria).

1, longitudinal myonemes; 2, sphincters of *Opisthonecta*; 3, contractile vacuole; 4, macronucleus; 5, *Endosphaera* with internal ciliated embryo; 6, *Endosphaera* releasing embryo; 7, micronucleus of host. (After Lynch and Noble, 1931.)

Metčnikov (1864) traced the whole developmental cycle of *Sphaerophrya* from its emergence as a ciliated embryo from one individual host, namely *Paramecium*, to its penetration into another individual. *Sphaerophrya* still retains the characteristics of Suctoria in that during part of its cycle it has tentacles radiating in all directions. The genus *Endosphaera*, encountered inside different Vorticellidae, has been considerably modified owing to its endoparasitism, having completely lost its tentacles. Its endoparasitic stage has the appearance of perfect globes, with a spherical macronucleus, micro-nucleus, and one contractile vacuole. Inside these spheres there arise by endogenous budding ciliated embryos, which leave the body of the mother and that of the host and serve to spread the infection.

Ectoparasitic Protozoa. Ectoparasitism represents, as it were, the first phase of the modifications produced in the organism of Protozoa by adaptation to a parasitic mode of life. The position of many ectoparasitic forms is doubtful, as it is sometimes difficult to tell whether they are parasites or merely epibionts, which do not enter into any trophic relations with their host. We propose to consider only those ectoparasites in which transition to parasitism has resulted in some modifications of either their structure or their life-cycle.

In Protozoa the transition to ectoparasitism might have proceeded in two main ways. Some parasitic forms are derived directly from free-living ones. They may retain this free-living mode of existence even after establishing themselves on their hosts, or they might, under the effect of the new conditions, pass over to an attached state.

In other cases the transition to a parasitic state is preceded by a sessile mode of life, when there is only a change of the object to which they are attached, viz. a dead substratum is replaced by a living one.

Illustrations of the first type of change to ectoparasitism are especially numerous among the ciliates. Thus, for example, among species of the genus *Chilodonella* some are free-living, others are ectoparasitic commensals of various crustaceans (*Orchestia*, *Asellus*, and others). Among these commensals *C. porcellionis*, which lives on the gills of the terrestrial wood-louse *Porcellio*, deserves special attention (Dogiel and Fursenko, 1921). Finally, the species *C. cyprini*, from the gills of fish, become a true ectoparasite, feeding at the expense of its host. We have observed this ciliate inserting its rod-shaped pharyngeal apparatus into the epithelium of the gill fringes. *C. cyprini* does not exhibit any special adaptations to parasitism, but the shape of its body, which is slightly concave on the ventral surface and convex on the dorsal side, with rows of cilia on the former, facilitates the transition of species of this genus to an ectoparasitic state. *C. cyprini* can adhere closely, by its convex ventral surface, to the surface of the gills, so as not to be washed away by the current of water.

The ciliates of the order *Thigmotricha*, which are commonly encountered on the gills of bivalve molluscs, present a whole series of transitions from the free-living state to ectoparasitism. Beginning from the typical Thigmotricha, which hardly touch their hosts with their thigmotactic cilia and feed on detritus, there are a number of transitions to such modified forms as *Sphenophrya*, which are devoid of cilia for most of their life and adhere closely to the body of their host (Fig. 147).

Similar ecological series of forms illustrating the transition to ectoparasitism may be constructed for sessile forms: for instance, for the peritrichous ciliates. Thus *Opercularia plicatilis* and *Epistylis plicatilis* attach themselves to various under-water objects, *O. stenostoma* settles on aquatic asellids and on water insects, i.e. on mobile objects but without much discrimination. On the other hand, *Epistylis cambari* chooses as its site of habitation the gills of the American crayfish *Cambarus*, while the genus *Ballodora*, resembling *Epistylis* (Dogiel and Fursenko, 1921), even follows its hosts, the wood-lice *Porcellio*, to the land, forming on the extremities of their gills small dentritic sessile colonies. These forms of Peritricha are mainly epibionts, but such forms as *Trichodina* and *Cyclochaeta*, which possess special organoids for mobile attachment to their host, apparently enter into a trophic association with it, becoming permanent parasites.

The localization of ectoparasitic Protozoa on the body of the host varies considerably, depending to a great extent on the external morphology of the host. The initial site was probably simply the surface of the body, but eventually the localization of the ectoparasites may have become more restricted and more definite according to the structure and biology of the host. The ectoparasites of benthonic free-living hosts naturally avoid the lower surface of the body on which the animal crawls. Such are, for instance, the trichodine ciliates from certain freshwater Turbellaria. Many ecto-parasites (*Chilodonella, Trichodina, Amphileptus branchiarum, Glossatella,* the suctorian *Trichophrya,* and others) show a predilection for areas of the body with the most delicate skin, owing to which in fishes the favourite site is very often the gills. For whole families of ciliates (Conchophthiridae, Ancistrumidae, Sphanophryidae, Hypocomidae) the pallial chamber and especially the gills of marine and freshwater lamellibranch and gastropod molluscs represent such choice sites. The establishment of ectoparasites on the gills of different animals was probably also influenced by abundant washing of the surface of the gills by water which brings to them particles of food. Apparently some ectoparasites are very sensitive to oxygen-deficiency, and perish rapidly when removed from the gills (*Trichodina* and others). Apart from everything else, the establishment of parasites in the pallial chamber or gill cavity reflects a tendency to leave the surface of the host's body and to occupy more sheltered sites, which protect them from being torn away from the body of the host. From this point of view further penetration into the body of the host is even more favourable, and accordingly we find a number of examples of a transition of ectoparasitic Protozoa to an endoparasitic existence. In this respect the trichodine ciliates of fish are particularly illustrative. The great majority of species of *Trichodina* lives on the surface of the body or on the gills of fish, but a whole group of species (*T. renicola* of pike, *T. urinicola* of perches in the rivers of the U.S.S.R.) found their way through the exterior urinary aperture into the urinary bladder of fish and firmly settled there.

Since their existence depends to a greater or lesser extent on their host, ectoparasitic Protozoa have developed adaptations for attachment to its body. These devices are particularly varied in parasitic ciliates. In some cases the attachment is limited to unstable contact with the body of the host, with a complete retention by the parasite of the capacity to move about on its surface. Such adhesion may be facilitated by the very shape of the concave lower side of the body of the parasite (for instance, in *Chilodonella*).

In other cases, as in the whole suborder Thigmotricha, temporary adhesion is secured by the development at the anterior end of the body of a special bundle of thigmotactic cilia, with which the ciliates are temporarily, as it were, suspended from the surface of the host's body. These devices are most frequently found in ciliates from the pallial chamber of different molluscs. Later a special area surrounded by the thigmotactic cilia becomes differentiated on the lower side of the anterior end of the body, while the rest of the ventral surface of the parasite may undergo a reduction of its ciliary cover. By gradual depression this area may be transformed into a more or less clearly defined sucking disk (*Conchophthirus discorphorus*, *Ptychostomum*). Finally, in such forms as *Sphenophrya* the whole lower side of the body is transformed into a sucking disk devoid of cilia, which adheres closely to the gill epithelium of the molluscan host.

The same pattern of development of a sucker is observed also on the aboral end of the body of ectoparasitic Peritricha, namely *Trichodina* and *Cyclochaeta*.

Some ectoparasites, e.g. *Trichodina*, have evolved an attachment apparatus in the form of hooks. Quite a peculiar method of attachment to their host was evolved in ectoparasitic stages of the life-cycle of many Astomata, which encyst in the phoront stage on the surface of the body of various crustacea. It is true that in this case the phoronts are merely passive lodgers on the host's body, and do not enter into any trophic relations with it. A somewhat similar method of attachment is found in the peculiar ciliates of the family Pilisuctoridae (*Conidophrys*).

The hemispherical, motile stage of *Conidophrys* has on its flat ventral side a mouth leading into a long, narrow pharyngeal canal, while a circlet of cilia is disposed on the periphery of the body. This free phase, or tomite, attaches itself to the ends of special excretory hairs of the amphipods *Corophium*, impaling itself on the end of a hair with its mouth or pharynx, as if on a stake: the excreta of the host enters into the body of the ciliate and are utilized by it, and the animal itself passes into the trophont stage. The body of the ciliate impaled on the hair is invested by a cyst, under the protection of which it begins to produce from its own posterior end motile tomites, which successively leave the cyst and infect new individuals of *Corophium*.

Finally, the ciliate *Ellobiophrya donacis* (Peritricha) from the gills of the lamellibranch mollusc *Donax* (Fig. 320) possesses a unique type of enveloping attachment. *Ellobiophrya* grasps one of the gill-threads of the host with two arm-like processes arising from its base in the form of a ring, and dangles freely from the thread like a padlock hanging from a staple.

Among the Mastigophora the ectoparasitic species of Blastodinidae attach themselves to the body of the host (various plankton organisms) by means of a short or long 'stalk', which penetrates through the integument of the host, and serves both for sucking in food and as an organ of attachment.

Ectoparasites (*Blastodinidae, Apostomata, Pilisuctoria*), and sometimes endoparasites, frequently multiply by the method just described for *Coni-*

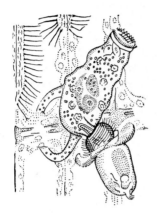

dophrys (Pilisuctoridae), i.e. by a form of terminal budding. It is associated with attachment to the body of the host and with loss of the organoids of locomotion. In this process the parasite attached to the host by one end of its body produces from its free end a series of cells, which acquire organoids of locomotion (flagella, cilia) and serve to spread the infection. Each of these cells frequently divides once more (palintomy). The attached part of the parasite, from which the daughter cells arise, is called the trophocyte, while the cells themselves are gonocytes.

FIG. 320. *Ellobiophrya donacis* (Peritricha) on gills of mollusc *Donax*. (After Chatton and Lwoff, 1929.)

In general in the Protozoa ectoparasitism is developed mainly among ciliates, much more rarely among flagellates (*Blastodinidae, Costia* from the skin of fish) and still more rarely in Sarcodina. Among the latter one may note especially *Hydramoeba hydroxena*, inhabiting the body of different species of *Hydra* and feeding on their epithelial cells.

Alternation of hosts in Protozoa, its origin and evolution

This phenomenon is characteristic of many parasites. In particular, among Protozoa it is found in one family of Mastigophora (Trypanosomidae), in one order of Ciliata (*Apostomata*), in many groups of Sporozoa (the family *Porosporidae* among the gregarines, the families *Aggregatidae* and *Haemogregarinidae* from the order *Coccidiida*, and the whole suborder *Haemosporidia*), and, finally, among the groups *Piroplasmoidea* and *Theileriidea* of uncertain origin.

The alternation of hosts ensures the spread of the parasite and facilitates its penetration into new hosts. This adaptation consists in a complication of the life-cycle of the parasite, by the intervention of the system of so-called intermediate hosts, which increases the chances of the parasite in its struggle for existence, providing it with the maximum possibilities of propagation.

The essential feature of the system of intermediate hosts is that the infective stages of the parasite, after leaving the organism of the host in which they were formed and before they find their way into another animal of the same species, must penetrate either actively or passively into a different animal; in this second animal the young parasites undergo certain changes—sometimes very complex—and only after completing this cycle are they capable of further development and of reproduction in the main host.

It is generally accepted in parasitology to denote the animal in which the parasite attains sexual maturity and reproduces sexually as the final host, while organisms in which the parasite lives in its embryonic or larval stage is called the intermediate host.

However, this terminology is not suitable for parasitic Protozoa: first of all because in a number of Protozoa (*Trypanosomidae, Piroplasmoidea*) sexual reproduction is absent altogether, so that the criterion determining the final host does not hold good. Therefore the vertebrate is conventionally regarded as the 'final' host, and the invertebrate one as the intermediate host or vector, transmitting the parasite from one vertebrate individual to another.

All the Protozoa, in which there is an alternation of hosts, may be divided into two main groups as regards their method of transmission from host to host.

I. The transfer from the first host to the second takes place through the outer medium; from the second to the first by the former being devoured as prey. In this case there is no host-vector, and the transfer is non-transmissive.

II. Transfer from the first host to the second and back takes place through the blood. One of the hosts acts as a vector, and the transfer is transmissive.

Apart from these two types there are several deviations from them. They can, however, be connected with one or the other of the two basic types.

First type—without transmissive transfer, is encountered in some of the Astomatous ciliates, in the Porosporid gregarines, and the cocciidium *Aggregata*.

(a) *Apostomata.* The life-cycle of these peculiar ciliates, which was studied in detail by Chatton and Lwoff (1935a, b), was described by us in another place, so that here we refer only to the alternation of hosts in these ciliates. The great majority of *Apostomata* (for instance the genus *Gymnodinioides*) have a single host—some kind of crustacean (crabs, hermit-crabs, amphipods, and others). They settle on the shell or gills of the host in the form of resting cysts (so-called phoronts); during ecdysis the phoront emerges from the cyst, penetrates into the moulted shell, and feeds there intensively on the exuvial fluid of the host, after which they are converted into the next stage, the trophont. The trophont then leaves the empty shell and encysts directly in water, forming the next stage, the tomont, which may be called, according to the usual nomenclature, the cyst of reproduction. The content of the cyst produces, by repeated transverse divisions, a chain of small individuals (tomites) representing the infective motile stage. The tomites escape from the cyst, settle on the gills of a new individual of the host, where each produces an encysted phoront. Owing to this purely ectoparasitic mode of life, Chatton and Lwoff were inclined to attribute the origin of such single-host *Apostomata* from certain free-living holotrichous ciliates, crawling on the surface of the body of various crustaceans, such as the genera *Dysteria* and *Larvulina*.

Another category of *Apostomata*, illustrated by the genus *Foettingeria*, have the same stages of development, but these are already distributed between two hosts. The resting cysts with the phoronts of *Foettingeria* attach themselves (as in the foregoing case) to the integuments of a great variety of crustaceans (Copepoda, Amphipoda, Isopoda, Decapoda). However, in this case the impulse for the phoront to encyst is given not by the moulting of the host (the encysted phoronts on the shell usually perish during ecdysis), but by the swallowing of the host by definite predators, namely the anemones. The phoront grows into a very large trophont in the alimentary tract of the anemone, and after a certain period (2–3 weeks) it leaves the actinia through its mouth together with the remains of its food, and forms a reproductive cyst. The trophont undergoes in it a number of changes and becomes a tomont, and the latter produces by repeated linear divisions (palintomy) a chain of small tomites. The tomites emerge from the cyst of reproduction, settle on the shell of crustaceans and encyst there, after which they are transformed into phoronts within the cyst. It is interesting that in some genera of Apostomata (*Spirophrya subparasitica*) the development from the resting cyst (phoront) to the reproductive cyst (tomont) may proceed in two ways: either without the participation of a second host (as in *Gymnodinioidea*), or involving a second host (the hydroid polyp *Cladonema*) within which the trophont stage develops (i.e. as in the *Foettingeria*).

On the basis of all the data mentioned, Chatton and Lwoff believe that the heteroxenous type of cycle in Astomata originated from a monoxenous type, along the line *Gymnodinioides*>*Spirophrya*>*Foettingeria*: furthermore, that the introduction of the second host (actinia, polyps) was at first facultative, but later became obligatory.

It is noteworthy that conjugation, i.e. the sexual process, is transferred in the heteroxenous forms (*Foettingeria*) to the second host, i.e. to the alimentary tract of actinia, where in general the entire active life of the parasite—nutrition, growth, sexual process—is passed. From this point of view, in the heteroxenous *Apostomata* the actinia should be regarded as the final host, i.e. the host secondarily intercalated in the cycle of *Apostomata*.

(*b*) *Porosporidae*. The great majority of typical gregarines (suborder Eugregarinida) have only a sexual method of reproduction, in the course of which each of the two associated gregarines within a cyst forms gametes; these unite in pairs and as a result of this fusion the number of zygotes or oocysts with 8 sporozoites inside is halved. Their entire development proceeds inside a single host.

However, in gregarines of the family *Porosporidae*, the process is different (Figs. 321, 322). The sporozoites of Porosporidae (for instance *Porospora gigantea* from the alimentary tract of the lobster) having found their way into the alimentary tract of the crustacean, grow there into typical

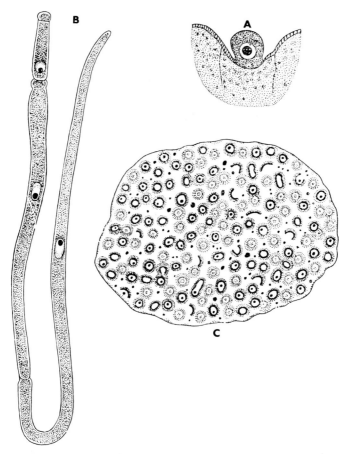

FIG. 321. *Porospora gigantea* (Gregarinidae) from gut of lobster.

(*A*) young trophozoite; (*B*) syzygy of adult *Porospora*; (*C*) cyst with mature gymnospores. (After Léger and Duboscq, 1913, from Doflein and Reichenow, 1929.)

polycystid gregarines, which encyst in the alimentary tract either singly or in groups of 2–3 together, but each produces huge numbers of naked individuals, the so-called 'gymnospores'. These are in fact the future gametes, but their copulation in *Porosporidae* is transferred from the gut of the crustacean to the body of the second host, which is a mollusc (Lamellibranchia or Gastropoda). When the gymnospores are discharged into the water from the hindgut of the crustacean, they have to find their way into the pallial chamber of the mollusc before they can develop further; they are carried there with the current of water washing the gills. The gymnospores usually penetrate into the gills of the mollusc (in the case of *Porospora* into *Mytilus*), where they accumulate in the blood lacunae. Here the gymnospores copulate (thereby revealing their equivalence to gametes) and the zygotes form oocysts, in each of which only one sporozoite develops.

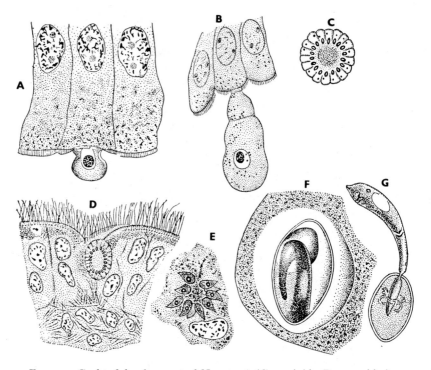

FIG. 322. Cycle of development of *Nematopsis* (Gregarinida, Porosporidae).

(*A*) young trophozoite attached to epithelium of gut of crab; (*B*) adult trophozoite; (*C*) section through gymnospore; (*D*) gymnospore in gill of mollusc; (*E*) sporozoites in tissues of mollusc 21 days after infection; (*F*) oocyst with one sporozoite; (*G*) emergence of sporozoite from oocyst in crab's gut. (After Léger and Duboscq, 1913.)

The crustaceans are infected with the sporozoites when eating infected molluscs.

Since the adult stages of *Porosporidae* are very similar to a number of gregarines of other families encountered in the alimentary tract of crustacea and insects, it would seem that here too the change in the cycle and the transition to an alternation of hosts was a secondary adaptation; furthermore, in the ancestors of *Porosporidae* the only hosts were crustacea. It may be noted here that the main stages of the sexual process (copulation of gametes and the formation of sporozoites) in this case were also transferred to a second host which was brought in later.

(*c*) *Aggregatidae* (Fig. 196) form a family of Coccidia in which schizogony proceeds within the intestinal walls of crustacea (for instance, *Aggregata eberthi* in the crab *Portunus*), while the sexual part of the cycle and sporogony take place in the intestinal walls of cephalopod molluscs (for instance, in *Sepia*). The micro- and macrogametocytes, produced by the merozoites which developed in the gut of the crab, are formed in the intestinal wall of *Sepia* after it has eaten an infected crab. The microgametocyte gives rise to 2–3 dozens of flagellated microgametes, while the macrogametocyte is transformed wholly into a single large, rounded macrogamete. After this copulation occurs, and then the fertilized macrogamete encysts and produces numerous spores. The intestinal walls of the infected *Sepia* become inflamed, pieces of its epithelium are cast off and are discharged through the anus. The crabs readily pick up the shreds of epithelium of *Sepia* falling to the bottom and thus swallow the spores of *Aggregata*. The sporozoites emerge from the spores, find their way into the intestinal wall of a crab, where they develop into large schizonts, which break up into hundreds of merozoites. Thus a regular alternation of hosts is established in the *Aggregatidae*, in the course of which one of the generations present in all the other *Coccidia*, namely the sexual one, is transferred to the second predatory host, while the asexual generation develops in the crustacean.

The problem regarding the primary host is more difficult to settle in the cycle of the *Aggregatidae* than it is in the case of *Porosporidae*. However, in view of the great similarity of the cycles in these two groups, we believe that here too the marine crustacea were the primary and exclusive hosts of the ancestors of *Aggregatidae*. The predatory molluscs must have been included in the cycle later, as in the case of the predatory coelenterates and the apostomatous ciliates.

Thus the non-transmissive transfer is always observed in aquatic, mostly marine, animals, and it is most frequently affected by the inclusion into the life-cycle of the parasite of a second predatory host. In all such cases the first host belongs to the class of crustacea, while the second one is not always but most often a mollusc; and the sexual part of the cycle is always transferred to a second host.

The second type—with transmissive transfer, is encountered in *Haemosporidia*, *Haemogregarinidae*, *Piroplasmoidea*, *Theileriidea*, and flagellata of the family *Trypanosomidae*. All the heteroxenous Protozoa of the second type spend a considerable part of their cycle in the blood of vertebrates, so that the problem of the origin of alternation of hosts in them is closely connected with that of the origin of blood parasitism. There can be no doubt that this form of parasitism is a phenomenon of a secondary order, originating from intestinal parasitism. However, it should be noted that this process probably proceeded differently in the Flagellata and Sporozoa. As regards the *Piroplasmoidea* and *Theileriidea*, at present no data are available for the assessment of the origin of blood parasitism in these groups.

The ancestors of the *Trypanosomidae* of vertebrates were apparently primarily exclusively intestinal parasites of various invertebrates, and only when their hosts acquired blood-sucking habits did the parasites gradually adapt themselves secondarily to a new medium of habitat, in the blood-stream of vertebrates, into which they found their way accidentally from their primary hosts during the act of blood-sucking. As they constantly returned into the alimentary tract of invertebrates, owing to the same act of blood-sucking, they did not lose their capacity to inhabit their primary medium and are at present equally well adapted for life in both hosts—in the alimentary tract of blood-sucking invertebrates and in the blood-stream of vertebrates.

In contrast to this the ancestors of the Haemosporidia and probably of the Haemogregarinidae of vertebrates were at first intestinal parasites of these hosts and only later became parasites of the blood-stream. They later gradually lost their ability to live in their primary habitat, instead of which they secondarily adapted themselves to parasitism of the alimentary tract of invertebrates. A good illustration of this process is provided by some members of the suborder *Eimeriidea*. The most characteristic feature of the majority of species of this suborder is the development of all stages in the intestinal epithelium. Thus, the schizonts, gamonts, and zygotes of *Eimeria intestinalis* and *E. perforans* are located only in the epithelial layer of the small intestine of the rabbit. The same may be said about *E. acervulina* and *E. mitis* from the intestine of fowls. However, in some cases various stages of development of Coccidia penetrate into the deeper layers of the intestinal wall, namely into the connective tissue. Thus, the gamonts of *Eimeria media* and *E. irresidua* in the alimentary tract of rabbit begin their development in the epithelium, and then invade the connective tissue of the villus. In *E. magna* not only the gamonts but the schizonts as well develop subepithelially (Chejsin, 1947). The same is observed in *E. subepithelialis* from the gut of carp and *Isospora bigemina* from that of dog, &c. During their passage into the connective tissue the epithelial cells occupied by the parasite are pushed out of the epithelial layer and sink into the layer below it, where the parasite continues its development. While the oocysts are formed there, their sporulation usually takes place only when they are discharged into the external medium.

It is thus seen that in different coccidia a gradual process of submergence of schizonts, gamonts, and zygotes (oocysts) into deeper layers of the walls of the alimentary tract is observed, while the oocysts retain their ability to pass into the external medium. These examples show no evidence of adaptations for the transmission of sporozoites into a different individual host by any other way except through the alimentary tract.

The further evolution of the intestinal parasites towards blood parasitism could have occurred only with the inclusion in their life-cycle of a new link, namely a vector represented by a blood-sucking invertebrate.

The first phase in this direction is represented by the development of the coccidium *Schellackia bolivari* (Fig. 323), parasitic in lizards. According to Reichenow (1919), the life-cycle of this coccidium begins from a passive transfer of the sporozoite into the alimentary tract of a lizard, where it penetrates into the epithelium and begins to multiply by schizogony. After

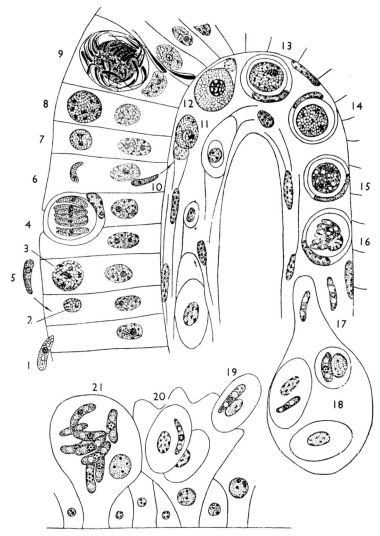

FIG. 323. Cycle of development of *Schellackia bolivari* from lizard and mite *Liponyssus saurarum*.

1, sporozoite penetrates epithelium of gut of lizard; 2–4, schizogony; 5, merozoite; 6–9, microgametogenesis; 10–11, growth of macrogamete; 12, fertilization; 13–16, encystment of zygote and sporogony; 17, sporozoite; 18, sporozoite penetrates into erythrocyte of lizard; 19–20, erythrocytes taken up into intestinal cells of mite, sporozoites accumulate in these cells, and emerge from digested erythrocytes. (After Reichenow, 1919.)

several asexual generations, and male and female gamonts are formed. The former develop in the same epithelial cells where asexual multiplication takes place, while the latter invade the subepithelial connective tissue. The male gametes formed from the microgametocyte also penetrate into the subepithelial tissues and fertilize the female macrogamete. The resulting zygote also develops there, but does not form spores; it ruptures and the sporozoites liberated from it find their way into a capillary blood-vessel, where they invade the red corpuscles. However, they do not develop in them, but remain there until they are taken up together with the blood into the alimentary tract of the mite *Liponyssus saurarum*, which is a temporary parasite on lizards. When the blood is ingested by the mite, the erythrocytes are taken up by the epithelial cells of its alimentary tract, together with the sporozoites enclosed in them. Within the cells the erythrocytes are digested and the sporozoites are liberated but not digested, remaining passive in the cells of the gut of the mite until it is devoured accidentally by a lizard, as often the case with *Liponyssus*. The mite is digested in the alimentary tract of the lizard, while the sporozoites actively penetrate into the epithelium of its intestine and initiate the development just described by us.

Thus in *Schellackia* we encounter a number of important changes in the life-cycle and morphology. First of all there is a temporary detachment of the parasite from the gut walls, and its transition to life in the erythrocytes. This part of the cycle is, however, comparatively insignificant (only one stage), not active, and unaccompanied by growth; in both hosts the parasite still lives for a long time in the cells of the gut, while the erythrocytic stage is only an indispensable vehicle for the transport from the gut cell of the lizard to that of the mite. Later, the transition into the blood becomes inevitably associated with the appearance of an intermediate host (the mite). Finally, the loss of the spore membrane represents a change in the morphology of the parasite. It is easily explained on biological grounds since *Schellackia* does not spend one moment of its life outside the bodies of its hosts, so that sporozoites require no protection and the spore membrane becomes superfluous.

The occidium *Lankesterella minima* (Fig. 324), parasitic in frogs, may serve as an example of the further development of blood parasitism. As in the case of *Schellackia* infection takes place through the alimentary tract. However, according to Nöller (1920), the sporozoite of *Lankesterella* finds its way into the intestinal capillaries directly through its epithelial and subepithelial layers, and then penetrates into the endothelial cells of the vessels of different organs. In these cells, the parasite undergoes asexual reproduction. The merozoites released from the cells find their way into the blood and invade new endothelial cells, where the asexual process of multiplication is repeated. As a result of a series of schizogonies gamonts are produced, which mature and undergo a process of fertilization in the same endothelial cells, giving rise to a zygote, which is invested in a membrane and becomes an oocyst, in which a large number of sporozoites are produced, without the formation of sporoblasts and spores. The sporozoites are liberated from the oocyst, enter the blood again, and penetrate into the erythrocytes. The

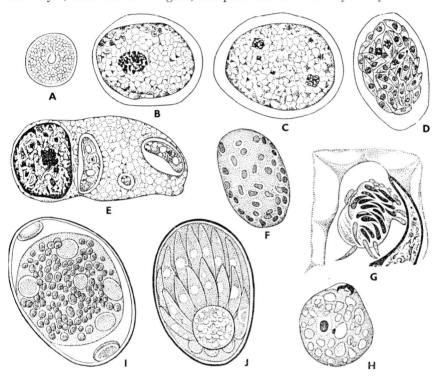

FIG. 324. Stages of development of *Lankesterella minima* in frogs.

(*A*)–(*D*) schizogony in endothelium of vessels; (*E*) gamonts in endothelial cells; (*F*) and (*G*) formation of microgametes; (*H*) fertilization of macrogamete; (*I*) undeveloped oocyst; (*J*) sporulated oocyst. (After Nöller, 1920.)

sporozoites remain entirely unchanged in them until they reach the alimentary tract of a leech, *Hemiclepsis marginata*, where they invade the cells of the intestinal epithelium. Like the sporozoites of *Schellackia* in the mite, those of *Lankesterella* do not develop at all in the organism of the leech, but are simply preserved there until they reach the alimentary tract of a frog, which habitually devours leeches. Here they begin their life-cycle again.

Thus, the entire life-cycle of *Lankesterella* takes place inside the endothelial cells, only the sporozoites penetrating into the erythrocytes. In the course of further evolution towards blood parasitism the parasites begin to invade the erythrocytes not in the sporozoite stage, but at earlier stages of development, as a result of which the period of development in the endothelium of the vessels is still more reduced.

In some Haemosporidia (*Haemoproteus*) the whole period of repeated schizogony takes place in the reticulo-endothelial system, and only the last generation of merozoites, which are converted into gamonts, invade the red-blood corpuscles. Finally, in *Plasmodium* only the first exoerythrocytic generations of schizonts multiply in the reticulo-endothelial system

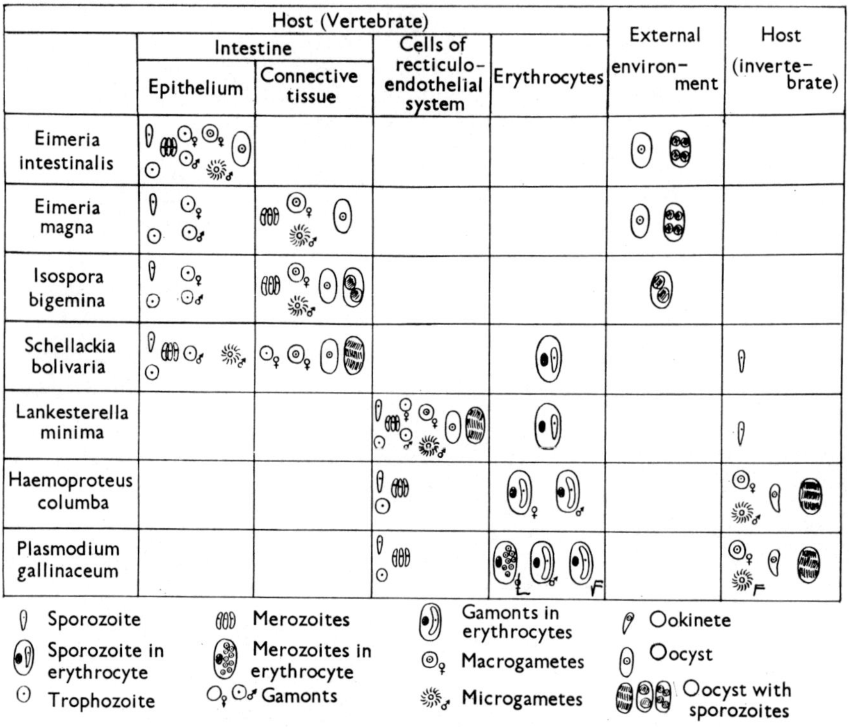

FIG. 325. Diagram, illustrating transition of sporozoa from intestinal parasitism to blood parasitism. (Original.)

or in cells of the liver, whereas the greater part of the period of schizogony and gametogenesis proceeds in the erythrocytes.

The examples given above show a clear pattern (Fig. 325) of the evolution from intestinal to blood parasitism, which proceeds as follows: the originally purely epithelial intestinal forms of coccidia first become facultatively subepithelial; then they temporarily break away from the epithelium of the gut of the vertebrate, while a short (only one phase, the sporozoite) endoerythrocytic stage (*Schellackia*) makes its appearance. Later (*Lankesterella*) the breakaway from the intestinal epithelium of the vertebrate becomes permanent (the epithelium serving only for the passage of the sporozoites through it), and the parasite undergoes its entire development in the endothelium of the vessels, i.e. still in an epithelium-like tissue; within the erythrocytes the parasite, as before, still spends only its sporozoite stage.

Finally, in the order Haemosporidia (*Haemoproteus–Plasmodium*) the enderythrocytic part of the cycle gradually becomes predominant and typical blood parasitism ensues.

However, from the moment when the erythrocytes harbour not sporozoites but the earlier stages, such as gametocytes, purely mechanical transmission from one host to another (such as takes place in *Schellackia* and *Lankesterella*) becomes inadequate. Transmission to a new vertebrate host becomes possible only after a preliminary development of the parasite terminating in the stage of sporozoite, which in these cases is transferred into the organism of the vector, represented by an invertebrate host. The method of transmission of the parasite changes after part of its cycle is transferred to a second host: the sporozoites return from the invertebrate host into the vertebrate during the act of blood-sucking. In *Haemosporidia* this method of transmission becomes the only one.

As regards blood flagellates of the family *Trypanosomidae*, there are clear indications that their distant ancestors lived in the alimentary tract of insects, which had not acquired specialized blood-sucking habits. This view is supported by the fact that there are at the present many insects (flies, fleas, and others) both blood-sucking and non-blood-sucking, whose alimentary tract is inhabited by forms allied to the trypanosomes, namely flagellates of the genera *Leptomonas* and *Crithidia*. The entire life-cycle of these flagellates (Fig. 326) takes place in the intestine, but the infection is transmitted through the mouth, i.e. they have no connexion with blood parasitism. When these insects eventually began to feed on the blood of vertebrates and became restricted to this diet, their intestinal flagellates came in contact with the vertebrates and were accidentally introduced into their blood during the sucking act. Blood proved to be not less nutritious than the contents of the alimentary tract, therefore the flagellates which found their way into the blood accidentally were able to live there for a long time and even continued to multiply. The prolonged stay in the blood gave them the opportunity to return into the alimentary tract of the insect during subsequent acts of blood-sucking. Not having lost their ability to live in the gut of the insect, the parasites, taken up with the blood of the vertebrate by the insect, survived in the latter and did not perish. Later the life-cycle of such flagellates became differentiated into a number of stages, through some of which they regularly passed in the vertebrate, while others were regularly spent in the alimentary tract of a blood-sucking insect (Hoare, 1960a). The trypanosomes find their way into the alimentary tract of the invertebrate host or vector only during blood-sucking. However, there are two ways whereby they return into the vertebrate host: first by inoculation, i.e. during blood-sucking, which is observed in the pathogenic African trypanosomes (*Trypanosoma vivax*, *T. congolense*, *T. brucei*, *T. gambiense*);

854352 U u

and secondly by contamination, when the infective stages of the trypanosomes are voided by the vector with its faeces on to the body of the vertebrate host, which accidentally licks them off and swallows them. In this
way rats are infected with *Trypanosoma lewisi* by fleas, and sheep with
T. melophagium by the sheep-ked (*Melophagus ovinus*). *T. cruzi*, which is
transmitted by Reduviid bugs and a number of other species, also belongs
to this type.

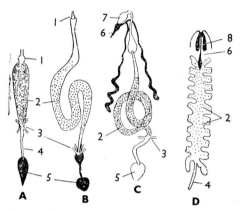

FIG. 326. Localization of trypanosomes in various vectors.

(*A*), (*B*) localization of trypanosomes with contami-
native transmission; (*C*), (*D*) with inoculative
transmission. (*A*) *Trypanosoma lewisi* in gut of flea;
(*B*) *T. melophagium* in sheep-ked; (*C*) *T. gambiense*
in tsetse fly; (*D*) *T. rotatorium* in leech. 1, gullet;
2, stomach; 3, Malpighian tubes; 4, hindgut; 5,
rectum; 6, proboscis; 7, pharynx; 8, proboscis
sheath. Sites of development of metacyclic trypanosomes are coloured black; sites with predominance
of crithidial forms are indicated by dots; sites of
development of trypanosome forms by circles.
(After Hoare, 1925.)

Finally, in a very few cases the blood-sucking vector was eliminated from
the cycle of the parasite, as in the case of *Trypanosoma equiperdum* causing
'dourine' in horses. These trypanosomes are transmitted from one horse
to another by direct contact during the sexual act, through the mucous
membranes of the genital tract.

A careful consideration of the life-cycles of Protozoa transmitted with
and without vectors reveals the following points.

Direct transmission without vectors occurs only between invertebrate
hosts, whereas in the case of indirect transmission an invertebrate (vector)
and a vertebrate host always take part. In all parasites with vectors (apart
from the trypanosomidae) the change of hosts is associated with an
alternation of sexual and asexual generations. In the case of direct
transmission, the development of a regular alternation of generations is not
obligatory. Thus it is absent in apostomatous ciliates.

When a change of hosts occurs the most important stages of the sexual process are usually transferred from the first, more ancient host into the second, which was included in the cycle later. Thus in heteroxenous Apostomata, conjugation, which is from time to time interpolated into the cycle, always takes place in the alimentary tract of coelenterates, but not in the body of crustaceans. In Porosporidae the copulation of gametes, and in Aggregatidae the entire formation of the gametes, proceed in the intestinal walls of cephalopods, but not in crustaceans. In Haemosporidia and Haemogregarinae, which originated as intestinal parasites of vertebrates, the sexual process and the development of the sexual generation takes place in the blood-sucking vectors.

The change of hosts does not stand in any genetic relation with the alteration of generations. Thus among Sporozoa it is observed in forms which possessed an alteration of generations before a change of hosts occurred, namely in coccidia, haemogregarines, and Haemosporidia, which doubtless originated from coccidia. On the other hand, a regular alteration of generations is absent altogether in Apostomata and *Trypanosomidae*.

Forms of mutual adaptation between parasite and host. The prolonged and extremely close physical and physiological contact between the parasite and the host involves multiple mutual relations between the two organisms. The interpretation of this relationship is one of the most important problems of parasitology. In the words of Hegner (1926): 'The relations between parasitic Protozoa and their hosts must . . . be studied as biological phenomena just as we are accustomed to study the relations between free-living Protozoa and their environment' (p. 393).

Here it should be added that the ecology of free-living organisms concerns mainly the behaviour of the organism in relation to its environment, i.e. the reactions by means of which the organism adapts itself to the changing conditions of its existence. However, the relationship between the parasite and its host is more complex, since the environment of the parasite, being a living organism like the one inhabiting it, sometimes reacts violently to the presence of the parasite. As a result of this the relationship between the parasites (in this case Protozoa) and their hosts is manifested in mutual adaptation, which enables the parasite to infect the host easily, and to exist within it, while the host develops the most effective means for dealing with the parasite's harmful activities, sometimes even turning the presence of entozoic inhabitants to its own advantage.

It may be said that the entire life of parasitic organisms consists in constant adaptation and adjustment of their relationship with the organism of their host. These adaptations are reflected both in the morphological and physiological peculiarities, and in fact in all the features of the ecology and life-cycle of the host.

Many of these adaptations of the parasite to its host have already been mentioned. The numerous and diverse attachment apparatus of parasitic

Protozoa are nothing but morphological adaptations enabling the parasite to hold on within the organism of the host. A similar adaptation, but in this case mainly of a physiological character, is the reduction of the special digestive apparatus and of the mouth (astomatism) in many parasitic Protozoa, especially in ciliates, and the adoption by such parasites of a saprophytic mode of nutrition. All the preceding paragraph, devoted to the problem of the origin of alternation of hosts, illustrates modifications in the life-cycle of Protozoa directed towards improvements of the methods of transmission of protozoal infection from host to host.

However, one of the best examples of the manifold and perfect adaptation of the structure and the whole mode of life of the parasite to the biology of the host may be observed from a study of the intestinal flagellates of termites, of the orders Polymastigida and Hypermastigida.

The main adaptations to the host are reflected in the life-cycle and the behaviour of these Mastigophora. Thus first of all most of them adopted the habit of feeding on large particles of wood that are ingested at the posterior pole of the body from which digital pseudopodia are produced (*Coronympha*). In others (*Trichonympha*) the posterior end of the body is invaginated in the shape of a cup; when small particles of wood enter it they are enveloped by the cup. Finally, some acquire temporarily a completely amoeboid form, retaining only a rudimentary miniature undulating membrane; these forms feed and move like amoebae. All these changes in the method of feeding are undoubtedly adaptations to the peculiarities of the host's diet (particles of cellulose).

Further, the method of transmission of the infection among termites reveals a second extremely important adaptation. None of the termites Mastigophora (except a few small Trichomonadidae) are capable of forming cysts, the habit of the termites of feeding on the liquid excreta of their companions is utilized for transmission. Thus the flagellates present in the droppings discharged through the anus are licked up by another termite and find their way into the gullet, whence they descend to their final habitat, the hindgut. As a result there is a continuous renewal of infection in adult termites and contamination of the young ones. Termite larvae are fed by worker termites, at first on the secretions of their salivary glands; while fed on these discharges the larvae are free of flagellates. Later the workers begin to feed the young on the liquid contents of their own hindgut, and from this moment Mastigophora appear in the hindgut of the young individuals.

Although the flagellates find their way through the mouth into the alimentary tract of new individuals, they encounter one more barrier on their way, namely the necessity of passing through sections of the alimentary tract that are unsuitable for their existence—the gullet and the midgut. In this connexion the flagellates of termites have developed another extremely important device. As was first shown by Dogiel (1916, 1926), among the ordinary flagellates present in the hindgut there is usually a small number of 'mummified' individuals. Such individuals either simply eject out of their protoplasm all the food contents (*Spirotrichonympha*), or the posterior end of their body, stuffed with pieces of wood, becomes detached (*Joenia, Pseudojoenia, Myxomonas*). Their cytoplasm becomes denser and homogenous, while their size diminishes. In forms completely covered with flagella, these form a thick felt round the body (*Spirotrichonympha*); in others the body becomes rounded (*Joenia, Myxomonas*). Such mummified forms pass unharmed through the digestive tract right down to the hindgut. Later Dogiel and, apparently independently, Duboscq and Grasse (1934) expressed the opinion that *Joenia annectens* behaved in the same manner.

Another interesting adaptation appears in the flagellates during ecdysis of their hosts. Each moulting period represents a critical moment both for the flagellates and their hosts, since during ecdysis all the lining of the hindgut together with all the Protozoa in it are removed from the hindgut. However, the experiments of Cleveland (1924) and of a number of other authors have conclusively proved that termites which had been artificially deprived of their flagellates or defaunated, for instance, by being kept for days at a temperature of 36° C., are doomed to perish within 3–4 weeks. Their death is caused by the fact that the enzymes of the alimentary tract of termites are unable to act on the cellulose unless it is predigested for them by the xylophagous flagellates. But if the defaunated termites are infected again with flagellates, they will continue to live for years in the laboratory. Hence the speedy re-establishment of the cellulose-digesting Protozoa in the hindgut is as important for the termites as it is, naturally, for their flagellates. However, all investigators of termites have for a long time been surprised by the absence of stages of reproduction (division) in the Mastigophora swarming in the hindgut of termites. Among these flagellates only an insignificant number showed some initial stages of division. This is the case in a normally functioning alimentary tract, but when defaunated termites are infected artificially or naturally (during moulting) then, as the American authors put it, real 'explosions of reproduction' take place among the Protozoa which found their way into the hindgut. All the flagellates observed during this period are in different stages of mitosis. This goes on until the concentration of flagellates in the hindgut reaches a certain level, when the mitoses cease and the living population of the hindgut apparently becomes more or less stabilized. The size of this stable population varies in different termites. Thus Andrew (1930) counted in the hindgut of *Termopsis angusticollis* on the average 25,000 large xylophagous flagellates *Trichonympha* and *Leidyopsis*, which satisfy to a considerable degree the trophic requirements of the host, and 500,000 small *Trichomonas*, which apparently take only a small part in the digestion of cellulose. At any rate the termites from which *Trichonympha* and *Leidyopsis* were removed artificially (by temperature) but *Trichomonas* were retained always perished in a few weeks. In the gut of normal termites there is one *Leidyopsis* to 1,000 *Trichonympha*. However, if all the *Trichonympha* are destroyed by artificial defaunation, leaving only the more tolerant *Leidyopsis*, the latter multiply intensively until their numbers approach the total number of the two species present before defaunation.

As regards the 'explosions of reproduction' this phenomenon points to an adaptation of the entire life-cycle of the flagellates to the host. And, indeed, it has been shown that the reproduction of these Protozoa does not depend on nutrition or any other factor affecting them directly, but on the moulting periods of their host: every ecdysis of the host is followed by a period of reproduction. It is thus seen that in the life of the flagellates of termites the most important features of their morphology, physiology, and biology are adapted to the peculiarities of their host.

Many similar examples from the life of other parasitic Protozoa might be cited, but we shall restrict ourselves to this one as being the clearest.

However, there is another side of the problem of adaptation of the parasite to the host which has been only inadequately studied and is in need of elucidation. This concerns the form of adaptation of the parasite to the host manifested in the lowering of its pathogenicity. Thus for the majority of animal parasites with a long life span, the preservation of longevity of their host ensures the perpetuation of the species. Under such conditions the duration of the infection may be prolonged, the multiplication of the infective stages may be increased, and so on.

Hence the lowering of pathogenicity favours the propagation of the parasite. A good illustration of this is provided by trypanosomes. Thus Nagana, a disease caused by *Trypanosoma brucei*, which, before the introduction of germanin, was fatal to horses, donkeys, and cattle, but is harmless to antelopes, is extremely limited in its distribution by its extreme pathogenicity for domestic animals. In contrast, *Trypanosoma theileri* of cattle, which is not pathogenic for its hosts, can spread its area of distribution wherever cattle and vectors of this trypanosome, represented by various horse-flies, are present.

The reverse picture, i.e. an advantage for the parasite from the death of its host, is observed in the rare cases when the emergence of the infective stages of the parasite is associated with the death of the host. Such parasites, among Protozoa, are represented by some Myxosporidia (*Lentospora cerebralis*, *Myxobolus neuro obius*) which are parasitic in organs (e.g. cartilaginous skeleton, the central nervous system) which do not provide them with any outlet from the host, except in the case of its death and decomposition of the body. After a certain period of active life these Sporozoa encyst and produce spores, which must find their way into the external medium for further development: this becomes possible only after the host's death. The death of the host might be advantageous for such parasites like cavitary gregarines, the spores of which have no other opportunity of escaping into the external environment.

However, in the great majority of cases the preservation of the life of the host is advantageous for the parasite, especially if it multiplies inside the host, or if its host transmits the infection when eaten by another animal, in which the parasite continues its life-cycle. In such cases the premature death of the intermediate host caused by the parasite may prevent it from becoming the prey of the final host, in which further development of the parasite must take place.

Moreover, a lowering of the virulence and pathogenicity of the parasite must, theoretically, reduce the defence reaction on the part of the host, thereby producing conditions favourable for the parasite.

The problem of non-pathogenicity as a gradually acquired adaptive characteristic of the parasite is of considerable interest, but has so far been very little investigated. Some authors have no doubt about the existence of this type of adaptation, and even assume that the degree of pathogenicity of a given parasite to a certain host can serve as a measure of the period of time during which the protozoon has been a parasite on the host in question. However, this does not seem to be a reliable criterion, since the speed of adaptation might vary considerably for different parasites and for the same parasite in different species of hosts. Nevertheless, the existence of adaptation of this type is highly probable, as it finds a ready explanation in the theory of evolution (see Ball, 1943, 1960). The host–parasite relationship has another essential characteristic. The action of the parasite on the host brings about response reactions from the latter, some of which have a definite protective function. These defence reactions may be either cellular or humoral. With their aid the host either rids itself entirely of the parasite or counteracts its harmful effect. Immunity in the host is thus developed in response to the effect of the appropriate parasite. We shall not dwell in detail on the problem of immunity, since this would require too much space, and moreover there are works specially devoted to this problem, to which the reader is referred (Taliaferro, 1929; Culbertson, 1941).

We shall only note briefly some aspects of this problem, mainly concerning the phenomenon of acquired immunity.

Acquired immunity is known mainly in the case of tissue and intercellular parasites, such as piroplasma, malaria parasites, coccidia, leishmanias, and trypanosomes and to a less extent in parasites inhabiting the lumen of the alimentary tract (for instance *Entamoeba histolytica*, *Giardia*, *Balantidium*, &c.).

It is often observed that resistance to repeated infection develops in the organism of the host when some parasites are retained from a previous infection. This form of immunity is called premunition (Sergent, 1935) or non-sterile immunity. Immunity against trypanosomiasis, caused by *Trypanosoma cruzi* or *T. brucei* as well as in malaria (*Plasmodium*), may serve as an example. The same type of immunity probably develops in man against *Leishmania tropica* (Taliaferro, 1948). On the other hand, sterile immunity develops in coccidiosis of rabbits and fowls. At the end of the primary infection rabbits or chickens are freed of the parasite, while on reinfection the invasion is slight and mortality from coccidioses is markedly reduced. Not infrequently the host becomes completely refractory to reinfection.

It has been established that the developing immunity may, on the one hand, restrict the existence and reproduction of the parasite in the host, and, on the other, inhibit the toxic effect of the parasite on the host. Thus, in human malaria in the course of development of the acute phase of the disease in patients left without treatment, the attacks may cease spontaneously, while the level of parasitaemia remains high, after which the number of parasites is reduced. Eventually the attacks cease altogether, but the parasites continue to circulate in the blood for a long time. Therefore in this case the host first becomes resistant to the clinical manifestations of the infection, after which resistance to the parasites develops.

In protozoal infections, in addition to actively acquired immunity, when the host itself develops a resistance to the parasite, there may also be passive immunity when the serum of another individual, possessing active immunity and containing antibodies in its blood, is introduced into the host. This type of immunity is less stable than the active one. It is known in the case of certain tissue-parasites, for example *Leishmania donovani, Trypanosoma lewisi, T. cruzi.*

In a whole series of protozoal diseases (malaria, piroplasmosis, and others) the development of resistance is determined largely by the activity of cellular reactions of phagocytosis. The cellular reaction may be accompanied by the appearance of antibodies in the blood, the two reactions frequently being simultaneous.

The essential characteristic of the defence reactions of the host is their strict specificity. In each host the parasite elicits the formation of antibodies acting only against the given species of parasite, but not on any other. This phenomenon is even used for the differentiation of allied species of parasitic Protozoa.

Among the various forms of immunity the non-sterile one acquires a special interest, as a definite phase in the mutual adaptation of parasite and host, which may lead to gradual development of an equilibrium between the two organisms, permitting the parasite to exist within its host without causing it any essential harm and without suffering from its defence reactions.

APPENDIX

SYSTEMATIC ARRANGEMENT OF THE PROTOZOA ADOPTED IN THIS BOOK

Type PROTOZOA
  Subtype Plasmodroma
    Class Sarcodina
      Subclass Rhizopoda
        Order Amoebida
        Order Piroplasmida
          Suborder Piroplasmina
          Suborder Theileriina
        Order Testacea
        Order Foraminifera
      Subclass Heliozoa
        Order Actinophrydia
        Order Centrohelidia
        Order Desmothoraca
      Subclass Radiolaria
        Order Acantharia
        Order Spumellaria
        Order Nassellaria
        Order Phaeodaria
        Order Sticholoncha
    Class Mastigophora (= Flagellata)
      Subclass Phytomastigina
        Order Chrysomonadida
        Order Silicoflagellida
        Order Cryptomonadida
        Order Heterochloridida
        Order Chloromonadida
        Order Euglenida
        Order Phytomonadida
        Order Dinoflagellata
      Subclass Zoomastigina
        Order Protomonadida
        Order Diplomonadida
        Order Polymastigida
        Order Hypermastigida
      Subclass Opalinina
    Class Sporozoa
      Subclass Gregarina

Order Schizogregarinida
Order Eugregarinida
Subclass Coccidia (= Coccidiomorpha)
Order Protococcidia
Order Adeleida
Order Coccidiida
Suborder Eimeriidea
Suborder Haemosporidia
Class Cnidosporidia
Order Myxosporidia
Order Microsporidia
Order Actinomyxidia
Subtype Ciliophora
Class Ciliata (= Infusoria)
Subclass Holotricha
Order Gymnostomata
Order Trichostomata
Order Hymenostomata
Order Astomata
Order Apostomata
Order Thigmotricha
Subclass Spirotricha
Order Heterotricha
Order Oligotricha
Order Tintinnoidea
Order Entodiniomorpha
Order Ctenostomata
Order Hypotricha
Subclass Peritricha
Order Sessilida
Order Mobilida
Subclass Chonotricha
Subclass Suctoria

Addendum. Groups of uncertain systematic position: (1) Sarcosporidia and (2) Toxoplasmida, both representing groups of Protozoa related to Sarcodina; Biocca (1956) unites them into one class, Toxoplasmatea; (3) Haplosporidia, which probably do not belong to the Protozoa; (4) Anaplasmida, which are not Protozoa but probably represent Rickettsias.

REFERENCES

ADLER, S., and KATZENELLENBOGEN, I., 1952, 'The Problem of the association between particular strains of *Leishmania tropica* and the clinical manifestations produced by them', *Ann. Trop. Med. Parasitol.* **46**, 25–32.

—— and THEODOR, O., 1929, 'Attempts to transmit *Leishmania tropica* by bite: the transmission of *L. tropica* by *Phlebotomus sergenti*', ibid., **23**, 1–16.

ALEKSANDROV, V. JA. (Alexandrov, W. J.), 1948, 'Specific and non-specific reactions of the cell to injury', *Proc. Inst. Histology and Embriology*, **3**, 3–82.

ALEKSEEV, A. G. (Alexeieff, A. G.), 1912, 'Le parasitisme des Eugléniens et la phylogénie des Sporozoaires *sensu stricto*', *Arch. Zool. exp. gén.* **10** (Notes et Rev.), 73–88.

—— 1925, 'Do soil Protozoa exist?' *Russian Arch. Protistol.* **4**, 127–32.

—— 1929, 'Nouvelles observations sur les chondriosomes chez les Protozoaires', *Arch. Protistenk.* **65**, 45–64.

ALLEN, R., 1961, 'Ameboid movement'. In.: *The Cell*. New York–London: 136–212.

—— and ROSLANSKY, J., 1958, 'An anterior-posterior gradient of refractive index in the ameba and its significance in ameboid movement', *J. Biophys. Biochem. Cytol.* **4**, 517–25.

ALLEN, S., and NANNEY, D., 1958, 'An analysis of nuclear differentiation in the selfers of *Tetrahymena*', *Amer. Natur.* **92**, 139–60.

AMBERSON, W., 1928, 'The influence of oxygen tension upon the respiration of unicellular organisms', *Biol. Bull.* **55**, 79–91.

ANDERSON, E., 1962, 'A cytological study of Chilomonas paramecium with particular reference to the so-called trichocysts', *J. Protozool.* **9**, 380–95.

—— and BEAMS, H., 1959a, 'Electron microscopic observations on the cytology of *Actinosphaerium eichhorni*', *J. Protozool.* **6**, Suppl.: 16.

—— —— 1959b, 'The cytology of *Tritrichomonas* as revealed by the electron microscope', *J. Morphol.* **104**, 205–35.

—— —— 1960, 'The fine structure of the Heliozoan *Actinosphaerium nucleofilum*', *J. Protozool.* **7**, 190–9.

—— SAXE, L., and BEAMS, H., 1956, 'Electron microscope observations of *Trypanosoma equiperdum*', *J. Parasitol.* **42**, 11–16.

ANDREEVA, E. V. (Andreewa, E. W.), 1929, 'Physiologische Studien an Protozoen. I. Die Wirkung der Elektrolyte auf einige Exkretionscrscheinungen bei den Infusorien', *Arch. Protistenk.* **68**, 587–608.

ANDREW, B., 1930, 'Method and rate of Protozoan refaunation in the termite Termopsis angusticollis Hagen', *Univ. Calif. Publ. Zool.* **33**, 449–70.

ARNOLD, Z., 1955, 'Life history and cytology of the foraminiferan Allogromia laticollaris', *Univ. Calif. Publ. Zool.* **61**, 251–62.

AUERBACH, M., 1910, 'Die Cnidosporidien (Myxosporidien, Actinomyxidien, Microsporidien)'. Eine monographische Studie. Leipzig.

AVAKJAN, A. A., 1955, 'Characteristics of the causative agent, epidemiology and clinical aspects of amebiasis', *J. Microbiol. Emidemiol. and Immunobiol.* **10**, 57–61.

AVERINCEV, S. V. (Awerinzew, S. W.), 1907, 'Die Struktur und die chemische Zusammensetzung der Gehäuse bei den Süßwasserrhizopoden', *Arch. Protistenk.* **8**, 95.

AVERINCEV S. V., 1909, 'Studien über parasitische Protozoen. I. Die Sporenbildung bei *Ceratomyxa drepanopsettae* mihi', *Arch. Protistenk.* **14**, 74–112.

—— 1925, 'Die Sporenbildung bei disporen Myxosporidien', *Russ. Arch. Protistol.* **3**, 171–7.

BAITSELL, G. A., 1914, 'Experiments on the reproduction of the hypotrichous infusoria. II. A study of the so-called life cycle in *Oxytricha fallax* and *Pleurotricha lanceolata*', *J. Exper. Zool.* **16**, 211–35.

BAKER, F., and BAUMBERG, J., 1941, 'The respiratory rate and the cytochrome content of ciliate protozoan (*Tetrahymena geleii*)', *J. Cell. Comp. Physiol.* **17**, 285–303.

BALAMUTH, W., 1951, 'Biological studies on *Entamoeba histolytica*. III. Induced encystation in several mediums, including an account of a new procedure', *J. Infect. Dis.* **88**, 230–6.

BALL, E., 1946, 'Malaria parasites growth *in vitro*', *Feder. Proc.* (*Baltimore*) **5**, 397–9.

——, ANFINSEN, C., GEIMAN, R., MEKEE, R., and ORMSBEE, R., 1945, '*In vitro* growth and multiplication of the malaria parasite *Plasmodium knowlesi*', *Science*, **101**, 2630, 342–4.

BALL, G., 1943, 'Parasitism and evolution', *Ann. Natur.* **78**, 345–64.

—— 1946, 'Attempts to cultivate the mosquito phase of *Plasmodium relictum*', *J. Parasitol.* **32**, sect. 2, Suppl.: 9.

—— 1960, 'Some considerations regarding the Sporozoa', *J. Protozool.* **7**, 1–6.

BARBARIN, V. V., 1937*a*, 'Factors determining the balance between fat and glycogen in *Paramecium caudatum*. I. Effect of starvation', *Biol. J.* **6**, 699–708.

—— 1937*b*, 'Factors determining the balance between fat and glycogen in *Paramecium caudatum*. II. Effect of different food on the accumulation of fat and glycogen', ibid., **6**, 709–20.

—— 1938, 'Factors determining the balance between fat and glycogen in *Paramecium caudatum*. III. Effect of asphyxia on the accumulation of fat and glycogen', ibid., **6**, 391–8.

—— 1954, 'Changes of oxidative processes and their adaptive significance in the life cycle of protozoa and in the ontogenesis of some invertebrates'. Author's abstract of Thesis. Leningrad.

—— and SOLOVJEVA, L. M., 1941, 'Changes in the intensity of respiration of *Bursaria truncatella* under the influence of starvation and of KCN', *Doklady Acad. Sci. U.S.S.R.* **31**, 72–74.

—— —— 1947, 'Respiration of the ciliate *Bursaria truncatella* during conjugation and during encystment', *Doklady Acad. Sci. U.S.S.R.* **55**, 677–80.

—— —— 1948, 'Changes in the intensity of respiration at different stages of the life cycle of *Bursaria truncatella*', *Scient. Trans. Herzen Leningrad State Pedag. Inst.* **70**, 49–66.

BARKER, D., and DEUTSCH, K., 1958, 'The chromatoid body of *Entamoeba invadens*', *Exper. Cell. Res.* **15**, 604–39.

BARKER, H., and TAYLOR, C., 1933, 'Studies on the excystment of *Colpoda cucullus*', *Physiol. Zool.* **6**, 127–36.

BARRAT, I., 1905, 'Die Kohlensäureproduktion von *Paramaecium aurelia*', *Z. allg. Physiol.* **5**, 66–72.

BASIN, F. N., 1945, 'Geographical distribution of shelled rhizopods'. Abstr. of Thesis.

BEALE, G., 1952, 'Antigen variation in *Paramecium aurelia*, variety I', *Genetics* 37, 1, 62–74.

—— 1954, 'The genetics of *Paramecium aurelia*', *Cambr. Monogr. Exper. Biol.* **2**, 1–17

BEAMS, H., TAHMISIAN, T., DEVINE, R., and ANDERSON, E., 1959, 'Studies on fine structure of a gregarine parasitic in the gut of the grasshopper, *Melanoplus differentialis*', *J. Protozool.* **6**, 136–46.

BEERS, C., 1925, 'Encystment and the life-cycle in the ciliate *Didinium nasutum*', *Proc. Nat. Acad. Sci.* **11**, 523–8.

—— 1926, 'The life cycle in the ciliate *Didinium nasutum*, with reference to encystment', *J. Morphol. Physiol.* **42**, 1–21.

—— 1927, 'The relation between hydrogen-ion concentration and encystment in *Didinium nasutum*', *J. Morphol.* **44**, 21–28.

—— 1930, 'Some effects of encystment in the ciliate *Didinium nasutum*', *J. Exper. Zool.* **56**, 193–209.

—— 1946, '*Tilina magna*: micronuclear number, encystment and vitality in diverse clones; capabilities of amicronucleate races', *Biol. Bull.* **91**, 256–71.

—— 1948a, 'Excystment in the ciliate *Bursaria truncatella*', ibid., **94**, 86–98.

—— 1948b, 'Observations on the ciliate *Bursaria ovata* n. sp., *J. Elisha Mitchell Sci. Soc.* **68**, 184–90.

BEJER, T. V., 1960, 'Cytological investigation of various stages of the life cycle of rabbit coccidia. Phosphomonoesterases in *Eimeria magna* Pérard, 1924', Symposium, *Problems of cytology and protistology*, 277–84.

BĚLÁŘ, K., 1922, 'Untersuchungen an *Actinophrys sol* Ehrenberg. I. Die Morphologie des Formwechsels', *Arch. Protistenk.* **46**, 1–96.

—— 1924, 'Untersuchungen an *Actinophrys sol* Ehrenberg. II. Beiträge zur Physiologie des Formwechsels', ibid., **48**, 371–434.

—— 1926, 'Der Formwechsel der Protistenkerne: eine vergleichendmorphologische Studie', *Ergebn. Zool.* **6**, 235–654.

BERGHE, L., VON DEN, 1946, 'A cytochemical study of the "Volutin granules" in Protozoa', *J. Parasitol.* **32**, 465–6.

BERNSTEIN, T., 1928, 'Untersuchungen an Flagellaten aus dem Darmkanal der Termiten aus Turkestan', *Arch. Protistenk.* **61**, 9–37.

—— 1932, 'Über einige arktische Radiolarien', ibid., **76**, 217–26.

BIENIARZ, B., 1950, 'Influence of vertebrate gonadotropic hormones upon the reproductive cycle of certain protozoa in frogs', *Nature*, **165**, 650.

BIOCCA, E., 1956, 'Alcune considerazioni sulla sistematica dei protozoi e sulla utilite di creare una nuova classe di protozoi', *Rev. Brasil. Malariol.* **8**, 91–102.

BLOCHMANN, F., and KIRCHNER, O., 1895, 'Die mikroskopische Tier- und Pflanzenwelt des Süßwassers', I. *Die Thierwelt*. 2. Aufl. Berlin.

BOCK, K., 1952, 'Zur Ökologie der Ciliaten des marinen Sandgrundes der Kieler Bucht I. und II.', *Kieler Meeresforschungen*, **9**, 77–89, 252–6.

BOELL, E., 1945, 'Respiratory enzymes in Paramecium I. Cytochrome oxydase', *Proc. Nat. Acad. Sci.* **31**, 396–402.

—— 1946, 'The effect of sodium acide on *Paramecium calkinsi*, *Biol. Bull.* **91**, 238–9.

—— and WOODRUFF, L., 1941, 'Respiratory metabolism of mating types in *Paramecium calkinsi*', *J. Exper. Zool.* **87**, 385–402.

BOEVA-PETRUŠEVSKAJA, T. N., 1933, 'Materials for the cycle of development of *Nyctotherus cordiformis*', *Trudy Leningrad Soc. Naturalists*, **42**, 27–40.

BOGDANOWICZ, A. K. (Bogdanovic, A. K.), 1930, 'Über die Konjugation von *Loxodes striatus* (Engelm.) Penard und *Loxodes rostrum* (O.F.M.)', *Ehrenb. Zool. Anz.* **87**, 209–22.

BORGERT, A., 1900, 'Untersuchungen über die Fortpflanzung der tripyleen Radiolarien speziell von *Aulacantha scolymantha*', *H. I. Teil. Zool. Jahrb.* Abt. 2, **14**, 203–76.

—— 1909, 'Untersuchungen über Fortpflanzung der tripyleen Radiolarien speziell von *Aulacantha scolymantha*', *H. II. Teil. Arch. Protistenk.* **14**, 134–263.

BOUGHTON, D., and VOLK, H., 1938, 'Avian hosts of Eimerian Coccidia', *Bird Banding*, **9**, 139–53.

BOYD, M., 1949, *Malariology*. I. Philadelphia and London.

BOZLER, E., 1924, 'Über die Morphologie der Ernährungsorganelle und die Physiologie der Nährungsaufnahme bei *Paramecium caudatum* Ehrbg', *Arch. Protistenk.* **49**, 163–215.

BRACHET, J., 1957, *Biochemical Cytology*. Acad. Press, New York.

BRAND, T., VON, 1946, *Anaerobiosis in invertebrates*. Berlin.

BRANDT, K., 1895, 'Die koloniebildende Radiolarien (Sphaerozoen) des Golfes von Neapel und der angrenzenden Meeresabschnitte', *Fauna u. Flora Golfes Neapel. Monogr.* 13.

—— 1907, Die Tintinnoideen der Plankton-Expedition. Systematischer Teil. Ergebn. Plankton-Exped. Humboldt-Stiftung, 3. Kiel–Leipzig.

BRANDT, P., 1958, 'A study of the mechanism of pinocytosis', *Exper. Cell. Res.* **15**, 300–13.

BRAY, R., 1957, *Studies in the Exo-erythrocytic cycle in the genus Plasmodium*. London.

BRESSLAU, E., 1919, 'Neue Versuche und Beobachtungen über die Hüllenbildung und Hüllsubstanz der Infusorien', *Verh. Deutsch. Zool. Ges.* **26**, 35–37.

—— 1921, 'Die experimentelle Erzeugung von Hüllen bei Infusorien als Paralelle zur Membranbildung bei der künstlichen Parthenogenese', *Naturwiss.* **9**, 57–62.

—— 1928, 'Die Stäbchenstruktur der Tektinhüllen', *Arb. a. Staatsinst. exp. Therapie*, **21**, 26–31.

BRETSCHNEIDER, L., 1934, 'Beiträge zur Strukturlehre der Ophryoscoleciden. II.', *Arch. Protistenk.* **82**, 298–330.

BRODSKIJ, A. L. (Brodsky, A. L.), 1929, 'Fauna of the bodies of water of Kara-Kum desert', *Proc. Middle Asian Univ.* (Series 12), **5**, 1–43.

—— 1937, *Investigation of the soil fauna*, Scient. Committee Uzbek S.S.R.

—— and JANKOVSKAJA, A. I. (Brodsky A. L. and Yankowskaja, A. I.), 1929, 'Materials on the soil fauna of Middle Asia. Part II. Soil protofauna of Kara-Kum desert', *Proc. Middle Asian Univ.* (Series 12), **6**, 1–36.

BROWN, H., 1945, 'On the structure and mechanisms of the protozoan flagellum', *Ohio J. Sci.* **45**, 247–78.

BROWN, V., 1930, 'Hypermastigote Flagellates from the termite *Reticulitermes: Torquenympha octoplus* gen. nov., sp. nov. and two new species of *Microjoena*', *Univ. Calif. Publ. Zool.* **36**, 67–80.

BRUMPT, E., 1925, 'Étude sommaire de l'Entamoeba dispara n. sp. Amibe à kystes quadrinucléés, parasite de l'homme', *Bull. Acad. med.* **49**, 943.

—— 1949, *Précis de Parasitologie*. I, 6 ed. Paris.

BÜNNING, E., and SCHNEIDERHOHN, G., 1956, 'Über das Aktionsspektrum der phototaktischen Reaktion von *Euglenia*', *Arch. Mikrobiol.* **24**, 80–90.

BURT, R., KIDDER, G., and CLAFF, C., 1941, 'Nuclear reorganization in the family Colpodidae', *J. Morphol.* **69**, 537–61.

BUSH, M., 1934, 'The morphology of *Haptophrya michiganensis* Woodhead, an astomatous ciliate from the intestinal tract of *Hemidactylium scutatum* (Schlegel)', *Univ. Calif. Publ. Zool.* **39**, 251–76.

BÜTSCHLI, O., 1889, 'Protozoa (Infusoria und System der Radiolaria)' in Bronns' *Klassen und Ordnungen des Thier-Reichs*, I. C. F. Winter, Leipzig, **3**, 1098 2035.

CACHON-ENJUMET, M., 1961, 'Contribution à l'étude des radiolaires Phaeodaries', *Arch. Zool. exp. gén.*, **100**, fasc. 3, 151–238.

CALDWELL, L., 1933, 'The production of the inherited diversities at endomixis in *Paramecium aurelia*', *J. Exper. Zool.* **66**, 371–407.

CALKINS, G., 1906, 'The Protozoan life cycle', *Biol. Bull.* **11**, 229–44.

—— 1911*a*, 'Effects produced by cutting *Paramecium* cells', ibid., **21**, 36–72.

—— 1911*b*, 'Regeneration and cell division in *Uronychia*', *J. Exper. Zool.* **10**, 95–116.

—— 1915*a*, '*Didinium nasutum*. I. The life history', *J. Exper. Zool.* **19**, 225–41.

—— 1915*b*, 'Cycles and rhythms and the problem of "immortality" in *Paramecium*', *Amer. Natur.* **49**, 65–76.

—— 1916, 'General Biology of the Protozoan life cycle', *Amer. Natur.* **50**, 257–70.

—— 1919*a*, '*Uroleptus mobilis* Engelm. I. History of the nuclei during division and conjugation', *J. Exper. Zool.* **27**, 293–357.

—— 1919*b*, '*Uroleptus mobilis* Engelm. II. Renewal of vitality through conjugation', ibid., **29**, 121–56.

—— 1919*c*, 'Restoration of vitality through conjugation', *Proc. Nat. Acad. Sci.* **5**, 95–102.

—— 1920, '*Uroleptus mobilis* Engelm. III. A study in the vitality', *J. Exper. Zool.* **31**, 287–305.

—— 1921, '*Uroleptus mobilis* Engelm. IV. The effect of cutting during conjugation', ibid., **34**, 449–70.

—— 1930, '*Uroleptus halseyi*. II. The origin and fate of the macronuclear chromatin', *Arch. Protistenk.* **69**, 151–74.

—— 1933. *The biology of the Protozoa*. 2nd ed. Philadelphia.

—— 1934, 'Factors controlling longevity in Protozoan protoplasm', *Biol. Bull.* **67**, 410–41.

—— and CULL, S., 1907, 'The conjugation of *Paramecium aurelia* (*caudatum*)', *Arch. Protistenk.* **10**, 375–415.

—— and SUMMERS, F. (editors), 1941, *Protozoa in biological Research*, Columb. Univ. Press, New York.

CARINI, A., and REICHENOW, E., 1935, 'Über Amöbeninfektionen in Zelleriellen', *Arch. Protistenk.* **84**, 175–85.

CAULLERY, M., 1953, 'Appendice aux Sporozoaires, classe de Haplosporidien', In *Traité de Zoologie* **1** (2), 922–34.

ČEHOVIĆ, G., 1956, 'Recherches expérimentales sur la corrélation hormonale entre le cycle saisonnier de la grenouille et celui de ses parasites', *C.R. Acad. Sci.* **242**, 2176–81

CÉPÈDE, C., 1910, 'Recherches sur les infusoires astomes. Anatomie, biologie, ethologie, parasitaire, systematique', *Arch. Zool. exp. gén.* (sér. 5), 341–609.

CHADEFAUD, M., 1936, 'Les Protistes trichocystifères ou protogastréades', *Ann. Protistol.* **5**, 323–41.

CHAMBERS, R., 1928, 'Intracellular hydrion concentration studies. I. The relation of the environment to the pH of the cytoplasm and of its inclusion bodies', *Biol. Bull.* **55**, 369–76.

CHANG, L., 1946, 'Studies on Entamoeba histolytica', *Parasitol.* **37**, 101–2.

CHAPMANN-ANDRESEN, C., and HOLTER, H., 1955, 'Studies on the ingestion of C^{14} glucose by pinocytosis in the amoeba *Chaos chaos*', *Exper. Cell Res. Suppl.* **3**, 52–63.

CHATTON, E., 1914, 'Les Cnidocystes du Péridinien *Polykrikos schwartzi* Bütschli. Structure, fonctionnement, ontogenèse, homologies. *Arch. Zool. exp. gén.* **54**, 157–94.

—— 1920*a*, 'Existence chez les Radiolaires de Péridiniens parasites considérés comme formes de reproduction de leurs hôtes', *C.R. Acad. Sci.* **170**, 413–15.

CHATTON, E., 1920b, 'Les Péridiniens parasites. Morphologie, reproduction, éthologie', Arch. Zool. exp. gén. 59, 1–475.

—— 1921, 'Réversion de la scission chez les ciliés. Réalisation d'individus distomes et polyénergides de Glaucoma scintillans se multipliant indéfiniment par la scissiparité', C.R. Acad. Sci. 173, 393–5.

—— 1924, 'Sur les connexions flagellaires des éléments flagellés. Centrosomes et mastigosomes. La cinétide, unité cinéto-flagellaire. Cinétides simples et cinétides composées', C.R. Soc. Biol. 91, 574–80.

—— 1927, 'La gamétogénèse méotique du Flagellé Paradinium poucheti, C.R. Acad. Sci. 185, 553–5.

—— 1931, 'Essai d'un schéma de l'énergide d'après une image objective et synthetique: le Dinoflagellé Polykrikos schwartzi Bütschli', Arch. Zool. 16, 169–87.

—— 1934, 'L'origine péridinienne des Radiolaires et l'interprétation parasitaire de l'anisporogenèse,' C.R. Acad. Sci. 198, 309–12.

—— 1937, 'Un nouvel élément de la structure des Sporozoaires: l'argyrome', ibid., 204, 633–7.

—— 1952, 'Classe de Dinoflagellés ou Péridiniens', Traité de Zoologie, 1 (1), 309–406.

—— and BIECHELER, B., 1934, 'Coccidinidae, Dinoflagellés coccidiomorphes parasites de Dinoflagellés et le phylum des Phytodinozoa', C.R. Acad. Sci. 199, 252–5.

—— —— 1936, 'Documents nouveaux relatifs aux Coccidinides (Dinoflagellés parasites). La sexualité du Coccidinium mesnili n. sp.', ibid., 203, 573–6.

—— and BRACHON, S., 1935a, 'Discrimination chez deux Infusoires du genre Glaucoma, entre système argentophile et infraciliature', C.R. Soc. Biol. 118, 399–403.

—— —— 1935b, 'Les relations du chondriome avec l'infraciliature chez divers ciliés. Mitochondries ciliaires et parabasaux', ibid., 118, 958–62.

—— and GRASSÉ, P., 1929, 'Le chondriome, le vacuome, les vésicules osmiophiles, le parabasal, les trichocystes et les cnidocystes du Dinoflagellé Polykrikos schwartzi Bütschli', ibid., 100, 281–5.

—— and HOVASSE, R., 1934, 'L'existence d'un réseau ectoplasmique chez les Polykrikos et les précisions qu'il fournit à la morphologie péridinienne', ibid., 115, 1036–9.

—— —— 1937, 'Actinidinium apsteini n. gen. n. sp. Péridinien parasite entérocœlomique des Acartia (Copépodes). Arch. Zool. exp. gén. 79, 24–29.

—— and LWOFF, A., 1921, 'Sur une famille nouvelle d'Acinétiens, les Sphenophryidae adaptés aux branchies des mollusques acéphales', C.R. Acad. Sci. 173, 1495–7.

—— —— 1929, 'Contributions à l'étude de l'adaptation. Elobiophrya donacis Ch. et Lw., péritriche vivant sur les branchies de l'Acéphale Donax vittatus da Costa', Bull. Biol. 63, 321–49.

—— —— 1930, 'Impregnation, par diffusion argentique, de l'infraciliature des ciliés marins et d'eau douce après fixation cytologique et sans dessication', C.R. Soc. Biol. 104, 834–6.

—— —— 1934, 'Sur un Infusoire parasite des poils sécréteurs des Crustacés edriophthalmes et la famille nouvelle des Pilisuctoridae', C.R. Acad. Sci. 199, 696–9.

—— —— 1935a, 'La constitution primitive de la strie ciliaire des infusoires. La desmodexie', C.R. Soc. Biol. 118, 1068–72.

—— —— 1935b, 'Les Ciliés apostomes. Morphologie, cytologie, éthologie, évolution et systématique. I. Aperçu historique et général, étude monographique des genres et des espèces', Arch. Zool. exp. gén. 77, 1–453.

CHATTON E., and LWOFF, A., 1936a, 'Les Pilisuctoridae Ch. et Lw. Ciliés parasites des poils sécréteurs des Crustacés Edriophthalmes. Polarité, orientation et desmodexie chez les Infusoires, *Bull. Biol.* **70**, 86-144.

—— —— 1936b, 'Technique par l'étude des protozoaires, spécialement de leurs structures superficielles (cinétome et argyrome)', *Bull. Soc. franç. micr.* **25**–39.

—— —— and LWOFF, M., 1931, 'L'origine infraciliaire et la genèse des trichocystes et des trichites chez les Ciliés Foettingeriidae', *C.R. Acad. Sci.* **193**, 670–3.

—— —— —— and MONOD, J., 1931, 'La formation l'ébauche buccale postérieure chez les Ciliés en division et ses relations de continuité topographique et génétique avec la bouche antérieure', *C.R. Soc. Biol.* **107**, 560–4.

—— —— —— and TELLIER, L., 1929, 'L'infraciliature et la continuité génétique des blépharoplastes chez l'acinétien *Podophrya fixa* O. F. Müller', *C.R. Soc. Biol.* **100**, 1191–6.

—— and PERARD, CH., 1921, 'Les Nicollellidae; infusoires intestinaux des Gondis et des Damans et le "cycle évolutif" des Ciliés', *Bull. Biol.* **55**, 86–151.

CHEJSIN, E. M. (Cheissin, Kheissin Heissin), 1930, 'Morphologische und systematische Studien über Astomata aus dem Baikalsee', *Arch. Protistenk.* **70**, 531–618.

—— 1932, 'Morphology and systematics of Baikal parasitic ciliates of the family Ptychostomidae', *Proc. Baikal Limnol.*, Station 2, 29–52.

—— 1935, 'Structure de l'oocyste et perméabilité de ses membranes chez les coccidies du lapin', *Ann. Parasitol.* **13**, 136-46.

—— 1939, 'Coccidiosis of rabbits. Duration of coccidial invasion in rabbits inoculated with *Eimeria magna* oocysts', *Ann. Microbiol., Epidemiol. and Parasitol.* **18**, 201–7.

—— 1940, 'Coccidiosin of rabbits. III. Cycle of development of *Eimeria magna*', *Sci. Trans. Herzen Leningr. Pedag. State Inst.* **30**, 65–91.

—— 1947, 'Coccidia in the alimentary tract of rabbits', *Monograph. Sci. Notes Herzen Leningr. Pedag. State Inst.* **51**, 1–229.

—— 1952, 'Dependence of the rate of pulsation of the contractile vacuole of parasitic ciliates on the living conditions of the host', *Zool. J.* **31**, 72–79.

—— 1956, 'On the systematic of sporozoa (class sporozoa, type Protozoa)', *Zool. Journ. (Moscow)*, **35**, 1281–98.

—— 1957, 'Topological differences in the conjugated species of coccidia of domestic rabbits', *Proc. Leningrad Soc. Naturalists*, **73**, 150–8.

—— 1958, 'Cytologische Untersuchungen verschiedener Studien des Lebenszyklus der Kaninchencoccidien. I. *Eimeria intestinalis* E. Cheissin, 1948', *Arch. Protistenk* **102**, 265–90.

—— 1960, 'Cytological investigation of the life cycle of rabbit coccidia. II. *Eimeria magna*', Symposium *Problems of Cytology and Protistology*, 258–76.

—— 1963, 'Electron microscope study of superficial structure of *Paramecium caudatum*'. *Voprosy morphologii and physiologii prosteishikh*, **3** (in press).

—— and MOSEVIČ, T. N. (Cheissin, E. M., and Mosievich, T. N.), 1962, 'An electron microscope study of *Colpidium colpoda*', *Arch. Protistenk.* **106**, 181–200.

—— and MURATOV, E. M., 1959, 'Cycle of development of *Piroplasma bigeminum* in ticks *Boophilus calcaratus*', *Zool. J.* **38**, 970–86.

—— OVCHINNICOVA, L., SELIVANOVA, G., and BUSE, E., 1963, 'Change of DNA-quantity from division to division in macronucleus of *Paramecium caudatum*', *Acta Protozool.* **1** (in press).

—— and PIC-LEVONTIN, E. M., 1946, 'Introduction of different lines of *Balantidium coli* from man and pig into the alimentary tract of a new host (rat)', *Zool. J.* **25**, 219–24.

CHEN, T., 1940a, 'Polyploidy and its origin in *Paramecium*', *J. Heredity*, **31**, 175–84.
—— 1940b, 'Conjugation in *Paramecium bursaria* between animals with diverse nuclear constitutions', *J. Heredity*, **31**, 185.
—— 1944, 'Mating types in *Paramecium caudatum*', *Amer. Natur.* **78**, 334–40.
—— 1946a, 'Conjugation in *Paramecium bursaria*. II. Nuclear phenomena in lethal conjugation between varieties', *J. Morphol.* **79**, 125–262.
—— 1946b, 'Varieties and mating types in *Paramecium bursaria*. I. New variety and types from England, Ireland and Czechoslovakia', *Proc. Nat. Acad. Sci.* **32**, 173–81.
—— 1948, 'Chromosomes in Opalinidae (Protozoa, Ciliata) with special reference to their behavior, morphology, individuality, diploidy, haploidy and association with nucleoli', *J. Morphol.* **83**, 281–358.
CHOCHLOV, S. S., 1946, 'Apomictic plants. Historical premises and evolutionary prospects', *Scient. Trans. Saratov Univ.* **16**, 3–74.
CHOLODKOVSKIJ, N. A., 1910, 'On biological species', *Proc. Imper. Acad. Sci.* **4**, 751–71.
CHRISTOPHERS, S., and FULTON, J., 1938, 'Observation on the respiratory metabolism of malaria parasite and trypanosomes', *Ann. Trop. Med. Parasitol.* **32**, 43–75.
CINGER, JA. A. (Zinger), 1929, 'Materials on the morphology and cytology of freshwater ciliates', *Russ. Arch. Protistology*, **8**, 51.
CLARK, T., and WALLACE, F., 1960, 'A comparative study of Kinetoplast ultrastructure in the Trypanosomatidae', *J. Protozool.* **7**, 115–24.
CLEVELAND, L., 1924, 'The physiological and symbiotic relationships between the intestinal Protozoa of Termites and their host, with special reference to *Reticulitermes flavipes* Kollar', *Biol. Bull.* **46**, 177–227.
—— 1925, 'The feeding habit of Termite castes and its relation to their intestinal Flagellates', *Biol. Bull.* **48**, 295–308.
—— 1938a, 'Longitudinal and transverse division in two closely related flagellates', *Biol. Bull.* **74**, 1–24.
—— 1938b, 'Origin and development of the achromatic figure', *Biol. Bull.* **74**, 41–55.
—— 1949a, 'Hormone-induced sexual cycles of flagellates. I. Gametogenesis, fertilization and meiosis in *Trichonympha*', *J. Morphol.* **85**, 197–295.
—— 1949b, 'The whole life cycle of chromosomes and their coiling systems (*Holomastigotoides*)', *Trans. Amer. Phil. Soc.* **39**, 1–100.
—— 1950a, 'Hormone-induced sexual cycles of flagellates. II. Gametogenesis, fertilization and one-division meiosis in *Oxymonas*', *J. Morphol.* **86**, 185–213.
—— 1950b, 'Hormone-induced sexual cycles of flagellates. III. Gametogenesis, fertilization and one-division meiosis in *Succinobaculus*', *J. Morphol.* **86**, 215–27.
—— 1950c, 'Hormone-induced sexual cycles of flagellates. IV. Meiosis after syngamy and before nuclear fusion in *Notila*', *J. Morphol.* **87**, 317–47.
—— 1950d, 'Hormone-induced sexual cycles of flagellates. V. Fertilization in *Euconympha*', *J. Morphol.* **87**, 349–67.
—— 1951, 'Hormone-induced sexual cycles of flagellates. VII. One-division meiosis and autogamy without cell division in *Urinympha*', *J. Morphol.* **88**, 385–439.
—— 1953, 'Hormone-induced sexual cycles of flagellates. IX. Haploid gametogenesis and fertilization in *Barbulanympha*', *J. Morphol.* **93**, 371–403.
—— 1954a, 'Hormone-induced sexual cycles of flagellates. X. Autogamy and endomitosis in *Barbulanympha* resulting from interruption of haploid gametogenesis', *J. Morphol.* **95**, 189–212.

CLEVELAND, L., 1954b, 'Hormone-induced sexual cycles of flagellates. XI. Reorganization in the zygote of *Barbulanympha* without nuclear or cytoplasmic division', *J. Morphol.* **95**, 213-35.

—— 1954c, 'Hormone-induced sexual cycles of flagellates. XII. Meiosis in *Barbulanympha* following fertilization, autogamy and endomitosis', *J. Morphol.* **95**, 557-619.

—— 1956a, 'Brief account of the sexual cycles of the flagellates of *Cryptocercus*', *J. Protozool.* **3**, 161-80.

—— 1956b, 'Hormone-induced sexual cycles of flagellates. XIV. Gametic meiosis and fertilization in *Macrospironympha*', *Arch. Protistenk.* **101**, 99-170.

—— 1957, 'Correlation between molting period of *Cryptocercus* and sexuality in its Protozoa', *J. Protozool.* **4**, 168-75.

—— BURKE, A., and KARLON, P., 1960, 'Ecdysone induced modifications in the sexual cycles of the Protozoa of *Cryptocercus*', *J. Protozool.* **7**, 229-39.

—— and DAY, M., 1958, 'Spirotrychonymphidae of *Stolotermes*', *Arch. Protistenk.* **103**, 1-53.

COHEN, B., 1934, 'The effect of conjugation within a clone of *Euplotes patella*', *Genetics*, **19**, 25-39.

COLLIN, B., 1909, 'La conjugation d'*Anoplophrya branchiarum* (Stein) (*A. circulans*, Balbiani)', *Arch. Zool. exp. gén.* (series 5), **1**, 345-88.

—— 1912, 'Étude monographique sur les Acinétiens. II. Morphologie, physiologie, systématique', *Arch. Zool. exp. gén.* **51**, 1-457.

CONNELL, F., 1930, 'The morphology and life cycle of *Oxymonas dimorpha* sp. nov., from *Neotermes simplicicornis* (Banks)', *Univ. Calif. Publ. Zool.* **36**, 51-66.

CORLISS, J., 1952, 'Le cycle autogamique de *Tetrahymena rostrata*', *C.R. Acad. Sci.* **235**, 399-402.

—— 1953, 'Comparative studies on holotrichous ciliates in the *Colpidium–Glaucoma–Leucophris–Tetrahymena* group. II. Morphology, life-cycle and systematic status of strains in pure culture', *Parasitol.* **43**, 49-87.

—— 1956a, 'Occurrence and study of autogamy in diverse strains of *Tetrahymena rostrata* (an abstract)', *J. Protozool.* **3** (Suppl.) 3.

—— 1956b, 'On the evolution and systematic of ciliated Protozoa', *Syst. Zool.* **5**, 68-91, 121-40.

—— 1959, 'An illustrated key to the higher groups of the ciliated Protozoa with definition of terms', *J. Protozool.* **6**, 265-81.

—— 1961a, 'The ciliated Protozoa. Characterization, classification and guide to the literature', *Intern. Ser. Monogr. Pure and Appl. Biol., Zool.* **7**, 1-310.

—— 1961b, *The ciliated Protozoa*. Pergamon Press.

CULBERTSON, J., 1941, *Immunity against animal parasites*, Columb. Univ. Press, New York.

CUNNINGHAM, A., 1915, 'Studies on soil Protozoa', *J. Agric. Sci.* **7**, 49-74.

CURASSON, G., 1943, *Traité de protozoologie vétérinaire et comparée*. Tome 1. Paris.

CUSHMAN, J., 1948, *Foraminifera: their classification and economic use*, 4 ed. Cambridge, Mass.

CVELKOV, V. N. (Zwetkow, W. N.), 1926, 'Eine neue Gregaringattung. *Enterocystis ensis* aus den Larven einer Eintagsfliege', *Arch. Russ. Protistol.* **5**, 45-55.

CZURDA, V., 1933a, 'Über einige Grundbegriffe der Sexualitätstheorie', *Bot. Zbl. Berich.* Abt. A, **50**, 196-210.

—— 1933b, 'Experimentelle Analyse der kopulationsauslösenden Bedingungen bei Mikroorganismen', *Berich. Bot. Zbl.* Abt. A, **51**, 711-62.

DACH, H., VON, 1942, 'Respiration of colorless flagellate, *Astasia klebsii*', *Biol. Bull.* **82**, 350-91.

DAIN, L., 1930, 'Die Konjugation von *Cryptochilum echini* Maupas', *Arch. Protistenk.* **70**, 192–216.

DALTON, A., and FELIX, M., 1957, 'Electron microscopy of mitochondrie and the Golgi complex', *Symp. Soc. Exper. Biol.* **10**, 148–159.

D'ANGELO, E., 1946, 'Micrurgical studies on *Chironomus* salivary gland chromosomes', *Biol. Bull.* **90**, 71.

DAS GUPTA, B., 1959, 'The Feulgen reaction in the different stages of the life cycles of certain Sporozoa', *Quart. J. Micr. Sci.* **100**, 241–55.

DASS, C., 1950, 'Chromatin elimination in Glaucoma pyriformis Ehreb', *Nature*, **165**, 693.

DATE, S., 1931, 'Concentration en ions d'hydrogène dans un corps unicellulaire', *C.R. Soc. Biol.* **106**, 89–93.

DAVENPORT, C. 1897, *Experimental Morphology*. I. New York.

DAWSON, J., and BELKIN, M., 1928, 'The digestion of oils by *Amoeba dubia*', *Proc. Soc. Exper. Biol. Med.* **25**, 790–3.

DECLOÎTRE, L., 1954, 'Biostatistique, biogéographie et Thécamœbiens d'A.-O. F.', *Bull. Inst. franç. Afrique Noire*, **16**, 414–37.

DEFLANDRE, G. 1928, 'Le genre *Arcella* Ehrenberg. Morphologie–biologie–essai phylogénétique et systématique', *Arch. Protistenk.* **64**, 152–287.

DEGEN, A., 1905, 'Untersuchungen über die contractile Vacuole und die Wabenstruktur des Protoplasmas', *Bot. Zbl.* **63**, 160–202.

DELLINGER, O., 1906, 'Locomotion of amoebae and allied forms', *J. Exper. Zool.* **3**, 337–58.

DEMBOVSKA, W., 1922, 'Über den Einfluß des farbigen Lichtes auf die Teilungsgeschwindigkeit von *Paramaecium caudatum*', *Trav. Lab. biol. génér. Inst. Nencki. Varsovie*, **1**, 1–24.

—— 1925, 'Studien über die Regeneration von *Stylonichia mytilus*', *Arch. mikr. Anat.* **104**, 185–209.

—— 1926, 'Studies on the regeneration of Protozoa', *J. Exper. Zool.* **43**, 485–504.

DEMBOWSKI, J., 1913, 'Versuche über die Merotomie der Gregarinen', *Arch. Protistenk.* **29**, 1–21.

DENNIS, E., 1932, 'The life cycle of *Babesia bigemina* (Smith and Kilbourne) of Texas cattle-fever in the tick *Margaropus annulatus* (Say), with notes on the embryology of *Margaropus*', *Univ. Calif. Publ. Zool.* **36**, 263–98.

DEUTSCH, K., and SWANN, M., 1959, 'An electron microscope study of a small free-living amoeba (*Hartmannella astromyxis*)', *Quart. J. Micr. Sci.* **100**, 13–15.

DEVIDÉ, Z., and GEITLER, L., 1947, 'Die Chromosomen der Ciliaten', *Chromosoma*, **3**, 110–36.

DIERKS, K., 1926, 'Lähmungsversuche an Stentor coeruleus durch Kaliumionen', *Zool. Anz.* **67**, 207–18.

DILLER, W., 1928, 'Binary fission and endomixis in the *Trichodina* from tadpoles (Protozoa, Ciliata)', *J. Morphol.* **46**, 521–61.

—— 1936, 'Nuclear reorganization processes in *Paramecium aurelia*, with descriptions of autogamy and "hemixis" ', *J. Morphol.* **59**, 11–67.

—— 1940, 'Nuclear variation in *Paramecium caudatum*', *J. Morphol.* **66**, 605–33.

—— 1948, 'Nuclear behaviour of *Paramecium trichium* during conjugation', *J. Morphol.* **82**, 1–30.

—— 1949, 'An abbreviated conjugation process in *Paramecium trichium*', *Biol. Bull.* **97**, 331–43.

—— 1954, 'Autogamy in *Paramecium polycaryum*', *J. Protozool.* **1**, 60–70.

DIWALD, K., 1938, 'Die ungeschlechtliche und geschlechtliche Fortpflanzung von *Glenodinium lubiniensiforme* sp. nov.', *Flora* (Jena), **32**, 174–92.

DOBELL, C., 1925, 'The life-history and chromosome cycle of *Aggregata eberthi*', *Parasitol.* **17**, 1–136.

—— and JEPPS, M., 1918, 'A study of the diverse races of *Entamoeba histolytica* distinguishable from another by the dimensions of their cysts', *Parasitol.* **10**, 320–51.

DOBZHANSKY, TH., 1937, *Genetics and the origin of species*, Columb. Univ. Press, New York.

—— 1941, *Genetics and the origin of species*. Columb. Univ. Press, 2nd ed., New York.

—— 1958, 'Species after Darwin', in *A Century of Darwin*, London.

DOFLEIN, F., 1909, *Lehrbuch der Protozoenkunde*, 2 Aufl. Jena.

—— and REICHENOW, E., 1929, *Lehrbuch der Protozoenkunde*, 5 Aufl. Jena.

—— 1953, *Lehrbuch der Protozoenkunde*, 6 Aufl. Jena.

DOGIEL, V. A., 1906*a*, 'Beiträge zur Kenntnis der Peridineen', *Mitt. Zool. Stat. Neapel*, **18**, 1–45.

—— 1906*b*, 'Beiträge zur Kenntnis der Gregarinen. I. *Cystobia chiridotae* nov. sp. und *Hyalosphaera gregarinicola* n. g. n. sp.', *Arch. Protistenk.* **7**, 106–29.

—— 1907, 'Beiträge zur Kenntnis der Gregarinen, III. *Schizocystis sipunculi* nov. sp.', *Arch. Protistenk.* **8**, 203–15.

—— 1910, 'Catenata. Organization of the genus *Haplozoon* and of some similar forms', Thesis: Univ. of St. Petersburg.

—— 1916, 'Investigations on parasitic Protozoa in the alimentary tract of termites. I. Tetramidae', *Zool. Ann.* **1**, 1–54.

—— 1920, 'Interesting convergences in the structure of the head organ of Trichonumphidae, of nematocysts of *Polykrikos* and spermia of Decapoda', *Trans. Petrograd Soci. Naturalists*, **51**, 37–45.

—— 1922, 'Investigations of parasitic Protozoa from the alimentary tract of termites. III. Trichonymphidae', *Arch. Russian Protistol. Soc.* **1**, 172–234.

—— 1923, 'Cellulose als Bestandteil des Skelettes bei einigen Infusorien', *Biol. Zbl.* **43**, 289–91.

—— 1925*a*, 'Die Geschlechtsprozesse bei Infusorien (speziell bei den Ophryosceliden); neue Tatsachen und theoretische Erwägungen', *Arch. Protistenk.* **50**, 283–442.

—— 1925*b*, 'How and on what do the ciliates parasitic in the alimentary tract of ungulates feed', *Trans. Leningr. Soc. Naturalists*, **54**, 69–93.

—— 1926, 'The present state of the problem of soil Protozoa', *Proc. State Inst. Exper. Agron.* **4**, 132–7.

—— 1927*a*, 'Monographie der Familie Ophryoscolecidae', *Arch. Protistenk.* **59**, 1–282.

—— 1927*b*, 'Physiologische Studien an Infusorien. I. Wirkung des Lithiumsulfats auf die Exkretion von Neutralrot bei *Cryptochilum echini*', *Zool. Anz.* **71**, 295–99.

—— 1928, 'Über die Konjugation von *Bütschlia parva*', *Arch. Protistenk.* **62**, 80–95.

—— 1929*a*, 'Die sogenannte "Konkrementenvacuole" der Infusorien als eine Statozyste betrachtet', *Arch. Protistenk.* **58**, 319–48.

—— 1929*b*, 'Polymerisation als ein Prinzip der progressiven Entwicklung bei Protozoen', *Biol. Zbl.* **49**, 451–69.

—— 1930, 'Die prospective Potenz der Syncaryonderivate an der Konjugation von *Paraisotricha* erläutert', *Arch. Protistenk.* **70**, 497–516.

—— 1935, 'La mode de conjugation de *Polytoma uvella*', *Arch. Zool. exp. gén.* **77**, 1–8.

—— 1936, 'Oligomerization of homologous organs as one of the processes of evolution of animal organisms', *Arch. Anat. Histol. Embryol.* **15**, 101–14.

DOGIEL, V. A., 1937, 'Type Protozoa': in *Text-book on Zoology*, vol. I. State Publ. Med. Biol. Lit. Moscow–Leningrad.

—— 1946, 'Phylogeny of ciliates from the stomach of ruminants in the light of palaeontological and ecologoparasitological data', *Zool. Journ.* (*Moscow*), **25**, 395–402.

—— 1947*a*, 'Phenomenon of polymerization and oligomerization of homologous organs in the animal kingdom and their evolutionary significance', *Bull. Acad. Sci. U.S.S.R.* (Biol. series), **4**, 471–86.

—— 1947*b*, 'Phylogeny of the stomach-infusorians of ruminants in the light of palaeontological and parasitological data', *Quart. Jour. micr. Sci.* **88**, 337–43.

—— 1949, 'Phenomenon of "conjugated species" in parasites and the evolutionary significance of this phenomenon', *Bull. Acad. Sci. Kazakh. S.S.R.* 74 series (Parasitol.), **7**, 3–15.

—— 1951, *General Protistology*. Moscow.

—— 1954, 'Oligomerization of homologous organs', Pub. Leningrad State Univ.

—— and FURSENKO, A. V., 1920, 'Ectoparasitic ciliates of land Isopoda', *Trans. Petrograd Soc. Naturalists*, **51**, 147–99.

—— and ISAKOVA-KEO, M. M., 1927, 'Physiologische Studien and Infusorien. II. Der Einfluß der Salzlösungen auf die Ernährung von *Paramecium*', *Biol. Zbl.* **47**, 577–86.

—— and REŠETNJAK, V. V. (Dogiel, V. A. and Rešchetnjak, V. V.), 1956, 'Vertical distribution of Radiolaria in the Kurilo-Kamchatka depression', *Proc. Probl. Them. Conferences, Zool. Inst. Acad. Sci. U.S.S.R.* **6**, 72–76.

DOROSZEWSKI, M., 1958, 'Experimental studies on the conductive role of ectoplasm and the silverline system in ciliates', *Acta Biol. Exper.* **18**, 69–88.

DOWNS, L., 1959, 'Mating types and their determination in Stylonychia putrina', *J. Protozool.* **6**, 285–92.

DOYLE, W., 1943, 'The nutrition of Protozoa', *Biol. Rev.* **18**, 119–36.

DRAGESCO, I., 1952*a*, 'The mucoid trichocystis of flagellates and ciliates', *Proc. Soc. Protozool.* **3**, 15.

—— 1952*b*, 'On the biology of sand-dwelling ciliates', *Science Progress*, **50**, 353–63.

—— 1960, 'Les Ciliés mesopsammiques littoraux (systématique, morphologie, écologie)', *Trav. Station Biol. Roscoff.*, N.S. **12**, 1–356.

DRYL, S., 1959, 'Effect of Adaptation to Environment on Chemotaxis of *Paramecium caudatum*', *Acta Biol. Experim.* **19**, 83–93.

DUBININ, V. B., 1954, 'Concept of species in parasitic animals with reference to the construction of a natural system', *Proc. Probl. Them. Conferences, Zool. Inst. Acad. Sci.* **7**, 163–86.

DUBOSCQ, O., and GRASSÉ, P., 1933, 'L'appareil parabasal des Flagellés avec des rémarques sur le trophosponge, l'appareil Golgi, les mitochondries et le vacuome', *Arch. Zool. exp. gén.* **73**, 381–621.

—— —— 1934, 'Notes sur les Protistes parasites des termites de France. IX. L'enkystement des Flagellés de Calotermes flavicollis', *Arch. Zool. exp. gén.* **76**, 66–72.

—— and TUZET, O., 1934, 'Sur le parabasal ou corps de Golgi des éponges calcaires', *Arch. Zool. exp. gén.* **76**, 78–89.

DYSART, M., 1960, 'Study of macronuclear chromatin extrusion in *Tetrahymena limacis* using tritiated thymidine', *J. Protozool.* **7** (Suppl.), 10–11.

EFIMOV, V. V., 1922, 'Freezing and supercooling of protozoa', *Arch. Russ. Protistol. Soc.* **1**, 153–68.

EGELHAAF, A., 1955, 'Cytologisch-entwicklungsphysiologische Untersuchungen zur Konjugation von *Paramecium bursaria* Focke', *Arch. Protistenk.* **100**, 447–514.

EHRENBERG, C., 1838, *Die Infusionsthierchen als vollkomene Organismen*, Leipzig.

EHRET, CH., and HALLER, G., 1961, 'Formation des organelles et des systèmes d'organelles cytoplasmiques au cours de la division chez Paramecium', *Proc. I. Intern. Conf. of Protozool, Praha* (in press).

—— and POWERS, E., 1959, 'The cell surface of *Paramecium*', *Intern. Rev. Cytol.* **8**, 97–133.

EISENBERG-HAMBURG, E., 1932, 'Einfluß der Sr-Salze auf die Bewegung von *Paramecium caudatum*', *Arch. Protistenk.* **77**, 108–24.

ELLIOTT, A., 1949, 'Growth-factor requirements of *Tetrahymena geleii*', *Anat. Rec.* **105**, 527.

—— 1950, 'The growth-factor requirements of *Tetrahymena geleii* E', *Physiol. Zool.* **23**, 85–91.

—— and HAYES, R., 1953, 'Mating types in *Tetrahymena*', *Biol. Bull.* **105**, 269–84.

—— —— 1955, '*Tetrahymena* from Mexico, Panama and Colombia with special reference to sexuality', *J. Protozool.* **2**, 75–80.

ELLIS, I., 1937, 'The morphology, division and conjugation of the salt-marsh Ciliate *Fabrea salina* Henneguy', *Univ. Calif. Publ. Zool.* **41**, 343–88.

ENGELMANN, T., 1875, 'Kontraktilität und Doppelbrechung', *Pflügers' Arch. ges. Physiol.* **11**, 432–64.

—— 1879, 'Über Reizung kontraktilen Protoplasmas durch plötzliche Beleuchtung', *Pflügers' Arch. ges. Physiol.* **19**, 1–7.

ENRIQUES, P., 1907, 'La coniugazione e il differenziamento sessuale negli Infusori', *Arch. Protistenk.* **9**, 195–296.

—— 1916, 'Due mila cinquecento generazione in un Infusorio senza coniugazione nè partenogenesi, nè depressioni', *Bologna Rend. Acc. Sci.*, N.S. **20**, 67–76.

EPSTEIN, T. V. (Epstejn, T. V.), 1941, *Parasitic amobae*, Medgiz, Moscow–Leningrad.

EVANS, F., 1944, 'A study of nuclear reorganization in the ciliate *Woodruffia metabolica*', *J. Morphol.* **74**, 101–27.

FAURÉ-FREMIET, E., 1910,' Étude sur les mitochondries de protozoaires et des cellules sexuelles', *Arch. Anat. Micr.* **2**, 457–648.

—— 1925, 'La structure permanente de l'appareil excréteur chez quelques vorticellides', *C.R. Soc. Biol.* **93**, 500–3.

—— 1932, 'Division et morphogenèse chez *Folliculina ampulla* O. F. Müller', *Bull. Biol.* **66**, 78–110.

—— 1950a, 'Écologie des Ciliés psammophiles littoraux', *Bull. Biol.* **84**, 35–75.

—— 1950b, 'Morphologie comparée et systématique des Ciliés', *Bull. Soc. Zool. Fr.* **75**, 109–22.

—— 1953a, 'Morphology of Protozoa', *Ann. Rev. Microbiol.* **7**, 1–18.

—— 1953b, 'L'hypothèse de la sénescence et les cycles de réorganisation nucléaire chez les Ciliés', *Rev. suisse Zool.* **60**, 426–38.

—— 1954, 'Réorganisation du type endomixique chez les Loxodidae et chez les Centrophorella', *J. Protozool.* **1**, 20–27.

—— 1961, 'Cils vibratiles et flagellés', *Biol. Rev.* **36**, 464–536.

—— FAVARD, P., and CURASSO, N., 1962, 'Étude au microscope électronique des ultrastructures d'*Epistylis anastatica* (Cilié Péritriche)', *Journ. Microsc.* **1**, 287–312.

—— and ROUILLER, C., 1955, 'Microscopie électronique des structures ectoplasmiques chez les Ciliés du genre *Stentor*', *C.R. Acad. Sci.* **241**, 678–80.

—— —— 1959, 'Le cortex de la vacuole contractile et sa ultrastructure chez les Ciliés', *J. Protozool.* **6**, 29–37.

FENYVESSY, B. VON, and REINER, L., 1928, 'Atmung und Glycolise der Trypano-somen. II.', *Bioch. Zeitschr.* **202**, 75–80.

FERMOR, X., 1913, 'Die Bedeutung der Enzystierung bei *Stylonychia pustulata*', *Ehrb. Zool. Anz.* **42**, 380–4.

FERNANDEZ-GALIANO, D., 1949, 'Sobre el aparato neuromotor y otras estructuras protoplásmicas de *Ophryoscolex purkinjei* Stein', *Trab. Inst. Cienc. Nat. Madrid*, ser. biol., **2**, 253–302.

FETTER, D., 1926, 'Determination of the protoplasmic viscosity of *Paramecium* by the centrifuge method', *J. Exper. Zool.* **44**, 279–83.

FIELD, J., 1942, 'Morphological variation in *Plasmodium vivax* Grassi et Feletti, 1890', *Parasitol.* **34**, 82–87.

FILIPČENKO, A. A., and CHEJSIN, E. M., 1937, 'On the existence of races in amoebae of the Histolytica type, differing in the sizes of their cysts and on the methods of their investigations', *Proc. Leningrad Pasteur Inst. Epidemiol. Bacteriol.* **3**, 1–7.

FINLEY, H., 1930, 'Toleration of fresh water Protozoa to increased Salinity', *Ecology*, **11**, 337–47.

—— 1943, 'Sexual differentiation in *Vorticella microstoma*', *Trans. Amer. Micr. Soc.* **62**, 97–121.

—— 1957, 'Electron microscope studies on *Vorticella* and *Spirostomum*', *J. Proto-zool.* **4** (Suppl.), 10.

—— and WILLIAMS, H., 1955, 'Chromatographic analysis of the asexual and sexual stages of a Ciliate (*Vorticella microstoma*)', *J. Protozool.* **2**, 13–18.

FLATHER, M., 1919, 'The influence of glandular extracts upon the contractile vacuoles of *Paramecium caudatum*', *Biol. Bull.* **37**, 22–39.

FÖRSTER, H., and WIESE, L., 1954, 'Gamonwirkungen bei *Chlamydomonas eugame-tos*', *Z. Naturf.* **9b**, 548–50.

FOSTER, E., BAYLOR, M., MEINKOTH, N., and CLARK, G., 1947, 'An electron microscope study of Protozoan flagella', *Biol. Bull.* **93**, 114–21.

FOTT, B., 1959, *Algenkunde*. Jena.

FREY-WYSSLING, A., 1948, *Submicroscopic Morphology of Protoplasm and its Deriva-tives*. New York.

FULTON, J., and CHRISTOPHERES, S., 1938, 'The inhibitive effect of drugs upon oxygen uptake by Trypanosomes (*T. rhodesiense*) and malaria parasites (*Plas-modium knowlesi*)', *Ann. Trop. Med. Parasitol.* **32**, 77–93.

FURSENKO, A. V. (Fursenko, A. W.), 1929, 'Lebenszyklus und Morphologie und Systematik der Infusorien des Baikalsee', *Arch. Protistenk.* **67**, 378–499.

GAEVSKAYA, N. S. (Gaewskaja, N. S.), 1924, 'On the role of pulsating and non-pulsating vacuoles in salt-water infusoria', *Russ. Hydrobiol. Journ.* **3**, 239–52.

—— 1925, 'On new salt-water infusoria, *Cladotricha koltzowi* n.g., n.sp., and *Palmarium salinum* n.g., n.sp.', *Arch. Russ. Protistol.* **4**, 255–88.

—— 1933, 'Zur Ökologie, Morphologie und Systematik der Infusorien des Baikal-sees', *Zoologica*, **32**, 1–298.

GALADZIEV, M. A., and MALM, E., 1929, 'The effect of some physico-chemical factors on marine Protozoa', *Doklady Acad. Sci.* (Series A), **18**, 433–6.

GALL, J., 1959, 'Macronuclear duplication in the ciliated protozoan *Euplotes*', *J. Biophys. Biochem. Cytol.* **5**, 295–308.

GARNHAM, P., 1948, 'The developmental cycle of *Hepatocystes* (*Plasmodium*) kochi in the monkey host', *Trans. Roy. Soc. Trop. Med. Hyg.* **41**, 601–16.

—— 1954, 'The life history of the malaria parasite', *Lecture on the scientific basis of medicine*, **2**, 323–33.

—— 1959, 'La ricerca del ciclo eso-eritrocitico nella malaria dei mammiferi', *R. Ist . sup. sanità*, **22**, 1–11.

GARNHAM P., BRAY, R., COOPER, W., LAINSON, R., AWAD, F., and WILLIAMSON, J., 1955, 'The preerytrocytic stage of Plasmodium ovale', *Trans. Roy. Soc. Trop. Med. Hyg.* **49**, 158–67.

GASSOVSKIJ, G. N. (Gassovsky, G. N.), 1918, 'On the microfauna of the alimentary tract of horse', *Trans. Petrograd Soc. Naturalists*, **49**, 20–37, 65–69.

GAUSE, G. F., 1932, 'Experimental studies on the struggle for existence. I. Mixed population of two species of yeast', *Journ. exper. Biol.* **9**, 389–402.

—— 1934a, 'On the processes of destruction of one species by another in ciliate populations', *Zool. J.* **13**, 18–26.

—— 1934b, 'Experimental investigation of the struggle for existence between *Paramaecium caudatum, Paramaecium aurelia* and *Stylonchia mytilus*', *Zool. J.* **13**, 1–17.

—— 1934c, *The Struggle for Existence.* Williams & Wilkins, Baltimore.

—— 1935a, 'Experimentelle Untersuchungen über die Konkurrenz zwischen *Paramaecium caudatum* und *Paramaecium aurelia*', *Arch. Protistenk.* **84**, 207–24.

—— 1935b, 'Experimental demonstrations of Volterra's periodic oscillations in the numbers of animals', *Journ. exper. Biol.* **12**, 44–48.

—— 1939, 'Investigation on natural selection in Protozoa. I. Adaptation of *Paramaecium aurelia* to increased salinity of the environment', *Zool. J.* **18**, 631–41.

—— NASTJUKOVA, O. K., and ALPATOVA, V. V., 1934, 'The effect of biological changes in the environment on the growth of a mixed population of *Paramaecium caudatum* and *Paramaecium aurelia*', *Zool. J.* **13**, 629–38.

GEDDES, M., and HUMPHREY, G., 1951, 'Glycolisis in *Paramecium caudatum*', *Austral. J. Exper. Biol. a. Med. Sci.* **29**, 187–93.

GEITLER, L., 1941, 'Das Wachstum des Zellkerns in tierischen und pflanzlichen Geweben', *Ergebn. Biol.* **18**, 1–54.

—— 1953, 'Endomitose und endomitotische Polyploidisierung', *Protoplasmologia* VI, C, 1–89.

GELEI, G. VON, 1937, 'Ein neues Fibrillensystem im Ectoplasma von *Paramecium*; zugleich ein Vergleich zwischen dem neuen und dem alten Gittersystem', *Arch. Protistenk.* **89**, 133–62.

—— 1939, 'Neuere Beiträge zum Bau und zu der Funktion des Exkretionssytems von *Paramecium*', *Arch. Protistenk.* **92**, 384–400.

—— 1925a, 'Ein neues *Paramaecium* aus der Umgebung von Szeged, *Paramaecium nephridiatum* n. sp.', *Állatorv. Közlem.*, **22**, 121–59, 245–8.

—— 1925b, 'Nephridial Apparat bei Protozoen', *Biol. Zbl.* **45**, 676–83.

—— 1928, 'Nochmals über den Nephridialapparat bei den Protozoen', *Arch. Protistenk.* **64**, 479–94.

—— 1929, 'Sensorischer Basalapparat der Tastborsten und der Syncilien bei Hypotrichen', *Zool. Anz.* **83**, 275–80.

—— 1932, 'Die reizleitenden Elemente der Ciliaten in naß hergestellten Silber- bzw. Goldpräparaten', *Arch. Protistenk.* **77**, 152–74.

—— 1934, 'Das Verhalten der ectoplasmatischen Elemente des *Parameciums* während der Teilung', *Zool. Anz.* **107**, 161–77.

—— 1938, 'Über die biologische Bedeutung der Pulsationsblase (kontraktile Vakuole) des Protisten', *Mat.-természettud. Ért. Budapest*, **57**, 1037–69.

—— 1950, 'Die Morphogenese des Einzeller mit Rücksicht auf die morphogenetischen Prinzipien von Sewertzoff', *Acta Biol. Acad. Sci. Hungar.* **1**, 69–134.

GEORGEVITCH, J., 1919, 'Études sur le développement de *Myxidium gadi*', *Arch. Zool. exp. gén.* **58**, 251–89.

—— 1935, 'Über Diplo- und Haplophase im Entwicklungskreise der Myxosporidien', *Arch. Protistenk.* **84**, 419–28.

GERARD, R., and HYMAN, L., 1931, 'The cyanide sensitivity of *Paramecium*', *Amer. J. Physiol.* **97**, 524–5.

GERISCH, G., 1959, 'Die Zelldifferenzierung bei *Pleodorina californica* Shaur und die Organization der Phytomonadinenkolonien (über Entwicklung, Koloniebau, Zellasymmetrie und Phototaxis der Phytomonadinen)', *Arch. Protistenk.* **104**, 292–358.

GIBBONS, I., and GRIMSTONE, A., 1960, 'On flagellar structure in certain flagellates', *J. Biophys., Biochem., Cytol.* **7**, 697–718.

GIERSBERG, H., 1922, 'Untersuchungen zum Plasmabau der Amöben im Hinblick auf Wabentheorie', *Arch. Entw. Mech. Organ.* **51**, 150–250.

GIESE, A., 1939, 'Studies on conjugation in *Paramecium multimicronucleatum*', *Amer. Natur.* **73**, 432–44.

—— 1941, 'Mating types in *Paramecium multimicronucleatum*', *Anat. Rec.* **81**, 131–2.

—— 1957, 'Mating types in *Paramecium multimicronucleatum*', *J. Protozool.* **4**, 120–4.

GILL, B., and RAY, H., 1954, 'Glycogen and its probable significance in *Eimeria tenella* Railliet et Lucet, 1891', *Ind. J. Veterin. Sci.* **24**, 223–9.

GILMAN, L., 1939, 'Mating types in *Paramecium caudatum*', *Amer. Natur.* **73**, 445.

—— 1949, 'Intervarietal mating reactions in *Paramecium caudatum*', *Biol. Bull.* **97**, 239.

—— 1956, 'Distribution of the varieties of *Paramecium caudatum*', *J. Protozool.* **3** (Suppl.), 4.

—— 1959, 'Nucleae reorganization in *Paramecium caudatum*', *J. Protozool.* **6**, 3 (Suppl.), 19.

GILMOUR, J., and GREGOR, J., 1939, 'Demes: a suggested new terminology', *Nature*, **144**, 333.

—— and HESLOP-HARRISON, J., 1954, 'The deme terminology and the units of micro-evolutionary change', *Genetics*, 27.

GLENN, S., and MANWELL, R., 1956, 'Further studies on the cultivation of the avian malaria parasites', *Exper. Parasitol.* **5**, 22–33.

GÖBEL, K., 1882, *Grundzüge der Systematik und speziellen Pflanzenmorphologie*, Berlin.

GOLDACRE, R., and LORCH, I., 1950, 'Folding and unfolding of protein molecules in relation to cytoplasmic streaming, amoeboid movement and osmotic work', *Nature*, **166**, 497–500.

GOODEY, T., 1912, 'A contribution to our knowledge of the Protozoa of the soil', *Proc. Roy. Soc.* **84**, 165–80.

—— 1913, 'The excystation of *Colpodia cucullus* from its resting cysts and the nature and properties of the cyst membrane', *Proc. Roy. Soc.* B. **86**, 427–39.

GOROZANKIN, I. N. (Goroschankin, I. N.), 1890, 'Beiträge zur Kenntnis der Morphologie und Systematik der Chlamydomonaden. I. *Chlamydomonas brounii* (mihi)', *Bull. Soc. imp. natur. Moscou*, 104.

GRASSÉ, P., 1926, 'Contribution à l'étude des Flagellés parasites', *Arch. Zool. exp. gén.* **65**, 345–602.

—— 1939, 'Étude de mécanique cellulaire: centromères et centrosomes dans la mitose de certains Flagellés', *C.R. Soc. Biol.* **131**, 1015–18.

—— (editor), 1952–3, *Traité de Zoologie*, **1** (1, 2) Paris.

—— 1956, 'L'ultrastructure de *Pyrsonympha vertens* (Zooflagellata *Pyrsonymphina*) les Flagellés et leur coaptation avec le corps, l'axostyle contractile, le paraxostyle, le cytoplasme', *Arch. Biol.* **67**, 595–611.

—— 1957, 'Ultrastructure, polarité et reproduction de l'appareil de Golgi', *C.R. Acad. Sci.* **245**, 1–4.

—— and DRAGESKO, J., 1957, 'L'ultrastructure du chromosome des Péridiniens et ses conséquences génétiques', *C.R. Acad. Sci.* **245**, 2447–52.

GRASSÉ, P., and HOLLANDE, A., 1941, 'Vacuoles pulsatiles et appareil de Golgi dans l'évolution de la cellule', *Arch. Zool. exp. gén.* **82**, 301–19.

—— —— 1951, 'Cytologie et mitose des *Pseudotrichonympha* Grassi et Foa, 1911', *Ann. Sci. Natur. Biol. anim.* (sér. 11), **13**, 237–46.

—— and THÉODORIDÈS, J., 1957, 'L'ultrastructure de la membrane nucléaire des Gregarines', *C.R. Acad. Sci.* **245**, 1985–6.

—— —— 1958, 'La présence de l'érgastoplasme chez les Protozoaires (cas des Grégarines)', *C.R. Acad. Sci.* **246**, 1352–3.

GRAYDILL, M., and SMITH, TH., 1920, 'Production of fatal blackhead in turkeys by feeding embrionated eggs of *Heterakis papillosa*', *J. Exper. Med.* **31**, 647–55.

GREBECKI, A., 1961, 'Conception électrobiologique du galvanotropisme du *Paramecium caudatum*', *Proc. 1. Int. Conf. of Protozool.* 123–4.

GREINER, J., 1921, 'Zytologische Untersuchungen der Gametenbildung und Befruchtung bei *Adelea ovata*', *Zool. Jahrb.*, Abt. Anat. **42**, 327–62.

GRELL, K., 1940, 'Der Kernphasenwechsel von Stylocephalus (*Stylorhynchus*) longicollis', *P. Stein. Arch. Protistenk.* **94**, 161–200.

—— 1949, 'Die Entwicklung der Makronukleusanlage im Exkonjuganten von *Ephelota gemmipara* R. Hertwig', *Biol. Zbl.* **68**, 289–312.

—— 1950, 'Der Kerndualismus der Ciliaten und Suktorien', *Naturwiss.* **37**, 347–56.

—— 1952 (1953), 'Der Stand unserer Kenntnisse über den Bau der Protistenkerne', *Verh. Dtsch. Zool. Ges.* 212–51.

—— 1953a, 'Die Konjugation von *Ephelota gemmipara* R. Hertwig', *Arch. Protistenk.* **98**, 287–326.

—— 1953b, 'Entwicklung und Geschlechtsbestimmung von *Eucoccidium dinophili*', *Arch. Protistenk.* **99**, 156–86.

—— 1953c, 'Die Chromosomen von *Aulacantha scolymantha* Haeckel', *Arch. Protistenk.* **99**, 1–54.

—— 1954, 'Der Generationswechsel der polythalamen Foraminifere *Rotaliella heterocaryotica*', *Arch. Protistenk.* **100**, 268–86.

—— 1956a, Protozoologie. Springer-Verlag, Berlin–Göttingen–Heidelberg.

—— 1956b, 'Der Kerndualismus der Foraminifere *Glabratella sulkata*', *Z. Naturf.* **11B**, 366–8.

—— 1957, 'Untersuchungen über die Fortpflanzung und Sexualität der Foraminiferen. I. *Rotaliella roscoffensis*', *Arch. Protistenk.* **102**, 147–64.

—— 1958a, 'Untersuchungen über die Fortpflanzung und Sexualität der Foraminiferen. II. *Rubratella intermedia*', *Arch. Protistenk.* **102**, 291–308.

—— 1958b, 'Untersuchungen über die Fortpflanzung und Sexualität der Foraminiferen. III. *Glabratella sulcata*', *Arch. Protistenk.* **102**, 449–72.

—— 1958c, 'Studien zum Differenzierungsproblem an Foraminiferen', *Naturwiss.* **45**, 25–32.

—— 1959, 'Untersuchungen über die Fortpflanzung und Sexualität der Foraminiferen. IV. *Patellina corrugata*', *Arch. Protistenk.* **104**, 211–35.

—— 1960, 'Zur Determination der Zellkerne bei der Foraminifera *Rotaliella heterocaryotica*', *Naturwiss.* **47**, 211–12.

GRIMSTONE, A., 1959, 'Cytoplasmic membranes and the nuclear membrane in the Flagellate *Trichonympha*', *J. Biophys., Biochem., Cytol.* **6**, 369–78.

—— 1961, 'Fine structure and morphogenesis in Protozoa', *Biol. Rev.* **36**, 97–150.

GROMOVA, E. N., 1941, 'The effect of external factors on the structure of the macronucleus in *Paramaecium caudatum*', *Zool. J.* **20**, 187–97.

—— 1948, 'Dynamics of nucleic acids in the process of conjugation of *Paramaecium caudatum*', *Doklady Acad. Sci. U.S.S.R.* **63**, 73–75.

GROSS, F., 1934, 'Zur Biologie und Entwicklungsgeschichte von *Noctiluca miliaris*', *Arch. Protistenk.* **83**, 178–96.

GRUCHY, D., 1955, 'The breeding system and distribution of *Tetrahymena pyriformis*', *J. Protozool.* **2**, 178–85.

GUERNE, J., DE, 1888, 'Sur les disséminations des organismes d'eau douce par les Palmipèdes', *C.R. Soc. Biol.*

GUILCHER, Y., 1951, 'Contribution à l'étude des Ciliés gemmipares, Chonotriches et Tentaculifères', *Ann. Sci. Natur. Zool.* sér. 11, **13**, 33–132.

GUTTES, E., and GUTTES, S., 1960, 'Incorporation of tritium-labelled thymidine into the macronucleus of *Stentor coeruleus*', *Exper. Cell. Res.* **19**, 626–8.

HAAGEN-SMIT, A., and THIMANN, K., 1938, 'The excystment of *Colpoda cucullus*. I. The chemical nature of the excysting factors in hay infusion', *J. Cell. Comp. Physiol.* **11**, 389–407.

HADZI, J., 1953, 'An attempt to reconstruct the system of animal classification', *Syst. Zool.* **2**, 145–54.

HAECKEL, E., 1826, 'Die Radiolarien (Rhizopoda, Radiolaria)', *Monographie*, Berlin.

—— 1868, 'Monographie der Moneren', *Jen. Zeitschr. Naturwiss.* 4.

—— 1887, 'Report on the Radiolaria collected by H.M.S. *Challenger*, during the year 1873–1876', *Chall. Rep. Zool.* i. 1–888; ii. 889–1809.

HAECKER, V., 1907, 'Zur Statik und Entwicklung des Coelographidenskelettes', *Arch. Protistenk.* **9**, 139–69.

—— 1908, 'Tiefseeradiolarien', *Wiss. Ergebn. Deutsch. Tiefsee-Exped. a. d. Dampfer "Valdivia"'*, i. 1–336; ii. 337–476; iii. 477–706.

—— 1909, 'Die Radiolarien in der Variations- und Artbildungslehre', *Z. Induct. Abstam.-u. Vererbungslehre*, **2**, 1–17.

HALL, R., 1923, 'Morphology and binary fission of *Menodinium incurvum* Klebs', *Univ. Calif. Publ. Zool.* **20**, 447–76.

—— 1925, 'Binary fission on *Oxyrrhis marina* Duj', *Univ. Calif. Publ. Zool.* **26**, 281–324.

—— 1941a, 'Food requirements and other factors influencing growth of Protozoa in pure cultures', In *Protozoa in Biological Research*. Ed. Calkins and Summers. New York.

—— 1941b, 'The effect of cyanide on oxygen consumption of *Colpidium campylum*', *Physiol. Zool.* **14**, 193–208.

—— 1941c, 'Populations of plant-like flagellates', *Amer. Natur.* **75**, 419–37.

—— 1953, *Protozoology*. Prentice-Hall, New York.

HAMMOND D., BOWMAN, G., DAVIS, L., and SIMENS, B., 1946, 'The endogenous phase of the life cycle of *Eimeria bovis*', *J. Parasitol.* **32**, 409–22.

HANSON, E., 1958, 'On the origin of the Eumetazoa', *Syst. Zool.* **7**, 16–47.

HARTMANN, M., 1909, 'Polyenergide Kerne. Studien über multiple Kernteilungen und generative Chromidien bei Protozoen', *Biol. Zbl.* **29**, 481–7, 491–500.

—— 1911, 'Die Konstitution der Protistenkerne und ihre Bedeutung für die Zellenlehre', G. Fischer, Jena.

—— 1921, 'Untersuchungen über die Morphologie und Physiologie des Formwechsels der Phytomonadinen (Volvocales). III. Die dauerndagame Zucht von *Eudorina elegans*, experimentelle Beiträge zum Befruchtungs- und Todproblem', *Arch. Protistenk.* **43**, 223–86.

—— 1924, 'Der Ersatz der Fortpflanzung von Amoeben durch fortgesetzte Regenerationen. Weitere Versuche zum Todproblem', *Arch. Protistenk.* **49**, 447–64.

—— 1925, 'Über relative Sexualität bei *Ectocarpus siliculosus*. Ein experimenteller Beitrag zur Sexualitätshypothese der Befruchtung', *Naturwiss.* **13**, 975–80.

—— 1928, 'Über experimentelle Unsterblichkeit von Protozoen-Individuen. Ersatz der Fortpflanzung von Amoeba proteus durch fortgesetzte Regeneration', *Zool. Jahrb., Abt. Allg. Zool. Physiol. Tiere*, **45**, 973–87.

HARTMANN, M, 1929, 'Verteilung, Bestimmung und Vererbung des Geschlechts bei den Protisten und Thallophyten', *Handb. d. Vererbungswiss.* **2**, 1–115.

—— 1952, 'Polyploide (polyenergide) Kerne bei Protozoen', *Arch. Protistenk.* **98**, 125–56.

—— 1956, Die Sexualität. 2 Aufl. G. Fischer, Stuttgart.

—— and NAGLER, K., 1908, 'Kopulation bei *Amoeba diploidae* n. sp. mit Selbständigbleiben der Gametenkerne während des ganzen Lebenszyklus', *S.B. Ges. Natur. Fr. Berl.* **5**, 112–25.

HAUSCHKA, T., 1943, 'Life history and chromosome cycle of the coccidian *Adelina deronis*', *J. Morphol.* **73**, 529.

HAWKING, F., 1954, 'Milk, p-aminobensoate and malaria of rats and monkeys', *Brit. Med. J.* **1**, 425–9.

HECKMANN, K., 1963, 'Paarungssystem und genabhängige Paarungsdifferenzierung bei dem hypotrichen Ciliaten Euplotes vannus O. F. Müller', *Arch. Protistenk.* **106**, 393–421.

HEGNER, R., 1919, 'Heredity variation and the appearance of diversities during the vegetative reproduction of *Arcella dentata*', *Genetics*, **4**, 95–150.

—— 1926, 'The biology of host-parasite relationships among Protozoa living in man', *Quart. Rev. Biol.* **1**, 393–418.

HEILBRUNN, L., 1929, 'Protoplasmic viscosity of amoeba at different temperatures', *Protoplasma*, **8**, 58–64.

—— 1936, 'Protein lipid binding in protoplasm', *Biol. Bull.* **71**, 299–305.

HERFS, A., 1922, 'Die pulsierende Vakuole der Protozoen, ein Schutzorgan gegen Aussüßung. Studien über Anpassung der Organismen an das Leben im Süßwasser', *Arch. Protistenk.* **44**, 227–60.

HERTWIG, R., 1877, 'Ueber den Bau und die Entwicklung der *Spirochona gemmipara*', *Jen. Zeitschr. Naturwiss.* **11**, 149–87.

—— 1889, 'Über die Konjugation der Infusorien', *Abhandl. Bayer. Akad. Wiss. München.* **17**, 1–83.

—— 1903, 'Über Korrelation von Zell- und Kerngröße, und ihre Bedeutung für die geschlechtliche Differenzierung und die Teilung der Zelle', *Biol. Zbl.* **23**, 49–62, 108–19.

—— 1914, 'Über Parthenogenesis der Infusorien und die Depressionszustände der Protozoen', *Biol. Zbl.* **34**, 557–81.

HIRSCHLER, J., 1924, 'Sur les composants lipoidifères du plasma des Protozoaires', *C.R. Soc. Biol.* **10**, 891–3.

—— 1927, 'Studien über sich mit Osmium schwarzenden Plasmakomponenten (Golgi Apparat, Mitochondrien) einiger Protozoenarten nebst Bemerkungen über die Morphologie der ersten von ihnen im Tierreiche', *Z. Zellforsch. mikr. Anat.* **5**, 704–86.

HIWATASHI, K., 1949, 'Studies on the conjugation of *Paramecium caudatum*. I. Mating types and groups in the races obtained in Japan. II. Induction of pseudoselfing pairs by formalin killed animals', *Sci. Rep. Tohoku Imp. Univ. Biol.* **18**. 137–443.

HOARE, C., 1925, 'The present state of our knowledge regarding the origin, evolution and classification of trypanosomes and allied forms', *Russian Arch. Protistol.* **3**, 177–85.

—— 1933, 'Studies on some new ophidian and avain Coccidia from Uganda, with a reversion of the classification of the Eimeriidae', *Parasitol.* **25**, 359–88.

—— 1938, 'Morphological and Taxonomic studies on Mammalian Trypanosomes. V. Diagnostic value of the Kinetoplast', *Trans. Roy. Soc. Trop. Med. Hyg.* **32**, 333–42.

HOARE, C., 1948, 'The relationship of the Haemoflagellates', *Proc. IV Intern. Congress Trop. Med. a. Malariol., Washington,* 87–88.

—— 1949, *Handbook of medical protozoology.* London.

—— 1954, 'The loss of the kinetoplast in Trypanosomes with special reference to *Trypanosoma evansi*', *J. Protozool.* **1**, 28–33.

—— 1956*a*, 'Morphological and Taxonomic studies on Mammalian Trypanosomes. VIII. Revision of *Trypanosoma evansi*', *Parasitol.* **46**, 130–72.

—— 1956*b*, 'Classification of Coccidia Eimeriidae in a "Periodic system" of Homologous genera', *Rev. Brasil. malarial.* **8**, 197–202.

—— 1956*c*, 'Intraspecific biological categories in pathogenic protozoa', *Zool. J.* **35**, 1113–17. (Also: *Refuah Veterinarith, Tel-Aviv,* **12**, 1955, 263.)

—— 1957, 'The spread of African Trypanosomes beyond their natural range.' (Essay on historical zoogeography of the host-parasite system.) *Trans. Leningrad Soc. Naturalists,* **73**, 111–16. (Also: *Zeitschr. Tropenmed.* **8**, 1957, 157–61.)

—— 1960*a*, 'Evolution and phylogeny of Haemoflagellates', *Zool. J.* **39**, 960–97.

—— 1960*b*, 'Host-parasite relations in amoebiasis', *Ann. Leningrad Univ.* **15**, 57–68.

—— and COUTELEN, F., 1933, 'Essai de classification des Trypanosomes des mammifères et de l'homme basé sur leurs caractères morphologiques et biologiques', *Ann. Parasitol.* **11**, 196–200.

HÖBER, R., 1945, *Physical chemistry of cells and tissues.* Philadelphia.

HOFFMANN-BEZLING, H., 1955, 'Geißelmodelle und Adenosentriphosphat', *Biochim. Biophys. Acta,* **16**, 146–54.

HOFKER, J., 1930, 'Der Generationswechsel von *Rotalia beccarii* var. *flevensis* nov. var', *Z. Zellforsch. mikr. Anat.* **10**, 756–68.

HOLLANDE, A., 1942, 'Étude cytologique et biologique de quelques Flagellés libres', *Arch. Zool. exp. gén.* **83**, 73–170.

—— and ENJUMET, M., 1954, 'Morphologie et affinité du Radiolaire *Sticholonche zanclea*', *Ann. Sci. Natur. Zool.* **16**, 337–42.

HOLTER, H., 1959*a*, 'Pinocytosis', *Intern. Rev. Cytol.* **8**, 481–503.

—— 1959*b*, 'Problems of pinocytosis with special regard to amoebae', *Ann. N.Y. Acad. Sci.* **78**, 524–37.

—— and LOWY, B., 1959, 'A study of the properties and localization of the acid phosphatase in the amoeba Chaos chaos', *C. R. Trav. Lab. Carlsberg,* **31**, 105–27.

—— and MARSHALL, J., 1954, 'Studies on pinocytosis in the amoeba *Chaos chaos*', *C. R. Trav. Lab. Carlsberg* (ser. Chim.), **29**, 7–26.

HOLZ, G., 1950, 'Synthesis of vitamins of the B-complex by *Chilomonas paramecium*', *Physiol. Zool.* **23**, 213–20,

HORNE, R., and NEWTON, B., 1958, 'Intracellular structures in *Strigomonas oncopelti*. II. Fine structure of the kinetoplast, blepharoplast-complex', *Exper. Cell. Res.* **15**, 103–11.

HORNING, E., 1927*a*, 'On the relation of mitochondria to the nucleus', *Austr. J. Exper. Biol.* **4**, 75–78.

—— 1927*b*, 'On the relation of mitochondria in the surface cytoplasm of infusorians', *Austr. J. Exper. Biol.* **4**, 187–90.

—— 1929, 'Studies on Mitochondria', *Austr. J. Exper. Biol.* **6**, 11–19.

HOSODA, S., 1928, 'Studien über die Entwicklung und Vermehrung der *Isospora lakazei* Labbe', *Fucuoka Acta Medica,* **21**, 885–930.

HOVASSE, R., 1924, 'Sur les Péridiniens parasites des Radiolaires coloniaux', *Bull. Soc. Zool. France,* **48**, 337.

—— 1937, 'Contribution à l'étude de l'appareil de Golgi des Flagellés libres: l'existence d'un corps parabasal chez *Cercomonas longicauda* Duj', *Arch. Zool. exp. gén.* (Notes et Rev.), **79**, 43–46.

HOVASSE, R., 1951, 'Contribution à l'étude de la Cnidogenèse chez les Péridiniens I. Cnidogenèse cyclique chez *Polykrikos schwartzi* Bütschli', *Arch. Zool. exp. gén.* **87**, 299–334.

HOWLAND, R., 1924*a*, 'On excretion of nitrogenous waste as a function of the contractile', *J. Exper. Zool.* **40**, 231–50.

—— 1924*b*, 'Experiments on the contractile vacuole of *Amoeba verrucosa* and *Paramecium caudatum*', *J. Exper. Zool.* **40**, 251–62.

HUFF, C., 1948, 'Exoerythrocytic stages of malarial parasites', *Amer. J. Trop. Med.* **28**, 527–31.

—— 1951, 'Observations on the pre-erythrocytic stages of *Plasmodium relictum, Plasmodium cathemerium* and *Plasmodium gallinaceum* in various birds', *J. Infect. Dis.* **88**, 17–26.

—— and GAMBRELL, E., 1934, 'Strains of *Plasmodium cathemerium* with and without gametocytes', *Amer. J. Hyg.* **19**, 404–15.

HUMPHREY, B., and HUMPHREY, G., 1947, 'Succinic dehydrogenase in Protozoa', *Nature*, **159**, 374.

—— —— 1948, 'Studies in the respiration of *Paramecium caudatum*', *J. Exper. Biol.* **25**, 123–34.

HUNGATE, R., 1939, 'Experiments on the nutrition of Zootermopsis. III. The anaerobic carbohydrate dissimilation by the intestinal Protozoa', *Ecology*, **20**, 230–45.

—— 1943, 'Further experiments on cellulose digestion by the Protozoa in the rumen of cattle', *Biol. Bull.* **84**, 157–63.

—— 1950, 'Mutualismus in Protozoa', *Ann. Rev. Microbiol.* **4**, 53–66.

—— 1955, 'Mutualistic intestinal Protozoa', *Biochemistry and Physiology of Protozoa*, **I**, 159–201.

HUNNINEN, A., and WICHTERMAN, R., 1936, 'Hyperparasitism: a species of *Hexamita* (Protozoa, Flagellata) found in the reproductive systems of *Deropristis inflata* (Trematoda) from marine Eels', *J. Parasitol.* **22**, 540.

HUTCHENS, J., 1939, 'Respiration in *Chilomonas paramecium*', *Biol. Bull.* **77**, 298.

HUTH, W., 1913, 'Zur Entwicklungsgeschichte der Thalassicolen', *Arch. Protistenk.* **30**, 1–124.

HUTNER, S., AARONSON, S., BAKER, H., and NATHAN, H., 1956, 'New problems with B₁₂ metabolism in Protozoa', *J. Protozool.* **3**, (Suppl.), 5.

—— and LWOFF, A. (editors), 1955, *Biochemistry and Physiology of Protozoa. II.* Academic Press Inc., New York.

HYMAN, L., 1917, 'Metabolic gradients in Amoeba and their relation to the mechanism of amoeboid movement', *J. Exper. Zool.* **24**, 55–99.

IKEDA, M., 1956, 'Factors necessary for *Eimeria tenella* infection on the chicken. III. Influence of the upper alimentary canal on infection. IV. Investigations of the site of action of the pancreatic juice on infection', *Jap. J. Vet. Sci.* **18**, 25–26, 45–51.

—— 1960, 'Factors necessary for *Eimeria tenella* infection of the chicken. Excystation of oocyst in vitro', *Jap. J. Vet. Sci.* **22**, 27–41.

INOKI, S., KITAURA, T., KUROGOCHI, Y., OSAKI, H., and NAKABAYASHI, T., 1952, 'Genetical studies on the antigenic variation in *Trypanosoma gambiense*', *Jap. J. Genetics*, **27**, 85–92.

IRLINA, I., 1963, 'Some physiological and cytochemical changes on *Paramecium caudatum* occurring on adaptation to different temperatures', *Cytologia*, **5**, 183–93.

IZJUMOV, G. I. (Isumov, G. I.), 1947, 'Digestive processes in *Tocophrya infusionum*', *Zool. J.* **26**, 263–8.

JAHN, T., 1941, 'Respiratory metabolism', In *Protozoa in Biological Research*, ed. G. Calxius and F. Souvriers, Columbia Univ. Press, New York, 352–453.

JAKOBS, L., 1941, 'Oxidation-reduction potentials in relation to the cultivation of *Entamoeba histolytica*', *J. Parasitol.* **27**, (6, Suppl.) 65.

JAKUS, M., 1945, 'The structure and properties of the trichocysts of *Paramecium*', *J. Exper. Zool.* **100**, 457–85.

—— and HALL, C., 1946, 'Electron microscope observations of the trichocysts and cilia of *Paramecium*', *Biol. Bull.* **91**, 141–4.

JAMES, W., 1953, *Plant Respiration*. Oxford Univ. Press.

JAMESON, A., 1920, 'The chromosome cycle of Gregarines, with special reference to *Diplocystis schneideri*', *Quart. J. Micr. Sci.* **64**, 207–25.

JANICKI, C., 1915, 'Untersuchungen an parasitischen Flagellaten. II. Teil. Die Gattungen *Devescovina, Parajoenia, Stephanonympha, Calonympha*', *Z. wiss. Zool.* **112**, 573–691.

JANKOVSKIJ, A. V., 1960, 'Process of conjugation in *Paramaecium trichium* Stokes. I. Amphimixis and autogamy', *Cytologia*, **2**, 581–8.

—— 1962, 'Processes of conjugation in *Paramaecium putrinum* C.L. (*P. trichium* Stokes). 2. Apomictic reorganization cycles. System of mixotypes', *Cytologia*, **4**, 434–44.

JENNINGS, H., 1900, 'Studies on Reactions to stimuli in unicellular Organisms. V. On the movements and motor Reflexes of the Flagellata and Ciliata', *Amer. J. Physiol.* **3**, 229–60.

—— 1904, 'Contribution to the behavior of lower organisms', *Pub. Carnegie Inst. Wash.* 257.

—— 1908, 'Heredity, variation and evolution in Protozoa. 1. The fate of new structural characters in *Paramecium* in connection with the problem of the inheritance of acquired characters in unicellular organisms', *J. Exper. Zool.* **5**, 577–632.

—— 1911, 'Assortative mating, variability and inheritance of size in the conjugation of *Paramecium*', *J. Exper. Zool.* **11**, 1–134.

—— 1913, 'The effect of conjugation on *Paramecium*', *J. Exper. Zool.* **14**, 279–391.

—— 1916, 'Heredity, variation and the results of selection in the uniparental reproduction of *Difflugia corona*', *Genetics*, **1**, 407–534.

—— 1929, 'Genetics of the Protozoa. Bibliographia', *Genetics*, **5**, 105–330.

—— 1939, 'Genetics of *Paramecium bursaria*. I. Mating types and groups, their interrelations and distributions, mating behavior and self sterility', *Genetics*, **24**, 202–33.

—— 1944a, '*Paramecium bursaria*: Life history. I. Immaturity, maturity and age', *Biol. Bull.* **86**, 131–45.

—— 1944b, '*Paramecium bursaria*: Life history. II. Age and death of clones in relation to the results of conjugation', *J. Exper. Zool.* **96**, 27–52.

—— 1944c, '*Paramecium bursaria*: Life history. III. Repeated conjugation in the same stock at different ages with and without inbreeding in relation to mortality at conjugation', *J. Exper. Zool.* **96**, 243–73.

—— 1944d, '*Paramecium bursaria:* Life history. IV. Relation of inbreeding to mortality of exconjugant clones', *J. Exper. Zool.* **97**, 165–97.

—— 1945, '*Paramecium bursaria*: Life history. V. Some relations of external conditions, past or present, to ageing and to mortality of exconjugants, with summary of conclusions on age and death', *J. Exper. Zool.* **99**, 15–31.

—— and OPITZ, P., 1944, 'Genetics of *Paramecium bursaria*. IV. A fourth variety from Russia', *Genetics*, **29**, 576–83.

JENSEN, P., 1893a, 'Über den Geotropismus niederer Organismen', *Pflügers' Arch. ges. Physiol.* **53**, 428.

JENSEN, P., 1893*b*, 'Die absolute Kraft einer Flimmerzelle', *Pflügers' Arch. ges. Physiol.* **54**, 537–51.

JIROVEC, O., WENIG, K., FOOT, B., BARTOŠ, E., WEISER, J., ŠRÁMEK-HUŠEK, R., 1953, *Protozoologie*. Praha.

JOLLOS, V., 1913, 'Experimentelle Untersuchungen an Infusorien', *Biol. Zbl.* **33**, 222–36.

—— 1921, 'Experimentelle Protistenstudien. I. Untersuchungen über Variabilität und Vererbung bei Infusorien', *Arch. Protistenk.* **43**, 1–222.

—— 1934, 'Dauermodifikationen und Mutationen bei Protozoen', *Arch. Protistenk.* **83**, 197–219.

JORGENSEN, E., 1905, 'The protist plancton', *Bergen Mus. Marine Investig.* **2**, 49–151.

JOSEPH, H., 1907, 'Beobachtungen über die Kernverhältnisse von Loxodes rostrum O. F. M.', *Arch. Protistenk.* **8**, 344–69.

JOYET-LAVERGNE, P., 1926, 'Recherches sur les cytoplasmes des Sporozoaires', *Arch. Anat. Micr.* **22**, 1–128.

JURAND, A., 1961, 'An electron microscope study of food vacuoles in *Paramecium aurelia*', *J. Protozool.* **8**, 185–90.

KAHL, A., 1913*a*, 'Über die verwandtschaftlichen Beziehungen der Suctorien zu den Prostomen Infusorien', *Arch. Protistenk.* **73**, 423–81.

—— 1931*b*, 'Urtiere oder Protozoa. I. Wimpertiere oder Ciliata (Infusoria)', In *Die Tierwelt Deutschlands*. Jena, **21**, 181–398.

—— 1932, 'Ctenostomata (Lauterborn) n. subordo. Vierte Unterordnung der Heterotricha', *Arch. Protistenk.* **77**, 231–304.

KATASHIMA, R., 1952, 'Studies on *Euplotes*. I. Conjugation and cytogamy induced by split pair method in *Euplotes harpa*', *J. Sci. Hiroshima Univ.* ser. B, **13**, 111–20.

KAY, M., 1946, 'Studien on *Oxytricha bifaria*', *Trans. Amer. Micr. Soc.* **65**, 132–48.

KAZANCEV, V. P. (Kasanzeff, W. P.), 1910, 'Zur Kenntnis von *Loxodes rostrum*', *Arch. Protistenk.* **20**, 79–96.

KEILIN, D., 1953, 'Occurrence of Haemoglobin in yeast and supposed stabilization of the oxygenated cytochrome oxidase', *Nature*, **172**, 390–3.

—— and RYLEY, I., 1953, 'Haemoglobin in Protozoa', *Nature*, **172**, 451.

KENT, S., 1880–2. *A Manual of the Infusoria*, I–III. David Bogue, London.

KEYSSELITZ, G., 1908, 'Die Entwicklung von *Myxobolus pfeifferi*', *Arch. Protistenk.* **11**, 252–308.

KIDDER, G., 1933, 'Studies on *Conchophthirius mytili* de Morgan. I. Morphology and division', *Arch. Protistenk.* **79**, 1–24.

—— 1938, 'Nuclear reorganization without cell division in *Paraclevelandia simplex* (Family Clevelandellidae), an endocommensal Ciliate of the wood-feeding roach, *Panesthia*', *Arch. Protistenk.* **81**, 69–77.

—— and CLAFF, G., 1938, 'Cytological investigations of *Colpoda cucullus*', *Biol. Bull.* **74**, 178–97.

—— and DEWEY, V., 1945, 'Studies on the biochemistry of *Tetrahymena*. IV. Aminoacids and their relation to the biosynthesis of thiamine', *Biol. Bull.* **89**, 131–43.

—— —— 1949, 'Studies on the biochemistry of *Tetrahymena*. XIII. B-vitamin requirements', *Arch. Biochem.* **21**, 66–73.

KIESEL, A., 1925, 'Untersuchungen über Protoplasma. I. Über die chemischen Bestandteile des Plasmodiums von *Reticularia lycoperdon*', *Hoppe-Seylers Zeitschr. Physiol. Chem.* **150**, 149.

—— 1927, 'Untersuchungen über Protoplasma. II. Über die chemischen Bestandteile des Plasmodiums von *Lycogala epidendron* und die Veränderung derselben während der Sporendifferenzierung', *Hoppe-Seylers Zeitschr. Physiol. Chem.* **164**, 103.

KIL, S. G., 1940, 'Experimental investigation on variation in *Diplodinium dentatum* (Ciliata, Ophryoscolecidae)', *Scient. Trans. Herzen, Leningr. State Pedag. Inst.* **30**, 25–50.

KIMBALL, R., 1939*a*, 'Change of mating type during vegetative reproduction in *Paramecium aurelia*', *J. Exper. Zool.* **81**, 165–79.

—— 1939*b*, 'Mating types in *Euplotes*', *Amer. Natur.* **73**, 451–6.

—— 1942, 'The nature and inheritance of mating types in *Euplotes patella*', *Genetics*, **27**, 269–85.

—— 1943, 'Mating types in the ciliate Protozoa', *Quart. Rev. Biol.* **18**, 30–45.

—— and BARKA, T., 1959, 'Quantitative cytochemical studies on *Paramecium aurelia*. II. Feulgen microspectrophotometry of the macronucleus during expotential growth', *Exper. Cell. Res.* **17**, 173–82.

—— and PRESCOTT, D., 1962, 'Deoxyribonucleic acid synthesis and distribution during growth and amitosis of the macronucleus of *Euplotes*', *J. Protozool.* **9**, 88–93.

KING, R., 1928, 'The contractile vacuole of *Paramecium trichium*', *Biol. Bull.* **55**, 59–64.

KINOSITA, H., 1938, 'Electric stimulation of *Spirostomum*', *J. Fac. Sci. Tokyo Univ.* **5**, 71–105.

—— 1939, 'Electrical stimulation of *Paramecium* with linearly increasing current', *J. Cell. Comp. Physiol.* **13**, 253–61.

KIRBY, H., 1928, 'A species of *Proboscidiella* from *Kalotermes* (*Cryptotermes*) *dudleyi* Banks, a termite of Central America, with remarks on the oxymonad flagellates', *Quart. J. Micr. Sci.* **72**, 355–86.

—— 1929, '*Snyderella* and *Coronympha*, two new genera of multinucleate flagellates from termites', *Univ. Calif. Publ. Zool.* **31**, 417–32.

—— 1939, 'Two new flagellates from Termites in the genera *Coronympha* Kirby and *Metacoronympha* Kirby, new genus', *Proc. Calif. Acad. Sci.* **22**, 207–20.

—— 1944, 'Some observations on cytology and morphogenesis in flagellate Protozoa', *J. Morphol.* **75**, 361–406.

KITCHING, J., 1939, 'The effect of lack of oxygen and low oxygen tensions on *Paramecium*', *Biol. Bull.* **77**, 339–53.

—— 1952, 'Contractile vacuoles', *Symposium of the Society for experimental biology*, **6**, 145–66.

—— 1956, 'Contractile vacuoles of Protozoa', *Protoplasmatologia*, **3** (D–3*a*), 1–45.

KLEBS, G., 1896, *Die Bedingungen der Fortpflanzung bei einigen Algen und Pilzen.* G. Fischer, Jena.

KLEIN, B., 1926, 'Ergebnisse mit einer Silbermethode bei Ciliaten', *Arch. Protistenk.* **56**, 243–79.

—— 1927, 'Die Silberliniensysteme der Ciliaten. Ihr Verhalten während Teilung und Conjugation, neue Silberbilder, Nachträge', *Arch. Protistenk.* **58**, 55–142.

—— 1943, 'Das Silberlinien- oder neuroformative System der Ciliaten', *Ann. Nat. Hist. Mus. Wien.* **53**, 156–336.

KLEIN, L., 1889, 'Morphologische und biologische Studien über die Gattung *Volvox*, I', *Teil. Prongsh. Jahrbuch. wiss. Bot.* **20**, 133.

KLITZKE, M., 1916, 'Ein Beitrag zur Kenntnis der Kernentwicklung bei den Ciliaten', *Arch. Protistenk.* **36**, 215–35.

KNOWLES, R., and DAS GUPTA, B., 1932, 'A study of monkey malaria and its experimental transmission to man. (A preliminary report)', *Ind. Med. Gaz.* **67**, 300–20.

KOEHLER, O., 1925, 'Galvanotaxis', *Handb. Norm. u. Pathol. Physiol.* **11**, 1027–49.

KOFFMAN, M., 1931, 'De egentliga jordprotozoerna. Deras Stalling till andra jord-microorganismen och deras roll vid de mikrobiologiska processerna i jorden', *Bakteriologiska avdelningen.* **55**, 3–67.

—— 1934, 'Die Mikrofauna des Bodens, ihr Verhältnis zu anderen Mikro-organismen und ihre Rolle bei den mikrobiologischen Vorgänge im Boden', *Arch. Mikrobiol.* **5**, 246–302.

KOFOID, CH., 1899, 'Plankton studies. III. On *Platydorina*, a new genus of the family *Volvocidae*, from the Plankton of the Illinois River', *Bull. Ill. St. Lab. Nat. Hist.* **5**, 419–40.

—— 1935, 'On two remarkable Ciliate Protozoa from the caecum of the Indian elephants', *Proc. Nat. Acad. Wash.* **21**, 501–6.

—— 1941, 'The life cycle of the Protozoa', In: *Protozoa in Biological Research*, N.Y. 565–82.

—— and MACLENNAN, R., 1932, 'Ciliates from *Bos indicus* Linn. II. A revision of *Diplodinium* Schuberg', *Univ. Calif. Publ. Zool.* **37**, 53–152.

—— and SWEZY, O., 1921, 'The free living unarmoured Dinoflagellates', *Calif. Univ. Memor.* **5**, 1–562.

—— —— 1922, 'Mitosis and fission in the active and encysted phases of *Giardia enterica* (Grassi) of man, with a discussion of the method of origin of bilateral symmetry in the polymastigote Flagellates', *Univ. Calif. Publ. Zool.* **20**, 199–234.

—— —— 1925, 'On the number of Chromosomes and the type of mitosis in *Endamoeba dysenteriae*', *Univ. Calif. Publ. Zool.* **26**, 331–52.

—— —— 1926a, 'On *Oxymonas*, a flagellate with an extensile and retractile proboscis from *Kalotermes* from British Guiana', *Univ. Calif. Publ. Zool.* **28**, 285–300.

—— —— 1926b, 'On *Proboscidiella multinucleata* gen. nov. sp. nov. from *Plano-cryptotermes nocens* from the Philippine Islands, a multinucleate flagellate with a remarkable organ of attachment', *Univ. Calif. Publ. Zool.* **28**, 301–10.

KOLCOV, N. K. (Koltzoff, N. K.), 1911, 'Investigation of the contractility of the stalk in *Zoothamnium alternans*', *Biol. J.* **2**, 55–136. (Reprinted from Kolcov's *Organization of the cell*, Biomedgiz, 1936, 263–333.)

—— 1912, 'Untersuchungen über Kontraktilität des Vorticellen Stiels', *Arch. Zellforsch.* **7**, 344–423.

KOMAROV, V. L., 1940, *The Concept of Species in Plants.* Pub. by Acad. Sci. U.S.S.R.

KONSULOFF, S., 1922, 'Untersuchungen über Opalina', *Arch. Protistenk.* **44**, 285–345.

KORŠIKOV, A. A. (Korschikov, A. A.), 1923, 'On the structure and aggregation of flagella in Volvocales and Flagellata', *Arch. Russian Protistol. Soc.* **2**, 195–205.

KOŠTOJANC, CH. S., and KOKINA, N. N., 1957, 'On the role of the system of acetylcholine esterase in the phenomena of galvanotaxis and the summation of irritation in *Paramecium*', *Biophysica*, **2**, 46 50.

KRAPIN, V., 1929, 'On Foraminifera of the rivers running into Lake Elton', *Russian Hydrobiol. J.* **8**, 187–92.

KRIJGSMAN, B., 1925, 'Beiträge zum Probleme der Geißelbewegung', *Arch. Protistenk.* **52**, 478–88.

KRÜGER, F., 1934, 'Bemerkungen über Flagellatentrichocysten', *Arch. Protistenk.* **83**, 321–33.

—— 1936, 'Die Trichocysten der Ciliaten im Dunkelfeldbild', *Zoologica*, **34**, 1–83.

KUDO, R., 1922, 'On the morphology and the life history of a Myxosporidian, *Leptotheca ohlmacheri*, parasitic in *Rana clamitans* and *R. pipiens*', *Parasitology*, **14**, 221–44.

—— 1926, 'On *Myxosoma catostomi* Kudo, 1923, a myxosporidia parasite of the sucker *Catostomus cammersonii*', *Arch. Protistenk.* **56**, 90–115.

—— 1954, *Protozoologie.* 4th ed. Thomas, Springfield, Illinois.

KÜMMEL, G., 1958, 'Die Gleitbewegung der Gregarinen. Elektronenmikroskopische und experimentelle Untersuchungen', *Arch. Protistenk.* **102**, 501–22.

LANDERS, E., 1960, 'Studies on excystation of coccidial oocysts', *J. Parasitol.* **46**, 195–200.

LARDY, H. (editor), 1949, *Respiratory enzymes.* Burgess, Minneapolis.

LATYŠEV, N. L., KOŽEVNIKOV, T. P., and POVALIŠINA, T. P., 1958, *Borovsky's disease (Cutaneous leishmaniasis, Pendeh soze, Ashkhabad ulcer).* Medgiz, Moscow.

LAUTERBORN, R., 1897, 'Kern- und Zellteilung von *Ceratium hirundinella* (O. F. M.)', *Inaugural—Dissertation der Hohen Math.-Naturwiss. Fakult. Univ. Heidelberg. Wiss. Zool.* **59**, 167–90.

—— 1908, 'Protozoen-Studien. V. Zur Kenntnis einiger Rhizopodea und Infusorien aus dem Gebiete des Oberrheins', *Z. wiss. Zool.* **90**, 645–69.

LE CALVEZ, J., 1935, 'Flagellispores du Radiolaire *Coelodendrum ramosissimum* (Haeckel)', *Arch. Zool. exp. gén.* **77**, 99–102.

—— 1937, 'Les chromosomes spiraux de la première mitose schizogonique du Foraminifère *Pattelina corrugata* Will', *C.R. Acad. Sci.* **205**, 1106–8.

—— 1938, 'Recherches sur les Foraminifères. I. Développement et reproduction', *Arch. Zool. exp. gén.* **80**, 163–333.

—— 1950, 'Recherches sur les Foraminifères. II. Place de la méïose et sexualité', *Arch. Zool. exp. gén.* **87**, 211–43.

—— 1953, Ordre des Foraminifères. In *Traité de Zoologie*, I (2), 149–265.

LE DANTEC, F., 1897, 'La Régénération du macronucleus chez quelques infusoires Ciliés', *C.R. Acad. Sci.* **125**, 51–52.

LÉGER, L., 1904, 'La reproduction sexuel chez les Stylorhynchus', *Arch. Protistenk.* **3**, 303–57.

—— 1907, 'Les Schizogrégarines des Trachéates. I. Le genre *Ophryocystis*', *Arch. Protistenk.* **8**, 159–202.

—— and DUBOSCQ, O., 1913, 'Le cycle évolutif de *Porospora portunidarum*', *C.R. Acad. Sci.* **156**, 1932–4.

—— and HOLLANDE, A., 1912, 'La réproduction sexuée chez les Coccidies monosporées du genre *Pfeifferellina*', *Arch. Zool. exp. gén.* **9**, 1–8.

LEICHSENRING, J., 1925, 'Factors influencing the rate consumption unicellular organisms', *Amer. J. Physiol.* **75**, 84–98.

LEPEŠKIN, V. V. (Lepeschkin, W. W.), 1925, 'Untersuchungen über das Protoplasma der Infusorien, Foraminiferen und Radiolarien', *Biol. Gen.* **1**, 368–95.

—— 1936a, *Kolloidchemie des Protoplasmas*, Dresden und Leipzig, 2 Aufl.

—— 1936b, 'Fortschritte der Kolloidchemie des Protoplasmas in den letzen zehn Jahren', *Protoplasma*, **25**, 124–49.

LERCHE, W., 1937, 'Untersuchungen über Entwicklung und Fortpflanzung in der Gattung *Dunaliella*', *Arch. Protistenk.* **88**, 236–68.

LEVINE, L., 1960, 'Cytochemical adenosine triphosphatase of vorticellid myonemes', *Science*, **131**, 1377–8.

LEVINE, P., 1940, 'The initiation of avian coccidial infection with merozoites', *J. Parasitol.* **26**, 337–43.

LEVINSON, L. B., 1941, 'Morphology and development of *Boveria zenkewitchi* n. sp.', *Zool. J.* **1**, 55–78.

LEWIN, R., 1954, 'Sex in unicellular algae', In *Sex in microorganisms. Symp. Amer. Assoc. Adv. Sci.* 100–73.

LEWIS, W., 1931, 'Pinocytosis', *Bull. Johns Hopkins Hosp.* **49**, 17–27.

LIGHT, S., 1927, '*Kofoidea*, a new Flagellate, from a Californian termite', *Univ. Calif. Publ. Zool.* **29**, 467–92.

LILLIE, F., 1896, 'On the smallest parts of *Stentor*, capable of regeneration, a contribution on the Limits of divisibility of living matter', *J. Morphol.* **12**, 239–49.

LOEFER, J., 1939, 'Acclimatization of fresh-water ciliates and flagellates to media of higher osmotic pressure', *Physiol. Zool.* **12**, 161–72.

—— and MACDANIEL, M., 1950, 'Acid formation by different strains of *Tetrahymena*', *Proc. Amer. Soc. Protozool.* **1**, 8.

LOUBATIÈRES, R., 1955, 'Contribution à l'étude des Gregarinomorphes Monocystidae parasites des Oligochètes du Languedoc–Roussilon', *Ann. Sci. Nat. Zool.* (Sér. 11), **17**, 73–201.

LOURIE, E., and O'CONNOR, R., 1937, 'A study of *Trypanosoma rhodesiense* relapse strains *in vitro*', *Ann. Trop. Med. Parasitol.* **31**, 319–40.

LOZINA-LOZINSKIJ, L. K. (Losina-Losinsky, L. K.), 1931, 'Zur Ernährungsphysiologie der Infusorien. Untersuchungen über die Nahrungsauswahl und Vermehrung bei *Paramecium caudatum*', *Arch. Protistenk.* **74**, 18–120.

—— and MARTYNOV, P. F., 1930, 'An investigation of the activity and the rate of propogation of Protozoa and bacteria in soils', *Bull. Scient. Meliorat. Inst.* **20**, 19–38.

LUBINSKY, G., 1957, 'Studies on the evolution of the Ophryoscolecidae (Ciliata: Oligotricha). I. A new species of *Entodinium* with "*caudatum*", "*loboso-spinosum*" and "*dubardi*" forms and some evolutionary trends in the genus *Entodinium*', *Canad. J. Zool.* **35**, 111–33.

LÜDICKE, M., and PLEKARSKI, G., 1952, 'Über die Gametanbildung von *Plasmodium falciparum* (Welch, 1897)', *Zbl. Bakter.* (Abt. 1), **57**, 522–39.

LUDWIG, W., 1928, 'Der Betriebsstoffwechsel von *Paramaecium caudatum*', *Arch. Protistenk.* **62**, 12–40.

LÜHE, M., 1913, 'Protozoa'. In Lang's *Handbuch der Morphologie der Wirbellosen Tiere*. Berlin.

LUND, E., 1918, 'Rate of oxidation in *Paramecium caudatum* and its independence of the toxic action of KCN', *Amer. J. Physiol.* **45**, 365–73.

—— 1921, 'Quantitative studies on intracellular respiration: V. The nature of the action of KCN on *Paramecium* and *Planaria* with an experimental test of criticism and certain explanations offered by Chlod and others', *Amer. J. Physiol.* **54**, 336–48.

—— 1933, 'A correlation of the silverline and neuromotor systems of *Paramecium*', *Univ. Calif. Publ. Zool.* **39**, 35–76.

LUNTZ, A., 1936, 'Unsterblichkeit von Protozoenindividuen, erhalten durch periodische Reizungen', *Arch. Protistenk.* **88**, 23–26.

LWOFF, A., 1936, 'Le cycle nucléaire de *Stephanopogon mesnili* Lw. (Cilié homocaryote)', *Arch. Zool. exp. gén.* **78**, 117–32.

—— 1949, 'Kinetosomes and the development of Ciliates', *Growth* **13** (Suppl.), 61–92.

—— 1950, *Problems of Morphogenesis in Ciliates. The kinetosomes in development, reproduction and evolution.* Wiley, New York.

—— (editor), 1951, *Physiology and Biochemistry of Protozoa*, New York.

LWOFF, M., 1934, 'Sur la respiration du Cilié *Glaucoma piriformis*', *C.R. Soc. Biol.* **115**, 237–41.

LYNCH, J., and NOBLE, A., 1931, 'Notes on the genus *Endosphaera* Engelman and on its occasional host *Opisthonecta henneguyi* Fauré-Fremiet', *Univ. Calif. Publ. Zool.* **36**, 97–114.

LYON, E., 1905, 'On the theory of geotropism in *Paramaecium*', *Amer. J. Physiol.* **14**, 421–32.

MacConnachie, E., 1960, 'Experiments on the encystation of Opalina in Rana temporaria', *Parasitol.* **50**, 171–81.

MacDougall, M., 1935, 'Cytological studies of the genus *Chilodonella* Strand, 1926 (*Chilodon Ehrbg.*, 1838). I. The conjugation of *Chilodonella* sp.', *Arch. Protistenk.* **84**, 199–206.

—— 1936, 'Étude cytologique de trois espèce du genre *Chilodonella* Strand', *Bull. Biol.* **70**, 308–31.

MacLennan, R., 1933, 'The pulsatory cycle of the contractile vacuoles in the Ophryoscolecidae Ciliates from the stomach of cattle', *Univ. Calif. Publ. Zool.* **39**, 205–50.

Maier, J., and Coggeshall, L., 1941, 'Respiration of Malaria plasmodia', *J. Infect. Dis.* **69**, 87–96.

Mainx, F., 1933, *Die Sexualität als Problem der Genetik. Versuch eines kritischen Vergleiches der wichtigsten Theorien.* G. Fischer, Jena.

Makarov, P. V., 1936, 'Experimental investigations on Protozoa in connexion with the problem of narcosis', *Proc. Physiol. Inst., Leningrad State Iniv.* **16**, 95–110.

—— 1940, 'Relationship between the vital staining capacity of the macronucleus of Protozoa and its ultramicroscopic structure', *Arch. Anatom. Histol. Embryol.* **25**, 105–12.

Manusova, M. V. (Manousova, M. V.), 1939, 'Seasonal changes in fat and glycogen in ciliates under natural conditions', *Zool. J.* **18**, 451–60.

Manwell, R., 1928, 'Conjugation, division and encystment in *Pleurotricha lanceolata*', *Biol. Bull.* **54**, 417–63.

Markova, T. G., 1945, 'Physiological differences of *Paramecium caudatum* of different ages', *Zool. J.* **24**, 32–41.

Mast, S., 1909, 'The reactions of *Didinium nasutum* with special reference to the feeding-habits and the function of trichocysts', *Biol. Bull.* **16**, 91–118.

—— 1911, *Light and the Behaviour of Organisms.* New York.

—— 1917, 'Conjugation and encystment in *Didinium nasutum* with especial reference to their significance', *J. Exper. Zool.* **23**, 335–59.

—— 1926a, 'Structure, movement, locomotion and stimulation in *Amoeba*', *J. Morphol.* **41**, 347–425.

—— 1926b, 'Reactions to light in *Volvox*, with special reference to the process of orientation', *Z. vergl. Physiol.* **4**, 637–58.

—— 1927, 'Structure and function of the eyespot in unicellular and colonial organisms', *Arch. Protistenk.* **60**, 197–220.

—— 1932, 'Localized stimulation, transmission of impulses and the nature of response in *Amoeba*', *Physiol. Zool.* **5**, 1–15.

—— 1938a, 'Factors involved in the process of orientation of lower organisms in light', *Biol. Rev.* **13**, 186–224.

—— 1938b, 'Digestion of fat by *Amoeba proteus*', *Biol Bull.* **75**, 389–412.

—— 1941, 'Motor response in unicellular animals', In *Protozoa in Biological Research.* Ed. Calkins and Summers. New York, 271–351.

—— and Doyle, W., 1934, 'Ingestion of fluid by *Amoeba*', *Protoplasma*, **20**, 555–60.

—— —— 1935, 'Structure, origin and function of cytoplasmic constituents of *Amoeba proteus*, I. Structure', *Arch. Protistenk.* **86**, 155–80.

—— and Nadler, J., 1926, 'Reversal of ciliary action in *Paramecium caudatum*', *J. Morphol.* **43**, 105–17.

Matevosjan, S. M., 1951, *Parasitology and Epidemiology of Amoebiasis.* Pub. by Aipetrat, Erevan.

Maupas, E., 1888, 'Recherches expérimentales sur la multiplication des Infusoires Ciliés', *Arch. Zool. exp. gén.* (sér. 2), **6**, 165–277.

MAUPAS, E., 1889, 'La rajeunissement karyogamique chez les Ciliés', *Arch. Zool. exp. gén.* (sér. 2), **7**, 149–517.

MEČNIKOV, I. (Metschnikoff, I.), 1864, 'Über die Gattung *Sphaerophrya*', *Arch. Anat. Physiol. wiss. Med.* 258–61.

MENDELSOHN, M., 1902, 'Recherches sur la thermotaxie des organismes unicellulaires', *J. Physiol. Pathol. Gén.* **4**, 393–409.

METALNIKOV, S. I. (Metalnikoff, S. I.), 1912, 'Contributions à l'étude de la digestion intracellulaire chez les protozoaires', *Arch. Zool. exp. gén.* (sér. 5), **9**, 373–499.

—— 1919, 'L'immortalité des organismes unicellulaires', *Ann. Inst. Pasteur*, **33**, 815–35.

—— 1924, *Immortalité et rajeunissement dans la biologie moderne.* Paris.

METCALF, M., 1932, 'The Opalinid ciliate infusorians', *Bull. U.S.A. Nat. Mus.* **120**, 1–484.

METZ, CH., 1954, 'Mating substances and the physiology of fertilization in Ciliates', In: *Sex in Microorganisms. Symp. Amer. Assoc. Adv. Sci.* 284–334.

—— and BUTTERFIELD, W., 1951, 'Action of various enzymes on the mating type substances of *Paramecium calkinsi*', *Biol. Bull.* **101**, 99–105.

—— and FOLEY, M., 1949, 'Fertilization studies on *Paramecium aurelia*: an experimental analysis of a nonconjugating stock', *J. Exper. Zool.* **112**, 505–28.

—— PITELKA, D., and WESTFALL, J., 1953, 'The fibrillar systems of Ciliates as revealed by the electron microscope. I. *Paramecium*', *Biol. Bull.* **104**, 408–25.

METZNER, P., 1921, 'Zur Kenntnis der photodynamischen Erscheinung. Die induzierte Phototaxis bei *Paramecium caudatum*', *Biochem. Zeitschr.* **113**, 145.

MEYER, A., 1904, 'Orientirende Untersuchungen über Verbreitung, Morphologie und Chemie des Volutins', *Botan. Zeitschr.* **62**, Jahrg. Abt. 1, 113.

MEYER, H., and QUEIROGA, L., 1960, 'Submicroscopical Aspects of Schizotrypanum cruzi in thin sections of tissue Culture Forms', *J. Protozool.* **7**, 124–7.

—— and OLIVEIRA MUSACCHIO, M. DE, ANDRADE MENDONCA, J. DE, 1958, 'Electron microscopic study of *Trypanosoma cruzi* in thin sections of infected tissue cultures and of blood-agar forms', *Parasitol.* **48**, 1–8.

MIGULA, W., 1888–9, 'Die Verbreitungsweise der Algen', *Biol. Zbl.* 8.

MINKIEWITZ, R., 1912, 'Un cas de reproduction extraordinaire chez Polyspira delagei', *C.R. Acad. Sci.* **155**, 733.

MITROFANOV, P. I., 1903, *On the Structure, Development and Mode of Action of Trichocysts in Paramecia.* Warsaw.

MOEWUS, F., 1934, 'Über Dauermodifikation bei *Chlamydomonaden*', *Arch. Protistenk.* **83**, 220–40.

—— 1935, 'Über die Vererbung des Geschlechtes bei *Polytoma pascheri* und bei *Polytoma uvella*', *Z. Ind. Abst. u. Vererb.-Lehre*, **69**, 376–417.

—— 1938, 'Vererbung des Geschlechts bei *Chlamydomonas eugametos* und verwandten Arten', *Biol. Zbl.* **58**, 516–36.

—— 1939, 'Untersuchungen über die relative Sexualität von Algen', *Biol. Zbl.* **59**, 40–58.

—— 1940, 'Caratinoid Derivate als Geschlechtsbestimmende Stoffe von Algen', *Biol. Zbl.* **60**, 143–66.

MOORE, E., 1924, 'Endomixis and encystment in *Spathidium spathula*', *J. Exper. Zool.* **39**, 317–37.

MOSES, M., 1950, 'Nucleic acids and proteins of the nuclei of *Paramecium*', *J. Morphol.* **87**, 493–536.

MOULDER, J., 1962, *The Biochemistry of Intracellular Parasitism.* Univ. of Chicago Press.

MUGARD, H., 1948, 'Contribution à l'étude des Infusoires hymenostomes histiophages', *Ann. Sci. Natur. Zool.* (sér. 11), **10**, 171–269.

MÜGGE, E., 1957, 'Die Konjugation von *Vorticella campanula* (Ehrbg.)', *Arch. Protistenk.* **102**, 165–208.

MÜLLER, M., and TÖRÖ, I., 1962, 'Studies on feeding and digestion in Protozoa. III. Acid phosphatase activity in food vacuoles of *Paramecium multimicronucleatum*', *J. Protozool.* **9**, 98–102.

—— TOTH, J., and TÖRÖ, I., 1962, 'Studies on feeding and digestion in Protozoa. IV. Acid phosphase and nonspecific asterase activity of food vacuoles in Amoeba proteus', *Acta Biol. Acad. Sci. Hung.* **13**, 105–16.

MULSOW, K., 1911, 'Über Fortpflanzungserscheinungen bei *Monocystis rostrata* n. sp.', *Arch. Protistenk.* **22**, 20–55.

MULSOW, W., 1913, 'Die Konjugation von *Stentor coeruleus* und *Stentor polymorphus*', *Arch. Protistenk.* **28**, 363–88.

MYERS, E., 1934, 'The life history of *Patellina corrugata*, a Foraminifera', *Science*, **79**, 436.

—— 1935, 'The life history of *Patellina corrugata* Williamcon, a Foraminiferan', *Bull. Scripps Inst. Ocean. Univ.* (tech. ser. 3), 355–75.

—— 1936, 'The life cycle of *Spirillina vivipara* Ehrenb. with notes on morphogenesis, systematics and distributions of the Foraminifera', *J. Roy. Micr. Soc.* **56**, 120–46.

—— 1940, 'Observations on the origin and fate of flagellated gametes in multiple tests of Discorbis (Foraminifera)', *J. Marine Biol. Assoc. U.K.* **24**, 201–26.

—— 1943, 'Life activities of Foraminifera in relation to marine ecology', *Proc. Amer. Phil. Soc.* **86**, 439–58.

NABIH, A., 1938, 'Studien über die Gattung Klossia, etc.', *Arch. Protistenk.* **91**, 474–515.

NANNEY, D., 1953, 'Mating type determination in *Paramecium aurelia* a model of nucleo-cytoplasmic interaction', *Proc. Nat. Acad. Sci. U.S.A.* **39**, 113–18.

—— 1954, 'Mating type determination in *Paramecium aurelia*. A study in cellular heredity', In *Sex in microorganisms. Symp. Amer. Assoc. Adv. Sci.* 266–83.

—— 1957, 'Vegetative mutants and the problem of senility in *Tetrahymena*', *J. Protozool.* **4** (Suppl.), 19.

—— and CAUGHEY, P., 1953, 'Mating type determination in *Tetrahymena pyriformis*', *Proc. Nat. Acad. Sci. U.S.A.* **39**, 1057–63.

NASONOV, D. N. (Nassonov, D. N.), 1924, 'Der Exkretionsapparat (Kontraktile Vacuole) der Protozoa als Homologe des Goldgischen Apparates der Metazoenzellen', *Arch. micr. Anat.* **103**, 437–82.

—— 1925, 'Zur Frage über den Bau und die Bedeutung des lipoiden Exkretionsapparates bei Protozoa (*Chilodon Dogielella*)', *Zeitschr. Zellforsch.* **2**, 87–97.

—— 1932, 'Vitalfärbung des Makronukleus aerober und anaerober Infusorien', *Protoplasma*, **17**, 218–38.

—— and ALEKSANDROV, V. JA., 1934, 'On the problem of changes in living matter during its reverse transition into a dead state', *Arch. biol. Sci.* **36**, 95–111.

—— —— 1940, 'Reaction of living matter to external stimulants', *Pub. Acad. Sci. U.S.S.R.*

NASTJUKOVA, O. K., 1939, 'The effect of conjugation on susceptibility of *Paramecium caudatum* to quinacrine', *Bull. exper. Biol. Med.* **7**, 254–7.

NATLAND, M., 1933, 'The temperature and depth-distribution of some recent and fossil Foraminifera in the Southern California region', *Bull. Scripps Inst. Ocean. Univ. Calif.* (techn. ser. 3), 225–30.

NAVILLE, A., 1927, 'Recherches sur le cycle évolutif et chromosomique de Klossia helecis', *Arch. Protistenk.* **57**, 427–74.

NAVILLE, A., 1928, 'La meiose, la fécondation et la dihaplophase de *Myxobolus guyénoti* sp. nov.', *Z. Zellforsch.* **7**, 228–56.

—— 1930, 'Recherches cytologiques sur les Schizogrégarines. I. Le cycle évolutif de *Mattesia dispora* n. g. n. sp.', *Z. Zellforsch.* **11**, 375–96.

NEAL, R., 1951, 'Some observations on the variation of virulence and response to chemotherapy of strains of *Entamoeba histolytica* in rats', *Trans. Roy. Soc. Trop. Med. Hyg.* **44**, 439–52.

—— 1954, 'The influence of encystation upon the virulence of *Entamoeba histolytica* to rats', *Trans. Roy. Soc. Trop. Med. Hyg.* **48**, 533–6.

—— 1958, 'The pathogenecity of *Entamoeba histolytica*', *Abstr. of Papers. Proceed. IV. Intern. Congr. Trop. Med. Malariol.*, London, **8**, 350–9.

NELSON, E., and KRÜGER, K., 1950, 'Effect of various inhibitors on the respiration of *Paramecium caudatum*', *Anat. Rec.* **108**, 534.

NERESHEIMER, E., 1903, 'Über die Höhe histologischer Differenzierung bei heterotrichen Ciliaten', *Arch. Protistenk.* **2**, 305–24.

NIKOLAEV, B. P., 1935, 'Experimental investigations on the incubation period in tertian malaria', *Proc. Leningr. Pasteur Inst. Epidem. Bact.* **2**, 82–107.

—— 1939, 'The duration and course of malaria infection in man', *Med. Parasitol. Parasit. Dis.* **8**, 28–45.

—— 1949, 'Subspecies of the parasite of tertian malaria', *Doklady Acad. Sci. U.S.S.R.* **67**, 201–4.

NIKOLJUK, 1948, 'Relict Foraminifera of Kara-Kum desert', *Bull. Acad. Sci. Uzbek U.S.S.R.* **1**, 79–88.

—— 1949, 'The effect of the root system of the cotton plant on soil Protozoa', *Doklady Acad. Sci. Uzbek S.S.R.* **4**, 22–24.

—— 1956, 'Soil Protozoa and their role in the cultivated soils of Uzbekstan', *Pub. Acad. Sci. Uzbek S.S.R.*, Tashkent.

NIRENSTEIN, E., 1905, 'Beiträge zur Ernährungsphysiologie der Protisten', *Z. allg. Physiol.* **5**, 435–510.

—— 1925, 'Über die Natur und Stärke der Säureabscheidung in den Nahrungsvacuolen von *Paramaecium caudatum*', *Z. wiss. Zool.* A, **125**, 513–18.

NOBLE, E., 1938, 'The life cycle of *Zygosoma globosum* sp. nov., a gregarine parasite of *Urechis caupo*', *Univ. Calif. Publ. Zool.* **43**, 41–66.

—— 1941, 'Nuclear cycles in the life history of the protozoan genus *Ceratomyxa*', *J. Morphol.* **69**, 455–79.

—— 1943, 'Nuclear cycles in the Protozoan parasite *Myxidium gasterostei* n. sp.', *J. Morphol.* **73**, 281–92.

—— 1944, 'Life cycle in the *Myxosporidia*', *Quart. Rev. Biol.* **19**, 213–35.

—— MacRARY, W., and BEAVER, E., 1953, 'Cell division in trypanosomes', *Trans. Amer. Micr. Soc.* **72**, 236–48.

NOIROT-TIMOTHÉE, C., 1957, 'L'ultrastructure de l'appareil de Golgi des Infusoires Ophryoscolecidae', *C.R. Acad. Sci.* **244**, 2847–9.

—— 1958, 'Étude au microscope électronique des fibres retrociliaires des Ophryoscolecidae: leur ultrastructure, leur insertion, leur rôle possible', *C.R. Acad. Sci.* **246**, 1286–9.

—— 1960, 'Étude d'une famille de Ciliés: les Ophryoscolecidae. Structure et ultrastructure', *Ann. Sci. Nat. Zool.* (sér. 12), **1**, 331–7.

NOLAND, L., 1927, 'Conjugation in the ciliate Metopus sigmoides C. and L.', *J. Morphol.* **44**, 341–61.

NÖLLER, W., 1920, 'Kleine Beobachtungen an parasitischen Protozoen (Zugleich vorläufige Mitteilung über die Befruchtung und Sporogonie von *Lankesterella minima* Chaussat)', *Arch. Protistenk.* **41**, 149–68.

NORTON, R., 1930, 'Ecologic relation of some Foraminifera', *Bull. Scripps. Inst. Ocean. Univ. Calif.* (Techn. ser.) **2**, 331–88.

NOVIKOFF, A. B., 1959, 'Lysosomes and the physiology and pathology of Cells', *Biol. Bull.* **117**, 385.

—— 1961, 'Lysosomes and related particles', In Brachet and Mirsky, *The Cell.* Acad. Press, N.Y., **2**, 423–88.

NOVIKOV, M. (Nowikow, M.), 1908, 'Über die Wirkung des Schilddrüsen-Extrakts und einiger anderer Organstoffe auf Ciliaten', *Arch. Protistenk.* **11**, 309–26.

—— 1922, 'On the problem of protozoa inhabiting the soil', *Russ. Arch. Protistology*, **I**, 141–7.

OLIPHANT, I., 1938, 'The effect of chemicals and temperature on reversal in ciliary action in *Paramecium*', *Physiol. Zool.* **11**, 19–30.

ORLOVA, A. F., 1941, 'Enduring modifications in *Paramaecium caudatum* and *P. multimicronucleatum*', *Zool. J.* **20**, 314–70.

—— 1947, 'On adaptations and enduring modifications in ciliates', *Zool. J.* **26**, 521–30.

ORMSBEE, R., and FISHER, K., 1944, 'The effect of urethane on the consumption of oxygen and the rate of cell division in the ciliate *Tetrahymena geleii*', *J. Gen. Physiol.* **27**, 461–8.

OWEN, H., 1947, 'Flagellar structure. I. A discussion of fixation and staining of the Protozoan flagellum', *Trans. Amer. Micr. Soc.* **66**, 50–58.

—— 1949, 'Flagellar structure. II. The flagellum as a taxonomic character', *Trans. Amer. Micr. Soc.* **68**, 261–74.

PACE, D., 1945, 'The effect of cyanidae on respiration in *Paramecium caudatum* and *Paramecium aurelia*', *Biol. Bull.* **89**, 76–83.

—— and KIMURA, K., 1944, 'The effect of Temperature on respiration in *Paramecium aurelia* and *Paramecium caudatum*', *J. Cell. Comp. Physiol.* **24**, 223–7.

—— and LYMAN, E., 1947, 'Oxygen consumption and carbon dioxide elimination in *Tetrahymena geleii* Furgason', *Biol. Bull.* **92**, 210–16.

PAINTER, T., 1945, 'Chromatin diminution', *Trans. Connecticut. Acad. Arts and Sci.* **36**, 443–6.

PALADE, G., 1955, 'Studies on the endoplasmic reticulum', *J. Biophys. Biochem. Cytol.* **1**, 567–82.

PANTIN, C., 1923, 'On the physiology of amoeboid movement. I', *J. Marine Biol. Assoc. U.K.* **13**, 24–69.

PAPPAS, G., 1959, 'Electron microscope studies on Amoebae', *Ann. N.Y. Acad. Sci.* **78**, 448–73.

—— and BRANDT, P., 1958, 'The fine structures of the contractile vacuole in *Amoeba*', *J. Biophys. Biochem. Cytol.* **4**, 485–8.

PÁRDUCZ, B., 1954, 'Reizphysiologische Untersuchungen an Ziliaten. II. Neuere Beiträge zum Bewegungs- und Koordinations-Mechanismus der Ziliatur', *Acta Biol. Hung.* **5**, 169–212.

—— 1955, 'Reizphysiologische Untersuchungen an Ziliaten. III. Über die Peristomalzilien von *Paramecium*', *Ann. Hist. Nat. Mus. Hung.*, N.S. **6**, 189–95.

—— 1962, 'On a new concept of cortical organization in *Paramecium*', *Acta Biol. Hung.* **13**, 299–322.

PASCHER, A., 1916, 'Über die Kreuzung einzelliger haploider Organismen *Chlamydomonas*', *Ber. deutsch. Bot. Gesellsch.* **34**, 228–56.

—— 1917, 'Von der merkwürdigen Bewegungsweise einiger Flagellaten', *Biol. Zbl.* **37**, 241–429.

PATTILO, W. and BECKER, E., 1955, 'Cytochemistry of *Eimeria brunetti* and *E. acervelina* of the Chicken', *J. Morphol.* **96**. 61–95.

PÉNARD, E., 1902, *Faune Rhizopodique du Basin du Léman*. Genève.

—— 1917, 'Le genre Loxodes', *Rev. suisse Zool.* **25**, 453–89.

—— 1922, *Les Protozoaires considerés sous le rapport de leur perfection organique.* Georg. et Cie, Genève.

PENN, A., 1937, 'Reinvestigation into the cytology of conjugation in *Paramecium caudatum*', *Arch. Protistenk.* **89**, 45–54.

PEŠKOVSKAJA, L. S., 1923 (Peschkowskaja, L. S.), 'On the biology and systematics of Trichodines', *Arch. Russ. Protistol.* **2**, 249–79.

—— 1936, 'Changes in the nuclear apparatus of *Climacostomum virens* during conjugation', *Biol. J.* **5**, 207–20.

—— 1948, 'Metamorphosis of nuclear apparatus during the sexual process in two species of Hypotricha', *Proc. Inst. Cytol. Histol. Embryol.* **3**, 201–8.

PESTEL, B., 1931, 'Beiträge zur Morphologie und Biologie des *Dendrocometes paradoxus* Stein', *Arch. Protistenk.* **75**, 403–71.

PETERS, R., 1929, 'Observations on the oxygen consumption of *Colpidium colpoda*', *J. Physiol.* **68**, 11–111.

PIEKARSKI, G., 1939, 'Cytologische Untersuchungen an einem normalen und einem micronucleuslosen Stamm von *Colpoda steini* Maupas', *Arch. Protistenk.* **92**, 117–30.

—— 1941, 'Endomitose beim Großkern der Ziliaten? Versuch einer Synthese', *Biol. Zbl.* **61**, 416–26.

PITELKA, D., 1961, 'Fine structure of the silverline and fibrillar systems of three tetrahymenid ciliates', *J. Protozool.* **8**, 75–89.

—— and SCHOOLEY, C., 1955, 'Comparative morphology of some protisten flagella', *Univ. Calif. Publ. Zool.* **61**, 79–128.

—— —— 1958, 'The fine structure of the flagellar apparatus in Trichonympha', *J. Morphol.* **102**, 199–246.

PITTS, R., 1932, 'Effect of cyanidae on respiration of the protozoan *Colpidium colpoda*', *Proc. Soc. Exper. Biol.* **4**, 542–4.

POLJANSKIJ, Ju. I. (Poljanskij, J. I.; Polyanski, Yu. I.; Poljansky, G. I.), 1926, 'Die Konjugation von *Dogielella sphaerii* (Infusoria, Holotricha, Astomata)', *Arch. Protistenk.* **53**, 407–35.

—— 1934, 'Geschlechtprozesse bei *Bursaria truncatella*. O.F.M.', *Arch. Protistenk.* **81**, 420–546.

—— 1938, 'Reconstruction of nuclear apparatus in *Bursaria truncatella* during experimental separation of conjugating couples', *Biol. J.* **8**, 123–31.

—— 1951, 'On certain parasitic ciliates from marine molluscs and Holothuria. Symposium of Parasitology', *Zool. Inst. Acad. Sci. U.S.S.R.* **13**, 355–70.

—— 1957, 'Temperature adaptations in ciliates. I. Heat resistance in *Paramecium caudatum* depending on temperature conditions of their existence', *Zool. J.* **36**, 1630–46.

—— 1959, 'Temperature adaptations in ciliates. II. Changes in heat and cold resistance in *Paramaecium caudatum* cultivated at low temperatures', *Cytologia*, **16**, 714–24.

—— and ORLOVA, A. F., 1948, 'On adaptive changes and enduring modifications in the ciliate *Paramaecium caudatum* caused by high or low temperatures', *Doklady Acad. Sci. U.S.S.R.* **59**, 1025–8.

—— and RAJKOV, I. B., 1960, 'The role of polyploidy in the evolution of Protozoa', *Cytologia*, **2**, 509–18.

—— —— 1961, 'Nature et origine du dualisme nucléaire chez les infusoires alliés', *Bull. Soc. Zool.* **86**, 402–11.

POLJANSKIJ, JU. I., and STRELKOV, A. A. (Strelkow, A. A.), 1937, 'On the processes of natural selection in some Entodiniomorpha Infusoria', *Zool. Journ. (Moscow)*, **26**, 77–87.

—— —— 1938*a*, 'Sexual processes in *Entodinium caudatum*', Stein. *Zool. J.* **27**, 74–81.

—— —— 1938*b*, 'Étude expérimentale sur la variabilité de quelques Ophryoscolécides', *Arch. Zool. exp. gén.* **80**, 1–123.

—— and CHEJSIN, E. M., 1959, 'Some observations on the development of *Babesiella bovis* in the tick-vector', *Bull. Karel. Section of Acad. Sci. U.S.S.R.* **14**, 5–13.

POLJANSKIJ, V. I. (Poljansky, V. I.), 1936, 'On the problem of the significance of taxonomic units in lower algae', *Proc. Bot. Inst. Acad. Sci. U.S.S.R.* (ser. 11), **3**, 7–97.

—— 1956, *On Species in Lower Algae*, Pub. Acad. Sci. U.S.S.R.

POLLACK, H., 1928, 'Intracellular hydrion concentration studies. III', *Biol. Bull.* **55**, 383–5.

POMRJASKINSKAJA, N. A., 1940, 'Observations on the cysts of the Hypotrichous ciliate *Oxytricha Hymenostoma*', *Scient. Trans. Herzen. Leningr. State Pedag. Inst.* **30**, 93–132.

POPOFF, M., 1908, 'Die Gametenbildung und die Konjugation von *Carchesium polypinum*', *L. Z. wiss. Zool.* **89**, 478–524.

POPOFSKY, A., 1904, 'Die Acantharia der Plankton Expedition. I. Acanthometra', *Ergebn. Plankton-Exped. Humboldt-Stiftung*, **3**, 1–58.

PORTER, K., 1954, *Dynamics of Growth Process*. Princeton Univ. Press. New Jersey.

—— 1957, 'The submicroscopic morphology of protoplasm', *The Harvey Lectures*, **51**, 175–228.

POWELSON, E., 1956, 'Differences in the silver-line system and various measurements in individuals, stocks and varieties of *Paramecium aurelia*', *J. Protozool.* **3** (Suppl.), 9.

POWERS, E., EHRET, C., and ROTH, L., 1955, 'Mitochondrial structure in *Paramecium* as revealed by electron microscopy', *Biol. Bull.* **108**, 182–95.

—— —— and MINCK, O., 1956, 'The internal organization of mitochondria', *J. Biophys. Biochem. Cytol.* **2** (Suppl.), 341–6.

POWERS, P., 1933, 'Studies on the Ciliates from sea urchins. II. *Entodiscus borealis* (Hentschel) (Protozoa, Ciliata), behaviour and morphology', *Biol. Bull.* **65**, 122–36.

PRANDTL, H., 1906, 'Die Konjugation von *Didinium nasutum* O.F.M.', *Arch. Protistenk.* **7**, 229–58.

PRESCOTT, D., 1960, 'Relation between cell growth and cell division. IV. The synthesis of DNA, RNA and Protein from division to division in Tetrahymena', *Exper. Cell. Res.* **19**, 228–38.

—— and KIMBALL, R., 1961, 'Relation between RNA, DNA and protein syntheses in the replicating nucleus of Euplotes', *Proc. Nat. Acad. Sci. U.S.A.* **47**, 686–93.

PRINGLE, C., 1956, Antigenic variation in *Paramecium aurelia*, variety 9', *Z. Ind. Abstm. u. Vererbungslehre*, **87**, 421–30.

PRINGSHEIM, E., 1937, 'Assimilation of different organic substances by saprophytic Flagellates', *Nature*, **139**, 196.

—— 1946, *Pure cultures of Algae, their Preparation and Maintenance*. Cambridge Univ. Press.

—— and ONDRATSCHEK, K., 1939, 'Untersuchungen über die Geschlechtsvorgänge bei Polytoma', *Beich. Bot. Zbl.* **59**, A, 117–72.

PUŠKAREV, B. (Puschkarew, B.), 1913, 'Über die Verbreitung der Süßwasserprotozoen durch die Luft', *Arch. Protistenk.* **28**, 323–62.

PÜTTER, A., 1905, 'Die Atmung der Protozoen', Z. allgem. Physiol. **5**, 566–612.

PUYTORAC, P. DE, 1958, 'Origine infraciliaire des fibres squelettiques de certains infusoires et présence d'un ergastoplasme chez ces Ciliés', C.R. Acad. Sci. **246**, 3186–8.

—— 1959, 'Le cytosquelette et les systèmes fibrillaires du Cilie Metaradiophrya gigas de Puytorac, d'après étude au microscope électronique', Arch. Anat. micr. Morph. exp. **48**, 49–62.

PYNE, C., 1958, 'Electron microscope investigations on the leptomonad form of Leishmania donovani', Exper. Cell. Res. **14**, 388–97.

—— 1960, 'Études sur la structure inframicroscopique des cinétoplaste chez "Leishmania tropica"', C.R. Acad. Sci. **251**, 2776–8.

—— and CHAKRABORTY, J., 1958, 'Electron microscopic studies on the larval apparatus of the flagellum in the Protozoan Leishmania donovani', J. Protozool. **5**, 264–8.

RAABE, H., 1947, 'L'appareil nucléaire d'Urostyla grandis Ehrb. II. Appareil macronucléaire', Ann. Univ. Curie-Skladowska, sect. C, **1**, 133–70.

RAFFEL, D., 1930, 'The effects of conjugation within a clone of Paramecium aurelia', Biol. Bull. **58**, 293–312.

RAJKOV, I., 1960, 'Interstitial fauna of Ciliates of a sandy beach of Dalnije Zelentzy (eastern Murman)', Trav. Inst. biol. de Murman, **2** (6), 172–85.

—— 1962a, 'Les Ciliés mésopsammiques du littoral de la Mer Blanche (U.R.S.S.) avec une description de quelques espèces nouvelles ou peu connues', Cahiers Biol. Marine, **3**, 325–61.

—— 1962, 'Der Kernapparat von Nassula ornata Ehrbg. (Ciliata, Holotricha). Zur Frage über den Chromosomenaufbau des Macronucleus', Arch. Protistenk. **105**, 463–88.

—— CHEISSIN, E., and BUZE, E., 1963, 'A photometric study of DNA content of macro- and micronuclei in Paramecium caudatum, Nassula ornata and Loxodes magnus', Acta Protozool. **1** (in press).

RAJKOV, I. B. (Raikov, I. B.), 1957, 'Reorganization of the nuclear apparatus in ciliates and the problem of the origin of their binuclearity', Ann. Leningr. Univ. **15** (Biol. series, 3), 21–37.

—— 1958a, 'Der Formwechsel des Kernapparates einiger niederer Ciliaten. I. Die Gattung Trachelocerca', Arch. Protistenk. **103**, 129–92.

—— 1958b, 'Conjugation in Holotrichous ciliate Trachelocerca phoenicopterus', Cohn. Zool. J. **37**, 781–800.

—— 1959a, 'Der Formwechsel des Kernapparates einiger niederer Ciliaten. II. Die Gattung Loxodes', Arch. Protistenk. **104**, 1–42.

—— 1959b, 'Cytological and cytochemical peculiarities of the nuclear apparatus in the Holotrichous ciliate Geleia nigriceps Kahl', Cytologia, **1**, 566–79.

RAMMELMEJER, E. S. (Rammelmeyer, E. S.), 1925, 'Zur Frage über die Glykogendifferenzierung bei Paramaecium caudatum', Arch. Protistenk. **51**, 184–8.

—— 1930, 'On the fauna of soil Protozoa of the Kamennostep Experimental station', Proc. Inst. agric. Microbiol. **4**, 173–6.

RANDALL, J., 1956, 'The fine structure of some Ciliate Protozoa', Nature, **178**, 9–14.

—— 1957, 'The fine structure of the Protozoan Spirostomum ambiguum', Symp. 10 Soc. Exper. Biol. 185–98.

—— 1959, 'Contractility in the stalks of Vorticellidae', J. Protozool. **6** (Suppl.), 30.

—— and JACKSON, S., 1958, 'Fine structure and function in Stentor polymorphus', J. Biophys. Biochem. Cytol. **4**, 807–30.

RAY, CH., 1956, 'Meiosis and nuclear behaviour in Tetrahymena pyriformis', J. Protozool. **3**, 88–96.

RAY, H., 1930. 'Studies on some Sporozoa in polychaete worms. II. *Dorisiella scolepidis*', *Parasitol.* **22**, 471–80.

—— and GILL, B., 1954, 'Preliminary observations on alkaline phosphatase in experimental *Eimeria tenella* infection in chicks', *Ann. Trop. Med. Parasitol.* **48**, 8–10.

—— and SEN GUPTA, P., 1954, 'A cytochemical study of *Entamoeba histolytica*', *Bull. Calc. Sch. Trop. Med.* **2**, 2–3.

REGENDANZ, P., and REICHENOW, E., 1933, 'Die Entwicklung von *Babesia canis* in *Dermacentor reticularis*', *Arch. Protistenk.* **79**, 50–71.

REICH, K., 1948, 'Studies in the respiration of an amoeba *Mayorella palestinensis*', *Physiol. Zool.* **21**, 390–414.

REICHENOW, E., 1909, 'Untersuchungen an *Haematococcus pluvialis* nebst Bemerkungen über andere Flagellaten', *Arb. Kais. Gesundh.* **33**, 1–45.

—— 1919, 'Der Entwicklungsgang der Hamococcidien *Karyolysus* und *Schellackia* n. gen. n. sp. Sitzungsber.', *Ges. Naturf. Freunde*, 440–7.

—— 1921, 'Die Hämococcidien der Eidechsen', *Arch. Protistenk.* **42**, 179–291.

—— 1928, 'Ergebnisse mit der Nuclealfärbung bei Protozoen', *Arch. Protistenk.* **61**, 144–66.

REŠETNJAK, V. V. (Reschetnjak, V. V.), 1955, 'Vertical Distribution of Radiolaria of the Kurilo-Kamchatka depression', *Trudy Zool. inst. Acad. Sci. U.S.S.R.* **21**, 94–101.

REYER, W., 1937, 'Infektionversuche mit *Barrouxia schneideri* an *Lithobius*, insbesondere zur Frage der Sexualität der Coccidiensporozoiten', *Z. Parasitenk.* **9**, 472–522.

RHUMBLER, L., 1891, 'Beiträge zur Kenntnis der Rhizopoden. Über Entstehung und sekundäres Wachstum der Gehäuse einiger Süßwasserrhizopoden', *Z. wiss. Zool.* **52**, 515–50.

—— 1905, 'Zur Theorie der Oberflächenkräfte der Amöben', *Z. wiss. Zool.* **83**, 1–52.

—— 1910, 'Die verschiedenartigen Nahrungsaufnahmen bei Amöben als Folge verschiedener Colloidalzustände ihrer Oberflächen', *Arch. Entw. Mech. Organ.* **30**, 194–223.

—— 1911, 'Die Foraminiferen der Plankton-Expedition', *Ergebn. Plankton-Exped. Humboldt-Stiftung*, **3**, Kiel u. Leipzig.

RICHTER, I., 1959, 'Bewegungsphysiologische Untersuchungen an Polycystiden Gregarinen unter Anwendung des Mikrozeitrafferfilmes', *Protoplasma*, **51**, 197–241.

ROBERTIS, E. DE, NOWINSKI, W., and SAEZ, F., 1960, *General Cytology*, 3rd ed. Philadelphia–London.

ROOT, W., 1930, 'The influence of carbon dioxide upon the oxygen consumption of *Paramecium* and the egg of *Arbacia*', *Biol. Bull.* **59**, 48–62.

ROSKIN, G. I. (Rosskin, G. I.), 1915, 'La structure des myonèmes contractiles de *Stentor coeruleus*', *Scient. Works Shanjavsky Univ. (Moscow)*, **1**, 1–3.

—— 1925, 'Über die Axopodien der Heliozoa und die Greiftentakeln der Ephilotiden', *Arch. Protistenk.* **52**, 207–16.

—— and LEVINSON, L. B. (Lewinson, L. B.), 1926, 'Die Oxydasen und Peroxydasen bei Protozoa', *Arch. Protistenk.* **56**, 145–66.

—— —— 1929, 'Die Kontraktilen- und Skelettelemente der Protozoen. I. Der Kontraktile und der Skelettapparat der Gregarinen (Monocystidae)', *Arch. Protistenk.* **66**, 355–401.

RÖSSLE, R., 1905, 'Spezifische Sera gegen Infusorien', *Arch. Hyg.* **54**, 1–31.

—— 1909, 'Zur Immunität einzelliger Organismen', *Verh. Deutsch. Path. Ges.* **13**, 158–62.

REFERENCES 703

ROSSOLIMO, L. L., 1916, 'Observations on *Loxodes rostrum* O. F. Müller', *Diary of Zool. section Moscow Soc. Nat. Hist., Anthrop. Etnogr.* (N.S.), **3**, 1–18.

—— and JAKIMOVIČ, K. (Jakimowich, K.), 1929, 'Die Kernteilung bei *Conchophthirius steenstrupii*', *St. Zool. Anz.* **84**, 323–33.

ROTH, L., 1956, 'Aspects of ciliary fine structure in *Euplotes patella*', *J. Biophys. Biochem. Cytol.* **2** (Suppl.), 235–40.

—— 1959, 'An electron microscope study of the cytology of the protozoan *Paranema trichophorum*', *J. Protozool.* **6**, 107–18.

—— 1960, 'Electron microscopy of pinocytosis and food vacuoles in *Pelomyxa*', *J. Protozool.* **7**, 176–85.

ROUBAND, E., COLAS-BELCOUR, I., and GASHEN, H., 1938, 'Le trypanosome des Antilles, *Trypanosoma viennei* a-t-il perdu l'aptitude à évoluer chez les glossines?', *Bull. Soc. Path. Exot.* **31**, 374–7.

ROUDABUSH, R., 1935, 'Merozoite infection in coccidiosis', *J. Parasitol.* **21**, 453–4.

—— 1937, 'The endogenous phases of the life cycles of *Eimeria nieschulzi, Eimeria separata* and *Eimeria miyairii*, coccidien parasite of the rat', *Iowa State Coll. J. Sci.* **11**, 135–63.

ROUILLER, C., and FAURÉ-FREMIET, E., 1957, 'L'ultrastructure des trichocystes fusiformes de Frontonia atra', *Bull. Micr. appl.* **7**, 135–9.

—— —— and GAUCHERY, M., 1956*a*, 'Les tentacules d'Ephelota: étude au microscope électronique', *J. Protozool.* **3**, 194–200.

—— —— —— 1956*b*, 'Origine ciliaire des fibrilles scléro protéique pédonculaires chez ciliés peritriches. Étude au microscope électronique', *Exp. Cell. Res.* **11**, 527–42.

ROZANOVA, M. L., 1946, *Experimental Basis of the Systematics of Plants*. Pub. Acad. Sci. U.S.S.R.

RUDZINSKA, M., 1956, 'The occurrence of hemixis in *Tokophrya infusionum*', *J. Protozool.* **3** (Suppl.), 3.

—— 1957, 'Mechanisms involved in the function of the contractile vacuole in *Tocophrya infusionum* as revealed by electron microscopy', *J. Protozool.* **4** (Suppl.), 9.

—— and PORTER, K., 1955, 'Observations on the fine structure of the macronucleus of *Tocophrya infusionum*', *J. Biophys. Biochem. Cytol.* **1**, 421–8.

—— and TRAGER, N., 1957, 'Intracellular phagotrophy by malaria parasites: an electron microscope study of *Plasmodium lophurae*', *J. Protozool.* **4**, 190–9.

—— and TRAGER, W., 1959, 'Phagotrophy and two new structures in the malaria parasite *Plasmodium berghei*', *J. Biophys. Biochem. Cytol.* **6**, 103–12.

RUMJANCEV, A. V., and VERMEL, E. M. (Rumjanzew, A. W., and Wermel, E. M.), 1925, 'Untersuchungen über den Protoplasmabau von Actinosphaerium *eichhornii*', *Arch. Protistenk.* **52**, 217–64.

RUNNSTRÖM, J., 1952, 'The Cytoplasm, its structure and role in metabolism, growth and differentiation', *Modern Trends in Physiol. Biochem.* New York, 47–76.

RUSSEL, E., and HUTCHINSON, H., 1909, 'The effect of partial sterilization of soil on the production of plant food', *J. Agric. Sci.* **3**, 111–44.

—— —— 1913, 'The effect of partial sterilization of soil on the production of plant food', *J. Agric. Sci.* **5**, 152–221.

RUTHMANN, A., 1963, 'Die Struktur des Chromatins und die Verteilung der Ribonucleinsäure im Makronucleus von Loxophyllum meleagris', *Arch. Protistenk.* **106**, 422–36.

—— and HECKMANN, K., 1961, 'Formwechsel and Struktur des Macronucleus von Bursaria Truncatella', *Arch. Protistenk.* **105**, 313–40.

RYLEY, J., 1952, 'Studies on the metabolism of the Protozoa. III. Metabolism of the ciliate *Tetrahymena pyriformis. (Glaucoma pyriformis)', Biochem. J.* **52**, 483–92.

RYLEY, J., 1953, 'Carbohydrate metabolism in Protozoa and metalbinding substances', *Nature*, **171**, 747–48.

RYLOV, W., 1924, 'Zur Biologie des seltenen planktonischen Infusoriums Epistylis rotans Svec', *Int. Rev. ges. Hydr.* **12**, 218–27.

SACHS, C., 1892, 'Physiologische Notizen. II. Beiträge zur Zellentheorie', *Flora Jahrb.* **75**, 57–67.

SAEDELEER, H. DE, 1930, 'L'appareil parabasal der Craspédomonadines et des Choanocytes des Éponges', *C.R. Soc. Biol.* **103**, 160–1.

SAITO, F., and TAMIJA, H., 1937, 'Über die Atmungsfarbstoffe von *Paramecium*', *Cytologia*, Fuji Jubilee Volume, 1133–8.

SANDON, H., 1927, *The Composition and Distribution of the Protozoan Fauna of the Soil.* Oliver & Boyd, Edinburgh.

SAUNDERS, J., 1925, 'The Trichocysts of *Paramecium*', *Proc. Cambr. Phil. Soc.* **1**, 249–69.

ŠČEDRINA, Z. G. (Schedrina, Z. G., Stschedrina, Z. G.), 1953, 'New data on the fauna of Foraminifera of the Okhotsk Sea and its distribution', *Proc. Zool. Inst. Acad. Sci. U.S.S.R.*, **13**, 12–13.

—— 1956, 'Results of investigation on the fauna of Foraminifera in the seas of the U.S.S.R.', *Problems of micropalaeontology*, Symposium 1, 23–26.

SCHAUDINN, F., 1900, 'Untersuchungen über den Generationswechsel bei Coccidien', *Zool. Jahrb., Abt. Anat.* **13**, 177–292.

—— 1903, 'Studien über krankheitserregende Protozoen', *Arb. Kais. Gesundh.* **19**, 169–250.

SCHELLACK, C., 1907, 'Über die Entwicklung und Fortpflanzung von *Echinomera hispida*', *Arch. Protistenk.* **9**, 297–345.

—— 1913, 'Coccidien-Untersuchungen. II. Die Entwicklung von *Adelina dimidiata* A. Schn. einem Coccidium aus *Scolopendra cingulata* Latr', *Arb. Kais. Gesundh.* **45**, 269–316.

—— and REICHENOW, E., 1913, 'Coccidien-Untersuchungen. I. *Barrouxia schneideri*', *Arb. Kais. Gesundh.* **44**, 30–77.

SCHNEIDER, A., 1867, 'Zur Kenntnis des Baues der Radiolarien (*Thalassicolla*)', *Arch. Anat. Physiol.* 509.

SCHNEIDER, L., 1960, 'Elektronenmikroskopische Untersuchungen über das Nephridialsystem von *Paramecium*', *J. Protozool.* **7**, 75–90.

SCHREIBER, E., 1925, 'Zur Kenntnis der Physiologie und Sexualität höherer Volvocales', *Z. Bot.* **17**, 337–76.

SCHRÖDER, B., 1914, 'Über Planktonepibionten', *Biol. Zbl.* **34**, 328–38.

SCHRÖDER, O., 1906, 'Eine gestielte Acanthometridae (*Podactinelius sessilis* n. gen. n. sp.)', *Verhandl. Naturhist. Medic. Vereins zu Heidelberg*, **8**, 369–70.

—— 1907, 'Beiträge zur Kenntnis von *Stentor coeruleus* Ehrbg. und *Stentor roeselii* Ehrbg.' *Arch. Protistenk.* **8**, 1–16.

—— 1910, 'Über die Anlage der Sporocyste (Pansporoblast) bei Sphaeromyxa sabrazesi Laveran et Mesnil', *Arch. Protistenk.* **40**, 27–35.

SCHUBERG, A., 1890, 'Zur Kenntnis des *Stentor coeruleus*', *Zool. Jahrb.*, Abt. 2, **4**, 197–238.

—— 1905, 'Über Cilien und Trichocysten einiger Infusorien', *Arch. Protistenk.* **6**, 61–110.

SCHULZ, H., and MACCLURE, E., 1961, 'Elektronenmikroskopische Untersuchungen der *Trypanosoma cruzi* mit besonderer Berücksichtigung der Periplasten und der Blepharoplasten', *Z. Zell.* **55**, 389–412.

SCHULZE, P., 1924, 'Der Nachweis und die Verbreitung des Chitins mit einem An-
hang über das komplizierte Verdauungssystem der Ophryoscoleciden', *Z. Mor-phol., Ökol. Thiere*, Abt. A, **2**, 643–66.

SCHÜTT, F., 1895, 'Die Peridineen der Plankton-Expedition', *Ergebn. Plankton-Exped. Humboldt-Stiftung*, **4**, Kiel u. Leipzig.

SCHWARTZ, V., 1935, 'Versuche über Regeneration und Kerndimorphismus bei
Stentor coeruleus Ehrbg.', *Arch. Protistenk.* **85**, 100–39.

—— 1956, 'Nukleolenformwechsel und Zyklen der Ribosennukleinsäure in der
vegetativen Entwicklung von *Paramecium bursaria*', *Biol. Zbl.* **75**, 1–16.

—— 1958, 'Chromosomen im Macronucleus von *Paramecium bursaria*', *Biol. Zbl.*
77, 347–64.

SCHWEYER, A., 1909, 'Zur Kenntnis des Tintinnoideenweichkörpers, nebst ein-
leitenden Worten über Hülsenstruktur und die Hülsenbildung', *Arch. Protis-tenk.* **18**, 134–89.

SEAMAN, G., 1951*a*, 'Localization of acetylcholinesterase activity in the protozoan
Tetrahymena geleii S.', *Proc. Soc. Exper. Biol. Med.* **76**, 169–70.

—— 1951*b*, 'Enzyme systems in *Tetrahymena geleii* S. III. Aerobic utilisation of
hexoses', *J. Biol. Chem.* **191**, 439–46.

—— 1951*c*, 'Studies on Protozoan metabolism and their relation to general problems of physiology and biochemistry', *Tex. Rep. Biol. Med.* **9**, 171–9.

—— 1952, 'The phosphagen of Protozoa', *Bioch. Biophys. Acta* **9**, 693–6.

—— 1953, 'The succinic dehydrogenase of *Trypanosoma cruzi*', *Exper. Parasitol.*
2, 236–41.

—— 1955, 'Metabolism of free-living Ciliates', In: *Biochemistry and Physiology
of Protozoa*, **2**, New York: 91–158.

SEAMAN, G. R., 1961, 'Acid phosphotase activity associated with phagotrophy in
the ciliate Tetrachymena', *J. Biophys. Biochem. Cytol.* **9**, 243–5.

—— and HOULIHAM, R., 1951, 'Enzyme systems in *Tetrahymena geleii* S. II. Acetil-
cholinesterase activity. Its relation to motility of the organism and to coordin-
ated ciliars action in general', *J. Cell. Comp. Physiol.* **37**, 309–21.

SEDAR, A., and PORTER, K., 1955, 'The fine structure of cortical components of
Paramecium multimicronucleatum', *J. Biophys. Biochem. Cytol.* **1**, 583–604.

—— and RUDZINSKA, M., 1956, 'Mitochondria of Protozoa', *J. Biophys. Biochem.
Cytol.* **2** (4, Suppl.), 333–6.

SEELER, A., and OTT, W., 1944, 'Effect of Riboflavin deficiency on the course of
Plasmodium lophurae infection in chicks', *J. Infect. Dis.* **75**, 175–8.

SEMENOV-TJANJ-ŠANSKIJ, A. P. (Semenov-Tjan-Schansky), 1910, 'Taxonomic
boundaries of the species and of its subdivisions. An attempt of an accurate
classification of the lower systematic units', *Trans. Imper. Acad. Sci.* (VIIIa,
Phys.-Math. series, section 25) **1** (4), 1–29. (Also in German: Berlin, Fried-
länder & Sohn.)

SERAVIN, L. N., 1957, 'Effect of solutions of chemical substances on phagocystosis
in *Paramecium caudatum*', *Ann. Leningr. State Univ.* (Biol. series), **3**, 85–100.

—— 1958, 'Changes in the activity of the contractile vacuole in *Paramecium caudatum* depending on the conditions of the environment', *Ann. Leningr. State
Univ.* (Biol. series), **3**, 85–100.

—— 1960, 'Changes of the resistance in the upper threshold of virubility and of
the rate of division of *Paramecium caudatum* during the process of adaption
to solutions of salts', *Trudy Petergof Biol. Institute*, **18**, 178–91.

—— 1961, 'The role of ATF in the ciliary-beating in the ciliates', *Biochimija*, **26**,
160–4.

SERGENT, ÉD., 1935, 'La prémunition dans le Paludisme', *Riv. Malariol. Rome*, **14**
(*Ser. II*), *Suppl. Confer. sulla malaria*, 5–25.

SERGENT, ED., DONATIEN, A., PARROT, L., and LESTOQUARD, F., 1936, 'Cycle évolutif du Sporozoaire *Theileria dispar*, agent de la théileriose bovine des pays méditerranéens chez les bœufs et chez une tique', *C. R. Acad. Sci.* **202**, 809–11.

—— —— —— —— 1945, *Études sur les piroplasmoses bovines. Alger.*, 1–816.

SESHACHAR, B., 1946, 'Nuclear reorganization in Epistylis (*Peritricha*)', *Current Sci.* **15**, 198.

—— and DASS, C., 1953, 'Macronuclear regeneration in *Epistylis articulata*', *Quart. J. Micr. Sci.* **94**, 185–92.

—— —— 1954, 'The macronucleus of *Epistylis articulata*. From., during conjugation: a photometric study', *Physiol. Zool.* **27**, 280–6.

SEVERCEV, A. N. (Sewertzow, A. N.), 1931, *Morphologische Gesetzmäßigkeiten der Evolution.* G. Fischer, Jena.

—— 1939, *Morphological Regularities in Evolution*, Pub. Acad. Sci. U.S.S.R.

ŠEVJAKOV, V. T. (Schewiakoff, W. T.), 1887, 'Über die karyokinetische Kernteilung der *Euglypha aloeolata*', *Morph. Jahrb.* **13**, 193–258.

—— 1892, 'Über die geographische Verbreitung der Süßwasser-Protozoen', *Verhandl. Naturhist.-Med. Vereins Heidlb.* N. F. **4, 5**, 1–24.

—— 1894, 'Über die Ursachen der fortschreitenden Bewegung der Gregarinen', *Z. Wiss. Zool.* **58**, 350–4.

—— 1896, 'Organization and systematics of Infusoria Aspirotricha (Holotricha)', *Mém. Acad. Imp. Sci.* (*St. Petersburg*) (series 8), **4**, 1–395.

—— 1926, 'Die Acantharia des Golfes von Neapel', *Fauna u. Flora d. Golfes von Neapel*, **37**.

SHARP, R., 1914, '*Diplodinium ecaudatum* with an account of its neuromotor apparatus', *Univ. Calif. Publ. Zool.* **13**, 42–122.

SHORTT, H., FAIRLEY, N., COVELL, G., SHUTE, P., and GARNCHAM, P., 1951, 'The pre-erythrocytic stage of *Plasmodium falciparum*', *Trans. Roy. Soc. Trop. Med.* **44**, 405–19.

SHUMWAY, W., 1917, 'Effects of thyroid diet upon paramecia', *J. Exper. Zool.* **22**, 529–62.

SIEGEL, R., 1952, 'The genetic analysis of mate-killing in *Paramecium aurelia*', *Genetics*, **37** (Abstr.), 625–6.

—— 1954, 'Mate-killing in *Paramecium aurelia* variety 8', *Physiol. Zool.* **27**, 89–100.

SILVERMANN, M., CEITHAML, J., TALIAFERO, L., and EVANS, E., 1944, 'The in vitro metabolism of *Plasmodium gallinaceum*', *J. Infect. Dis.* **75**, 212–30.

SIMONSEN, D., and WAGTENDONK, VON W., 1952, 'Respiratory studies on *Paramecium aurelia* variety 4, killers and sensitives', *Biochem. Biophys. Acta*, **9**, 515–27.

SINSKAJA, E. N., 1948, *Dynamics of the Species*, Agric. State Pub.

ŠKREB-GUILCHER, J., 1955, 'Quelques remarques sur un protozoaire Cilié. Le tentaculifère *Stylocometes digitatus*', *Stein. Bull. Micr. Appl.* **5**, 118–21.

SMARAGDOVA, N. P., 1941, 'Geographical variation in paramecia and the role of stabilizing selection in the origin of geographical differences', *J. gen. Biol.* **2**, 71–84.

SMETANA, H., 1933, 'Coccidiosis of the liver in rabits. I', *Arch. Pathol.* **15**, 175–92.

SNYDER, T., and MELENEY, H., 1941, 'The excystation of *Entamoeba histolytica* in bacteriologically sterile media', *Amer. J. Trop. Med.* **21**, 63–72.

—— —— 1943, 'Anaerobiosis and cholesterol as growth requirements of *Entamoeba histolytica*', *J. Parasitol.* **29**, 278–84.

SOKOLOV, B. F. (Sokolow, B. F., Ssokoloff, B. F.), 1912, 'Studien über Physiologie der Gregarin', *Arch. Protistenk.* **27**, 260–314.

—— 1924, 'Das Regenerationsproblem bei Protozoen', *Arch. Protistenk.* **47**, 143–252.

SOKOLOV, D. (Sokoloff, D.), 1933, 'Algunas nuevas formas de flagelados del Valle de México', *An. Inst. México*, **4**, 197–206.

SOLOVJEVA, L. M., 1946, 'Changes in sensitivity to certain external factors at different stages of conjugation in *Bursaria truncatella*', *Zool. J.* **25**, 3–14.

SONNEBORN, T., 1937, 'Sex, sex inheritance and sex determination in *Paramecium aurelia*', *Proc. Nat. Acad. Sci. Wash.* **23**, 378–95.

—— 1938a, 'The delayed occurrence and total omission of endomixis in selected lines of *Paramecium aurelia*', *Biol. Bull.* **74**, 76–82.

—— 1938b, 'Mating types in *Paramecium aurelia*: diverse conditions for mating in different stocks; occurrence, number and interrelations of the types', *Proc. Amer. Phil. Soc.* **79**, 411–34.

—— 1939, '*Paramecium aurelia*: mating types and groups lethal interactions: determination and inheritance', *Amer. Natur.* **73**, 390–413.

—— 1943, 'Gene and cytoplasm. Ia. II', *Proc. Nat. Acad. Sci.* **29**, 329–43.

—— 1947, 'Recent advances in the genetics of *Paramecium* and *Euplotes*', *Adv. Genetics*, **1**, 264–358.

—— 1948, 'Symposium on plasmagenes, genes and characters in *Paramecium aurelia*', *Amer. Natur.* **82**, 26–34.

—— 1950, 'The kinetosome in cytoplasmic heredity', *J. Heredity*, **41**, 222–4.

—— 1954a, 'Patterns of nucleo-cytoplasmic integration in *Paramecium*', *Proc. 9. Intern. Congr. Genet.*, publ. in *Caryologia*, **6** (Suppl.), 307–25.

—— 1954b, 'The relation of autogamy to senescence and rejuvenescence in *Paramecium aurelia*', *J. Protozool.* **1**, 38–53.

—— 1957, 'Breeding systems, reproductive methods and species problems in Protozoa, Symp. *The Species Problem*, Amer. Assoc. Adv. Sci. Wash., 155–324.

—— 1959, 'Kappa and related particles in *Paramecium*', *Adv. Virus. Res.* **6**, 229–356.

—— and DIPPELL, R., 1943, 'Sexual isolation, mating types and sexual responses to diverse conditions in variety 4, *Paramecium aurelia*', *Biol. Bull.* **85**, 36–43.

—— and LYNCH, R., 1932, 'Racial differences in the early physiological effects of conjugation in *Paramecium aurelia*', *Biol. Bull.* **62**, 258–93.

SOTELO, J., and TRUJILLO-CENOZ, O., 1959, 'The fine structure of an elementary contractile system', *J. Biophys. Biochem. Cytol.* **6**, 126–7.

SPECHT, H., 1935, 'Aerobic respiration in Spirostomum ambiguum and the production of ammonia', *J. Cell. Comp. Physiol.* **5**, 319–33.

SPECK, J., and EVANS, E., 1945, 'The biochemistry of the malaria parasite. II. Glycolysis in cell-free preparations of the Malaria parasite', *J. Biol. Chem.* **159**, 71–81.

—— MOULDER, W., and EVANS, E., 1940, 'The biochemistry of Malaria parasite', *J. Biol. Chem.* **164**, 119–44.

SPRAGUE, V., 1941, 'Studies on *Gregarina blattarum* with particular reference to the chromosome cycle', *Illin. Biol. Monogr.* **18**, 2–20.

SPRINCE, H., and KUPFERBERG, A., 1947, 'The nutrition of Protozoa. 1. A simplified medium for the investigation of unknown factors in blood serum essential for the sustained growth of *Trichimonas vaginalis*', *J. Bact.* **53**, 435–9.

STANIEWICZ, W., 1910, 'Études expérimentales sur la digestion de la graisse dans les Infusoires ciliés', *Krakow Bull. Intern. Acad.*, 199–214.

STATKEVIČ, P. (Statkewitsch, P.), 1903, 'Über die Wirkung der Induktionsschläge auf einige Ciliata', *Russian Journ. Physiol.* **3**, 1–55.

—— 1907, 'Galvanotropismus und Galvanotaxis der Ciliata', *Zeitschr. Allg. Physiol.* **6**, 13–43.

STEIN, FR., 1878, *Der Organismus der Infusionstiere. Der Organismus der Flagellaten. Abt. III. Die Naturgeschichte der Flagellaten oder Geißelinfusorien. I. Der noch nicht abgeschlossenen allgemeinen Theil nebst Erklärung der sämtlichen Abbildungen.* Wilhelm Engelmann, Leipzig.

STEIN, FR., 1883, *Der Organismus der Infusionstiere. Der Organismus der Flagellaten. Abt. III. Die Naturgeschichte der Flagellaten oder Geißelinfusorien. II. Einleitung und Erklärung der Abbildungen.* Wilhelm Engelmann, Leipzig.

STEINERT, G., FIRKET, H., and STEINERT, M., 1958, 'Synthèse d'acide desoxyribonucléique dans le corps parabasal de *Trypanosoma mega*', *Exp. Cell. Res.* **15**, 632–5.

STEINERT, M., 1960, 'Mitichondria associated with the kinetonucleus of *Trypanosoma mega*', *J. Biophys. Biochem. Cytol.* **8**, 542–6.

ŠTEJN, G. A. (Stein, G. A.), 1960, 'Cytological investigation on different stages in the life cycles of the gregarines from the larvae of dragon flies', *Cytologia*, **2**, 74–87.

STRELKOV, A. A. (Strelkow, A. A.), 1929, 'Morphologische Studien über oligotriche Infusorien aus dem Darme des Pferdes. I. Äußere Morphologie und Skelett der Gattung *Cycloposthium* Bundle', *Arch. Protistenk.* **68**, 503–54.

—— 1930, 'On soil Protozoa in the experiment on drying of fallow', *Proc. Inst. Agric. Microbiol.* **4**, 177–80.

—— 1931, 'Morphologische Studien über oligotriche Infusorien aus dem Darme der Pferdes. III. Körperbau von *Tripalmaria dogieli* Gassovsky', *Arch. Protistenk.* **75**, 221–54.

—— 1939, 'Parasitic ciliates from the alimentary tract of the perissodactyle family Equidae', *Sci. Proc. Herzen. Leningrad State Pedag. Inst.* **17**, 1–262.

ŠUBNIKOVA, E., 1947, 'Ribonucleic acid in the life cycle of a protozoan cell', *Doklady Acad. Sci. U.S.S.R.* **55**, 521–4.

SUCHANOVA, K. N. (Sukhanova, K. N.), 1953, 'The effect of factors of the external environment on the life cycle of *Opalina ranarum*', *Sci. Proc. Herzen. Leningrad State Pedag. Inst.* **91**, 31–69.

—— 1960, 'Cytophysiological characteristics of the life cycle of ciliates of the genus *Balantidium* from amphibia', Symposium: *Problems of Cytology and Protistology*, 285–311.

SUGDEN, B., and OXFORD, A., 1952, 'Some cultural studies with Holotrich ciliate Protozoa of the sheep's rumen', *J. Gen. Microb.* **7**, 145–53.

SUMMERS, F., 1935, 'The division and reorganization of the macronuclei of *Aspidisca lynceus* Müller, *Diophrys appendiculata* Stein and *Stylonychia pustulata* Ehrbg', *Arch. Protistenk.* **85**, 173–210.

SWARCZEWSKY, B., 1928, 'Zur Kenntnis der Baikalprotistenfauna. Die an den Baikalgammariden lebenden Infusorien. II. Dendrocometidae', *Arch. Protistenk.* **62**, 41–79.

SWELLENGREBEL, N., SWELLENGREBEL-DE GRAAT, J., and BUCK, A. DE, 1929, 'Le paludisme aux Pays-Bas, concentration automne ne se manifeste que pendant l'été suivant', *Bull. Soc. Exot.* **22**, 642–5.

SWEZY, O., 1923, 'The pseudopodial method of feeding by Trichonymphid Flagellates parasitic in wood-feeding Termites', *Univ. Calif. Publ. Zool.* **20**, 391–400.

TALIAFERRO, W., 1929, *The Immunology of Parasitic Infections.* New York–London.

—— 1948, 'The inhibition of reproduction of parasites by immune factors (Trypanosomes and malaria parasites)', *Bact. Rev.* **12**, 1–17.

TARTAR, V., 1939, 'The so-called racial variation in the power of regeneration in *Paramecium*', *J. Exper. Zool.* **81**, 181–208.

—— 1957, 'Equivalence of macronuclear nodes', *J. Exper. Zool.* **135**, 387–401.

—— 1961, *The Biology of Stentor.* Pergamon Press, New York, London, Paris. 413 pp.

TAYLOR, C., and FARBER, W., 1924, 'Fatal effect of the removal of the micronucleus in *Euplotes*', *Univ. Calif. Publ. Zool.* **26**, 131–44.

TEN KATE, C., 1927, 'Über das Fibrillensystem der Ciliaten', *Arch. Protistenk.* **57**, 362–426.

—— 1928, 'Über das Fibrillensystem der Ciliaten. II. Das Fibrillensystem der Isotrichen (*Isotricha* und *Dasytricha*)', *Arch. Protistenk.* **62**, 328–54.

THOMAS, J., 1942, 'The anaerobic carbohydrate metabolism of *Tetrahymena geleii*', Thesis, Stanford Univ., Calif.

THOMSON, J., 1917, 'Notes on Malaria', *J. Roy. Army Med. Corps*, **29**, 379–411.

TIMOTHÉE, C., 1953, 'Le système fibrillaire d'*Epidinium ecaudatum* Grawly (Inf., Ophryoscolecidae)', *Ann. Sci. Nat. Zool.* (sér. 11), **4**, 375–92.

TÖNNINGES, G., 1914, 'Die Trichocysten von *Frontonia leucas* und ihr chromidialer Ursprung', *Arch. Protistenk.* **32**, 298–378.

TRAGER, W., 1934, 'The cultivation of cellulose-digesting flagellate, *Trichomonas termopsidis*, and of certain other termite Protozoa', *Biol. Bull.* **66**, 182–90.

—— 1947, 'The relation to the course of avain malaria of biotin and fat-soluble material having the biological activities of biotin', *J. Exper. Med.* **85**, 663–83.

—— 1957a, 'Nutrition of a hemoflagellate (*Leishmania tarentolae*) having an interchangeable requirement for choline pyridoxal', *J. Protozool.* **4**, 269–76.

—— 1957b, 'The nutrition of an intracellular parasite (Avian malaria)', *Acta. Trop.* **14**, 289–301.

—— 1958. 'Folinic acid and nondialysable materials in the nutrition of malaria parasites', *J. Exper. Med.* **108**, 753–72.

TRAUBE, J., 1904, 'Oberflächendruck und seine Bedeutung im Organismus', *Pflüger's Arch. ges. Physiol.* **105**, 559–72.

TSENG, H., 'Über die gegenseitige Beeinflussung verschiedener Trypanosomen bei Mischinfektion', *Zbl. Bakt.* (I. Orig.), **134**, 153.

TSUNODA, K., and ICHIKAWA, O., 1955, 'Histochemical studies of chicken Coccidia (*Eimeria tenella*). I. On the nucleic acids, polysaccharides and phosphomonoesterases in their several development stages', *Exper. Rep. Gov. Exper. Station for Anim. Hyg.* **29**, 181–92.

TUFFRAU, M., 1953, 'Les processus cytologiques de la conjugation chez *Spirochona gemmipara* Stein', *Bull. Biol.* **87**, 314–22.

—— 1962, 'Les processus régulateurs de la "caryophtisis" du macronucleus de *Nassulopsis lagenula* Fauré-Fremiet, 1959. I. Cycle évolutif', *Arch. Protistenk.* **106**, 201–10.

TURESSON, G., 1922, 'The genotipical response of the Plant species to the habitat', *Hereditas*, **3**, 100–13.

—— 1929, 'Zur Natur und Begrenzung der Arteinheit', *Hereditas*, **12**, 323–4.

TURNER, J., 1930, 'Division and conjugation in *Euplotes patella* with special reference to the nuclear phenomena', *Univ. Calif. Publ. Zool.* **33**, 193–258.

TYZZER, E., 1927, 'Species and strains of Coccidia in Poultry', *J. Parasitol.* **13**, 215.

—— 1929, 'Coccidiosis in gallinaceus birds', *Amer. J. Hyg.* **10**, 269–383.

—— 1932, 'Criteria and methods in the investigation of avian coccidiosis', *Science*, **75**, 324.

VAVILOV, N. I., 1931, 'The Linnean Species as a System', Agric. State Pub., Leningrad.

VERMEL, E. M. (Wermel, E. M.), 1925, 'Beiträge zur Cytologie der *Amoeba hydroxena* Entz.', *Arch. Protistenk.* **4**, 95–120.

VERWORN, M., 1903, *Allgemeine Physiologie*. Jena.

VILLENEUVE-BRACHON, S., 1940, 'Recherches sur les Ciliés hétérotriches', *Arch. Zool. exp. gén.* **82**, 1–180.

VINBERG, G. T. (Wingerg, G. T.), 1949, 'Intensity of metabolism in Protozoa', *Advances in Contemporary Biology*, **28**, 226–45.

VISSCHER, I., 1927, 'Conjugation in the ciliate of protozoan *Dileptus gigas* with special reference to the nuclear phenomena', *J. Morphol.* **44**, 383–415.

VIVIER, E., 1960, 'Contribution à l'étude de la conjugation chez *Paramecium caudatum*', *Ann. Sci. Natur. Zool.* (ser. 12), **2**, 387–506.

VLADIMIRSKIJ, A. P. (Wladimirsky, A. P.), 1916, 'Are ciliates capable of "learning" to choose their food?', *Ann. Zool.* **1**, 448–506.

VLK, W., 1938, 'Über den Bau der Geißel', *Arch. Protistenk.* **90**, 448–88.

VVDEENSKIJ, N. E., 1886, *Correlation between Excitation and Stimulation in Tetanus.* St. Petersburg.

WAKSMANN, S., 1916, 'Protozoa as affecting bacterial activities in the soil', *Soil Sci.* **2**, 363–76.

—— 1932, *Principles of Soil Microbiology.* Baltimore.

WALLENGREN, H., 1901, 'Zur Kenntnis des Neubildungs- und Resorptionsprozess bei Teilung der hypotrichen Infusorien', *Zool. Jahrb., Abt. Anat.* **15**, 1–58.

WATSON-KAMM, M., 1922, 'Studies on Gregarines. II. Cynopsis of the Polycystid Gregarines of the world, excluding those from the Myriapoda, Orthoptera and Coleoptera', *Illin. Biol. Monogr.* **7**, 1–104.

WEATHERBY, I.,1927, 'The function of the contractile vacuole in *Paramecium caudatum*, with special reference to the nitrogenous compounds', *Biol. Bull.* **52**, 208–22.

WEDEKIND, G., 1927, 'Zytologische Untersuchungen an *Barrouxia schneideri*', *Z. Zellforsch.* **5**, 505–650.

WEINREB, S., 1955, 'Homalozoon vermiculare. II. Pharingeal granules and trichites. *J. Protozool.* **2**, 67–70.

WEISER, J., 1961, 'Die Mikrosporidien als Parasiten der Insecten', *Monogr. zur angew. Entomol.* Nr. 17, Hamburg.

WEISMANN, A., 1884, *Über Leben und Tod.* Jena.

—— 1902, *Vorträge über Descendenztheorie.* Jena.

WEISS, E., and BALL, G., 1947, 'Nutritional requirements of *Tritrichomonas foetus* with special reference to partially digested proteins', *Proc. Soc. Exper. Biol. Med.* **65**, 278–83.

WEISZ, P., 1948a, 'The role of carbohydrate reserves in the regeneration of Stentor fragments', *J. Exper. Zool.* **108**, 263–76.

—— 1948b, 'On the growth of regenerating fragments in *Stentor coeruleus*', *J. Exper. Zool.* **109**, 427–38.

—— 1949a, 'A cytochemical and cytological study of differentiation in normal and reorganizational stages of *Stentor coeruleus*', *J. Morphol.* **84**, 335–64.

—— 1949b, 'The role of specific macronuclear nodes in the differentiation and the maintenance of the oral area in a *Stentor*', *J. Exper. Zool.* **111**, 145–55.

—— 1949c, 'The role of the macronucleus in the differentiation of *Blepharisma undulans*', *J. Morphol.* **85**, 503–18.

—— 1950, 'A correlation between macronuclear thymonucleic acid and the capacity of morphogenesis in *Stentor*', *J. Morphol.* **87**, 275–86.

—— 1951, 'An experimental analysis of morphogenesis in *Stentor coeruleus*', *J. Exper. Zool.* **116**, 231–58.

—— 1954, 'Morphogenesis in Protozoa', *Quart. Rev. Biol.* **29**, 207–29.

WENDEL, W., 1943, 'Respiratory and carbohydrate metabolism of malaria parasites (*Plasmodium knowlesi*)', *J. Biol. Chem.* **148**, 21–34.

WENYON, C., 1926, *Protozoology, I, II.* Baillière, Tindall & Cox, London.

—— and O'CONNOR, R., 1917, *Human intestinal Protozoa in the Near East.* Wellcome Bur. Scient. Res., London.

WESCHENFELDER, R., 1938, 'Die Entwicklung von *Actinocephalus parvus* Wellmer', *Arch. Protistenk.* **91**, 1–60.

WESTPHAL, A., 1934, 'Studien über Ophryoscoleciden in der Kultur', *Z. Parasitenk.* **7**, 71–117.

WETZEL, A., 1925, 'Vergleichendcytologische Untersuchungen an Ziliaten', *Arch. Protistenk.* **51**, 209–304.

—— 1928, 'Der Faulschlamm und seine ziliaten Leitformen', *Z. Morphol. Ökol. Tiere*, **13**, 181–328

WEYER, G., 1930, 'Untersuchungen über die Morphologie und Physiologie des Formwechsels der *Gastrostyla steinii* Engelmann', *Arch. Protistenk.* **71**, 139–228.

WICHTERMAN, R., 1937, 'Division and conjugation in *Nyctotherus cordiformis*. (Ehrb) Stein (Protozoa, Ciliata) with special reference to the nuclear phenomena', *J. Morphol.* **60**, 563–611.

—— 1940, 'Cytogamy: a sexual process occurring in living joined pairs of *Paramecium caudatum* and its relation to their sexual phenomena', *J. Morphol.* **66**, 423–51.

—— 1943, 'Conjugation and fate exconjugants of Zoochlorella-free *Paramecium bursaria*', *Anat. Rec.* **87**, 478.

—— 1951, 'The ecology, cultivation structural characteristic and mating types of *Paramecium calkinsi*', *Proc. Nat. Acad. Sci.* **25**, 51–65.

—— 1953, *The Biology of Paramecium*. Blakiston, Philadelphia.

WILBRANDT, W., 1938, 'Die Permeabilität der Zelle', *Ergebn. Physiol. exp. Pharmacol.* **40**, 204–41.

WILLET, K., and FAIRBRAIN, H., 1955, 'The Tinde experiment: a study of *Trypanosoma rhodesiense* during eighteen years of cyclical transmission', *Ann. Trop. Med. Parasitol.* **49**, 278–92.

WILSON, S. G., 1949, '*Trypanosoma uniforme–Trypanosoma vivax* infections in bovines and *Trypanosoma uniforme* infections in goats and sheep at Entebbe, Uganda', *Parasitology*, **39**, 198.

WOHLFARTH-BOTTERMANN, K., and KRÜGER, F., 1954, 'Protistenstudien. VI. Die Feinstruktur der Axopodien und der Skelettnadbeln von Heliozoen', *Protoplasma*, **43**, 177–91.

WOLCOTT, G., 1952, 'Mitosis in *Trypanosoma lewisi*', *J. Morphol.* **90**, 189–99.

—— 1954, 'The chromosomes of the four species of human malaria', *J. Parasitol.* **40** (Suppl.), 31.

—— 1957, 'Chromosome studies in the genus *Plasmodium*', *J. Protozool.* **4**, 48–51.

WOLKEN, J., 1956, 'A molecular morphology of *Euglena gracilis* var. *bacillaris*', *J. Protozool.* **3**, 211–21.

WOLTERECK, R., 1913, 'Über Funktion, Herkunft und Entstehungsursache der sogenannten "Schwebe-Fortsätze" pelagischer Cladoceren', *Zoologica* **26**, 474–548.

WOODARD, J., GELBER, B., and SWIFT, H., 1961, 'Nucleoprotein changes during the mitotic cycle in *Paramecium aurelia*', *Exp. Cell. Res.* **23**, 258–64.

WOODRUFF, L., 1911, 'Two thousand generations of *Paramecium*', *Arch. Protistenk.* **21**, 26–6.

—— 1915, 'The problem of rejuvenescence in Protozoa', *Biochem. Bull.* **4**, 371–8.

—— 1917, 'Rhythms and endomixis in various races of *Paramecium aurelia*', *Biol. Bull.* **33**, 51–56.

—— 1921, 'The present status of the long-continued pedigree-culture of *Paramecium aurelia* at Yale University', *Proc. Nat. Acad. Sci.* **7**, 41–44.

—— 1925a, 'Eleven thousand generations of *Paramecium*', *Quart. Rev. Biol.* **1**, 436–8.

—— 1925b, 'The physiological significance of conjugation and endomixis in the Infusoria', *Amer. Natur.* **59**, 225–49.

WOODRUFF, L., 1941, 'Endomixis'. In: *Protozoa in Biological Research.* (Ed. by G. Calkins and F. Summers.) New York: 645–65.

—— and ERDMANN, R., 1914, 'A normal periodic reorganization process without cell fusion in *Paramecium*', *J. Exper. Zool.* **17**, 425–518.

—— and SPENCER, H., 1922, 'Studies on *Spathidium spathula*. I. The structure and behaviour of *Spathidium* with special reference to the capture and ingestion of its prey', *J. Exper. Zool.* **35**, 189–205.

—— —— 1924, 'Studies on *Spathidium spathula*. II. The significance of conjugation', *J. Exper. Zool.* **39**, 133–96.

WORLEY, L., 1934, 'Ciliary metachronism and reversal in *Paramecium, Spirostomum* and *Stentor*', *J. Cell. Comp. Physiol.* **5**, 53–72.

YAGIU, R., 1940, 'The division, conjugation and nuclear reorganization of *Entorhipidium echini* Lynch', *J. Sci. Hirosima Univ.*, ser. B, I (Zool.), 125–56.

—— and SHIGENAKA, Y., 1959, 'Electron microscopical observations of *Condylostoma spatiosum* in ultra-thin section. IV. The fibrils between the basal granule and the longitudinal fibrillar bundle', *Zool. Mag.* **68**, 414–18.

YAMASAKI, M., 1937, 'Studies on the intestinal Protozoa of Termites. IV. Glycogen in the body of *Trichonympha agilis* var japonica under Experimental conditions', *Mem. Coll. Sci. Kyoto Imper. Univ.*, ser. B, **12**, 222–35.

YARWOOD, E., 1937, 'The life cycle of *Adelina cryptocerci* sp. nov. a coccidian parasite of the Roach *Cryptocercus puntulatus*', *Parasitol.* **29**, 370–90.

YOUNG, D., 1922, 'A contribution to the morphology and physiology of the genus *Uronychia*', *J. Exper. Zool.* **36**, 353–95.

ZACHVATKIN, A. A., 1949, 'Comparative embryology of lower invertebrates', *Sov. Sci. Moscow.*

ZASUCHIN, D. N. (Sassuchin, Sassoukhine, Zassoukhin), 1929, 'Conditions of habitat, structure and development of *Entamoeba blattae*', *Russian Arch. Protistol.* **8**, 163–244.

—— KABANOVA, N. M., and NEISVESTNOVA, E. S. (Neiswestnova), 1927, 'Investigation on the microscopic population of alluvial sands in the bed of the river Oka', *Russian Hydrobiol. J.* **6**, 59–83.

ZEDERBAUER, E., 1904, 'Geschlechtliche und ungeschlechtliche Fortpflanzung von *Ceratium hirundinella*', *Bericht. Deutsch. Botan. Ges.* **22**, 1–8.

ZENKEVIČ, L. A. (Zenkevitch, L. A.), 1947, 'Fauna and biological productivity of the sea', *Sov. Sci. Moscow.*

ZERNOV, S. A., 1934, *General Hydrobiology.* Moscow-Leningrad.

ZIMMERMANN, W., 1921, 'Zur Entwicklungsgeschichte und Zytologie von *Volvox*', *Jahrb. wiss. Bot.* **60**, 256–94.

ŽINKIN, L. N. (Zhinkin, L. N.), 1929, 'Fat and the causes of its formation in the ciliate *Stentor polymorphus*', *Proc. Petergof. Inst. Nat. Sci.* **6**, 199–215.

—— 1930, 'Zur Frage Der Reservestoffe bei Infusorien (Fett und Glykogen bei *Stentor Polymorphus*)', *Z. Morph. Ökol. Tiere*, **18**, 217–48.

ZSCHOKKE, F., 1889, 'Beitrag zur Kenntnis der Fauna von Gebirgseen', *Zool. Anz.* Nr. 326, 37–40.

ZÜELZER, M., 1909, 'Bau und Entwicklung von *Wagnerella borealis* Mezesch', *Arch. Protistenk.* **17**, 135.

—— 1910, 'Über den Einfluß des Meerwassers auf die pulsierende Vakuole', *Roux Arch. Entwicklungsmech. Organ.* **29**, 632–40.

ZWEIBAUM, J., 1922, 'Ricerche sperimentale sulla conjugazione degli infusori. II. Influenza della conjugazione sulla produzione dei materialie di reserva nel *Paramecium caudatum*', *Arch. Protistenk.* **44**, 375–96.

AUTHOR INDEX

SUBJECT INDEX

The page numbers in italics refer to illustrations.

ABYSSAL PLAIN, 582.

Acantharia, forms, series of, 511–14.

—, gamete structure in, 327, *328*.

—, myoneme system in, 108–10.

—, polymerization in, 555.

—, rhizopodia in, 147.

—, skeleton in, 78, 92–94.

—, spicules, convergence in, 523–5.

—, vertical distribution, 580–1.

Acanthocystis, budding in, 267.

Acanthodinium, convergence in, 530.

　A. caryophyllum, convergence in, 529.

Acanthometra, spicules, convergence, *524*.

　A. pellucida, gametes, *328*.

Acanthometron pellucidum, contractile apparatus in, *109*.

Acanthostaurus, 92.

　A. purpurscens, gametes, *328*.

Acervuline shell, 86.

Acetic acid, 243.

Acetylcholin-cholinesterase system, in ciliary movement, 121–2.

Achromonas, mitosis in, 47.

Acid, effect on gamones, 413.

—, — — paramecia, 156–7.

Acid hydrolase, 217.

— phosphatase, 217.

Acidity, cytoplasmic, in amoeboid movement, 150.

Actinobolus, growth on Halteria cultures, 120.

—, phylogeny, 508.

　A. radians, tentacles, *184*.

Actinocephalus parvus, sex-determination in, 417.

Actinodinium apsteini, body shape, 529.

Actinomyxidia, parasitism in, 619.

Actinophrys, cyst in, *350*, 351.

—, meiosis in, 301.

—, mitosis in, 47.

—, progamous period in, 341.

　A. sol, chromosomes in, number, 61.

—, meiosis in, *302*.

—, nuclear division in, *48*.

—, paedogomy in, *321*–2.

—, sex-determination in, 418.

Actinospaerium, birefringence, 9.

—, cyst, *350*, 351, 473.

Activation scheme, during sexual processes in paramecia, *405*.

Adaptation, mutual, between parasite and host, 659–64.

Adaptation to environment, in freshwater Protozoa, 606.

Adeleidae, cyst in, *350*.

—, life-cycle, 432.

Adelina, cysts in, 349, *350*, 351.

—, life-cycle, *339*.

Adenosine triphosphate (ATP), energy source for flagella and cilia, 145.

— —, in biochemistry of stalk contraction, 108.

— —, in ciliary action, 145.

— — production, and mitochondria, 22.

Adoral apparatus, 209.

— —, in choice of food, 211.

— cilia, 207 et seq.

— membranelles, 209.

Adsorption theory (Nasonov-Aleksandrov), of cytoplasmic permeability, 12.

Afferent canal, 223.

Agamete (merozoite), 442.

Agamogony, in foraminifers, 440.

Agamous reproduction. *See* Reproduction, agamous.

Agarella, convergence in, 530, *531*.

Age polymorphism, in Apostomata, 464.

Agglutination, in *Chlamydomonas eugametes*, *412*.

—, reaction of, 403, 410.

Aggregata, chromosome pattern in, 63.

—, development cycle in, *338*, 339.

—, karyokinesis in, 51.

—, life-cycle, 356.

—, paramitosis in, 50.

—, progressive coenogenetic gamete formation in, 346.

　A. eberthi, nuclear division during sporogony, *51*.

Aggregatidae, alternation of hosts in, 650–1.

Aikinetocystis, convergence in, 532.

Algae, symbiotic, 245.

Alimentary apparatus, of Entodiniomorpha, 210.

— —, primitive, in Mastigophora, 201.

— system, in ciliates, 206.

— tract, parasites, 624–32.

— —, relationship with outer environment, 623.

Allantosoma, endoparasitism in, 639, *640*.

Allogromia laticolaris, number of chromosomes in, 61.

Alloplasmatic structure, *77*.

3 B

Shell, phylogenetic development, 84.
—, planospiral, 86.
—, sandy, phylogenetic development, 85.
—, sessile, 88.
—, siliceous, 84.
—, spiral type, 86.
—, stalked, 88.
—, tubular, shortening of, 85.
—, turbospiral, 86.
Shelter, in population studies on ciliates, 569.
SH-groups, 34.
Shock reaction, 155, 157.
'Sichelstadium', 305.
Silica, in inorganic skeleton, 78.
— in shells, 84.
— in skeleton of radiolarians, 90.
Silver impregnation, 113 et seq.
Silver-line system of fibrils, *114. See also* Argyrome, of Chatton.
— — — —, composition, 115.
Size, body, and polymerization, 562.
—, of protozoon, and polymerization, 561.
Skeleton, absence of, in radiolarians, 90.
— and body shape, in plankton, 577.
—, astroid, convergence to spheroid type, 525.
—, —, in Acantharia, 92.
—, chemical composition, 77–79.
— completely covering, 79–82.
—, complicating division, 250.
— continuous, in Dinoflagellata, 80.
— convergence, 517–39.
—, external, 79–88.
— functions, 77.
— in buoyancy of plankton, 577, 579.
— in heliozoans, 90 et seq.
— in radiolarians, 90 et seq.
— in Sarcodina, and nutrition, 204.
— in transition to parasitism, 619.
—, inorganic, 78.
—, internal, 88–96.
—, —, continuous, 88.
—, —, of separate supporting elements, 89.
—, morphology, 79.
—, organic, 76.
— plate, of Entodiniomorpha, 95.
—, radiolarian, convergence with spicules of Porifera, 583–9.
—, —, shape, 92.
—, spheroid, convergence to astroid type, 525.
—, —, in Spumellaria, 94.
— structure, 77–96.
— supporting structures, fibrillar, 89, 96–103.
— — —, non-fibrillar, 89, 90–96.
Soil, depth, and protozoan population, 614.
—, nature, and protozoan population, 615.

Soil Protozoa, calculation, 613–14.
— —, composition, qualitative, 613.
— —, number of, 613.
— protozoology, 612.
— protozoan population, 608–13.
— sterilization, and death of protozoan population, 612.
—, temperature of, effect on Protozoa, 614.
Solation, amoeboid, 151.
Somatella, 426, 552.
— evolution, 553.
Soviet Seas, plankton in, 584–5.
Spathidium spatula, feeding, *183.*
Speciation, in parasites, 505–6.
— intraspecific groups leading to, 505.
Species, biological aspects, 484.
—, concept of, 484–507.
—, conjoint, 506.
—, constitution in Protozoa, 484–507.
—, definition, 484.
— of marine Protozoa, distribution, 574.
— polymorphism, 487.
— reality, 486.
Specificity, of host, 664.
Spenophrya, 643.
Spermatozoa, crustacean, Trichonymphidae, and cnidocysts of Polykrikos— mutual convergence, 535, *536*, 537.
— metazoan, and flagelloid gametes, mutual convergence, 535.
Sphaenophryidae, budding in, 265, *266.*
Sphaerophrya, endoparasitism in other Protozoa, 642.
Sphaerospora, budding in, *267*, 268.
Spasmoneme, in stalk of *Vorticella*, 107.
Specific gravity, of cytoplasm, 5, 6.
Spermatic nuclei, 38.
Spheroid colonies, 280.
Spicules, convergence in structure, in radiolarians, 521.
— in skeleton of radiolarians, 90.
—, mineral, in radiolarian skeleton, 90.
— of Porifera, 84.
— —, convergence with radiolarian spicules, 537, 538.
— on shells of Globigerinidae, function, 86.
— radial, convergences, 523, *524.*
— radiolarian, convergence with spicules, of Porifera, 537.
— —, structure, *91.*
Spirochona gemmipara, budding in, 265.
— —, conjugation in, 370.
S. subparasitica, life-cycle, 458–62.
Spirostomum, myoneme system in, 103, 104.
S. ambiguum, 66.
—, ciliary movement, 146.
Spirotrichonympha polygura, number of chromosomes in, 61.

PRINTED IN GREAT BRITAIN
AT THE UNIVERSITY PRESS, OXFORD
BY VIVIAN RIDLER
PRINTER TO THE UNIVERSITY